Henry James

Henry James OM (15 April 1843 – 28 February 1916) was an American-British author regarded as a key transitional figure between literary realism and literary modernism, and is considered by many to be among the greatest novelists in the English language. He was the son of Henry James Sr. and the brother of renowned philosopher and psychologist William James and diarist Alice James.

He is best known for a number of novels dealing with the social and marital interplay between émigré Americans, English people, and continental Europeans. Examples of such novels include The Portrait of a Lady, The Ambassadors, and The Wings of the Dove. His later works were increasingly experimental. In describing the internal states of mind and social dynamics of his characters, James often made use of a style in which ambiguous or contradictory motives and impressions were overlaid or juxtaposed in the discussion of a character's psyche.(Source: Wikipedia)

Literary works:

Watch and Ward (1871)

Roderick Hudson (1875)

The American (1877)

The Europeans (1878)

Confidence (1879)

Washington Square (1880)

The Portrait of a Lady (1881)

The Bostonians (1886)

The Princess Casamassima (1886)

The Reverberator (1888)

The Tragic Muse (1890)

The Other House (1896)

The Spoils of Poynton (1897)

What Maisie Knew (1897)

The Awkward Age (1899)

The Sacred Fount (1901)

THE COLLECTED WORKS
OF
HENRY JAMES
VOL. 11 (OF 24)

A LITTLE TOUR IN FRANCE
THE SACRED FOUNT
THE SPOILS OF POYNTON

BOOKLAND
CLASSICS

An Imprint of Bookland Classics LLC

A Wholly Owned Subsidiary of Queenior LLC

A Melodragon Company

First Printing: 2020

ISBN 978-1-6627-1484-9 (Paperback)

ISBN 978-1-6627-1485-6 (Hardcover)

Published by Bookland Classics

www.booklandclassics.com

Contents

THE COLLECTED WORKS

OF

HENRY JAMES

VOL. 11 (OF 24)

A LITTLE TOUR IN FRANCE

PREFACE

The notes presented in this volume were gathered, as will easily be perceived, a number of years ago and on an expectation not at that time answered by the event, and were then published in the United States. The expectation had been that they should accompany a series of drawings, and they themselves were altogether governed by the pictorial spirit. They made, and they make in appearing now, after a considerable interval and for the first time, in England, no pretension to any other; they are impressions, immediate, easy, and consciously limited; if the written word may ever play the part of brush or pencil, they are sketches on "drawing-paper" and nothing more. From the moment the principle of selection and expression, with a tourist, is not the delight of the eyes and the play of fancy, it should be an energy in every way much larger; there is no happy mean, in other words, I hold, between the sense and the quest of the picture, and the surrender to it, and the sense and the quest of the constitution, the inner springs of the subject—springs and connections social, economic, historic.

One must really choose, in other words, between the benefits of the perception of surface—a perception, when fine, perhaps none of the most frequent—and those of the perception of very complex underlying matters. If these latter had had, for me, to be taken into account, my pages would not have been collected. At the time of their original appearance the series of illustrations to which it had been their policy to cling for countenance and company failed them, after all, at the last moment, through a circumstance not now on record; and they had suddenly to begin to live their little life without assistance. That they have seemed able in any degree still to prolong even so modest a career might perhaps have served as a reason for leaving them undisturbed. In fact, however, I have too much appreciated—for any renewal of inconsistency—the opportunity of granting them at last, in an association with Mr. Pennell's admirable drawings, the benefit they have always lacked. The little book thus goes forth finally as the picture-book it was designed to be. Text and illustrations are, altogether and alike, things of the play of eye and hand and fancy—views, head-pieces, tail-pieces; through the artist's work, doubtless, in a much higher degree than the author's.

But these are words enough on a minor point. Many things come back to me on reading my pages over—such a world of reflection and emotion as I can neither leave unmentioned nor yet, in this place, weigh them down with the full expression of. Difficult indeed would be any full expression for one who, deeply devoted always to the revelations of France, finds himself, late in life, making of the sentiment no more substantial, no more direct record than this mere revival of an accident. Not one of these small chapters but suggests to me a regret that I might not, first or last, have gone farther, penetrated deeper, spoken oftener—closed, in short, more intimately with the great general subject; and I mean, of course, not in such a form as the present, but in many another, possible and impossible. It all comes back, doubtless, this vision of missed occasions and delays overdone, to the general truth that the observer, the enjoyer, may, before he knows it, be practically too far in for all that free testimony and pleasant, easy talk that are incidental to the earlier or more detached stages of a relation. There are relations that soon get beyond all merely showy appearances of value for us. Their value becomes thus private and practical, and is represented by the process—the quieter, mostly, the better—of absorption and assimilation of what the relation has done for us. For persons thus indebted to the genius of France—however, in its innumerable ways, manifested—the profit to be gained, the lesson to be learnt, is almost of itself occupation enough. They feel that they bear witness by the intelligent use and application of their advantage, and the consciousness of the artist is therefore readily a consciousness of pious service. He may repeatedly have dreamt of some such happy combination of mood and moment as shall launch him in a profession of faith, a demonstration of the interesting business; he may have had inner glimpses of an explicit statement, and vaguely have sketched it to himself as one of the most candid and charming ever drawn up; but time, meanwhile, has passed, interruptions have done their dismal work, the indirect tribute, too, has perhaps, behind the altar, grown and grown; and the reflection has at all events established itself that honour is more rendered by seeing and doing one's work in the light than by brandishing the torch on the house-tops. Curiosity and admiration have operated continually, but with as little waste as they could. The drawback is only that in this case, to be handsomely consequent, one would perhaps rather not have appeared to celebrate any rites. The moral of all of which is that those here embodied must pass, at the best, but for what they are worth.

H. J.

August 9, 1900.

INTRODUCTORY

Though the good city of Paris appears to be less in fashion than in other days with those representatives of our race—not always, perhaps, acknowledged as the soundest and stiffest—curious of foreign opportunity and addicted to foreign sojourns, it probably none the less remains true that such frequentations of France as may be said still to flourish among us have as much as ever the wondrous capital, and the wondrous capital alone, for their object. The taste for Paris, at all events, is—or perhaps I should say was, alluding as I do, I fear, to a vanished order—a taste by itself; singularly little bound up, of necessity, with such an interest in the country at large as would be implied by an equal devotion, in other countries, to other capitals. Putting aside the economic inducement, which may always operate, and limiting the matter to the question of free choice, it is sufficiently striking that the free chooser would have to be very fond of England to quarter himself in London, very fond of Germany to quarter himself in Berlin, very fond of America to quarter himself in New York. It had, on the other hand, been a common reflection for the author of these light pages that the fondness for France (throughout the company of strangers more or less qualified) was oddly apt to feed only on such grounds for it as made shift to spread their surface between the Arc de Triomphe and the Gymnase Theatre: as if there were no good things in the *doux pays* that could not be harvested in that field. It matters little how the assumption began to strike him as stupid, especially since he himself had doubtless equally shared in the guilt of it. The light pages in question are but the simple record of a small personal effort to shake it off. He took, it must be confessed, no extraordinary measures; he merely started, one rainy morning in mid-September, for the charming little city of Tours, where he felt that he might as immediately as anywhere else see it demonstrated that, though France might be Paris, Paris was by no means France. The beauty of the demonstration—quite as prompt as he could have desired—drew him considerably farther, and his modest but eminently successful adventure begot, as aids to amused remembrance, a few informal notes.

CHAPTER I. TOURS

I AM ashamed to begin with saying that Touraine is the garden of France; that remark has long ago lost its bloom. The town of Tours, however, has something sweet and bright, which suggests that it is surrounded by a land of fruits. It is a very agreeable little city; few towns of its size are more ripe, more complete, or, I should suppose, in better humour with themselves and less disposed to envy the responsibilities of bigger places. It is truly the capital of its smiling province; a region of easy abundance, of good living, of genial, comfortable, optimistic, rather indolent opinions. Balzac says in one of his tales that the real Tourangeau will not make an effort, or displace himself even, to go in search of a pleasure; and it is not difficult to understand the sources of this amiable cynicism. He must have a vague conviction that he can only lose by almost any change. Fortune has been kind to him: he lives in a temperate, reasonable, sociable climate, on the banks of a river which, it is true, sometimes floods the country around it, but of which the ravages appear to be so easily repaired that its aggressions may perhaps be regarded (in a region where so many good things are certain) merely as an occasion for healthy suspense. He is surrounded by fine old traditions, religious, social, architectural, culinary; and he may have the satisfaction of feeling that he is French to the core. No part of his admirable country is more characteristically national. Normandy is Normandy, Burgundy is Burgundy, Provence is Provence; but Touraine is essentially France. It is the land of Rabelais, of Descartes, of Balzac, of good books and good company, as well as good dinners and good houses. George Sand has somewhere a charming passage about the mildness, the convenient quality, of the physical conditions of central France—"son climat souple et chaud, ses pluies abondantes et courtes." In the autumn of 1882 the rains perhaps were less short than abundant; but when the days were fine it was impossible that anything in the way of weather could be more charming. The vineyards and orchards looked rich in the fresh, gay light; cultivation was everywhere, but everywhere it seemed to be easy. There was no visible poverty; thrift and success presented themselves as matters of good taste. The white caps of the women glittered in the sunshine, and their well-made sabots clicked cheerfully on the hard, clean roads. Touraine is a land of old châteaux,—a gallery of architectural specimens and of large hereditary properties. The peasantry have less of the luxury of ownership than in most other parts of France; though they have enough of it to give them quite their share of that shrewdly conservative look which, in the little chaffering *place* of the market-town, the stranger observes so often in the wrinkled brown masks that surmount the agricultural blouse. This is, moreover, the heart of the old French monarchy; and as that monarchy was splendid and picturesque, a reflection of the splendour still glitters in the current of the Loire. Some of the most striking events of French history have occurred on the banks of that river, and the soil it waters bloomed for a while with the flowering of the Renaissance. The Loire gives a great "style" to a landscape of which the features are not, as the phrase is, prominent, and carries the eye to distances even more poetic than the green horizons of Touraine. It is a very fitful stream, and is sometimes observed to run thin and expose all the crudities of its channel—a great defect certainly in a river which is so much depended upon to give an air to the places it waters. But I speak of it as I saw it last; full, tranquil, powerful, bending in large slow curves and sending back half the light of the sky. Nothing can be finer than the view of its course which you get from the battlements and terraces of Amboise. As I looked down on it from that elevation one lovely Sunday morning, through a mild glitter of autumn sunshine, it seemed the very model of a generous, beneficent stream. The most charming part of Tours is naturally the shaded quay that overlooks it, and looks across too at the friendly faubourg of Saint Symphorien and at the terraced heights which rise above this. Indeed, throughout Touraine it is half the charm of the Loire that you can travel beside it. The great dyke which protects it, or protects the country from it, from Blois to Angers, is an admirable road; and on the other side as well the highway constantly keeps it company. A wide river, as you follow a wide road, is excellent company; it brightens and shortens the way.

Tours

The inns at Tours are in another quarter, and one of them, which is midway between the town and the station, is very good. It is worth mentioning for the fact that every one belonging to it is extraordinarily polite—so unnaturally polite as at first to excite your suspicion that the hotel has some hidden vice, so that the waiters and chambermaids are trying to pacify you in advance. There was one waiter in especial who was the most accomplished social being I have ever encountered; from morning till night he kept up an inarticulate murmur of urbanity, like the hum of a spinning-top. I may add that I discovered no dark secrets at the Hôtel de l'Univers; for it is not a secret to any traveller to-day that the obligation to partake of a lukewarm dinner in an overheated room is as imperative as it is detestable. For the rest, at Tours there is a certain Rue Royale which has pretensions to the monumental; it was constructed a hundred years ago, and the houses, all alike, have on a moderate scale a pompous eighteenth-century look. It connects the Palais de Justice, the most important secular building in the town, with the long bridge which spans the Loire—the spacious, solid bridge pronounced by Balzac, in "Le Curé de Tours," "one of the finest monuments of French architecture." The Palais de Justice was the seat of the Government of Léon Gambetta in the autumn of 1870, after the dictator had been obliged to retire in his balloon from Paris and before the Assembly was constituted at Bordeaux. The Germans occupied Tours during that terrible winter: it is astonishing, the number of places the Germans occupied. It is hardly too much to say that, wherever one goes in certain parts of France, one encounters two great historic facts: one is the Revolution; the other is the German invasion. The traces of the Revolution remain in a hundred scars and bruises and mutilations, but the visible marks of the war of 1870 have passed away. The country is so rich, so living, that she has been able to dress her wounds, to hold up her head, to smile again, so that the shadow of that darkness has ceased to rest upon her. But what you do not see you still may hear; and one remembers with a certain shudder that only a few short years ago this province, so intimately French, was under the heel of a foreign foe. To be intimately French was apparently not a safeguard; for so successful an invader it could only be a challenge. Peace and plenty, however, have succeeded that episode; and among the gardens and vineyards of Touraine it seems only a legend the more in a country of legends.

It was not, all the same, for the sake of this chequered story that I mentioned the Palais de Justice and the Rue Royale. The most interesting fact, to my mind, about the high-street of Tours was that as you walk toward the bridge on the right hand *trottoir* you can look up at the house, on the other side of the way, in which Honoré de Balzac first saw the light. That violent and complicated genius was a child of the good-humoured and succulent Touraine. There is something anomalous in this fact, though, if one thinks about it a little, one may discover certain correspondences between his character and that of his native province. Strenuous, laborious, constantly infelicitous in spite of his great successes, he suggests at times a very different set of influences. But he had his jovial, full-feeding side—the side that comes out in the "Contes Drolatiques," which are the romantic and epicurean chronicle of the old manors and abbeys of this region. And he was, moreover, the product of a soil into which a great deal of history had been trodden. Balzac was genuinely as well as affectedly monarchical, and he was saturated with a sense of the past. Number 39 Rue Royale—of which the basement, like all the basements in the Rue Royale, is occupied by a shop—is not shown to the public; and I know not whether tradition designates the chamber in which the author of "Le Lys dans la Vallée" opened his eyes into a world in which he was to see and to imagine such extraordinary things. If this were the case I would willingly have crossed its threshold; not for the sake of any relic of the great novelist which it may possibly contain, nor even for that of any mystic virtue which may be supposed to reside within its walls, but simply because to look at those four modest walls can hardly fail to give one a strong impression of the force of human endeavour. Balzac, in the maturity of his vision, took in more of human life than any one, since Shakspeare, who has attempted to tell us stories about it; and the very small scene on which his consciousness dawned is one end of the immense scale that he traversed. I confess it shocked me a little to find that he was born in a house "in a row"—a house, moreover, which at the date of his birth must have been only about twenty years old. All that is contradictory. If the tenement selected for this honour could not be ancient and embrowned, it should at least have been detached.

Tours

There is a charming description in his little tale of "La Grenadière" of the view of the opposite side of the Loire as you have it from the square at the end of the Rue Royale—a square that has some pretensions to grandeur, overlooked as it is by the Hôtel de Ville and the Musée, a pair of edifices which directly contemplate the river, and ornamented with marble images of François Rabelais and René Descartes. The former, erected a few years since, is a very honourable production; the pedestal of the latter could, as a matter of course, only be inscribed with the *Cogito ergo Sum*. The two statues mark the two opposite poles to which the wondrous French mind has travelled; and if there were an effigy of Balzac at Tours it ought to stand midway between them. Not that he by any means always struck the happy mean between the sensible and the metaphysical; but one may say of him that half of his genius looks in one direction and half in the other. The side that turns toward François Rabelais would be, on the whole, the side that takes the sun. But there is no statue of Balzac at Tours; there is only in one of the chambers of the melancholy museum a rather clever, coarse bust. The description in "La Grenadière" of which I just spoke is too long to quote; neither have I space for anyone of the brilliant attempts at landscape-painting which are woven into the shimmering texture of "Le Lys dans la Vallée." The little manor of Clochegourde, the residence of Madame de Mortsauf, the heroine of that extraordinary work, was within a moderate walk of Tours, and the picture in the novel is presumably a copy from an original which it would be possible to-day to discover. I did not, however, even make the attempt. There are so many châteaux in Touraine commemorated in history that it would take one too far to look up those which have been commemorated in fiction. The most I did was to endeavour to identify the former residence of Mademoiselle Gamard, the sinister old maid of "Le Curé de Tours." This terrible woman occupied a small house in the rear of the cathedral, where I spent a whole morning in wondering rather stupidly which house it could be. To reach the cathedral from the little *place* where we stopped just now to look across at the Grenadière, without, it must be confessed, very vividly seeing it, you follow the quay to the right and pass out of sight of the charming *côteau* which, from

25

beyond the river, faces the town—a soft agglomeration of gardens, vineyards, scattered villas, gables and turrets of slate-roofed châteaux, terraces with grey balustrades, moss-grown walls draped in scarlet Virginia-creeper. You turn into the town again beside a great military barrack which is ornamented with a rugged mediæval tower, a relic of the ancient fortifications, known to the Tourangeaux of to-day as the Tour de Guise. The young Prince of Joinville, son of that Duke of Guise who was murdered by the order of Henry II. at Blois, was, after the death of his father, confined here for more than two years, but made his escape one summer evening in 1591, under the nose of his keepers, with a gallant audacity which has attached the memory of the exploit to his sullen-looking prison. Tours has a garrison of five regiments, and the little red-legged soldiers light up the town. You see them stroll upon the clean, uncommercial quay, where there are no signs of navigation, not even by oar, no barrels nor bales, no loading nor unloading, no masts against the sky nor booming of steam in the air. The most active business that goes on there is that patient and fruitless angling in which the French, as the votaries of art for art, excel all other people. The little soldiers, weighed down by the contents of their enormous pockets, pass with respect from one of these masters of the rod to the other, as he sits soaking an indefinite bait in the large, indifferent stream. After you turn your back to the quay you have only to go a little way before you reach the cathedral.

CHAPTER II. TOURS. THE CATHEDRAL

IT IS a very beautiful church of the second order of importance, with a charming mouse-coloured complexion and a pair of fantastic towers. There is a commodious little square in front of it, from which you may look up at its very ornamental face; but for purposes of frank admiration the sides and the rear are perhaps not sufficiently detached. The cathedral of Tours, which is dedicated to Saint Gatianus, took a long time to build. Begun in 1170, it was finished only in the first half of the sixteenth century; but the ages and the weather have interfused so well the tone of the different parts that it presents, at first at least, no striking incongruities, and looks even exceptionally harmonious and complete. There are many grander cathedrals, but there are probably few more pleasing; and this effect of delicacy and grace is at its best towards the close of a quiet afternoon, when the densely decorated towers, rising above the little Place de l'Archevêché, lift their curious lanterns into the slanting light and offer a multitudinous perch to troops of circling pigeons. The whole front, at such a time, has an appearance of great richness, although the niches which surround the three high doors (with recesses deep enough for several circles of sculpture) and indent the four great buttresses that ascend beside the huge rose-window, carry no figures beneath their little chiselled canopies. The blast of the great Revolution blew down most of the statues in France, and the wind has never set very strongly towards putting them up again. The embossed and crocketed cupolas which crown the towers of Saint Gatien are not very pure in taste; but, like a good many impurities, they have a certain character. The interior has a stately slimness with which no fault is to be found and which in the choir, rich in early glass and surrounded by a broad passage, becomes very bold and noble. Its principal treasure perhaps is the charming little tomb of the two children (who died young) of Charles VIII. and Anne of Brittany, in white marble embossed with symbolic dolphins and exquisite arabesques. The little boy and girl lie side by side on a slab of black marble, and a pair of small kneeling angels, both at their head and at their feet, watch over them. Nothing could be more elegant than this monument, which is the work of

Tours: the Cathedral

Michel Colomb, one of the earlier glories of the French Renaissance; it is really a lesson in good taste. Originally placed in the great abbey-church of Saint Martin, which was for so many ages the holy place of Tours, it happily survived the devastation to which that edifice, already sadly shattered by the wars of religion and successive profanations, finally succumbed in 1797. In 1815 the tomb found an asylum in a quiet corner of the cathedral.

I ought perhaps to be ashamed to acknowledge that I found the profane name of Balzac capable of adding an interest even to this venerable sanctuary.

Those who have read the terrible little story of "Le Curé de Tours" will perhaps remember that, as I have already mentioned, the simple and childlike old Abbé Birotteau, victim of the infernal machinations of the Abbé Troubert and Mademoiselle Gamard, had his quarters in the house of that lady (she had a specialty of letting lodgings to priests), which stood on the north side of the cathedral, so close under its walls that the supporting pillar of one of the great flying buttresses was planted in the spinster's garden. If you wander round behind the church in search of this more than historic habitation you will have occasion to see that the side and rear of Saint Gatien make a delectable and curious figure. A narrow lane passes beside the high wall which conceals from sight the palace of the archbishop and beneath the flying buttresses, the far-projecting gargoyles, and the fine south porch of the church. It terminates in a little dead grass-grown square entitled the Place Grégoire de Tours. All this part of the exterior of the cathedral is very brown, ancient, Gothic, grotesque; Balzac calls the whole place "a desert

Tours: the Cathedral

of stone." A battered and gabled wing or out-house (as it appears to be) of the hidden palace, with a queer old stone pulpit jutting out from it, looks down on this melancholy spot, on the other side of which is a seminary for young priests, one of whom issues from a door in a quiet corner, and, holding it open a moment behind him, shows a glimpse of a sunny garden, where you may fancy other black young figures strolling up and down. Mademoiselle Gamard's house, where she took her two abbés to board, and basely conspired with one against the other, is still farther round the cathedral. You cannot quite put your hand upon it to-day, for the dwelling of which you say to yourself that it must have been Mademoiselle Gamard's does not fulfil all the conditions mentioned in Balzac's description. The edifice in question, however, fulfils conditions enough; in particular, its little court offers hospitality to the big buttress of the church. Another buttress, corresponding with this (the two, between them, sustain the gable of the north transept), is planted in the small cloister, of which the door on the farther side of the little soundless Rue de la Psalette, where nothing seems ever to pass, opens opposite to that of Mademoiselle Gamard. There is a very genial old sacristan, who introduced me to this cloister from the church. It is very small and solitary, and much mutilated; but it nestles with a kind of wasted friendliness beneath the big walls of the cathedral. Its lower arcades have been closed, and it has a small plot of garden in the middle, with fruit-trees which I should imagine to be too much overshadowed. In one corner is a remarkably picturesque turret, the cage of a winding staircase which ascends (no great distance) to an upper gallery, where an old priest, the *chanoine-gardien* of the church, was walking to and fro with his breviary. The turret, the gallery, and even the chanoine-gardien, belonged, that sweet September morning, to the class of objects that are dear to painters in water-colours.

CHAPTER III. TOURS: SAINT MARTIN

I HAVE mentioned the church of Saint Martin, which was for many years the sacred spot, the shrine of pilgrimage, of Tours. Originally the simple burial-place of the great apostle who in the fourth century Christianised Gaul and who, in his day a brilliant missionary and worker of miracles, is chiefly known to modern fame as the worthy that cut his cloak in two at the gate of Amiens to share it with a beggar (tradition fails to say, I believe, what he did with the other half), the abbey of Saint Martin, through the Middle Ages, waxed rich and powerful, till it was known at last as one of the most luxurious religious houses in Christendom, with kings for its titular abbots (who, like Francis I., sometimes turned and despoiled it) and a great treasure of precious things. It passed, however, through many vicissitudes. Pillaged by the Normans in the ninth century and by the Huguenots in the sixteenth, it received its death-blow from the Revolution, which must have brought to bear upon it an energy of destruction proportionate to its mighty bulk. At the end of the last century a huge group of ruins alone remained, and what we see to-day may be called the ruin of a ruin. It is difficult to understand how so vast an edifice can have been so completely obliterated. Its site is given up to several ugly streets, and a pair of tall towers, separated by a space which speaks volumes as to the size of the church and looking across the close-pressed roofs to the happier spires of the cathedral, preserve for the modern world the memory of a great fortune, a great abuse, perhaps, and at all events a great penalty. One may believe that to this day a considerable part of the foundations of the great abbey is buried in the soil of Tours. The two surviving towers, which are dissimilar in shape, are enormous; with those of the cathedral they form the great landmarks of the town. One of them bears the name of the Tour de l'Horloge; the other, the so-called Tour Charlemagne, was erected (two centuries after her death) over the tomb of Luitgarde, wife of the great Emperor, who died at Tours in 800. I do not pretend to understand in what relation these very mighty and effectually detached masses of masonry stood to each other, but in their grey elevation and loneliness they are striking and suggestive to-day; holding their hoary heads far above the modern life of the town and looking sad and conscious, as they had outlived all uses. I know not what is supposed to have become of the bones

Tours: Saint Martin

of the blessed saint during the various scenes of confusion in which they may have got mislaid; but a mystic connection with his wonder-working relics may be perceived in a strange little sanctuary on the left of the street, which opens in front of the Tour Charlemagne—whose immemorial base, by the way, inhabited like a cavern, with a diminutive doorway where, as I passed, an old woman stood cleaning a pot, and a little dark window decorated with homely flowers, would be appreciated by a painter in search of "bits." The present shrine of Saint Martin is enclosed (provisionally, I suppose) in a very modern structure of timber, where in a dusky cellar, to which you descend by a wooden staircase adorned with votive tablets and paper roses, is placed a tabernacle surrounded by twinkling tapers and prostrate worshippers. Even this crepuscular vault, however, fails, I think, to attain solemnity; for the whole place is strangely vulgar and garish. The Catholic Church, as churches go to-day, is certainly the most spectacular; but it must feel that it has a great fund of impressiveness to draw upon when it opens such sordid little shops of sanctity as this. It is impossible not to be struck with the grotesqueness of such an establishment as the last link in the chain of a great ecclesiastical tradition.

In the same street, on the other side, a little below, is something better worth your visit than the shrine of Saint Martin. Knock at a high door in a white wall (there is a cross above it), and a fresh-faced sister of the convent of the Petit Saint Martin will let you into the charming little cloister, or rather fragment of cloister. Only one side of this surpassing structure remains, but the whole place is effective. In front of the beautiful arcade, which is terribly bruised and obliterated, is one of those walks of interlaced *tilleuls* which are so frequent in Touraine, and into which the green light filters so softly through a lattice of clipped twigs. Beyond this is a garden, and beyond the garden are the other buildings of the convent, where the placid sisters keep a school—a test, doubtless, of placidity. The imperfect arcade, which dates from the beginning of the sixteenth century (I know nothing of it but what is related in Mrs. Pattison's "Renaissance in France"), is a truly enchanting piece of work; the cornice and the angles of the arches being covered with the daintiest sculpture of arabesques, flowers, fruit, medallions, cherubs, griffins, all in the finest and most attenuated relief. It is like the chasing of a bracelet in stone. The taste, the fancy, the elegance, the refinement, are of the order that straightens up again our drooping standard of distinction. Such a piece of work is the purest flower of the French Renaissance; there is nothing more delicate in all Touraine.

Tours: Saint Julian

There is another fine thing at Tours which is not particularly delicate, but which makes a great impression—the very interesting old church of Saint Julian, lurking in a crooked corner at the right of the Rue Royale, near the point at which this indifferent thoroughfare emerges, with its little cry of admiration, on the bank of the Loire. Saint Julian stands to-day in a kind of neglected hollow, where it is much shut in by houses; but in the year 1225, when the edifice was begun, the site was doubtless, as the architects say, more eligible. At present indeed, when once you have caught a glimpse of the stout, serious Romanesque tower—which is not high, but strong—you feel that the building has something to say and that you must stop to listen to it. Within, it has a vast and splendid nave, of immense height, the nave of a cathedral, with a shallow choir and transepts and some admirable old glass. I spent half an hour there one morning, listening to what the church had to say, in perfect solitude. Not a worshipper entered, not even an old man with a broom. I have always thought there be a sex in fine buildings; and Saint Julian, with its noble nave, is of the gender of the name of its patron.

It was that same morning, I think, that I went in search of the old houses of Tours; for the town contains several goodly specimens of the domestic architecture of the past. The dwelling to which the average Anglo-Saxon will most promptly direct his steps, and the only one I have space to mention, is the so-called Maison de Tristan l'Hermite—a gentleman whom the readers of "Quentin Durward" will not have forgotten—the hangman-in-ordinary to that great and prompt chastener Louis XI. Unfortunately the house of Tristan is not the house of Tristan at all; this illusion has been cruelly dispelled. There are no illusions left at all, in the good city of Tours, with regard to Louis XI. His terrible castle of Plessis, the picture of which sends a shiver through the youthful reader of Scott, has been reduced to suburban insignificance; and the residence of his *triste compère*, on the front of which a festooned rope figures as a motive for decoration, is observed to have been erected in the succeeding century. The Maison de Tristan may be visited for itself, however, if not for Sir Walter; it is an exceedingly picturesque old façade, to which you pick your way through a narrow and tortuous street—a street terminating, a little beyond it, in the walk beside the river. An elegant Gothic doorway is let into the rusty-red brickwork, and strange little beasts crouch at the angles of the windows, which are surmounted by a tall graduated gable, pierced with a small orifice, where the large surface of brick, lifted out of the shadow of the street, looks yellow and faded. The whole thing is disfigured and decayed; but it is a capital subject for a sketch in colours. Only I must wish the sketcher better luck—or a better temper—than my own. If he ring the bell to be admitted to see the court, which I believe is more sketchable still, let him have patience to wait till the bell is answered. He can do the outside while they are coming.

Tours: Plessis-les-Tours

The Maison de Tristan, I say, may be visited for itself; but I hardly know for what the remnants of Plessis-les-Tours may be investigated. To reach them you wander through crooked suburban lanes, down the course of the Loire, to a rough, undesirable, incongruous spot, where a small, crude building of red brick is pointed out to you by your cabman (if you happen to drive) as the legendary frame of the grim portrait, and where a strong odour of pigsties and other unclean things so prostrates you for the moment that you have no energy to protest against this obvious fiction. You enter a yard encumbered with rubbish and a defiant dog, and an old woman emerges from a shabby lodge and assures you that you stand deep in historic dust. The red brick building, which looks like a small factory, rises on the ruins of the favourite residence of the dreadful Louis. It is now occupied by a company of night-scavengers, whose huge carts are drawn up in a row before it. I know not whether this be what is called the irony of fate; in any case, the effect of it is to accentuate strongly the fact (and through the most susceptible of our senses) that there is no honour for the authors of great wrongs. The dreadful Louis is reduced simply to an offence to the nostrils. The old woman shows you a few fragments—several dark, damp, much-encumbered vaults, denominated dungeons, and an old tower staircase in good condition. There are the outlines of the old moat; there is also the outline of the old guard-room, which is now a stable; and there are other silhouettes of the undistinguishable, which I have forgotten. You need all your imagination, and even then you cannot make out that Plessis was a castle of large extent, though the old woman, as your eye wanders over the neighbouring *potagers*, discourses much of the gardens and the park. The place looks mean and flat; and as you drive away you scarcely know whether to be glad or sorry that all those bristling horrors have been reduced to the commonplace.

Tours: Marmoutier

A certain flatness of impression awaits you also, I think, at Marmoutier, which is the other indispensable excursion in the near neighbourhood of Tours. The remains of this famous abbey lie on the other bank of the stream, about a mile and a half from the town. You follow the edge of the big brown river; of a fine afternoon you will be glad to go farther still. The abbey has gone the way of most abbeys; but the place is a restoration as well as a ruin, inasmuch as the Sisters of the Sacred Heart have erected a terribly modern convent here. A large Gothic doorway, in a high fragment of ancient wall, admits you to a garden-like enclosure, of great extent, from which you are further introduced into an extraordinarily tidy little parlour, where two good nuns sit at work. One of these came out with me and showed me over the place—a very definite little woman, with pointed features, an intensely distinct enunciation, and those pretty manners which (for whatever other teachings it may be responsible) the Catholic Church so often instils into its functionaries. I have never seen a woman who had got her lesson better than this little trotting, murmuring, edifying nun. The interest of Marmoutier to-day is not so much an interest of vision, so to speak, as an interest of reflection—that is, if you choose to reflect (for instance) upon the wondrous legend of the seven sleepers (you may see where they lie in a row), who lived together—they were brothers and cousins—in primitive piety, in the sanctuary constructed by the blessed Saint Martin (emulous of his precursor, Saint Gatianus), in the face of the hillside that overhung the Loire, and who, twenty-five years after his death, yielded up their seven souls at the same moment and enjoyed the rare convenience of retaining in their faces, in spite of mortality, every aspect of health. The abbey of Marmoutier, which sprang from the grottos in the cliff to which Saint Gatianus and Saint Martin retired to pray, was therefore the creation of the latter worthy, as the other great abbey, in the town proper, was the monument of his repose. The cliff is still there; and a winding staircase, in the latest taste, enables you conveniently to explore its recesses. These sacred niches are scooped out of the rock, and will give you an impression if you cannot do without one. You will feel them to be sufficiently venerable when you learn that the particular pigeon-hole of Saint Gatianus, the first Christian missionary to Gaul, dates from the third century. They have been dealt with as the Catholic Church deals with most of such places to-day; polished and furbished up, labelled and ticketed—*edited*, with notes, in short, like an old book. The process is a mistake—the early editions had more sanctity. The modern buildings (of the Sacred Heart), on which you look down from these points of vantage, are in the vulgar taste which sets its so mechanical stamp on all new Catholic work; but there was nevertheless a great sweetness in the scene. The afternoon was lovely, and it was flushing to a close. The large garden stretched beneath us, blooming with fruit and wine and succulent promise, and beyond it flowed the shining river. The air was still, the shadows were long, and the place, after all, was full of memories, most of which might pass for virtuous. It certainly was better than Plessis-les-Tours.

CHAPTER IV. BLOIS

YOUR business at Tours is to make excursions; and if you make them all you will be always under arms. The land is a rich reliquary, and an hour's drive from the town in almost any direction will bring you to the knowledge of some curious fragment of domestic or ecclesiastical architecture, some turreted manor, some lonely tower, some gabled village, some scene of something. Yet even if you do everything—which was not my case—you cannot hope to tell everything, and, fortunately for you, the excursions divide themselves into the greater and the less. You may achieve most of the greater in a week or two; but a summer in Touraine (which, by the way, must be a delectable thing) would hold none too many days for the others. If you come down to Tours from Paris your best economy is to spend a few days at Blois, where a clumsy but rather attractive little inn on the edge of the river will offer you a certain amount of that familiar and intermittent hospitality which a few weeks spent in the French provinces teaches you to regard as the highest attainable form of accommodation. Such an economy I was unable to practise. I could only go to Blois (from Tours) to spend the day; but this feat I accomplished twice over. It is a very sympathetic little town, as we say nowadays, and a week there would be sociable even without company. Seated on the north bank of the Loire, it presents a bright, clean face to the sun and has that aspect of cheerful leisure which belongs to all white towns that reflect themselves in shining waters. It is the water-front only of Blois, however, that exhibits this fresh complexion; the interior is of a proper brownness, as old sallow books are bound in vellum. The only disappointment is perforce the discovery that the castle, which is the special object of one's pilgrimage, does not overhang the river, as I had always allowed myself to understand. It overhangs the town, but is scarcely visible from the stream. That peculiar good fortune is reserved for Amboise and Chaumont.

The Château de Blois is one of the most beautiful and elaborate of all the old royal residences of this part of France, and I suppose it should have all the honours of my description. As you cross its threshold you step straight into the sunshine and storm of the French Renaissance. But it is too rich to describe—I can only pick out the high lights. It must be premised that in speaking of it as we see it to-day we speak of a monument unsparingly restored. The work of restoration has been as ingenious as it is profuse, but it rather chills the imagination. This is perhaps almost the first thing you feel as you approach the castle from the streets of the town. These little streets, as they leave the river, have pretensions to romantic steepness; one of them, indeed, which resolves itself into a high staircase with divergent wings (the *escalier monumental*), achieved this result so successfully as to remind me vaguely—I hardly know why—of the great slope of the Capitol, beside the Ara Cœli, at Rome. The view of that part of the castle which figures to-day as the back (it is the only aspect I had seen reproduced) exhibits the marks of restoration with the greatest assurance. The long façade, consisting only of balconied windows deeply recessed, erects itself on the summit of a considerable hill, which gives a fine, plunging movement to its foundations. The deep niches of the windows are all aglow with colour. They have been repainted with red and blue, relieved with gold figures; and each of them looks more like the royal box at a theatre than like the aperture of a palace dark with memories. For all this, however, and in spite of the fact that, as in some others of the châteaux of Touraine (always excepting the colossal Chambord, which is not in Touraine), there is less vastness than one had expected, the least hospitable aspect of Blois is abundantly impressive. Here, as elsewhere, lightness and grace are the keynote; and the recesses of the windows, with their happy proportions, their sculpture and their colour, are the hollow sockets of the human ornament. They need the figure of a Francis I. to complete them, or of a Diane de Poitiers, or even of a Henry III. The stand of this empty gilt cage emerges from a bed of light verdure which has been allowed to mass itself there and which contributes

Blois

to the springing look of the walls; while on the right it joins the most modern portion of the castle, the building erected, on foundations of enormous height and solidity, in 1635, by Gaston d'Orléans. This fine frigid mansion—the proper view of it is from the court within—is one of the masterpieces of François Mansard, whom a kind providence did not allow to make over the whole palace in the superior manner of his superior age. That had been a part of Gaston's plan—he was a blunderer born, and this precious project was worthy of him. This execution of it would surely have been one of the great misdeeds of history. Partially performed, the misdeed is not altogether to be regretted; for as one stands in the court of the castle and lets one's eye wander from the splendid wing of Francis I.—which is the last word of free and joyous invention—to the ruled lines and blank spaces of the ponderous pavilion of Mansard, one makes one's reflections upon the advantage, in even the least personal of the arts, of having something to say, and upon the stupidity of a taste which had ended by becoming an aggregation of negatives. Gaston's wing, taken by itself, has much of the *bel air* which was to belong to the architecture of Louis XIV.; but, taken in contrast to its flowering, laughing, living neighbour, it marks the difference between inspiration and calculation. We scarcely grudge it its place, however, for it adds a price to the rest of the pile.

We have entered the court, by the way, by jumping over the walls. The more orthodox method is to follow a modern terrace which leads to the left, from the side of the edifice that I began by speaking of, and passes round, ascending, to a little square on a considerably higher level, a square not, like the rather prosaic space on which the back (as I have called it) looks out, a thoroughfare. This small empty *place*, oblong in form, at once bright and quiet, and which ought to be grass-grown, offers an excellent setting to the entrance-front of the palace—the wing of Louis XII. The restoration here has been lavish; but it was perhaps but an inevitable reaction against the injuries, still more lavish, by which the unfortunate building had long been overwhelmed. It had fallen into a state of ruinous neglect, relieved only by the misuse proceeding from successive generations of soldiers, for whom its charming chambers served as barrack-room. Whitewashed, mutilated, dishonoured, the castle of Blois may be said to have escaped simply with its life. This is the history of Amboise as well, and is to a certain extent the history of Chambord. Delightful, at any rate, was the refreshed façade of Louis XII. as I stood and looked at it one bright September morning. In that soft, clear, merry light of Touraine, everything shows, everything speaks. Charming are the taste, the happy proportions, the colour of this beautiful front, to which the new feeling for a purely domestic architecture—an architecture of security and tranquillity, in which art could indulge itself—gave an air of youth and gladness. It is true that for a long time to come the castle of Blois was neither very safe nor very quiet; but its dangers came from within, from the evil passions of its inhabitants, and not from siege or invasion. The front of Louis XII. is of red brick, crossed here and there with purple; and the purple slate of the high roof, relieved with chimneys beautifully treated and with the embroidered caps of pinnacles and arches, with the porcupine of Louis, the ermine and the festooned rope which formed the devices of Anne of Brittany—the tone of this decorative roof carries out the mild glow of the wall. The wide, fair windows open as if they had expanded to let in the rosy dawn of the Renaissance. Charming, for that matter, are the windows of all the châteaux of Touraine, with their squareness corrected (as it is not in the Tudor architecture) by the curve of the upper corners, which gives this line the look, above the expressive aperture, of a pencilled eyebrow. The low door of this front is crowned by a high, deep niche, in which, under a splendid canopy, stiffly astride of a stiffly-draped charger, sits in profile an image of the good King Louis. Good as he had been—the father of his people, as he was called (I believe he remitted various taxes)—he was not good enough to pass muster at the Revolution; and the effigy I have just described is no more than a reproduction of the primitive statue demolished at that period.

Pass beneath it into the court, and the sixteenth century closes round you. It is a pardonable flight of fancy to say that the expressive faces of an age in which human passions lay very near the surface seem to peep out at you from the windows, from the balconies, from the thick foliage of the sculpture. The portion of the wing of Louis XII. that fronts toward the court is supported on a deep arcade. On your right is the wing erected by Francis I., the reverse of the mass of building which you see on approaching the castle. This exquisite, this extravagant, this transcendent piece of architecture is the most joyous utterance of the French Renaissance. It is covered with an embroidery of sculpture in which every detail is worthy of the hand of a goldsmith. In the middle of it, or rather a little to the left, rises the famous winding staircase (plausibly, but I believe not religiously, restored), which even the ages which most misused it must vaguely have admired. It forms a kind of chiselled cylinder, with wide interstices, so that the stairs are open to the air. Every inch of this structure, of its balconies, its pillars, its great central columns, is wrought over with lovely images, strange and ingenious devices, prime among which is the great heraldic salamander of Francis I. The salamander is everywhere at Blois—over the chimneys, over the doors, on the walls. This whole quarter of the castle bears the stamp of that eminently pictorial prince. The running cornice along the top of the front is like an unfolded, an elongated bracelet. The windows of the attic are like shrines for saints. The gargoyles, the medallions, the statuettes, the festoons are like the elaboration of some precious cabinet rather than the details of a building exposed to the weather and to the ages. In the interior there is a profusion of restoration, and it is all restoration in colour. This has been, evidently, a work of great energy and cost, but it will easily strike you as overdone. The universal freshness is a discord, a false note; it seems to light up the dusky past with an unnatural glare. Begun in the reign of Louis Philippe, this terrible process—the more terrible always the better case you conceive made out for it—has been carried so far that there is now scarcely a square inch of the interior that preserves the colour of the past. It is true that the place had been so coated over with modern abuse that something was needed to keep it alive; it is only perhaps a pity the clever doctors, not content with saving its life, should have undertaken to restore its bloom. The love of consistency, in such a business, is a dangerous lure. All the old apartments have been rechristened, as it were; the geography of the castle has been re-established. The guard-rooms, the bedrooms, the closets, the oratories have recovered their identity. Every spot connected with the murder of the

Blois

Duke of Guise is pointed out by a small, shrill boy, who takes you from room to room and who has learned his lesson in perfection. The place is full of Catherine de'Medici, of Henry III., of memories, of ghosts, of echoes, of possible evocations and revivals. It is covered with crimson and gold. The fireplaces and the ceilings are magnificent; they look like expensive "sets" at the grand opera.

I should have mentioned that below, in the court, the front of the wing of Gaston d'Orléans faces you as you enter, so that the place is a course of French history. Inferior in beauty and grace to the other portions of the castle, the wing is yet a nobler monument than the memory of Gaston deserves. The second of the sons of Henry IV.—who was no more fortunate as a father than as a husband—younger brother of Louis XIII. and father of the great Mademoiselle, the most celebrated, most ambitious, most self-complacent and most unsuccessful *fille à marier* in French history, passed in enforced retirement at the castle of Blois the close of a life of clumsy intrigues against Cardinal Richelieu, in which his rashness was only equalled by his pusillanimity and his ill-luck by his inaccessibility to correction, and which, after so many follies and shames, was properly summed up in the project— begun, but not completed—of demolishing the beautiful habitation of his exile in order to erect a better one. With Gaston d'Orléans, however, who lived there without dignity, the history of the Château de Blois declines. Its interesting period is that of the wars of religion. It was the chief residence of Henry III., and the scene of the principal events of his depraved and dramatic rule. It has been restored more than enough, as I have said, by architects and decorators; the visitor, as he moves through its empty rooms, which are at once brilliant and ill-lighted (they have not been refurnished), undertakes a little restoration of his own. His imagination helps itself from the things that remain; he tries to see the life of the sixteenth century in its form and dress—its turbulence, its passions, its loves and hates, its treacheries, falsities, sincerities, faith, its latitude of personal development, its presentation of the whole nature, its nobleness of costume, charm of speech, splendour of taste, unequalled picturesqueness. The picture is full of movement, of contrasted light and darkness, full altogether of abominations. Mixed up with them all is the great theological motive, so that the drama wants little to make it complete. What episode was ever more perfect—looked at as a dramatic occurrence—than the murder of the Duke of Guise? The insolent prosperity of the victim; the weakness, the vices, the terrors, of the author of the deed; the perfect execution of the plot; the accumulation of horror in what followed it—render it, as a crime, one of the classic things.

But we must not take the Château de Blois too hard: I went there, after all, by way of entertainment. If among these sinister memories your visit should threaten to prove a tragedy, there is an excellent way of removing the impression. You may treat yourself at Blois to a very cheerful afterpiece. There is a charming industry practised there, and practised in charming conditions. Follow the bright little quay down the river till you get quite out of the town and reach the point where the road beside the Loire becomes sinuous and attractive, turns the corner of diminutive headlands and makes you wonder what is beyond. Let not your curiosity induce you, however, to pass by a modest white villa which overlooks the stream, enclosed in a fresh little court; for here dwells an artist—an artist in faience. There is no sort of sign, and the place looks peculiarly private. But if you ring at the gate you will not be turned away. You will, on the contrary, be ushered upstairs into a parlour—there is nothing resembling a shop—encumbered with specimens of remarkably handsome pottery. The ware is of the best, a careful reproduction of old forms, colours, devices; and the master of the establishment is one of those completely artistic types that are often found in France. His reception is as friendly as his work is ingenious; and I think it is not too much to say that you like the work better because he has produced it. His vases, cups and jars, lamps, platters, *plaques*, with their brilliant glaze, their innumerable figures, their family likeness and wide variations, are scattered through his occupied rooms; they serve at once as his stock-in-trade and as household ornament. As we all know, this is an age of prose, of machinery, of wholesale production, of coarse and hasty processes. But one brings away from the establishment of the very intelligent M. Ulysse the sense of a less eager activity and a greater search for perfection. He has but a few workmen and he gives them plenty of time. The place makes a little vignette, leaves an impression—the quiet white house in its garden on the road by the wide, clear river, without the smoke, the bustle, the ugliness, of so much of our modern industry. It struck me as an effort Mr. Ruskin might have inspired and Mr. William Morris—though that be much to say—have forgiven.

CHAPTER V. CHAMBORD

THE second time I went to Blois I took a carriage for Chambord, and came back by the Château de Cheverny and the forest of Russy—a charming little expedition, to which the beauty of the afternoon (the finest in a rainy season that was spotted with bright days) contributed not a little. To go to Chambord you cross the Loire, leave it on one side and strike away through a country in which salient features become less and less numerous and which at last has no other quality than a look of intense and peculiar rurality—the characteristic, even when it be not the charm, of so much of the landscape of France. This is not the appearance of wildness, for it goes with great cultivation; it is simply the presence of the delving, drudging, economising peasant. But it is a deep, unrelieved rusticity. It is a peasant's landscape; not, as in England, a landlord's. On the way to Chambord you enter the flat and sandy Sologne. The wide horizon opens out like a great *potager*, without interruptions, without an eminence, with here and there a long, low stretch of wood. There is an absence of hedges, fences, signs of property; everything is absorbed in the general flatness—the patches of vineyard, the scattered cottages, the villages, the children (planted and staring and almost always pretty), the women in the fields, the white caps, the faded blouses, the big sabots. At the end of an hour's drive (they assure you at Blois that even with two horses you will spend double that time), I passed through a sort of gap in a wall which does duty as the gateway of the domain of a proscribed pretender. I followed a straight avenue through a disfeatured park—the park of Chambord has twenty-one miles of circumference; a very sandy, scrubby, melancholy plantation, in which the timber must have been cut many times over and is to-day a mere tangle of brushwood. Here, as in so many spots in France, the traveller perceives that he is in a land of revolutions. Nevertheless its great extent and the long perspective of its avenues give this frugal shrubbery a certain state; just as its shabbiness places it in agreement with one of the strongest impressions awaiting you. You pursue one of these long perspectives a proportionate time, and at last you see the chimneys and pinnacles of Chambord rise apparently out of the ground. The filling-in of the wide moats that formerly surrounded it has, in vulgar parlance, let it down and given it a monstrous over-crowned air that is at the same time a magnificent Orientalism. The towers, the turrets, the cupolas, the gables, the lanterns, the chimneys look more like the spires of a city than the salient points of a single building. You emerge from the avenue and find yourself at the foot of an enormous fantastic mass. Chambord has a strange mixture of society and solitude. A little village clusters within view of its liberal windows, and a couple of inns near by offer entertainment to pilgrims. These things of course are incidents of the political proscription which hangs its thick veil over the place. Chambord is truly royal—royal in its great scale, its grand air, its indifference to common considerations. If a cat may look at a king, a tavern may look at a palace. I enjoyed my visit to this extraordinary structure as much as if I had been a legitimist; and indeed there is something interesting in any monument of a great system, any bold presentation of a tradition.

You leave your vehicle at one of the inns, which are very decent and tidy and in which every one is very civil, as if in this latter respect the neighbourhood of a Court veritably set the fashion, and you proceed across the grass and the gravel to a small door, a door infinitely subordinate and conferring no title of any kind on those who enter it. Here you ring a bell, which a highly respectable person answers (a person perceptibly affiliated, again, to the old regime), after which she ushers you over a vestibule into an inner court. Perhaps the strongest impression I got at Chambord came to me as I stood in this court. The woman who admitted me did not come with

43

me; I was to find my guide somewhere else. The specialty of Chambord is its prodigious round towers. There are, I believe, no less than eight of them, placed at each angle of the inner and outer square of buildings; for the castle is in the form of a larger structure which encloses a smaller one. One of these towers stood before me in the court; it seemed to fling its shadow

Chambord

over the place; while above, as I looked up, the pinnacles and gables, the enormous chimneys, soared into the bright blue air. The place was empty and silent; shadows of gargoyles, of extraordinary projections, were thrown across the clear grey surfaces. One felt that the whole thing was monstrous. A cicerone appeared, a languid young man in a rather shabby livery, and led me about with a mixture of the impatient and the desultory, of condescension and humility. I do not profess to understand the plan of Chambord, and I may add that I do not even desire to do so; for it is much more entertaining to think of it, as you can so easily, as an irresponsible, insoluble labyrinth. Within it is a wilderness of empty chambers, a royal and romantic barrack. The exiled prince to whom it gives its title has not the means to keep up four hundred rooms; he contents himself with preserving the huge outside. The repairs of the prodigious roof alone must absorb a large part of his revenue. The great feature of the interior is the celebrated double staircase, rising straight through the building, with two courses of steps, so that people may ascend and descend without meeting. This staircase is a truly majestic piece of humour; it gives you the note, as it were, of Chambord. It opens on each landing to a vast guard-room, in four arms, radiations of the winding shaft. My guide made me climb to the great open-work lantern which, springing from the roof at the termination of the rotund staircase (surmounted here by a smaller one), forms the pinnacle of the bristling crown of the pile. This lantern is tipped with a huge *fleur-de-lis* in stone—the only one, I believe, that the Revolution did not succeed in pulling down. Here, from narrow windows, you look over the wide, flat country and the tangled, melancholy park, with the rotation of its straight avenues. Then you walk about the roof in a complication of galleries, terraces, balconies, through the multitude of chimneys and gables. This roof, which is in itself a sort of castle in the air, has an extravagant, fabulous quality, and with its profuse ornamentation—the salamander of Francis I. is a constant motive—its lonely pavements, its sunny niches, the balcony that looks down over the closed and grass-grown main entrance, a strange, half-sad, half-brilliant charm. The stonework is covered with fine mould. There are places that reminded me of some of those quiet mildewed corners of courts and terraces into which the traveller who wanders through the Vatican looks down from neglected windows. They show you two or three furnished rooms, with Bourbon portraits, hideous tapestries from the ladies of France, a collection of the toys of the *enfant du miracle*, all military and of the finest make. "Tout cela fonctionne," the guide said of these miniature weapons; and I wondered, if he should take it into his head to fire off his little cannon, how much harm the Comte de Chambord would do.

From below the castle would look crushed by the redundancy of its upper protuberances if it were not for the enormous girth of its round towers, which appear to give it a robust lateral development. These towers, however, fine as they are in their way, struck me as a little stupid; they are the exaggeration of an exaggeration. In a building erected after the days of defence and proclaiming its peaceful character from its hundred embroideries and cupolas, they seem to indicate a want of invention. I shall risk the accusation of bad taste if I say that, impressive as it is, the Château de Chambord seemed to me to have altogether a touch of that quality of stupidity. The trouble is that it stands for nothing very momentous; it has not happened, in spite of sundry vicissitudes, to have a strongly-marked career. Compared with that of Blois and Amboise its past is rather vacant; and one feels to a certain extent the contrast between its pompous appearance and its spacious but somewhat colourless annals. It had indeed the good fortune to be erected by Francis I., whose name by itself expresses a good deal of history. Why he should have built a palace in those sandy plains will ever remain an unanswered question, for kings have never been obliged to give reasons. In addition to the fact that the country was rich in game and that Francis was a passionate hunter, it is suggested by M. de la Saussaye, the author of the very complete little account of the place which you may buy at the bookseller's at Blois, that he was governed in his choice of the site by the chance that a charming woman had previously lived there. The Comtesse de Thoury had a manor in the neighbourhood, and the Comtesse de Thoury had been the object of a youthful passion on the part of the most susceptible of princes before his accession to the throne. This great pile was reared, therefore, according to M. de la Saussaye, as a *souvenir de premières amours*! It is certainly a very massive memento; and if these tender passages were proportionate to the building that commemorates them, the flame blazed indeed. There has been much discussion as to the architect employed by Francis I., and the honour of having designed this splendid residence has been claimed for several of the Italian artists who early in the sixteenth century came to seek patronage in France. It seems well established to-day, however, that Chambord was the work neither of Primaticcio, of

Chambord

Vignola, nor of Il Rosso, all of whom have left some trace of their sojourn in France; but of an obscure yet very complete genius, Pierre Nepveu, known as Pierre Trinqueau, who is designated in the papers which preserve in some degree the history of the origin of the edifice, as the *maistre de l'œuvre de maçonnerie*. Behind this modest title, apparently, we must recognise one of the most original talents of the French Renaissance; and it is a proof of the vigour of the artistic life of that period that, brilliant production being everywhere abundant, an artist of so high a value should not have been treated by his contemporaries as a celebrity. We make our celebrities to-day at smaller cost.

The immediate successors of Francis I. continued to visit Chambord; but it was neglected by Henry IV. and was never afterwards a favourite residence of any French king. Louis XIV. appeared there on several occasions, and the apparition was characteristically brilliant; but Chambord could not long detain a monarch who had gone to the expense of creating a Versailles ten miles from Paris. With Versailles, Fontainebleau, Saint-Germain and Saint-Cloud within easy reach of their capital, the later French sovereigns had little reason to take the air in the dreariest province of their kingdom. Chambord therefore suffered from royal indifference, though in the last century a use was found for its deserted halls. In 1725 it was occupied by the luckless

Stanislaus Leczynski, who spent the greater part of his life in being elected King of Poland and being ousted from his throne, and who, at this time a refugee in France, had found a compensation for some of his misfortunes in marrying his daughter to Louis XV. He lived eight years at Chambord and filled up the moats of the castle. In 1748 it found an illustrious tenant in the person of Maurice de Saxe, the victor of Fontenoy, who, however, two years after he had taken possession of it, terminated a life which would have been longer had he been less determined to make it agreeable. The Revolution, of course, was not kind to Chambord. It despoiled it in so far as possible of every vestige of its royal origin, and swept like a whirlwind through apartments to which upwards of two centuries had contributed a treasure of decoration and furniture. In that wild blast these precious things were destroyed or for ever scattered. In 1791 an odd proposal was made to the French Government by a company of English Quakers, who had conceived the bold idea of establishing in the palace a manufacture of some peaceful commodity not to-day recorded. Napoleon allotted Chambord, as a "dotation," to one of his marshals, Berthier, for whose benefit it was converted, in Napoleonic fashion, into the so-called principality of Wagram. By the Princess of Wagram, the marshal's widow, it was, after the Restoration, sold to the trustees of a national subscription which had been established for the purpose of presenting it to the infant Duke of Bordeaux, then prospective King of France. The presentation was duly made; but the Comte de Chambord, who had changed his title in recognition of the gift, was despoiled of his property by the government of Louis Philippe. He appealed for redress to the tribunals of his country; and the consequence of his appeal was an interminable litigation, by which, however, finally, after the lapse of twenty-five years, he was established in his rights. In 1871 he paid his first visit to the domain which had been offered him half a century before, a term of which he had spent forty years in exile. It was from Chambord that he dated his famous letter of the 5th of July of that year—the letter, directed to his so-called subjects, in which he waves aloft the white flag of the Bourbons. This rare miscalculation—virtually an invitation to the French people to repudiate, as their national ensign, that immortal tricolour, the flag of the Revolution and the Empire, under which they have won the glory which of all glories has hitherto been dearest to them and which is associated with the most romantic, the most heroic, the epic, the consolatory, period of their history—this luckless manifesto, I say, appears to give the measure of the political wisdom of the excellent Henry V. The proposal should have had less simplicity or the people less irony.

Chambord

On the whole Chambord makes a great impression; and the hour I was there, while the yellow afternoon light slanted upon the September woods, there was a dignity in its desolation. It spoke, with a muffled but audible voice, of the vanished monarchy, which had been so strong, so splendid, but to-day had become a vision almost as fantastic as the cupolas and chimneys that rose before me. I thought, while I lingered there, of all the fine things it takes to make up such a monarchy; and how one of them is a superfluity of mouldering, empty palaces. Chambord is touching—that is the best word for it; and if the hopes of another restoration are in the follies of the Republic, a little reflection on that eloquence of ruin ought to put the Republic on its guard. A sentimental tourist may venture to remark that in presence of all the haunted houses that appeal in this mystical manner to the retrospective imagination it cannot afford to be foolish. I thought of all this as I drove back to Blois by the way of the Château de Cheverny. The road took us out of the park of Chambord, but through a region of flat woodland, where the trees were not mighty, and again into the prosy plain of the Sologne—a thankless soil to sow, I believe, but lately much amended by the magic of cheerful French industry and thrift. The light had already begun to fade, and my drive reminded me of a passage in some rural novel of Madame Sand. I passed a couple of timber and plaster churches, which looked very old, black and crooked, and had lumpish wooden porches and galleries encircling the base. By the time I reached Cheverny the clear twilight had approached. It was late to ask to be allowed to visit an inhabited house; but it was the hour at which I like best to visit almost anything. My coachman drew up before a gateway, in a high wall, which opened upon a short avenue, along which I took my way on foot; the coachmen in those parts being, for reasons best known to themselves, mortally averse to driving up to a house. I answered the challenge of a very tidy little portress who sat, in company with a couple of children, enjoying the evening air in front of her lodge, and who told me to walk a little farther and turn to the right. I obeyed her to the letter, and my turn brought me into sight of a house as charming as an old manor in a fairy tale. I had but a rapid and partial view of Cheverny; but that view was a glimpse of perfection. A light, sweet mansion stood looking over a wide green lawn, over banks of flowers and groups of trees. It had a striking character of elegance, produced partly by a series of Renaissance busts let into circular niches in the façade. The place looked so private, so reserved, that it seemed an act of violence to ring, a stranger and foreigner, at the graceful door. But if I had not rung I should be unable to express—as it is such a pleasure to do—my sense of the exceeding courtesy with which this admirable house is shown. It was near the dinner-hour—the most sacred hour of the day; but I was freely conducted into the inhabited apartments. They are extremely beautiful. What I chiefly remember is the charming staircase of white embroidered stone, and the great *salle des gardes* and *chambre à coucher du roi* on the second floor. Cheverny, built in 1634, is of a much later date than the other royal residences of this part of France; it belongs to the end of the Renaissance and has a touch of the rococo. The guard-room is a superb apartment; and as it contains little save its magnificent ceiling and fireplace and certain dim tapestries on its walls, you the more easily take the measure of its noble proportions. The servant opened the shutters of a single window, and the last rays of the twilight slanted into the rich brown gloom. It was in the same picturesque fashion that I saw the bedroom (adjoining) of Henry IV., where a legendary-looking bed, draped in folds long unaltered, defined itself in the haunted dusk. Cheverny remains to me a very charming, a partly mysterious vision. I drove back to Blois in the dark, some nine miles, through the forest of Russy, which belongs to the State and which, though consisting apparently of small timber, looked under the stars sufficiently vast and primeval. There was a damp autumnal smell and the occasional sound of a stirring thing; and as I moved through the evening air I thought of Francis I. and Henry IV.

CHAPTER VI. AMBOISE

YOU may go to Amboise either from Blois or from Tours; it is about half-way between these towns. The great point is to go, especially if you have put it off repeatedly; and to go, if possible, on a day when the great view of the Loire, which you enjoy from the battlements and terraces, presents itself under a friendly sky. Three persons, of whom the author of these lines was one, spent the greater part of a perfect Sunday morning in looking at it. It was astonishing, in the course of the rainiest season in the memory of the oldest Tourangeau, how many perfect days we found to our hand. The town of Amboise lies, like Tours, on the left bank of the river—a little white-faced town staring across an admirable bridge and leaning, behind, as it were, against the pedestal of rock on which the dark castle masses itself. The town is so small, the pedestal so big and the castle so high and striking, that the clustered houses at the base of the rock are like the crumbs that have fallen from a well-laden table. You pass among them, however, to ascend by a circuit to the château, which you attack, obliquely, from behind. It is the property of the Comte de Paris, another pretender to the French throne; having come to him remotely, by inheritance, from his ancestor, the Duc de Penthièvre, who toward the close of the last century bought it from the Crown, which had recovered it after a lapse. Like the castle of Blois, it has been injured and defaced by base uses, but, unlike the castle of Blois, it has not been completely restored. "It is very, very dirty, but very curious"—it is in these terms that I heard it described by an English lady who was generally to be found engaged upon a tattered Tauchnitz in the little *salon de lecture* of the hotel at Tours. The description is not inaccurate; but it should be said that if part of the dirtiness of Amboise is the result of its having served for years as a barrack and as a prison, part of it comes from the presence of restoring stonemasons, who have woven over a considerable portion of it a mask of scaffolding. There is a good deal of neatness as well, and the restoration of some of the parts seems finished. This process, at Amboise, consists for the most part simply of removing the vulgar excrescences of the last two centuries.

The interior is virtually a blank, the old apartments having been chopped up into small modern rooms; it will have to be completely reconstructed. A worthy woman with a military profile and that sharp, positive manner which the goodwives who show you through the châteaux of Touraine are rather apt to have, and in whose high respectability, to say nothing of the frill of her cap and the cut of her thick brown dress, my companions and I thought we discovered the particular note, or *nuance*, of Orleanism—a competent, appreciative, peremptory person, I say—attended us through the particularly delightful hour we spent upon the ramparts of Amboise. Denuded and disfeatured within and bristling without with bricklayers' ladders, the place was yet extraordinarily impressive and interesting. I should mention that we spent a great deal of time in looking at the view. Sweet was the view, and magnificent; we preferred it so much to certain portions of the interior, and to occasional effusions of historical information, that the old lady with the profile sometimes lost patience with us. We laid ourselves open to the charge of preferring it even to the little chapel of Saint Hubert, which stands on the edge of the great terrace and has, over the portal, a wonderful sculpture of the miraculous hunt of that holy man. In the way of plastic art this elaborate scene is the gem of Amboise. It seemed to us that we had never been in a place where there are so many points of vantage to look down from. In the matter of position Amboise is certainly supreme in the list of perched places; and I say this with a proper recollection of the claims of Chaumont and of Loches—which latter, by the way (the afterthought is due), is not on the Loire. The platforms, the bastions, the terraces, the high-niched windows and balconies, the hanging gardens and dizzy crenellations, of this complicated structure, keep you in perpetual intercourse with an immense horizon. The great feature of the place is the obligatory round tower which occupies the northern end of it, and which has now been completely restored. It is of astounding size, a fortress in itself, and contains, instead of a staircase, a wonderful inclined plane, so wide and gradual that a coach and four may be driven to the top. This colossal cylinder has to-day no visible use; but it corresponds, happily enough, with the great circle of the prospect. The gardens of Amboise, lifted high aloft, covering the irregular remnants of the platform on which the castle stands and making up in picturesqueness what they lack in extent, constitute of course but a scanty domain. But bathed, as we found them, in the autumn sunshine and doubly private from their aerial site, they offered irresistible opportunities for a stroll interrupted, as one leaned against their low parapets, by long contemplative pauses. I remember in particular a certain terrace planted with clipped limes upon which we looked down from the summit of the big tower. It seemed from that point to be absolutely necessary to one's happiness to go down and spend the rest of the morning there; it was an ideal place to walk to and fro and talk. Our venerable conductress, to whom our relation had gradually become more filial, permitted us to gratify this innocent wish—to the extent, that is, of taking a turn or two under the mossy *tilleuls*. At the end of this terrace is the low door, in a wall, against the top of which, in 1498, Charles VIII., according to an accepted tradition, knocked his head to such good purpose that he died. It was within the walls of Amboise that his widow, Anne of Brittany, already in mourning for three children, two of whom we have seen commemorated in sepulchral marble at Tours, spent the first violence of that grief which was presently dispelled by a union with her husband's cousin and successor, Louis XII. Amboise was a frequent resort of the French Court during the sixteenth century; it was here that the young Mary Stuart spent sundry hours of her first marriage. The wars of religion have left here the ineffaceable stain which they left wherever they passed. An imaginative visitor at Amboise to-day may fancy that the traces of blood are mixed with the red rust on the crossed iron bars of the grim-looking balcony to which the heads of the Huguenots executed on the discovery of the conspiracy of La Renaudie are rumoured to have been suspended. There was room on the stout balustrade—an admirable piece of work—for a ghastly array. The same rumour represents Catherine de'Medici and the young queen as watching from this balcony the *noyades* of the captured Huguenots in the Loire. The facts of history are bad enough; the fictions are, if possible, worse; but there is little doubt that the future Queen of Scots learnt the first lessons of life at a horrible school. If in subsequent years she was a prodigy of innocence and virtue, it was not the fault of her whilom mother-in-law, of her uncles of the house of Guise, or of the examples presented to her either at the windows of the castle of Amboise or in its more private recesses.

Chaumont

It was difficult to believe in these dark deeds, however, as we looked through the golden morning at the placidity of the far-shining Loire. The ultimate consequence of this spectacle was a desire to follow the river as far as the castle of Chaumont. It is true that the cruelties practised of old at Amboise might have seemed less phantasmal to persons destined to suffer from a modern form of inhumanity. The mistress of the little inn at the base of the castle-rock—it stands very pleasantly beside the river, and we had breakfasted there—declared to us that the Château de Chaumont, which is often during the autumn closed to visitors, was at that particular moment standing so wide open to receive us that it was our duty to hire one of her carriages and drive thither with speed. This assurance was so satisfactory that we presently found ourselves seated in this wily woman's most commodious vehicle and rolling, neither too fast nor too slow, along the margin of the Loire. The drive of about an hour, beneath constant clumps of chestnuts, was charming enough to have been taken for itself; and indeed when we reached Chaumont we saw that our reward was to be simply the usual reward of virtue, the consciousness of having attempted the right. The Château de Chaumont was inexorably closed; so we learned from a talkative lodge-keeper, who gave what grace she could to her refusal. This good woman's dilemma was almost touching; she wished to reconcile two impossibles. The castle was not to be visited, for the family of its master was staying there; and yet she was loath to turn away a party of which she was good enough to say that it had a *grand genre*; for, as she also remarked, she had her living to earn. She tried to arrange a compromise, one of the elements of which was that we should descend from our carriage and trudge up a hill which would bring us to a designated point where, over the paling of the garden, we might obtain an oblique and surreptitious view of a small portion of the castle walls. This suggestion led us to inquire (of each other) to what degree of baseness it is lawful for an enlightened lover of the picturesque to resort in order not to have a blank page in his collection. One of our trio decided characteristically against any form of derogation; so she sat in the carriage and sketched some object that was public property while her two companions, who were not so proud, trudged up a muddy ascent which formed a kind of back-stairs. It is perhaps no more than they deserved that they were disappointed. Chaumont is feudal, if you please; but the modern spirit is in possession. It forms a vast clean-scraped mass, with big round towers, ungarnished with a leaf of ivy or a patch of moss, surrounded by gardens of moderate extent (save where the muddy lane of which I speak passes near it), and looking rather like an enormously magnified villa. The great merit of Chaumont is its position, which almost exactly resembles that of Amboise; it sweeps the river up and down and seems to look over half the province. This, however, was better appreciated as, after coming down the hill and re-entering the carriage, we drove across the long suspension-bridge which crosses the Loire just beyond the village and over which we made our way to the small station of Onzain, at the farther end, to take the train back to Tours. Look back from the middle of this bridge; the whole picture composes, as the painters say. The towers, the pinnacles, the fair front of the château, perched above its fringe of garden and the rusty roofs of the village and facing the afternoon sky, which is reflected also in the great stream that sweeps below, all this makes a contribution to your happiest memories of Touraine.

CHAPTER VII. CHENONCEAUX

WE never went to Chinon; it was a fatality. We planned it a dozen times; but the weather interfered, or the trains didn't suit, or one of the party was fatigued with the adventures of the day before. This excursion was so much postponed that it was finally postponed to everything. Besides, we had to go to Chenonceaux, to Azay-le-Rideau, to Langeais, to Loches. So I have not the memory of Chinon; I have only the regret. But regret, as well as memory, has its visions; especially when, like memory, it is assisted by photographs. The castle of Chinon in this form appears to me as an enormous ruin, a mediæval fortress of the extent almost of a city. It covers a hill above the Vienne, and after being impregnable in its time is indestructible to-day. (I risk this phrase in the face of the prosaic truth. Chinon, in the days when it was a prize, more than once suffered capture, and at present it is crumbling inch by inch. It is apparent, however, I believe, that these inches encroach little upon acres of masonry.) It was in the castle that Jeanne Dare had her first interview with Charles VII., and it is in the town that François Rabelais is supposed to have been born. To the castle, moreover, the lover of the picturesque is earnestly recommended to direct his steps. But one always misses something, and I would rather have missed Chinon than Chenonceaux. Fortunate exceedingly were the few hours we passed on the spot on which we missed nothing.

"In 1747," says Jean-Jacques Rousseau in his "Confessions," "we went to spend the autumn in Touraine, at the Château of Chenonceaux, a royal residence upon the Cher, built by Henry II. for Diana of Poitiers, whose initials are still to be seen there, and now in possession of M. Dupin, the farmer-general. We amused ourselves greatly at this fine place; the living was of the best, and I became as fat as a monk. We made a great deal of music and acted comedies."

This is the only description that Rousseau gives of one of the most romantic houses in France and of an episode that must have counted as one of the most agreeable in his uncomfortable career. The eighteenth century contented itself with general epithets; and when Jean-Jacques has said that Chenonceaux was a "beau lieu," he thinks himself absolved from further characterisation. We later sons of time have, both for our pleasure and our pain, invented the fashion of special terms, and I am afraid that even common decency obliges me to pay some larger tribute than this to the architectural gem of Touraine. Fortunately I can discharge my debt with gratitude. In going from Tours you leave the valley of the Loire and enter that of the Cher, and at the end of about an hour you see the turrets of the castle on your right, among the trees, down in the meadows, beside the quiet little river. The station and the village are about ten minutes' walk from the château, and the village contains a very tidy inn, where, if you are not in too great a hurry to commune with the shades of the royal favourite and the jealous queen, you will perhaps stop and order a dinner to be ready for you in the evening. A straight, tall avenue leads to the grounds of the castle; what I owe to exactitude compels me to add that it is crossed by the railway-line. The place is so arranged, however, that the château need know nothing of passing trains—which pass, indeed, though the grounds are not large, at a very sufficient distance. I may add that the trains throughout this part of France have a noiseless, desultory, dawdling, almost stationary quality, which makes them less of an offence than usual. It was a Sunday afternoon and the light was yellow save under the trees of the avenue, where, in spite of the waning of September, it was duskily green. Three or four peasants, in festal attire, were strolling about. On a bench at the beginning of the avenue sat a man with two women. As I advanced with my companions he rose, after a sudden stare, and approached me with a smile in which (to be Johnsonian for a moment) certitude was mitigated by modesty and eagerness was embellished with respect. He came toward me with a salutation that I had seen before, and I am happy to say that after an instant I ceased to be guilty of the brutality of not knowing where. There was only one place in the world where people smile like that, only one place where the art of salutation has that perfect grace. This excellent creature used to crook his arm, in Venice, when I stepped into my gondola; and I now laid my hand on that member with the familiarity of glad recognition; for it was only surprise that had kept me even for a moment from accepting the genial Francesco as an ornament of the landscape of Touraine. What on earth—the phrase is the right one—was a Venetian gondolier doing at Chenonceaux? He had been brought from Venice, gondola and all, by the mistress of the charming house, to paddle about on the Cher. Our meeting was affectionate, though there was a kind of violence in seeing him so far from home. He was too well dressed, too well fed; he had grown stout, and his nose had the tinge of good claret. He remarked that the life of the household to which he had the honour to belong was that of a *casa regia*; which must have been a great change for poor Checco, whose habits in Venice were not regal. However, he was the sympathetic Checco still; and for five minutes after I left him I thought less about the little pleasure-house by the Cher than about the palaces of the Adriatic.

But attention was not long in coming round to the charming structure that presently rose before us. The pale yellow front of the château, the small scale of which is at first a surprise, rises beyond a considerable court, at the entrance of which a massive and detached round tower, with a turret on its brow (a relic of the building that preceded the actual villa), appears to keep guard. This court is not enclosed—or is enclosed at least only by the gardens, portions of which are at present in process of radical readjustment. Therefore, though Chenonceaux has no great height, its delicate façade stands up boldly enough. This façade, one of the most finished things in Touraine, consists of two storeys, surmounted by an attic which, as so often in the buildings of the French Renaissance, is the richest part of the house. The high-pitched roof contains three windows of beautiful design, covered with embroidered caps and flowering into crocketed spires. The window above the door is deeply niched; it opens upon a balcony made in the form of a double pulpit—one of the most charming features of the front. Chenonceaux is not large, as I say, but into its delicate compass is packed a great deal of history—history which differs from that of Amboise and Blois in being of the private and sentimental kind. The echoes of the place, faint and far as they are to-day, are not political, but personal. Chenonceaux dates, as a residence, from the year 1515, when the shrewd Thomas Bohier, a public functionary who had grown rich in handling the finances of Normandy and had acquired the estate from a family which, after giving it many feudal lords, had fallen into poverty, erected the present structure on the foundations of an old mill. The design is attributed, with I know not what justice, to Pierre Nepveu, *alias* Trinqueau, the audacious architect of Chambord. On the death of Bohier the house passed to his son, who, however, was forced, under cruel pressure, to surrender it to the Crown in compensation for a so-called deficit in the official accounts of this rash parent and predecessor. Francis I. held the place till his death; but Henry II., on ascending the throne, presented it out of hand to that mature charmer, the admired of two generations, Diana of Poitiers. Diana enjoyed it till the death of her protector; but when this event occurred the widow of the monarch, who had been obliged to submit in silence, for years, to the ascendency of a rival, took the most pardonable of all the revenges with which the name of Catherine de'Medici is associated and turned her out of doors. Diana was not in want of refuges, Catherine went through the form of giving her Chaumont in exchange; but there was only one Chenonceaux. Catherine devoted herself to making the place more completely unique. The feature that renders it sole of its kind is not appreciated till you wander round to either side of the house. If a certain springing lightness is the characteristic of Chenonceaux, if it bears in every line the aspect of a place of recreation—a place intended for delicate, chosen pleasures—nothing can confirm this expression better than the strange, unexpected movement with which, from behind, it carries itself across the river. The earlier building stands in the water; it had inherited the foundations of the mill destroyed by Thomas Bohier. The first step therefore had been taken upon solid piles of masonry; and the ingenious Catherine—she was a *raffinée*—simply proceeded to take the others. She continued the piles to the opposite bank of the Cher, and over them she threw a long, straight gallery of two tiers. This part of the château, which mainly resembles a house built upon a bridge and occupying its entire length, is of course the great curiosity of Chenonceaux. It forms on each floor a charming corridor, which, within, is illuminated from either side by the flickering river-light. The architecture of these galleries, seen from without, is less elegant than that of the main building, but the aspect of the whole thing is delightful. I have spoken of Chenonceaux as a "villa," using the word advisedly, for the place is neither a castle nor a palace. It is a very exceptional villa, but it has the villa-quality—the look of being intended for life in common. This look is not at all contradicted by the wing across the Cher, which only suggests indoor perspectives and intimate pleasures—walks in pairs on rainy days; games and dances on autumn nights; together with as much as may be of moonlighted dialogue (or silence) in the course of evenings more genial still, in the well-marked recesses of windows.

Chenonceaux

It is safe to say that such things took place there in the last century, during the kindly reign of Monsieur and Madame Dupin. This period presents itself as the happiest in the annals of Chenonceaux. I know not what festive train the great Diana may have led, and my imagination, I am afraid, is only feebly kindled by the records of the luxurious pastimes organised on the banks of the Cher by that terrible daughter of the Medici whose appreciation of the good things of life was perfectly consistent with a failure to perceive why others should live to enjoy them. The best society that ever assembled there was collected at Chenonceaux during the middle of the eighteenth century. This was surely, in France at least, the age of good society, the period when the "right people" made every haste to be born in time. Such people must of course have belonged to the fortunate few—not to the miserable many; for if a society be large enough to be good, it must also be small enough. The sixty years that preceded the Revolution were the golden age of fireside talk and of those amenities that proceed from the presence of women in whom the social art is both instinctive and acquired. The women of that period were, above all, good company; the fact is attested in a thousand documents. Chenonceaux offered a perfect setting to free conversation; and infinite joyous discourse must have mingled with the liquid murmur of the Cher. Claude Dupin was not only a great man of business, but a man of honour and a patron of knowledge; and his wife was gracious, clever, and wise. They had acquired this famous property by purchase (from one of the Bourbons, as Chenonceaux, for two centuries after the death of Catherine de'Medici, remained constantly in princely hands), and it was transmitted to their son, Dupin de Francueil, grandfather of Madame George Sand. This lady, in her Correspondence, lately published, describes a visit that she paid more than thirty years ago to those members of her family who were still in possession. The owner of Chenonceaux to-day[a] is the daughter of an Englishman naturalised in France. But I have wandered far from my story, which is simply a sketch of the surface of the place. Seen obliquely, from either side, in combination with its bridge and gallery, the structure is singular and fantastic, a striking example of a wilful and capricious conception. Unfortunately all caprices are not so graceful and successful, and I grudge the honour of this one to the false and blood-polluted Catherine. (To be exact, I believe the arches of the bridge were laid by the elderly Diana. It was Catherine, however, who completed the monument.) Within, the house has been, as usual, restored. The staircases and ceilings, in all the old royal residences of this part of France, are the parts that have suffered least; many of them have still much of the life of the old time about them. Some of the chambers of Chenonceaux, however, encumbered as they are with modern detail, derive a sufficiently haunted and suggestive look from the deep setting of their beautiful windows, which thickens the shadows and makes dark corners. There is a charming little Gothic chapel, with its apse hanging over the water, fastened to the left flank of the house. Some of the upper balconies, which look along the outer face of the gallery and either up or down the river, are delightful protected nooks. We walked through the lower gallery to the other bank of the Cher; this fine apartment appeared to be for the moment a purgatory of ancient furniture. It terminates rather abruptly; it simply stops, with a blank wall. There ought, of course, to have been a pavilion here, though I prefer very much the old defect to any modern remedy. The wall is not so blank, however, but that it contains a door which opens on a rusty drawbridge. This drawbridge traverses the small gap which divides the end of the gallery from the bank of the stream. The house, therefore, does not literally rest on opposite edges of the Cher, but rests on one and just fails to rest on the other. The pavilion would have made that up; but after a moment we ceased to miss this imaginary feature. We passed the little drawbridge, and wandered awhile beside the river. From this opposite bank the mass of the château looked more charming than ever; and the little peaceful, lazy Cher, where two or three men were fishing in the eventide, flowed under the clear arches and between the solid pedestals of the part that spanned it, with the softest, vaguest light on its bosom. This was the right perspective; we were looking across the river of time. The whole scene was deliciously mild. The moon came up; we passed back through the gallery and strolled about a little longer in the gardens. It was very still. I met my old gondolier in the twilight. He showed me his gondola, but I hated, somehow, to see it there. I don't like, as the French say, to *mêler les genres*. A gondola in a little flat French river? The image was not less irritating, if less injurious, than the spectacle of a steamer in the Grand Canal, which had driven me away from

Chenonceaux

Venice a year and a half before. We took our way back to the Bon Laboureur, and waited in the little inn-parlour for a late train to Tours. We were not impatient, for we had an excellent dinner to occupy us; and even after we had dined we were still content to sit awhile and exchange remarks upon the superior civilisation of France. Where else, at a village inn, should we have fared so well? Where else should we have sat down to our refreshment without condescension? There were a couple of countries in which it would not have been happy for us to arrive hungry, on a Sunday evening, at so modest an hostelry. At the little inn at Chenonceaux the *cuisine* was not only excellent, but the service was graceful. We were waited on by mademoiselle and her mamma; it was so that mademoiselle alluded to the elder lady as she uncorked for us a bottle of Vouvray mousseux. We were very comfortable, very genial; we even went so far as to say to each other that Vouvray mousseux was a delightful wine. From this opinion indeed one of our trio differed; but this member of the party had already exposed herself to the charge of being too fastidious by declining to descend from the carriage at Chaumont and take that back-stairs view of the castle.

CHAPTER VIII. AZAY-LE-RIDEAU

WITHOUT fastidiousness it was fair to declare on the other hand that the little inn at Azay-le-Rideau was very bad. It was terribly dirty and it was in charge of a fat *mégère* whom the appearance of four trustful travellers—we were four, with an illustrious fourth, on that occasion—roused apparently to fury. I attached great importance to this incongruous hostess, for she uttered the only uncivil words I heard spoken (in connection with any business of my own) during a tour of some six weeks in France. Breakfast not at Azay-le-Rideau therefore, too trustful traveller; or if you do so, be either very meek or very bold. Breakfast not, save under stress of circumstance; but let no circumstance whatever prevent your going to see the great house of the place, which is a fair rival to Chenonceaux. The village lies close to the gates, though after you pass these gates you leave it well behind. A little avenue, as at Chenonceaux, leads to the castle, making a pretty vista as you approach the sculptured doorway. Azay is a most perfect and beautiful thing; I should place it third in any list of the great houses of this part of France in which these houses should be ranked according to charm. For beauty of detail it comes after Blois and Chenonceaux, but it comes before Amboise and Chambord. On the other hand, of course it is inferior in majesty to either of these vast structures. Like Chenonceaux, it is a watery place, though it is more meagrely moated than the small château on the Cher. It consists of a large square *corps de logis*, with a round tower at each angle, rising out of a somewhat too slumberous pond. The water—the water of the Indre—surrounds it, but it is only on one side that it bathes its feet in the moat. On one of the others stretches a little terrace, treated as a garden, and in front prevails a wide court formed by a wing which, on the right, comes forward. This front, covered with sculptures, is of the richest, stateliest effect. The court is approached by a bridge over the pond, and the house would reflect itself in this wealth of water if the water were a trifle less opaque. But there is a certain stagnation—it affects more, senses than one—about the picturesque pools of Azay. On the hither side of the bridge is a garden overshadowed by fine old sycamores—a garden shut in by greenhouses and by a fine last-century gateway flanked with twin lodges. Beyond the château and the standing waters behind it is a so-called *parc*, which, however, it must be confessed, has little of park-like beauty. The old houses—a large number—remain in France; but the old timber does not remain, and the denuded aspect of the few acres that surround the châteaux of Touraine is pitiful to the traveller who has learned to take the measure of such things from the country of "stately homes." The garden-ground of the lordly Chaumont is that of an English suburban villa; and in that and in other places there is little suggestion, in the untended aspect of walk and lawns, of the gardener the British Islands know. The manor as we see it dates from the early part of the sixteenth century; and the industrious Abbé Chevalier, in his very entertaining though slightly rose-coloured book on Touraine,[b] speaks of it as "perhaps the purest expression of the *belle Renaissance françoise.*" "Its height," he goes on "is divided between two storeys, terminating under the roof in a projecting entablature which imitates a row of machicolations. Carven chimneys and tall dormer windows, covered with imagery, rise from the roofs; turrets on brackets, of elegant shape, hang with the greatest lightness from the angles of the building. The soberness of the main lines, the harmony of the empty spaces and those that are filled out, the prominence of the crowning parts, the delicacy of all the details, constitute an enchanting whole." And then the Abbé speaks of the admirable staircase which adorns the north front and which, with its extension inside, constitutes the principal treasure of Azay. The staircase passes beneath one of the richest of porticos—a portico over which a monumental salamander indulges in the most decorative contortions. The sculptured vaults of stone which cover the windings of the staircase within, the fruits, flowers, ciphers, heraldic signs, are of the noblest effect. The interior of the château is rich, comfortable, extremely modern; but it makes no picture that compares with its external face, about which, with its charming proportions, its profuse yet not extravagant sculpture, there is something very tranquil and pure.

Azay-le-Rideau

I took a particular fancy to the roof, high, steep, old, with its slope of bluish slate, and the way the weather-worn chimneys seemed to grow out of it—living things in a deep soil. The single defect of the house is the blankness and bareness of its walls, which have none of that delicate parasitic deposit that agrees so well—to the eye—with the surface of old dwellings. It is true that this bareness results in a kind of silvery whiteness of complexion which carries out the tone of the quiet pools and even that of the scanty and shadeless park.

CHAPTER IX. LANGEAIS

I HARDLY know what to say about the tone of Langeais, which, though I have left it to the end of my sketch, formed the objective point of the first excursion I made from Tours. Langeais is rather dark and grey; it is perhaps the simplest and most severe of all the castles of the Loire. I don't know why I should have gone to see it before any other, unless it be because I remembered that Duchesse de Langeais who figures in several of Balzac's novels, and found this association very potent. The Duchesse de Langeais is a somewhat transparent fiction; but the castle from which Balzac borrowed the title of his heroine is an extremely solid fact. My doubt just above as to whether I should pronounce it exceptionally grey came from my having seen it under a sky which made most things look dark. I have, however, a very kindly memory of that moist and melancholy afternoon, which was much more autumnal than many of the days that followed it.

Langeais lies down the Loire, near the river, on the opposite side from Tours, and to go to it you will spend half an hour in the train. You pass on the way the Château de Luynes, which, with its round towers catching the afternoon light, looks uncommonly well on a hill at a distance; you pass also the ruins of the castle of Cinq-Mars, the ancestral dwelling of the young favourite of Louis XIII., the victim of Richelieu, the hero of Alfred de Vigny's novel, which is usually recommended to young ladies engaged in the study of French. Langeais is very imposing and decidedly sombre; it marks the transition from the architecture of defence to that of elegance. It rises, massive and perpendicular, out of the centre of the village to which it gives its name and which it entirely dominates; so that as you stand before it in the crooked and empty street there is no resource for you but to stare up at its heavy overhanging cornice and at the huge towers surmounted with extinguishers of slate. If you follow this street to the end, however, you encounter in abundance the usual embellishments of a French village: little ponds or tanks, with women on their knees on the brink, pounding and thumping a lump of saturated linen; brown old crones, the tone of whose facial hide makes their nightcaps (worn by day) look dazzling; little alleys perforating the thickness of a row of cottages and showing you behind, as a glimpse, the vividness of a green garden. In the rear of the castle rises a hill which must formerly have been occupied by some of its appurtenances and which indeed is still partly enclosed within its court. You may walk round this eminence, which, with the small houses of the village at its base, shuts in the castle from behind. The enclosure is not defiantly guarded, however; for a small, rough path, which you presently reach, leads up to an open gate. This gate admits you to a vague and rather limited *parc*, which covers the crest of the hill and through which you may walk into the gardens of the castle. These gardens, of small extent, confront the dark walls with their brilliant parterres and, covering the gradual slope of the hill, form, as it were, the fourth side of the court. This is the stateliest view of the structure, which looks to you sufficiently grim and grey as, after asking leave of a neat young woman who sallies out to learn your errand, you sit there on a garden bench and take the measure of the three tall towers attached to this inner front and forming severally the cage of a staircase. The huge bracketed cornice (one of the features of Langeais), which is merely ornamental, as it is not machicolated, though it looks so, is continued on the inner face as well. The whole thing has a fine feudal air, though it was erected on the ruins of feudalism.

Langeais

The main event in the history of the castle is the marriage of Anne of Brittany to her first husband, Charles VIII., which took place in its great hall in 1491. Into this great hall we were introduced by the neat young woman— into this great hall and into sundry other halls, winding staircases, galleries, chambers. The cicerone of Langeais is in too great a hurry; the fact is pointed out in the excellent Guide-Joanne. This ill-dissimulated vice, however, is to be observed, in the country of the Loire, in every one who carries a key. It is true that at Langeais there is no great occasion to indulge in the tourist's weakness of dawdling; for the apartments, though they contain many curious odds and ends of antiquity, are not of first-rate interest. They are cold and musty indeed, with that touching smell of old furniture, as all apartments should be through which the insatiate American wanders in the rear of a bored domestic, pausing to stare at a faded tapestry or to read the name on the frame of some simpering portrait.

To return to Tours my companion and I had counted on a train which (as is not uncommon in France) existed only in the "Indicateur des Chemins de Fer;" and instead of waiting for another we engaged a vehicle to take us home. A sorry *carriole* or *patache* it proved to be, with the accessories of a lumbering white mare and a little wizened, ancient peasant, who had put on, in honour of the occasion, a new blouse of extraordinary stiffness and blueness. We hired the trap of an energetic woman, who put it "to" with her own hands; women in Touraine and the Blésois appearing to have the best of it in the business of letting vehicles, as well as in many other industries. There is, in fact, no branch of human activity in which one is not liable, in France, to find a woman engaged. Women, indeed, are not priests; but priests are, more or less, women. They are not in the army, it may be said but then they *are* the army. They are very formidable. In France one must count with the women. The drive back from Langeais to Tours was long, slow, cold; we had an occasional spatter of rain. But the road passes most of the way close to the Loire, and there was something in our jog-trot through the darkening land, beside the flowing river, which it was very possible to enjoy.

CHAPTER X. LOCHES

THE consequence of my leaving to the last my little mention of Loches is that space and opportunity fail me; and yet a brief and hurried account of that extraordinary spot would after all be in best agreement with my visit. We snatched a fearful joy, my companion and I, the afternoon we took the train for Loches. The weather this time had been terribly against us: again and again a day that promised fair became hopelessly foul after lunch. At last we determined that if we could not make this excursion in the sunshine we would make it with the aid of our umbrellas. We grasped them firmly and started for the station, where we were detained an unconscionable time by the evolutions, outside, of certain trains laden with liberated (and exhilarated) conscripts, who, their term of service ended, were about to be restored to civil life. The trains in Touraine are provoking; they serve as little as possible for excursions. If they convey you one way at the right hour, it is on the condition of bringing you back at the wrong; they either allow you far too little time to examine the castle or the ruin, or they leave you planted in front of it for periods that outlast curiosity. They are perverse, capricious, exasperating. It was a question of our having but an hour or two at Loches, and we could ill afford to sacrifice to accidents. One of the accidents, however, was that the rain stopped before we got there, leaving behind it a moist mildness of temperature and a cool and lowering sky which were in perfect agreement with the grey old city. Loches is certainly one of the greatest impressions of the traveller in central France—the largest cluster of curious things that presents itself to his sight. It rises above the valley of the Indre, the charming stream set in meadows and sedges, which wanders through the province of Berry and through many of the novels of Madame George Sand; lifting from the summit of a hill, which it covers to the base, a confusion of terraces, ramparts, towers, and spires. Having but little time, as I say, we scaled the hill amain and wandered briskly through this labyrinth of antiquities. The rain had decidedly stopped and, save that we had our train on our minds, we saw Loches to the best advantage. We enjoyed that sensation with which the conscientious tourist is—or ought to be—well acquainted and for which, at any rate, he has a formula in his rough-and-ready language. We "experienced," as they say (most irregular of verbs), an "agreeable disappointment." We were surprised and delighted; we had for some reason suspected that Loches was scarce good.

I hardly know what is best there: the strange and impressive little collegial church, with its romanesque atrium or narthex, its doorways covered with primitive sculpture of the richest kind, its treasure of a so-called pagan altar embossed with fighting warriors, its three pyramidal domes, so unexpected, so sinister, which I have not met elsewhere in church architecture; or the huge square keep of the eleventh century—the most cliff-like tower I remember, whose immeasurable thickness I did not penetrate; or the subterranean mysteries of two other less striking but not less historic dungeons, into which a terribly imperative little cicerone introduced us, with the aid of downward ladders, ropes, torches, warnings, extended hands, and many fearful anecdotes—all in impervious darkness. These horrible prisons of Loches, at an incredible distance below daylight, enlivened the consciousness of Louis XI. and were for the most part, I believe, constructed by him. One of the towers of the castle is garnished with the hooks or supports of the celebrated iron cage in which he confined the Cardinal La Balue, who survived so much longer than might have been expected this extraordinary mixture of seclusion and exposure. All these things form part of the castle of Loches, whose enormous *enceinte* covers the whole of the top of the hill and abounds in dismantled gateways, in crooked passages, in winding lanes that lead to postern doors, in long façades that look upon terraces interdicted to the visitor, who perceives with irritation that they command magnificent views. These views are the property of the sub-prefect of the department, who resides at the Château de Loches and who has also the enjoyment of a garden—a garden compressed and curtailed, as those of old castles that perch on hill-tops are apt to be—containing a horse-chestnut tree of fabulous size, a tree of a circumference so vast and so perfect that the whole population of Loches might sit in concentric rows beneath its boughs. The gem of the place, however, is neither the big *marronier*, nor the collegial church, nor the mighty dungeon, nor the hideous prisons of Louis XI.; it is simply the tomb of Agnes Sorel, *la belle des belles*, so many years the mistress of Charles VII. She was buried in 1450, in the collegial church, whence, in the beginning of the present century, her remains, with the monument that marks them, were transferred to one of the towers of the castle. She has always, I know not with what justice, enjoyed a fairer fame than most ladies who have occupied her position, and this fairness is expressed in the delicate statue that surmounts her tomb. It represents her lying there in lovely demureness, her hands folded with the best modesty, a little kneeling angel at either side of her head, and her feet, hidden in the folds of her decent robe, resting upon a pair of couchant lambs, innocent reminders of her name. Agnes, however, was not lamb-like, inasmuch as, according to popular tradition at least, she exerted herself sharply in favour of the expulsion of the English from France. It is one of the suggestions of Loches that the young Charles VII., hard put to it as he was for a treasury and a capital—"le roi de Bourges," he was called at Paris—was yet a rather privileged mortal, to stand up as he does before posterity between the noble Joan and the *gentille Agnes*; deriving, however, much more honour from one of these companions than from the other. Almost as delicate a relic of antiquity as this fascinating tomb is the exquisite oratory of Anne of Brittany, among the apartments of the castle the only chamber worthy of note. This small room, hardly larger than a closet, and forming part of the addition made to the edifice by Charles VIII., is embroidered over with the curious and remarkably decorative device of the ermine and festooned cord. The objects in themselves are not especially graceful, but the constant repetition of the figure on the walls and ceiling produces an effect of richness in spite of the modern whitewash with which, if I remember rightly, they have been endued. The little streets of Loches wander crookedly down the hill and are full of charming pictorial "bits:" an old town-gate, passing under a medieval tower, which is ornamented by Gothic windows and the empty niches of statues; a meagre but delicate *hotel de ville* of the Renaissance nestling close beside it; a curious *chancellerie* of the middle of the sixteenth century, with mythological figures and a Latin inscription on the front—both of these latter buildings being rather unexpected features of the huddled and precipitous little town. Loches has a suburb on the other side of the Indre, which we had contented ourselves with looking down at from the heights while we wondered whether, even if it had not been getting late and our train were more accommodating, we should care to take our way across the bridge and look up that bust in terra-cotta of Francis I. which is the principal ornament of the Château de Sansac and the faubourg of Beaulieu. I think we decided that we should not, that we had already often measured the longest nose in history.

CHAPTER XI. BOURGES

I KNOW not whether the exact limits of an excursion as distinguished from a journey have ever been fixed; at any rate, it seemed none of my business at Tours to settle the question. Therefore, though the making of excursions had been the purpose of my stay, I thought it vain, while I started for Bourges, to determine to which category that little expedition might belong. It was not till the third day that I returned to Tours; and the distance, traversed for the most part after dark, was even greater than I had supposed. That, however, was partly the fault of a tiresome wait at Vierzon, where I had more than enough time to dine, very badly, at the *buffet* and to observe the proceedings of a family who had entered my railway carriage at Tours and had conversed unreservedly, for my benefit, all the way from that station—a family whom it entertained me to assign to the class of *petite noblesse de province*. Their noble origin was confirmed by the way they all "made *maigre*" in the refreshment-room (it happened to be a Friday), as if it had been possible to do anything else. They ate two or three omelets apiece and ever so many little cakes, while the positive, talkative mother watched her children as the waiter handed about the roast fowl. I was destined to share the secrets of this family to the end; for while I took my place in the empty train that was in waiting to convey us to Bourges the same vigilant woman pushed them all on top of me into my compartment, though the carriages on either side contained no travellers at all. It was better, I found, to have dined (even on omelets and little cakes) at the station at Vierzon than at the hotel at Bourges, which, when I reached it at nine o'clock at night, did not strike me as the prince of hotels. The inns in the smaller provincial towns in France are all, as the term is, commercial, and the *commis-voyageur* is in triumphant possession. I saw a great deal of him for several weeks after this; for he was apparently the only traveller in the southern provinces, and it was my daily fate to sit opposite to him at tables d'hôte and in railway trains. He may be known by two infallible signs—his hands are fat and he tucks his napkin into his shirt-collar. In spite of these idiosyncrasies, he seemed to me a reserved and inoffensive person, with singularly little of the demonstrative good-humour that he has been described as possessing. I saw no one who reminded me of Balzac's "illustre Gaudissart;" and indeed in the course of a month's journey through a large part of France I heard so little desultory conversation that I wondered whether a change had not come over the spirit of the people. They seemed to me as silent as Americans when Americans have not been "introduced," and infinitely less addicted to exchanging remarks in railway trains and at tables d'hôte than the colloquial and cursory English; a fact perhaps not worth mentioning were it not at variance with that reputation which the French have long enjoyed of being a pre-eminently sociable nation. The common report of the character of a people is, however, an indefinable product, and is apt to strike the traveller who observes for himself as very wide of the mark. The English, who have for ages been described (mainly by the French) as the dumb stiff, unapproachable race, present to-day a remarkable appearance of good-humour and garrulity and are distinguished by their facility of intercourse. On the other hand, any one who has seen half-a-dozen Frenchmen pass a whole day together in a railway-carriage without breaking silence is forced to believe that the traditional reputation of these gentlemen is simply the survival of some primitive formula. It was true, doubtless, before the Revolution; but there have been great changes since then. The question of which is the better taste, to talk to strangers or to hold your tongue, is a matter apart; I incline to believe that the French reserve is the result of a more definite conception of social behaviour. I allude to it only because it is at variance with the national fame and at the same time compatible with a very easy view of life in certain other directions. On some of these latter points the Boule d'Or at Bourges was full of instruction; boasting as it did of a hall of reception in which, amid old boots that had been brought to be cleaned, old linen that was being sorted for the wash, and lamps of evil odour that were awaiting replenishment, a strange, familiar, promiscuous household life went forward. Small scullions in white caps and aprons slept upon greasy benches; the Boots sat staring at you while you fumbled, helpless, in a row of pigeon-holes, for your candlestick or your key; and, amid the coming and going of the *commis-voyageurs*, a little sempstress bent over the under-garments of the hostess—the latter being a heavy, stern, silent woman, who looked at people very hard.

Bourges: the Cathedral

It was not to be looked at in that manner that one had come all the way from Tours; so that within ten minutes after my arrival I sallied out into the darkness to form somehow and somewhere a happier relation. However late in the evening I may arrive at a place, I never go to bed without my impression. The natural place at Bourges to look for it seemed to be the cathedral; which, moreover, was the only thing that could account for my presence *dans cette galère*. I turned out of a small square in front of the hotel and walked up a narrow, sloping street paved with big, rough stones and guiltless of a footway. It was a splendid starlight night; the stillness of a sleeping *ville de province* was over everything; I had the whole place to myself. I turned to my right, at the top of the street, where presently a short, vague lane brought me into sight of the cathedral. I approached it obliquely, from behind; it loomed up in the darkness above me enormous and sublime. It stands on the top of the large but not lofty eminence over which Bourges is scattered—a very good position as French cathedrals go, for they are not all so nobly situated as Chartres and Laon. On the side on which I approached it (the south) it is tolerably well exposed, though the precinct is shabby; in front, it is rather too much shut in. These defects, however, it makes up for on the north side and behind, where it presents itself in the most admirable manner to the garden of the Archevêché, which has been arranged as a public walk, with the usual formal alleys of the *jardin français*. I must add that I appreciated these points only on the following day. As I stood there in the light of the stars, many of which had an autumnal sharpness, while others were shooting over the heavens, the huge, rugged vessel of the church overhung me in very much the same way as the black hull of a ship at sea would overhang a solitary swimmer. It seemed colossal, stupendous, a dark leviathan.

The next morning, which was lovely, I lost no time in going back to it, and found with satisfaction that the daylight did it no injury. The cathedral of Bourges is indeed magnificently huge, and if it is a good deal wanting in lightness and grace, it is perhaps only the more imposing. I read in the excellent handbook of M. Joanne that it was projected "*dès* 1172," but commenced only in the first years of the thirteenth century. "The nave," the writer adds, "was finished *tant bien que mal, faute de ressources*; the façade is of the thirteenth and fourteenth centuries in its lower part, and of the fourteenth in its upper." The allusion to the nave means the omission of the transepts. The west front consists of two vast but imperfect towers; one of which (the south) is immensely buttressed, so that its outline slopes forward like that of a pyramid. This is the taller of the two. If they had spires these towers would be prodigious; as it is, given the rest of the church, they are wanting in elevation. There are five deeply recessed portals, all in a row, each surmounted with a gable, the gable over the central door being exceptionally high. Above the porches, which give the measure of its width, the front rears itself, piles itself, on a great scale, carried up by galleries, arches, windows, sculptures, and supported by the extraordinarily thick buttresses of which I have spoken and which, though they embellish it with deep shadows thrown sidewise, do not improve its style. The portals, especially the middle one, are extremely interesting; they are covered with curious early sculptures. The middle one, however, I must describe alone. It has no less than six rows of figures—the others have four—some of which, notably the upper one, are still in their places. The arch at the top has three tiers of elaborate imagery. The upper of these is divided by the figure of Christ in judgment, of great size, stiff and terrible, with outstretched arms. On either side of him are ranged three or four angels, with the instruments of the Passion. Beneath him in the second frieze stands the angel of justice with the scales; and on either side of him is the vision of the last judgment. The good prepare, with infinite titillation and complacency, to ascend to the skies; while the bad are dragged, pushed, hurled, stuffed, crammed, into pits and caldrons of fire. There is a charming detail in this section. Beside the angel, on the right, where the wicked are the prey of demons, stands a little female figure, that of a child, who, with hands meekly folded and head gently raised, waits for the stern angel to decide upon her fate. In this fate, however, a dreadful big devil also takes a keen interest: he seems on the point of appropriating the tender creature; he has a face like a goat and an enormous hooked nose. But the angel gently lays a hand upon the shoulder of the little girl—the movement is full of dignity— as if to say: "No; she belongs to the other side." The frieze below represents the general resurrection, with the good and the wicked emerging from their sepulchres. Nothing can be more quaint and charming than the difference shown in their way of responding to the final trump. The good get out of their tombs with a certain modest gaiety, an alacrity tempered by respect; one of them kneels to pray as soon as he has disinterred himself. You may know the wicked, on the other hand, by their extreme shyness; they crawl out slowly and fearfully; they hang back, and seem to say "Oh, dear!" These elaborate sculptures, full of ingenuous intention and of the reality of early faith, are in a remarkable state of preservation; they bear no superficial signs of restoration and appear scarcely to have suffered from the centuries. They are delightfully expressive; the artist had the advantage of knowing exactly the effect be wished to produce.

Bourges: the Cathedral

The interior of the cathedral has a great simplicity and majesty and, above all, a tremendous height. The nave is extraordinary in this respect; it dwarfs everything else I know. I should add, however, that I am in architecture always of the opinion of the last speaker. Any great building seems to me while I look at it the ultimate expression. At any rate, during the hour that I sat gazing along the high vista of Bourges the interior of the great vessel corresponded to my vision of the evening before. There is a tranquil largeness, a kind of infinitude, about such an edifice; it soothes and purifies the spirit, it illuminates the mind. There are two aisles, on either side, in addition to the nave—five in all—and, as I have said, there are no transepts; an omission which lengthens the vista, so that from my place near the door the central jewelled window in the depths of the perpendicular choir seemed a mile or two away. The second or outward of each pair of aisles is too low and the first too high; without this inequality the nave would appear to take an even more prodigious flight. The double aisles pass all the way round the choir, the windows of which are inordinately rich in magnificent old glass. I have seen glass as fine in other churches, but I think I have never seen so much of it at once.

Beside the cathedral, on the north, is a curious structure of the fourteenth or fifteenth century, which looks like an enormous flying buttress, with its support, sustaining the north tower. It makes a massive arch, high in the air, and produces a romantic effect as people pass under it to the open gardens of the Archevêché, which extend to a considerable distance in the rear of the church. The structure supporting the arch has the girth of a largeish house, and contains chambers with whose uses I am unacquainted, but to which the deep pulsations of the cathedral, the vibration of its mighty bells and the roll of its organ-tones must be transmitted even through the great arm of stone.

The archiepiscopal palace, not walled in as at Tours, is visible as a stately habitation of the last century, at the time of my visit under repair after a fire. From this side and from the gardens of the palace the nave of the cathedral is visible in all its great length and height, with its extraordinary multitude of supports. The gardens aforesaid, accessible through tall iron gates, are the promenade—the Tuileries—of the town, and, very pretty in themselves, are immensely set off by the overhanging church. It was warm and sunny; the benches were empty; I sat there a long time in that pleasant state of mind which visits the traveller in foreign towns, when he is not too hurried, while he wonders where he had better go next. The straight, unbroken line of the roof of the cathedral was very noble; but I could see from this point how much finer the effect would have been if the towers, which had dropped almost out of sight, might have been carried still higher. The archiepiscopal gardens look down at one end over a sort of esplanade or suburban avenue lying on a lower level on which they open, and where several detachments of soldiers (Bourges is full of soldiers) had just been drawn up. The civil population was also collecting, and I saw that something was going to happen. I learned that a private of the Chasseurs was to be "broken" for stealing, and every one was eager to behold the ceremony. Sundry other detachments arrived on the ground, besides many of the military who had come as a matter of taste. One of them described to me the process of degradation from the ranks, and I felt for a moment a hideous curiosity to see it, under the influence of which I lingered a little. But only a little; the hateful nature of the spectacle hurried me away at the same that others were hurrying forward. As I turned my back upon it I reflected that human beings are cruel brutes, though I could not flatter myself that the ferocity of the thing was exclusively French. In another country the concourse would have been equally great, and the moral of it all seemed to be that military penalties are as terrible as military honours are gratifying.

CHAPTER XII. BOURGES. JACQUES COEUR

THE cathedral is not the only lion of Bourges; the house of Jacques Cœur awaits you in posture scarcely less leonine. This remarkable man had a very strange history, and he too was "broken" like the wretched soldier whom I did not stay to see. He has been rehabilitated, however, by an age which does not fear the imputation of paradox, and a marble statue of him ornaments the street in front of his house. To interpret him according to this image—a womanish figure in a long robe and a turban, with big bare arms and a dramatic pose—would be to think of him as a kind of truculent sultana. He wore the dress of his period, but his spirit was very modern; he was a Vanderbilt or a Rothschild of the fifteenth century. He supplied the ungrateful Charles VII. with money to pay the troops who, under the heroic Maid, drove the English from French soil. His house, which to-day is used as a Palais de Justice, appears to have been regarded at the time it was built very much as the residence of Mr. Vanderbilt is regarded in New York to-day. It stands on the edge of the hill on which most of the town is planted, so that, behind, it plunges down to a lower level, and, if you approach it on that side, as I did, to come round to the front of it you have to ascend a longish flight of steps. The back, of old, must have formed a portion of the city wall; at any rate it offers to view two big towers which Joanne says were formerly part of the defence of Bourges. From the lower level of which I speak—the square in front of the post-office—the palace of Jacques Cœur looks very big and strong and feudal; from the upper street, in front of it, it looks very handsome and delicate. To this street it presents two tiers and a considerable length of façade; and it has both within and without a great deal of curious and beautiful detail. Above the portal, in the stonework, are two false windows, in which two figures, a man and a woman, apparently household servants, are represented, in sculpture, as looking down into the street. The effect is homely, yet grotesque, and the figures are sufficiently living to make one commiserate them for having been condemned, in so dull a town, to spend several centuries at the window. They appear to be watching for the return of their master, who left his beautiful house one morning and never came back.

Bourges: Jacques Cœur

The history of Jacques Cœur, which has been written by M. Pierre Clément in a volume crowned by the French Academy, is very wonderful and interesting, but I have no space to go into it here. There is no more curious example, and few more tragical, of a great fortune crumbling from one day to the other, or of the antique superstition that the gods grow jealous of human success. Merchant, millionaire, banker, ship-owner, royal favourite and minister of finance, explorer of the East and monopolist of the glittering trade between that quarter of the globe and his own, great capitalist who had anticipated the brilliant operations of the present time, he expiated his prosperity by poverty, imprisonment, and torture. The obscure points in his career have been elucidated by M. Clément, who has drawn, moreover, a very vivid picture of the corrupt and exhausted state of France during the middle of the fifteenth century. He has shown that the spoliation of the great merchant was a deliberately calculated act, and that the king sacrificed him without scruple or shame to the avidity of a singularly villanous set of courtiers. The whole story is an extraordinary picture of high-handed rapacity—the crudest possible assertion of the right of the stronger. The victim was stripped of his property, but escaped with his life, made his way out of France and, betaking himself to Italy, offered his services to the Pope. It is proof of the consideration that he enjoyed in Europe, and of the variety of his accomplishments, that Calixtus III. should have appointed him to take command of a fleet which his Holiness was fitting out against the Turks. Jacques Cœur, however, was not destined to lead it to victory. He died shortly after the expedition had started, in the island of Chios, in 1456. The house at Bourges, his native place, testifies in some degree to his wealth and splendour, though it has in parts that want of space which is striking in many of the buildings of the Middle Ages. The court indeed is on a large scale, ornamented with turrets and arcades, with several beautiful windows and with sculptures inserted in the walls, representing the various sources of the great fortune of the owner. M. Pierre Clément describes this part of the house as having been of an "incomparable richesse"—an estimate of its charms which seems slightly exaggerated to-day. There is, however, something delicate and familiar in the bas-reliefs of which I have spoken, little scenes of agriculture and industry which show that the proprietor was not ashamed of calling attention to his harvests and enterprises. To-day we should question the taste of such allusions, even in plastic form, in the house of a "merchant prince" however self-made. Why should it be, accordingly, that these quaint little panels at Bourges do not displease us? It is perhaps because things very ancient never, for some mysterious reason, appear vulgar. This fifteenth-century millionaire, with his palace, his "swagger" sculptures, may have produced that impression on some critical spirits of his own day.

The portress who showed me into the building was a dear little old woman, with the gentlest, sweetest, saddest face—a little white, aged face, with dark, pretty eyes—and the most considerate manner. She took me up into an upper hall, where there were a couple of curious chimney-pieces and a fine old oaken roof, the latter representing the hollow of a long boat. There is a certain oddity in a native of Bourges—an inland town if ever there was one, without even a river (to call a river) to encourage nautical ambitions—

having found his end as admiral of a fleet; but this boat-shaped roof, which is extremely graceful and is repeated in another apartment, would suggest that the imagination of Jacques Cœur was fond of riding the waves. Indeed, as he trafficked in Oriental products and owned many galleons, it is probable that he was personally as much at home in certain Mediterranean ports as in the capital of the pastoral Berry. If, when he looked at the ceilings of his mansion, he saw his boats upside down, this was only a suggestion of the shortest way of emptying them of their treasures. He is presented in person above one of the great stone chimney-pieces, in company with his wife, Macée de Léodepart—I like to write such an extraordinary name. Carved in white stone, the two sit playing at chess at an open window, through which they appear to give their attention much more to the passers-by than to the game. They are also exhibited in other attitudes; though I do not recognise them in the composition on top of one of the fireplaces which represents the battlements of a castle, with the defenders (little figures between the crenellations) hurling down missiles with a great deal of fury and expression. It would have been hard to believe that the man who surrounded himself with these friendly and humorous devices had been guilty of such wrong-doing as to call down the heavy hand of justice.

It is a curious fact, however, that Bourges contains legal associations of a purer kind than the prosecution of Jacques Cœur, which, in spite of the rehabilitations of history, can hardly be said yet to have terminated, inasmuch as the law-courts of the city are installed in his quondam residence. At a short distance from it stands the Hôtel Cujas, one of the curiosities of Bourges and the habitation for many years of the great jurisconsult who revived in the sixteenth century the study of the Roman law and professed it during the close of his life in the university of the capital of Berry. The learned Cujas had, in spite of his sedentary pursuits, led a very wandering life; he died at Bourges in the year 1590. Sedentary pursuits are perhaps not exactly what I should call them, having read in the "Biographie Universelle" (sole source of my knowledge of the renowned Cujacius) that his usual manner of study was to spread himself on his belly on the floor. He did not sit down, he lay down; and the "Biographie Universelle" has (for so grave a work) an amusing picture of the short, fat, untidy scholar dragging himself *à plat ventre*, across his room, from one pile of books to the other. The house in which these singular gymnastics took place, and which is now the headquarters of the gendarmerie, is one of the most picturesque at Bourges. Dilapidated and discoloured, it has a charming Renaissance front. A high wall separates it from the street, and on this wall, which is divided by a large open gateway, are perched two overhanging turrets. The open gateway admits you to the court, beyond which the melancholy mansion erects itself, decorated also with turrets, with fine old windows and with a beautiful tone of faded red brick and rusty stone. It is a charming encounter for a provincial by-street; one of those accidents in the hope of which the traveller with a propensity for sketching (whether on a little paper block or on the tablets of his brain) decides to turn a corner at a venture. A brawny gendarme in his shirtsleeves was polishing his boots in the court; an ancient, knotted vine, forlorn of its clusters, hung itself over a doorway and dropped its shadow on the rough grain of the wall. The place was very sketchable. I am sorry to say, however, that it was almost the only "bit." Various other curious old houses are supposed to exist at Bourges, and I wandered vaguely about in search of them. But I had little success, and I ended by becoming sceptical. Bourges is a *ville de province* in the full force of the term, especially as applied invidiously. The streets, narrow, tortuous, and dirty, have very wide cobble-stones; the houses for the most part are shabby, without local colour. The look of things is neither modern nor antique—a kind of mediocrity of middle age. There is an enormous number of blank walls—walls of gardens, of courts, of private houses—that avert themselves from the street as if in natural chagrin at there being so little to see. Round about is a dull, flat, featureless country, on which the magnificent cathedral looks down. There is a peculiar dulness and ugliness in a French town of this type, which, I must immediately add, is not the most frequent one. In Italy everything has a charm, a colour, a grace; even desolation and ennui. In England a cathedral city may be sleepy, but it is pretty sure to be mellow. In the course of six weeks spent *en province*, however, I saw few places that had not more expression than Bourges.

Bourges: Jacques Cœur

I went back to the cathedral; that, after all, was a feature. Then I returned to my hotel, where it was time to dine, and sat down, as usual, with the *commis-voyageurs*, who cut their bread on their thumb and partook of every course; and after this repast I repaired for a while to the café, which occupied a part of the basement of the inn and opened into its court. This café was a friendly, homely, sociable spot, where it seemed the habit of the master of the establishment to *tutoyer* his customers and the practice of the customers to *tutoyer* the waiter. Under these circumstances the waiter of course felt justified in sitting down at the same table with a gentleman who had come in and asked him for writing materials. He served this gentleman with a horrible little portfolio covered with shiny black cloth and accompanied with two sheets of thin paper, three wafers, and one of those instruments of torture which pass in France for pens—these being the utensils invariably evoked by such a request; and then, finding himself at leisure, he placed himself opposite and began to write a letter of his own. This trifling incident reminded me afresh that France is a democratic country. I think I received an admonition to the same effect from the free, familiar way in which the game of whist was going on just behind me. It was attended with a great deal of noisy pleasantry, flavoured every now and then with a dash of irritation. There was a young man of whom I made a note; he was such a beautiful specimen of his class. Sometimes he was very facetious, chattering, joking, punning, showing off; then, as the game went on and he lost and had to pay the *consommation*, he dropped his amiability, slanged his partner, declared he wouldn't play any more, and went away in a fury. Nothing could be more perfect or more amusing than the contrast. The manner of the whole affair was such as, I apprehend, one would not have seen among our English-speaking people; both the jauntiness of the first phase and the petulance of the second. To hold the balance straight, however, I may remark that if the men were all fearful "cads," they were, with their cigarettes and their inconsistency, less heavy, less brutal, than our dear English-speaking cad; just as the bright little café where a robust materfamilias, doling out sugar and darning a stocking, sat in her place under the mirror behind the *comptoir*, was a much more civilised spot than a British public-house or a "commercial room," with pipes and whisky, or even than an American saloon.

CHAPTER XIII. LE MANS

IT IS very certain that when I left Tours for Le Mans it was a journey and not an excursion; for I had no intention of coming back. The question indeed was to get away, no easy matter in France in the early days of October, when the whole *jeunesse* of the country is returning to school. It is accompanied, apparently, with parents and grandparents, and it fills the trains with little pale-faced *lycéens*, who gaze out of the windows with a longing, lingering air not unnatural on the part of small members of a race in which life is intense, who are about to be restored to those big educative barracks that do such violence to our American appreciation of the opportunities of boyhood. The train stopped every five minutes; but fortunately the country was charming—hilly and bosky, eminently good-humoured, and dotted here and there with a smart little château. The old capital of the province of the Maine, which has given its name to a great American State, is a fairly interesting town, but

I confess that I found in it less than I expected to admire. My expectations had doubtless been my own fault; there is no particular reason why Le Mans should fascinate. It stands upon a hill, indeed—a much better hill than the gentle swell of Bourges. This hill, however, is not steep in all directions; from the railway, as I arrived, it was not even perceptible. Since I am making comparisons, I may remark that, on the other hand, the Boule d'Or at Le Mans is an appreciably better inn than the Boule d'Or at Bourges. It looks out upon a small market-place which has a certain amount of character and seems to be slipping down the slope on which it lies, though it has in the middle an ugly *halle*, or circular market-house, to keep it in position. At Le Mans, as at Bourges, my first business was with the cathedral, to which I lost no time in directing my steps. It suffered by juxtaposition to the great church I had seen a few days before; yet it has some noble features. It stands on the edge of the eminence of the town, which falls straight away on two sides of it, and makes a striking mass, bristling behind, as you see it from below, with rather small but singularly numerous flying buttresses. On my way to it I happened to walk through the one street which contains a few ancient and curious houses, a very crooked and untidy lane, of really mediæval aspect, honoured with the denomination of the Grand Rue. Here is the house of Queen Berengaria—an absurd name, as the building is of a date some three hundred years later than the wife of Richard Cœur de Lion, who has a sepulchral monument in the south aisle of the cathedral. The structure in question—very sketchable, if the sketcher could get far enough away from it—is an elaborate little dusky façade, overhanging the street, ornamented with panels of stone, which are covered with delicate Renaissance sculpture. A fat old woman standing in the door of a small grocer's shop next to it—a most gracious old woman, with a bristling moustache and a charming manner—told me what the house was, and also indicated to me a rotten-looking brown wooden mansion in the same street, nearer the cathedral, as the Maison Scarron. The author of the "Roman Comique" and of a thousand facetious verses enjoyed for some years, in the early part of his life, a benefice in the cathedral of Le Mans, which gave him a right to reside in one of the canonical houses. He was rather an odd canon, but his history is a combination of oddities. He wooed the comic muse from the arm-chair of a cripple, and in the same position—he was unable even to go down on his knees—prosecuted that other suit which made him the first husband of a lady of whom Louis XIV. was to be the second. There was little of comedy in the future Madame de Maintenon; though, after all, there was doubtless as much as there need have been in the wife of a poor man who was moved to compose for his tomb such an epitaph as this, which I quote from the "Biographie Universelle":

"Celui qui cy maintenant dort,

Fit plus de pitié que d'envie,

Et souffrit mille fois la mort,

Avant que de perdre la vie.

Passant, ne fais icy de bruit,

Et garde bien qu'il ne s'éveille.

Car voicy la première nuit,

Que le pauvre Scarron sommeille."

Le Mans

There is rather a quiet, satisfactory *place* in front of the cathedral, with some good "bits" in it; notably a turret at the angle of one of the towers and a very fine steep-roofed dwelling, behind low walls, which it overlooks, with a tall iron gate. This house has two or three little pointed towers, a big black, precipitous roof, and a general air of having had a history. There are houses which are scenes, and there are houses which are only houses. The trouble with the domestic architecture of the United States is that it is not scenic, thank goodness, and the characteristic of an old structure like the turreted mansion on the hillside of Le Mans is that it is not simply a house. It is a person, as it were, as well. It would be well, indeed, if it might have communicated a little of its personality to the front of the cathedral, which has none of its own. Shabby, rusty, unfinished, this front has a romanesque portal, but nothing in the way of a tower. One sees from without, at a glance, the peculiarity of the church—the disparity between the romanesque nave, which is small and of the twelfth century, and the immense and splendid transepts and choir, of a period a hundred years later. Outside, this end of the church rises far above the nave, which looks merely like a long porch leading to it, with a small and curious romanesque porch in its own south flank. The transepts, shallow but very lofty, display to the spectators in the *place* the reach of their two clere-storey windows, which occupy, above, the whole expanse of the wall. The south transept terminates in a sort of tower, which is the only one of which the cathedral can boast. Within, the effect of the choir is superb; it is a church in itself, with the nave simply for a point of view. As I stood there I read in my Murray that it has the stamp of the date of the perfection of pointed Gothic, and I found nothing to object to the remark. It suffers little by confrontation with Bourges and, taken in itself, seems to me quite as fine. A passage of double aisles surrounds it, with the arches that divide them supported on very thick round columns, not clustered. There are twelve chapels in this passage, and a charming little lady-chapel filled with gorgeous old glass. The sustained height of this almost detached choir is very noble; its lightness and grace, its soaring symmetry, carry the eye up to places in the air from which it is slow to descend. Like Tours, like Chartres, like Bourges (apparently like all the French cathedrals, and unlike several English ones), Le Mans is rich in splendid glass. The beautiful upper windows of the choir make, far aloft, a brave gallery of pictures, blooming with vivid colour. It is the south transept that contains the formless image—a clumsy stone woman lying on her back—which purports to represent Queen Berengaria aforesaid.

Le Mans

The view of the cathedral from the rear is, as usual, very fine. A small garden behind it masks its base; but you descend the hill to a large *place de foire*, adjacent to a fine old public promenade which is known as Les Jacobins, a sort of miniature Tuileries, where I strolled for a while in rectangular alleys destitute of herbage and received a deeper impression of vanished things. The cathedral, on the pedestal of its hill, looks considerably farther than the fair-ground and the Jacobins, between the rather bare poles of whose straightly planted trees you may admire it at a convenient distance. I admired it till I thought I should remember it (better than the event has proved), and then I wandered away and looked at another curious old church, Notre-Dame-de-la-Couture. This sacred edifice made a picture for ten minutes, but the picture has faded now. I reconstruct a yellowish-brown façade and a portal fretted with early sculptures; but the details have gone the way of all incomplete sensations. After you have stood awhile, in the choir of the cathedral there is no sensation at Le Mans that goes very far. For some reason not now to be traced I had looked for more than this. I think the reason was to some extent simply in the name of the place; for names, on the whole, whether they be good reasons or not, are very active ones. Le Mans, if I am not mistaken, has a sturdy, feudal sound; suggests something dark and square, a vision of old ramparts and gates. Perhaps I had been unduly impressed by the fact, accidentally revealed to me, that Henry II., first of the English Plantagenets, was born there. Of course it is easy to assure one's self in advance, but does it not often happen that one had rather not be assured? There is a pleasure sometimes in running the risk of disappointment. I took mine, such as it was, quietly enough, while I sat before dinner at the door of one of the cafés in the market-place with a *bitter-et-curaçao* (invaluable pretext at such an hour!) to keep me company. I remember that in this situation there came over me an impression which both included and excluded all possible disappointments. The afternoon was warm and still; the air was admirably soft. The good Manceaux, in little groups and pairs, were seated near me; my ear was soothed by the fine shades of French enunciation, by the detached syllables of that perfect tongue. There was nothing in particular in the prospect to charm; it was an average French view. Yet I felt a charm, a kind of sympathy, a sense of the completeness of French life and of the lightness and brightness of the social air, together with a desire to arrive at friendly judgments, to express a positive interest. I know not why this transcendental mood should have descended upon me then and there; but that idle half-hour in front of the café, in the mild October afternoon suffused with human sounds, is perhaps the most abiding thing I brought away from Le Mans.

CHAPTER XIV. ANGERS

I AM shocked at finding, just after this noble declaration of principles, that in a little note-book which at that time I carried about with me the celebrated city of Angers is denominated a "sell."

I reproduce this vulgar word with the greatest hesitation, and only because it brings me more quickly to my point. This point is that Angers belongs to the disagreeable class of old towns that have been, as the English say, "done up." Not the oldness, but the newness, of the place is what strikes the sentimental tourist to-day, as he wanders with irritation along second-rate boulevards, looking vaguely about him for absent gables. "Black Angers," in short, is a victim of modern improvements and quite unworthy of its admirable name—a name which, like that of Le Mans, had always had, to my eyes, a highly picturesque value. It looks particularly well on the Shakespearean page (in "King John"), where we imagine it uttered (though such would not have been the utterance of the period) with a fine grinding insular accent. Angers figures with importance in early English history: it was the capital city of the Plantagenet race, home of that Geoffrey of Anjou who married, as second husband, the Empress Maud, daughter of Henry I. and competitor of Stephen, and became father of Henry II., first of the Plantagenet kings, born, as we have seen, at Le Mans. These facts create a natural presumption that Angers will look historic; I turned them over in my mind as I travelled in the train from Le Mans, through a country that was really pretty and looked more like the usual English than like the usual French scenery, with its fields cut up by hedges and a considerable rotundity in its trees. On my way from the station to the hotel, however, it became plain that I should lack a good pretext for passing that night at the Cheval Blanc; I foresaw that I should have contented myself before the end of the day. I remained at the White Horse only long enough to discover that it was an exceptionally good provincial inn, one of the best that I encountered during six weeks spent in these establishments.

"Stupidly and vulgarly modernised"—that is another flower from my note-book, and note-books are not obliged to be reasonable. "There are some narrow and tortuous streets, with a few curious old houses," I continue to quote; "there is a castle, of which the exterior is most extraordinary, and there is a cathedral of moderate interest." It is fair to say that the Château d'Angers is by itself worth a pilgrimage; the only drawback is that you have seen it in a quarter of an hour. You cannot do more than look at it, and one good look does your business. It has no beauty, no grace, no detail, nothing that charms or detains you; it is simply very old and very big—so big and so old that this simple impression is enough, and it takes its place in your recollections as a perfect specimen of a superannuated stronghold. It stands at one end of the town, surrounded by a huge, deep moat, which originally contained the waters of the Maine, now divided from it by a quay. The water-front of Angers is poor—wanting in colour and in movement; and there is always an effect of perversity in a town lying near a great river and yet not upon it. The Loire is a few miles off; but Angers contents itself with a meagre affluent of that stream. The effect was naturally much better when the vast dark bulk of the castle, with its seventeen prodigious towers, rose out of the protecting flood. These towers are of tremendous girth and solidity; they are encircled with great bands, or hoops, of white stone, and are much enlarged at the base. Between them hang high curtains of infinitely old-looking masonry, apparently a dense conglomeration of slate, the material of which the town was originally built (thanks to rich quarries in the neighbourhood), and to which it owed its appellation of the Black. There are no windows, no apertures, and to-day no battlements nor roofs. These accessories were removed by Henry III., so that, in spite of its grimness and blackness, the place has not even the interest of looking like a prison; it being, as I suppose, the essence of a prison not to be open to the sky. The only features of the enormous structure are the blank, sombre stretches and protrusions of wall, the effect of which, on so large a scale, is strange and striking. Begun by Philip Augustus and terminated by St. Louis, the Château d'Angers has of course a great deal of history. The luckless Fouquet, the extravagant minister of finance of Louis XIV., whose fall from the heights of grandeur was so sudden and complete, was confined here in 1661, just after his arrest, which had taken place at Nantes. Here also Huguenots and Vendeans suffered effective captivity.

Angers

I walked round the parapet which protects the outer edge of the moat (it is all up-hill, and the moat deepens and deepens), till I came to the entrance which faces the town, and which is as bare and strong as the rest. The concierge took me into the court; but there was nothing to see. The place is used as a magazine of ammunition, and the yard contains a multitude of ugly buildings. The only thing to do is to walk round the bastions for the view; but at the moment of my visit the weather was thick, and the bastions began and ended with themselves. So I came out and took another look at the big, black exterior, buttressed with white-ribbed towers, and perceived that a desperate sketcher might extract a picture from it, especially if he were to bring in, as they say, the little black bronze statue of the good King René (a weak production of David d'Angers), which, standing within sight, ornaments the melancholy faubourg. He would do much better, however, with the very striking old timbered house (I suppose of the fifteenth century) which is called the Maison d'Adam and is easily the first specimen at Angers of the domestic architecture of the past. This admirable house, in the centre of the town, gabled, elaborately timbered, and much restored, is a really imposing monument. The basement is occupied by a linen-draper, who flourishes under the auspicious sign of the Mère de Famille; and above his shop the tall front rises in five overhanging storeys. As the house occupies the angle of a little *place*, this front is double, and the black beams and wooden supports, displayed over a large surface and carved and interlaced, have a high picturesqueness. The Maison d'Adam is quite in the grand style, and I am sorry to say I failed to learn what history attaches to its name. If I spoke just above of the cathedral as "moderate," I suppose I should beg its pardon; for this serious charge was probably prompted by the fact that it consists only of a nave, without side aisles. A little reflection now convinces me that such a form is a distinction; and indeed I find it mentioned, rather inconsistently, in my note-book, a little further on, as "extremely simple and grand." The nave is spoken of in the same volume as "big, serious, and Gothic," though the choir and transepts are noted as very shallow. But it is not denied that the air of the whole thing is original and striking; and it would therefore appear, after all, that the cathedral of Angers, built during the twelfth and thirteenth centuries, is a sufficiently honourable church; the more that its high west front, adorned with a very primitive Gothic portal, supports two elegant tapering spires, between which, unfortunately, an ugly modern pavilion has been inserted.

I remember nothing else at Angers but the curious old Café Serin, where, after I had had my dinner at the inn, I went and waited for the train which, at nine o'clock in the evening, was to convey me, in a couple of hours, to Nantes—an establishment remarkable for its great size and its air of tarnished splendour, its brown gilding and smoky frescoes, as also for the fact that it was hidden away on the second floor of an unassuming house in an unilluminated street. It hardly seemed a place where you would drop in; but when once you had found it, it presented itself, with the cathedral, the castle, and the Maison d'Adam, as one of the historical monuments of Angers.

CHAPTER XV. NANTES

IF I spent two nights at Nantes, it was for reasons of convenience rather than of sentiment; though indeed I spent them in a big circular room which had a stately, lofty, last-century look—a look that consoled me a little for the whole place being dirty. The high, old-fashioned inn (it had a huge windy *porte-cochère*, and you climbed a vast black stone staircase to get to your room) looked out on a dull square, surrounded with other tall houses and occupied on one side by the theatre, a pompous building decorated with columns and statues of the muses. Nantes belongs to the class of towns which are always spoken of as "fine," and its position near the mouth of the Loire gives it, I believe, much commercial movement. It is a spacious, rather regular city, looking, in the parts that I traversed, neither very fresh nor very venerable. It derives its principal character from the handsome quays on the Loire, which are overhung with tall eighteenth-century houses (very numerous too in the other streets)—houses with big *entresols* marked by arched windows, classic pediments, balcony-rails of fine old iron-work. These features exist in still better form at Bordeaux; but, putting Bordeaux aside, Nantes is quite architectural. The view up and down the quays has the cool, neutral tone of colour that one finds so often in French water-side places— the bright greyness which is the tone of French landscape art. The whole city has rather a grand, or at least an eminently well-established, air. During a day passed in it of course I had time to go to the Musée; the more so that I have a weakness for provincial museums—a sentiment that depends but little on the quality of the collection. The pictures may be bad, but the place is often curious; and indeed from bad pictures, in certain moods of the mind, there is a degree of entertainment to be derived. If they are tolerably old they are often touching; but they must have a relative antiquity, for I confess I can do nothing with works of art of which the badness is of recent origin. The cool, still, empty chambers in which indifferent collections are apt to be preserved, the red brick tiles, the diffused light, the musty odour, the mementos around you of dead fashions, the snuffy custodian in a black skull-cap, who pulls aside a faded curtain to show you the lustreless gem of the museum—these things have a mild historical quality, and the sallow canvases after all illustrate something. Many of those in the museum of Nantes illustrate the taste of a successful warrior, having been bequeathed to the city by Napoleon's marshal Clarke (created Duc de Feltre). In addition to these there is the usual number of specimens of the contemporary

French school, culled from the annual Salons and presented to the museum by the State. Wherever the traveller goes, in France, he is reminded of this very honourable practice—the purchase by the Government of a certain number of "pictures of the year," which are presently distributed in the provinces. Governments succeed each other and bid for success by different devices; but the "patronage of art" is a plank, as we should say here, in every platform. The works of art are often ill-selected—there is an official taste which you immediately recognise—but the custom is essentially liberal, and a Government which should neglect it would be felt to be painfully common. The only thing in this particular Musée that I remember is a fine portrait of a woman by Ingres—very flat and Chinese, but with an interest of line and a great deal of style.

There is a castle at Nantes which resembles in some degree that of Angers, but has, without, much less of the impressiveness of great size, and, within, much more interest of detail. The court contains the remains of a very fine piece of late Gothic—a tall elegant building of the sixteenth century. The château is naturally not wanting in history. It was the residence of the old Dukes of Brittany, and was brought, with the rest of the province, by the Duchess Anne, the last representative of that race, as her dowry, to Charles VIII. I read in the excellent handbook of M. Joanne that it has been visited by almost every one of the kings of France, from Louis XI. downward; and also that it has served as a place of sojourn less voluntary on the part of various other distinguished persons, from the horrible Maréchal de Retz, who in the fifteenth century was executed at Nantes for the murder of a couple of hundred young children, sacrificed in abominable rites, to the ardent Duchess of Berry, mother of the Count of Chambord, who was confined there for a few hours in 1832, just after her arrest in a neighbouring house. I looked at the house in question—you may see it from the platform in front of the château—and tried to figure to myself that embarrassing scene. The Duchess, after having unsuccessfully raised the standard of revolt (for the exiled Bourbons) in the legitimist Bretagne, and being "wanted," as the phrase is, by the police of Louis Philippe, had hidden herself in a small but loyal house at Nantes, where, at the end of five months of seclusion, she was betrayed, for gold, to the austere M. Guizot by one of her servants, an Alsatian Jew named Deutz. For many hours before her capture she had been compressed into an interstice behind a fireplace, and by the time she was drawn forth into the light she had been ominously scorched. The man who showed me the castle indicated also another historic spot, a house with little *tourelles* on the Quai de la Fosse, in which Henry IV. is said to have signed the Edict revoked by Louis XIV. I am, however, not in a position to answer for this pedigree.

There is another point in the history of the fine old houses which command the Loire, of which, I suppose, one may be tolerably sure; that is their having, placid as they stand there to-day, looked down on the horrors of the Terror of 1793, the bloody reign of the monster Carrier and his infamous *noyades*. The most hideous episode of the Revolution was enacted at Nantes, where hundreds of men and women, tied together in couples, were set afloat upon rafts and sunk to the bottom of the Loire. The tall eighteenth-century house, full of the *air noble*, in France always reminds me of those dreadful years—of the street-scenes of the Revolution. Superficially, the association is incongruous, for nothing could be more formal and decorous than the patent expression of these eligible residences. But whenever I have a vision of prisoners bound on tumbrels that jolt slowly to the scaffold, of heads carried on pikes, of groups of heated *citoyennes* shaking their fists at closed coach-windows, I see in the background the well-ordered features of the architecture of the period—the clear grey stone, the high pilasters, the arching lines of the *entresol*, the classic pediment, the slate-covered attic. There is not much architecture at Nantes except the domestic. The cathedral, with a rough west front and stunted towers, makes no impression as you approach it. It is true that it does its best to recover its reputation as soon as you have passed the threshold. Begun in 1434 and finished about the end of the fifteenth century, as I discover in Murray, it has a magnificent nave, not of great length, but of extraordinary height and lightness. On the other hand, it has no choir whatever. There is much entertainment in France in seeing what a cathedral will take upon itself to possess or to lack; for it is only the smaller number that have the full complement of features. Some have a very fine nave and no choir; others a very fine choir and no nave. Some have a rich outside and nothing within; others a very blank face and a very glowing heart. There are a hundred possibilities of poverty and wealth, and they make the most unexpected combinations.

Nantes

The great treasure of Nantes is the two noble sepulchral monuments which occupy either transept, and one of which has (in its nobleness) the rare distinction of being a production of our own time. On the south side stands the tomb of Francis II., the last of the Dukes of Brittany, and of his second wife, Margaret of Foix, erected in 1507 by their daughter Anne, whom we have encountered already at the Château de Nantes, where she was born; at Langeais, where she married her first husband; at Amboise, where she lost him; at Blois, where she married her second, the "good" Louis XII., who divorced an impeccable spouse to make room for her, and where she herself died. Transferred to the cathedral from a demolished convent, this monument, the masterpiece of Michel Colomb, author of the charming tomb of the children of Charles VIII. and the aforesaid Anne, which we admired at Saint Gatien of Tours, is one of the most brilliant works of the French Renaissance. It has a splendid effect and is in perfect preservation. A great table of black marble supports the reclining figures of the duke and duchess, who lie there peacefully and majestically, in their robes and crowns, with their heads each on a cushion, the pair of which are supported from behind by three charming little kneeling angels; at the foot of the quiet couple are a lion and a greyhound, with heraldic devices. At each of the angles of the table is a large figure in white marble of a woman elaborately dressed, with a symbolic meaning, and these figures, with their contemporary faces and clothes, which give them the air of realistic portraits, are truthful and living, if not remarkably beautiful. Round the sides of the tomb are small images of the apostles. There is a kind of masculine completeness in the work, and a certain robustness of taste.

In nothing were the sculptors of the Renaissance more fortunate than in being in advance of us with their tombs: they have left us nothing to say in regard to the great final contrast—the contrast between the immobility of death and the trappings and honours that survive. They expressed in every way in which it was possible to express it the solemnity of their conviction that the marble image was a part of the personal greatness of the defunct, and the protection, the redemption, of his memory. A modern tomb, in comparison, is a sceptical affair; it insists too little on the honours. I say this in the face of the fact that one has only to step across the cathedral of Nantes to stand in the presence of one of the purest and most touching of modern tombs. Catholic Brittany has erected in the opposite transept a monument to one of the most devoted of her sons, General de Lamoricière, the defender of the Pope, the vanquished of Castelfidardo. This noble work, from the hand of Paul Dubois, one of the most interesting of that new generation of sculptors who have revived in France an art of which our over-dressed century had begun to despair, has every merit but the absence of a certain prime feeling. It is the echo of an earlier tune—an echo with a beautiful cadence. Under a Renaissance canopy of white marble elaborately worked with arabesques and cherubs, in a relief so low that it gives the work a certain look of being softened and worn by time, lies the body of the Breton soldier with a crucifix clasped to his breast and a shroud thrown over his body. At each of the angles sits a figure in bronze, the two best of which, representing Charity and Military Courage, had given me extraordinary pleasure when they were exhibited (in the clay) in the Salon of 1876. They are admirably cast and not less admirably conceived: the one a serene, robust young mother, beautiful in line and attitude; the other a lean and vigilant young man, in a helmet that overshadows his serious eyes, resting an outstretched arm, an admirable military member, upon the hilt of a sword. These figures contain abundant assurance that M. Paul Dubois has been attentive to Michael Angelo, whom we have all heard called a splendid example and a bad model. The visor-shadowed face of his warrior is more or less a reminiscence of the figure on the tomb of Lorenzo de' Medici at Florence; but it is doubtless none the worse for that. The interest of the work of Paul Dubois is its peculiar seriousness, a kind of moral good faith which is not the commonest feature of French art, and which, united as it is in this case with exceeding knowledge and a remarkable sense of form, produces an impression of deep refinement. The whole monument is a proof of exquisitely careful study; but I am not sure that this impression on the part of the spectator is the happiest possible. It explains much of the great beauty, and it also explains perhaps a little of the slight pedantry. That word, however, is scarcely in place; I only mean that M. Dubois has made a visible effort, which has visibly triumphed. Simplicity is not always strength, and our complicated modern genius contains treasures of intention. This fathomless modern element is an immense charm on the part of M. Paul Dubois. I am lost in admiration of the deep æsthetic experience, the enlightenment of taste, revealed by such work. After that I only hope that, Giuseppe Garibaldi may have somewhere or other some commemoration as distinguished.

CHAPTER XVI. LA ROCHELLE

TO go from Nantes to La Rochelle you travel straight southward across the historic *bocage* of La Vendée, the home of royalist bush-fighting. The country, which is exceedingly pretty, bristles with copses, orchards, hedges, and with trees more spreading and sturdy than the traveller is apt to find the feathery foliage of France. It is true that as I proceeded it flattened out a good deal, so that for an hour there was a vast featureless plain, which offered me little entertainment beyond the general impression that I was approaching the Bay of Biscay (from which, in reality, I was yet far distant). As we drew near La Rochelle, however, the prospect brightened considerably, and the railway kept its course beside a charming little canal, or canalised river, bordered with trees and with small, neat, bright-coloured and yet old-fashioned cottages and villas, which stood back, on the farther side, behind small gardens, hedges, painted palings, patches of turf. The whole effect was Dutch and delightful; and in being delightful, though not in being Dutch, it prepared me for the charms of La Rochelle, which from the moment I entered it I perceived to be a fascinating little town, a quite original mixture of brightness and dulness. Part of its brightness comes from its being extraordinarily clean—in which, after all, it *is* Dutch; a virtue not particularly noticeable at Bourges, Le Mans, and Angers. Whenever I go southward, if it be only twenty miles, I begin to look out for the south, prepared as I am to find the careless grace of those latitudes even in things of which it may be said that they may be south of something, but are not southern. To go from Boston to New York (in this state of mind) is almost as soft a sensation as descending the Italian side of the Alps; and to go from New York to Philadelphia is to enter a zone of tropical luxuriance and warmth. Given this absurd disposition, I could not fail to flatter myself, on reaching La Rochelle, that I was already in the Midi, and to perceive in everything, in the language of the country, the *caractère méridional*. Really a great many things had a hint of it. For that matter it seems to me that to arrive in the south at a bound—to wake up there, as it were—would be a very imperfect pleasure. The full pleasure is to approach by stages and gradations; to observe the successive shades of difference by which it ceases to be the north. These shades are exceedingly fine, but your true south-lover has an eye for them all. If he perceives them at New York and Philadelphia—we imagine him boldly as liberated from Boston—how could he fail to perceive them at La Rochelle? The streets of this dear little city are lined with arcades—good, big, straddling arcades of stone, such as befit a land of hot summers and which recalled to me, not to go further, the dusky porticos of Bayonne. It contains, moreover, a great wide *place d'armes* which looked for all the world like the piazza of some dead Italian town, empty, sunny, grass-grown, with a row of yellow houses overhanging it, an unfrequented café with a striped awning, a tall, cold, florid, uninteresting cathedral of the eighteenth century on one side, and on the other a shady walk which forms part of an old rampart. I followed this walk for some time, under the stunted trees, beside the grass-covered bastions; it is very charming, winding and wandering, always with trees. Beneath the rampart is a tidal river, and on the other side, for a long distance, the mossy walls of the immense garden of a seminary. Three hundred years ago La Rochelle was the great French stronghold of Protestantism, but to-day it appears to be a nursery of Papists.

La Rochelle

The walk upon the rampart led me round to one of the gates of the town, where I found some small modern fortifications and sundry red-legged soldiers, and, beyond the fortifications, another shady walk—a *mail*, as the French say, as well as a *champ de manœuvre*—on which latter expanse the poor little red-legs were doing their exercise. It was all very quiet and very picturesque, rather in miniature; and at once very tidy and a little out of repair. This, however, was but a meagre back-view of La Rochelle, or poor side-view at best. There are other gates than the small fortified aperture just mentioned; one of them, an old grey arch beneath a fine clock-tower, I had passed through on my way from the station. This substantial Tour de l'Horloge separates the town proper from the port; for beyond the old grey arch the place presents its bright, expressive little face to the sea. I had a charming walk about the harbour and along the stone piers and sea-walls that shut it in. This indeed, to take things in their order, was after I had had my breakfast (which I took on arriving) and after I had been to the *hôtel de ville*. The inn had a long narrow garden behind it, with some very tall trees; and passing through this garden to a dim and secluded *salle à manger*, buried in the heavy shade, I had, while I sat at my repast, a feeling of seclusion which amounted almost to a sense of incarceration. I lost this sense, however, after I had paid my bill, and went out to look for traces of the famous siege, which is the principal title of La Rochelle to renown. I had come thither partly because I thought it would be interesting to stand for a few moments in so gallant a spot, and partly because, I confess, I had a curiosity to see what had been the starting-point of the Huguenot emigrants who founded the town of New Rochelle in the State of New York, a place in which I had passed sundry memorable hours. It was strange to think, as I strolled through the peaceful little port, that these quiet waters, during the wars of religion, had swelled with a formidable naval power. The Rochelais had fleets and admirals, and their stout little Protestant bottoms carried defiance up and down.

To say that I found any traces of the siege would be to misrepresent the taste for vivid whitewash by which La Rochelle is distinguished to-day. The only trace is the dent in the marble top of the table on which, in the *hôtel de ville*, Jean Guiton, the mayor of the city, brought down his dagger with an oath when in 1628 the vessels and regiments of Richelieu closed about it on sea and land. This terrible functionary was the soul of the resistance; he held out from February to October in the midst of pestilence and famine. The whole episode has a brilliant place among the sieges of history; it has been related a hundred times, and I may only glance at it and pass. I limit my ambition in these light pages to speaking of those things of which I have personally received an impression, and I have no such impression of the defence of La Rochelle. The *hôtel de ville* is a pretty little building, in the style of the Renaissance of Francis I.; but it has left much of its interest in the hands of the restorers. It has been "done up" without mercy; its natural place would be at Rochelle the New. A sort of battlemented curtain, flanked with turrets, divides it from the street and contains a low door (a low door in a high wall is always felicitous), which admits you to an inner court, where you discover the face of the building. It has statues set into it and is raised upon a very low and very deep arcade. The principal function of the deferential old portress who conducts you over the place is to call your attention to the indented table of Jean Guiton; but she shows you other objects of interest besides. The interior is absolutely new and extremely sumptuous, abounding in tapestries, upholstery, morocco, velvet, satin. This is especially the case with a really beautiful *grande salle*, where, surrounded with the most expensive upholstery, the mayor holds his official receptions. (So at least said my worthy portress.) The mayors of La Rochelle appear to have changed a good deal since the days of the grim Guiton; but these evidences of municipal splendour are interesting for the light they throw on French manners. Imagine the mayor of an English or an American town of twenty thousand inhabitants holding magisterial soirées in the town hall! The said *grande salle*, which is unchanged in form and in its larger features, is, I believe, the room in which the Rochelais debated as to whether they should shut themselves up, and decided in the affirmative. The table and chair of Jean Guiton have been restored, like everything else, and are very elegant and coquettish pieces of furniture—incongruous relics of a season of starvation and blood. I believe that Protestantism is somewhat shrunken to-day at La Rochelle, and has taken refuge mainly in the *haute société* and in a single place of worship. There was nothing particular to remind me of its supposed austerity as, after leaving the *hôtel de ville*, I walked along the empty porticos and out of the Tour de l'Horloge, which I have already mentioned. If I stopped and looked up at this venerable monument, it was not to ascertain the hour, for I foresaw that I should have more time at La Rochelle than I knew what to do with; but because its high, grey, weather-beaten face was an obvious subject for a sketch.

La Rochelle

The little port, which has two basins and is accessible only to vessels of light tonnage, had a certain gaiety and as much local colour as you please. Fisher-folk of picturesque type were strolling about, most of them Bretons; several of the men with handsome, simple faces, not at all brutal, and with a splendid brownness—the golden-brown colour on cheek and beard that you see on an old Venetian sail. It was a squally, showery day, with sudden drizzles of sunshine; rows of rich-toned fishing-smacks were drawn up along the quays. The harbour is effective to the eye by reason of three battered old towers which at different points overhang it and look infinitely weather-washed and sea-silvered. The most striking of these, the Tour de la Lanterne, is a big grey mass of the fifteenth century, flanked with turrets and crowned with a Gothic steeple. I found it was called by the people of the place the Tour des Quatre Sergents, though I know not what connection it has with the touching history of the four young sergeants of the garrison of La Rochelle who were arrested in 1821 as conspirators against the Government of the Bourbons, and executed, amid general indignation, in Paris in the following year. The quaint little walk, with its label of Rue sur les Murs, to which one ascends from beside the Grosse Horloge, leads to this curious Tour de la Lanterne and passes under it. This walk has the top of the old town-wall, towards the sea, for a parapet on one side, and is bordered on the other with decent but irregular little tenements of fishermen, where brown old women, whose caps are as white as if they were painted, seem chiefly in possession. In this direction there is a very pretty stretch of shore, out of the town, through the fortifications (which are Vauban's, by the way); through, also, a diminutive public garden or straggling shrubbery which edges the water and carries its stunted verdure as far as a big Établissement des Bains. It was too late in the year to bathe, and the Établissement had the bankrupt aspect which belongs to such places out of the season; so I turned my back upon it and gained, by a circuit in the course of which there were sundry water-side items to observe, the other side of the cheery little port, where there is a long breakwater and a still longer sea-wall, on which I walked a while, to inhale the strong, salt breath of the Bay of Biscay. La Rochelle serves, in the months of July and August, as a *station de bains* for a modest provincial society; and, putting aside the question of inns, it must be charming on summer afternoons.

CHAPTER XVII. POITIERS

IT is an injustice to Poitiers to approach her by night, as I did some three hours after leaving La Rochelle; for what Poitiers has of best, as they would say at Poitiers, is the appearance she presents to the arriving stranger who puts his head out of the window of the train. I gazed into the gloom from such an aperture before we got into the station, for I remembered the impression received on another occasion; but I saw nothing save the universal night, spotted here and there with an ugly railway lamp. It was only as I departed, the following day, that I assured myself that Poitiers still makes something of the figure she ought on the summit of her considerable hill. I have a kindness for any little group of towers, any cluster of roofs and chimneys, that lift themselves from an eminence over which a long road ascends in zigzags; such a picture creates for the moment a presumption that you are in Italy, and even leads you to believe that if you mount the winding road you will come to an old town-wall, an expanse of creviced brownness, and pass under a gateway surmounted by the arms of a mediæval despot. Why I should find it a pleasure in France to imagine myself in Italy, is more than I can say; the illusion has never lasted long enough to be analysed. From the bottom of its perch Poitiers looks large and high; and indeed, the evening I reached it, the interminable climb of the omnibus of the hotel I had selected, which I found at the station, gave me the measure of its commanding position. This hotel, "magnifique construction ornée de statues," as the Guide-Joanne, usually so reticent, takes the trouble to announce, has an omnibus, and, I suppose, has statues, though I didn't perceive them; but it has very little else save immemorial accumulations of dirt. It is magnificent, if you will, but it is not even relatively proper; and a dirty inn has always seemed to me the dirtiest of human things—it has so many opportunities to betray itself.

Poitiers covers a large space, and is as crooked and straggling as you please; but these advantages are not accompanied with any very salient features or any great wealth of architecture. Although there are few picturesque houses, however, there are two or three curious old churches. Notre Dame la Grande, in the market-place, a small romanesque structure of the twelfth century, has a most interesting and venerable exterior. Composed, like all the churches of Poitiers, of a light brown stone with a yellowish tinge, it is covered with primitive but ingenious sculptures, and is really an impressive monument. Within, it has lately been daubed over with the most hideous decorative painting that was ever inflicted upon passive pillars and indifferent vaults. This battered yet coherent little edifice has the touching look that resides in everything supremely old; it has arrived at the age at which such things cease to feel the years; the waves of time have worn its edges to a kind of patient dulness; there is something mild and smooth, like the stillness, the deafness, of an octogenarian, even in its rudeness of ornament, and it has become insensible to differences of a century or two. The cathedral interested me much less than Our Lady the Great, and I have not the spirit to go into statistics about it. It is not statistical to say that the cathedral stands half-way down the hill of Poitiers, in a quiet and grass-grown *place*, with an approach of crooked lanes and blank garden-walls, and that its most striking dimension is the width of its façade. This width is extraordinary, but it fails, somehow, to give nobleness to the edifice, which looks within (Murray makes the remark) like a large public hall. There are a nave and two aisles, the latter about as high as the nave; and there are some very fearful modern pictures, which you may see much better than you usually see those specimens of the old masters that lurk in glowing side-chapels, there being no fine old glass to diffuse a kindly gloom. The sacristan of the cathedral showed me something much better than all this bright bareness; he led me a short distance out of it to the small Temple de Saint-Jean, which is the most curious object at Poitiers. It is an early Christian chapel, one of the earliest in France; originally, it would seem—that is, in the sixth or seventh century—a baptistery, but converted into a church while the Christian era was still comparatively young. The Temple de Saint-Jean is therefore a monument even more venerable than Notre Dame la Grande, and that numbness of age which I imputed to Notre Dame ought to reside in still larger measure in its crude and colourless little walls. I call them crude, in spite of their having been baked through by the centuries, only because, although certain rude arches and carvings are let into them and they are surmounted at either end with a small gable, they have (so far as I can remember) little fascination of surface. Notre Dame is still expressive, still pretends to be alive; but the temple has delivered its message and is completely at rest. It retains a kind of atrium, on the level of the street, from which you descend to the original floor, now uncovered, but buried for years under a false bottom. A semicircular apse was, apparently at the time of its conversion into a church, thrown out from the east wall. In the middle is the cavity of the old baptismal font. The walls and vaults are covered with traces of extremely archaic frescoes, attributed, I believe, to the twelfth century. These vague, gaunt, staring fragments of figures are, to a certain extent, a reminder of some of the early Christian churches in Rome; they even faintly recalled to me the great mosaics of Ravenna. The Temple de Saint-Jean has neither the antiquity nor the completeness of those extraordinary monuments, nearly the most impressive in Europe; but, as one may say, it is very well for Poitiers.

Poitiers

Not far from it, in a lonely corner which was animated for the moment by the vociferations of several old women who were selling tapers, presumably for the occasion of a particular devotion, is the graceful romanesque church erected in the twelfth century to Saint Radegonde—a lady who found means to be a saint even in the capacity of a Merovingian queen. It bears a general resemblance to Notre Dame la Grande, and, as I remember it, is corrugated in somewhat the same manner with porous-looking carvings; but I confess that what I chiefly recollect is the row of old women sitting in front of it, each with a tray of waxen tapers in her lap, and upbraiding me for my neglect of the opportunity to offer such a tribute to the saint. I know not whether this privilege is occasional or constant; within the church there was no appearance of a festival, and I see that the name-day of Saint Radegonde occurs in August, so that the importunate old women sit there always perhaps and deprive of its propriety the epithet I just applied to this provincial corner. In spite of the old women, however, I suspect that the place is lonely; and indeed it is perhaps the old women who have made the desolation.

The lion of Poitiers in the eyes of the natives is doubtless the Palais de Justice, in the shadow of which the statue-guarded hotel, just mentioned, erects itself; and the gem of the court-house, which has a prosy modern front, with pillars and a high flight of steps, is the curious *salle des pas perdus*, or central hall, out of which the different tribunals open. This is a feature of every French court-house, and seems the result of a conviction that a palace of justice—the French deal in much finer names than we—should be in some degree palatial. The great hall at Poitiers has a long pedigree, as its walls date back to the twelfth century and its open wooden roof, as well as the remarkable trio of chimney-pieces at the right end of the room as you enter, to the fifteenth. The three tall fireplaces, side by side, with a delicate gallery running along the top of them, constitute the originality of this ancient chamber, and make one think of the groups that must formerly have gathered there—of all the wet boot-soles, the trickling doublets, the stiffened fingers, the rheumatic shanks, that must have been presented to such an incomparable focus of heat. To-day, I am afraid, these mighty hearths are for ever cold; justice is probably administered with the aid of a modern *calorifère*, and the walls of the palace are perforated with regurgitating tubes. Behind and above the gallery that surmounts the three fireplaces are high Gothic windows, the tracery of which masks, in some sort, the chimneys; and in each angle of this and of the room to the right and left of the trio of chimneys is an open-work spiral staircase, ascending to—I forget where; perhaps to the roof of the edifice. The whole side of the *salle* is very lordly, and seems to express an unstinted hospitality, to extend the friendliest of all invitations, to bid the whole world come and get warm. It was the invention of John, Duke of Berry and Count of Poitou, about 1395. I give this information on the authority of the Guide-Joanne, from which source I gather much other curious learning; as, for instance, that it was in this building, when it had surely a very different front, that Charles VII. was proclaimed king in 1422; and that here Jeanne Darc was subjected, in 1429, to the inquisition of sundry doctors and matrons.

Poitiers

The most charming thing at Poitiers is simply the Promenade de Blossac—a small public garden at one end of the flat top of the hill. It has a happy look of the last century (having been arranged at that period), and a beautiful sweep of view over the surrounding country, and especially of the course of the little river Clain, which winds about a part of the base of the big mound of Poitiers. The limit of this dear little garden is formed, on the side that turns away from the town, by the rampart erected in the fourteenth century and by its big semicircular bastions. This rampart, of great length, has a low parapet; you look over it at the charming little vegetable-gardens with which the base of the hill appears exclusively to be garnished. The whole prospect is delightful, especially the details of the part just under the walls, at the end of the walk. Here the river makes a shining twist which a painter might have invented, and the side of the hill is terraced into several hedges—a sort of tangle of small blooming patches and little pavilions with peaked roofs and green shutters. It is idle to attempt to reproduce all this in words; it should be reproduced only in water-colours. The reader, however, will already have remarked that disparity in these ineffectual pages, which are pervaded by the attempt to sketch without a palette or brushes. He will doubtless also be struck with the grovelling vision which, on such a spot as the ramparts of Poitiers, peoples itself with carrots and cabbages rather than with images of the Black Prince and the captive king. I am not sure that in looking out from the Promenade de Blossac you command the old battle-field; it is enough that it was not far off, and that the great rout of Frenchmen poured into the walls of Poitiers, leaving on the ground a number of the fallen equal to the little army (eight thousand) of the invader. I did think of the battle. I wondered, rather helplessly, where it had taken place; and I came away (as the reader will see from the preceding sentence) without finding out. This indifference, however, was a result rather of a general dread of military topography than of a want of admiration of this particular victory, which I have always supposed to be one of the most brilliant on record. Indeed, I should be almost ashamed, and very much at a loss, to say what light it was that this glorious day seemed to me to have left for ever on the horizon, and why the very name of the place had always caused my blood gently to tingle. It is carrying the feeling of race to quite inscrutable lengths when a vague American permits himself an emotion because more than five centuries ago, on French soil, one rapacious Frenchman got the better of another. Edward was a Frenchman as well as John, and French were the cries that urged each of the hosts to the fight. French is the beautiful motto graven round the image of the Black Prince as he lies for ever at rest in the choir of Canterbury: *à la mort ne pensai-je mye.* Nevertheless, the victory of Poitiers declines to lose itself in these considerations; the sense of it is a part of our heritage, the joy of it a part of our imagination, and it filters down through centuries and migrations till it titillates a New Yorker who forgets in his elation that he happens at that moment to be enjoying the hospitality of France. It was something done, I know not how justly, for England; and what was done in the fourteenth century for England was done also for New York.

CHAPTER XVIII. ANGOULÊME

IF it was really for the sake of the Black Prince that I had stopped at Poitiers (for my prevision of Notre Dame la Grande and of the little temple of St. John was of the dimmest), I ought to have stopped at Angoulême for the sake of David and Eve Séchard, of Lucien de Rubempré and of Madame de Bargeton, who when she wore a *toilette étudiée* sported a Jewish turban ornamented with an Eastern brooch, a scarf of gauze, a necklace of cameos, and a robe of "painted muslin," whatever that may be; treating herself to these luxuries out of an income of twelve thousand francs. The persons I have mentioned have not that vagueness of identity which is the misfortune of historical characters; they are real, supremely real, thanks to their affiliation to the great Balzac, who had invented an artificial reality which was as much better than the vulgar article as mock-turtle soup is than the liquid it emulates. The first time I read

"Les Illusions Perdues" I should have refused to believe that I was capable of passing the old capital of Anjou without alighting to visit the Houmeau. But we never know what we are capable of till we are tested, as I reflected when I found myself looking back at Angoulême from the window of the train just after we had emerged from the long tunnel that passes under the town. This tunnel perforates the hill on which, like Poitiers, Angoulême rears itself, and which gives it an elevation still greater than that of Poitiers. You may have a tolerable look at the cathedral without leaving the railway carriage, for it stands just above the tunnel and is exposed, much foreshortened, to the spectator below. There is evidently a charming walk round the plateau of the town commanding those pretty views of which Balzac gives an account. But the train whirled me away, and these are my only impressions. The truth is that I had no need, just at that moment, of putting myself into communication with Balzac, for opposite to me in the compartment were a couple of figures almost as vivid as the actors in the "Comédie Humaine." One of these was a very genial and dirty old priest, and the other was a reserved and concentrated young monk—the latter (by which I mean a monk of any kind) being a rare sight to-day in France. This young man indeed was mitigatedly monastic. He had a big brown frock and cowl, but he had also a shirt and a pair of shoes; he had, instead of a hempen scourge round his waist, a stout leather thong, and he carried with him a very profane little valise. He also read, from beginning to end, the *Figaro* which the old priest, who had done the same, presented to him; and he looked altogether as if, had he not been a monk, he would have made a distinguished officer of engineers.

Angoulême

When he was not reading the *Figaro* he was conning his breviary or answering, with rapid precision and with a deferential but discouraging dryness, the frequent questions of his companion, who was of quite another type. This worthy had a bored, good-natured, unbuttoned, expansive look; was talkative, restless, almost disreputably human. He was surrounded by a great deal of small luggage, and had scattered over the carriage his books, his papers, and fragments of his lunch, and the contents of an extraordinary bag which he kept beside him—a kind of secular reliquary—and which appeared to contain the odds and ends of a lifetime, as he took from it successively a pair of slippers, an old padlock (which evidently did not belong to it), an opera-glass, a collection of almanacs, and a large sea-shell, which he very carefully examined. I think that if he had not been afraid of the young monk, who was so much more serious than he, he would have held the shell to his ear like a child. Indeed, he was a very childish and delightful old priest, and his companion evidently thought him quite frivolous. But I liked him the better of the two. He was not a country curé, but an ecclesiastic of some rank, who had seen a good deal both of the church and of the world; and if I too had not been afraid of his colleague, who read the *Figaro* as seriously as if it had been an encyclical, I should have entered into conversation with him.

All this while I was getting on to Bordeaux, where I permitted myself to spend three days. I am afraid I have next to nothing to show for them, and that there would be little profit in lingering on this episode, which is the less to be justified as I had in former years examined Bordeaux attentively enough. It contains a very good hotel—an hotel not good enough, however, to keep you there for its own sake. For the rest, Bordeaux is a big, rich, handsome, imposing commercial town, with long rows of fine old eighteenth-century houses which overlook the yellow Garonne. I have spoken of the quays of Nantes as fine, but those of Bordeaux have a wider sweep and a still more architectural air. The appearance of such a port as this makes the Anglo-Saxon tourist blush for the sordid water-fronts of Liverpool and New York, which, with their larger activity, have so much more reason to be stately. Bordeaux gives a great impression of prosperous industries, and suggests delightful ideas, images of prune-boxes and bottled claret. As the focus of distribution of the best wine in the world, it is indeed a sacred city—dedicated to the worship of Bacchus in the most discreet form. The country all about it is covered with precious vineyards, sources of fortune to their owners and of satisfaction to distant consumers: and as you look over to the hills beyond the Garonne you see them, in the autumn sunshine, fretted with the rusty richness of this or that immortal *clos*. But the principal picture, within the town, is that of the vast curving quays, bordered with houses that look like the *hôtels* of farmers-general of the last century, and of the wide, tawny river, crowded with shipping and spanned by the largest of bridges. Some of the types on the water-side are of the sort that arrest a sketcher—figures of stalwart, brown-faced Basques, such as I had seen of old in great numbers at Biarritz, with their loose circular caps, their white sandals, their air of walking for a wager. Never was a tougher, a harder race. They are not mariners nor watermen, but, putting questions of temper aside, they are the best possible dock-porters. "Il s'y fait un commerce terrible," a *douanier* said to me, as he looked up and down the interminable docks; and such a place has indeed much to say of the wealth, the capacity for production, of France—the bright, cheerful, smokeless industry of the wonderful country which produces, above all, the agreeable things of life, and turns even its defeats and revolutions into gold. The whole town has an air of almost depressing opulence, an appearance which culminates in the great *place* which surrounds the Grand-Théatre—an establishment of the highest style, encircled with columns, arcades, lamps, gilded cafés. One feels it to be a monument to the virtue of the well-selected bottle. If I had not forbidden myself to linger, I should venture to insist on this and, at the risk of being called fantastic, trace an analogy between good claret and the best qualities of the French mind; pretend that there is a taste of sound Bordeaux in all the happiest manifestations of that fine organ, and that, correspondingly, there is a touch of French reason, French completeness, in a glass of Pontet-Canet. The danger of such an excursion would lie mainly in its being so open to the reader to take the ground from under my feet by saying that good claret doesn't exist. To this I should have no reply whatever. I should be unable to tell him where to find it. I certainly didn't find it at Bordeaux, where I drank a most vulgar fluid; and it is of course notorious that a large part of mankind is occupied in vainly looking for it. There was a great pretence of putting it forward at the Exhibition which was going on at Bordeaux at the time of my visit, an "exposition philomathique," lodged in a collection of big temporary buildings in the Allées d'Orléans, and regarded by the Bordelais for the moment as the most brilliant feature of their city. Here were pyramids of bottles, mountains of bottles, to say nothing of cases and cabinets of bottles. The contemplation of these glittering tiers was of course not very convincing; and indeed the whole arrangement struck me as a high impertinence. Good wine is not an optical pleasure, it is an inward emotion; and if there was a chamber of degustation on the premises, I failed to discover it. It was not in the search for it, indeed, that I spent half an hour in this bewildering bazaar. Like all "expositions," it seemed to me to be full of ugly things, and gave one a portentous idea of the quantity of rubbish that man carries with him on his course through the ages. Such an amount of luggage for a journey after all so short! There were no individual objects; there was nothing but dozens and hundreds, all machine-made and expressionless, in spite of the repeated grimace, the conscious smartness, of "the last new thing," that was stamped on all of them. The fatal facility of the French *article* becomes at last as irritating as the refrain of a popular song. The poor "Indiens Galibis" struck me as really more interesting—a group of stunted savages who formed one of the attractions of the place and were confined in a pen in the open air, with a rabble of people pushing and squeezing, hanging over the barrier, to look at them. They had no grimace, no pretension to be new, no desire to catch your eye. They looked at their visitors no more than they looked at each other, and seemed ancient, indifferent, terribly bored.

CHAPTER XIX. TOULOUSE

THERE is much entertainment in the journey through the wide, smiling garden of Gascony; I speak of it as I took it in going from Bordeaux to Toulouse. It is the south, quite the south, and had for the present narrator its full measure of the charm he is always determined to find in countries that may even by courtesy be said to appertain to the sun. It was, moreover, the happy and genial view of these mild latitudes, which, goodness knows, often have a dreariness of their own; a land teeming with corn and wine and speaking everywhere (that is everywhere the phylloxera had not laid it waste) of wealth and plenty. The road runs constantly near the Garonne, touching now and then its slow, brown, rather sullen stream, a sullenness that encloses great dangers and disasters. The traces of the horrible floods of 1875 have disappeared, and the land smiles placidly enough while it waits for another immersion. Toulouse, at the period I speak of, was up to its middle (and in places above it) in water, and looks still as if it had been thoroughly soaked—as if it had faded and shrivelled with a long steeping. The fields and copses, of course, are more forgiving. The railway line follows as well the charming Canal du Midi, which is as pretty as a river, barring the straightness, and here and there occupies the foreground, beneath a screen of dense, tall trees, while the Garonne takes a larger and more irregular course a little way beyond it. People who are fond of canals—and, speaking from the pictorial standpoint, I hold the taste to be most legitimate—will delight in this admirable specimen of the class, which has a very interesting history, not to be narrated here. On the other side of the road (the left), all the way, runs a long, low line of hills, or rather one continuous hill, or perpetual cliff, with a straight top, in the shape of a ledge of rock, which might pass for a ruined wall. I am afraid the reader will lose patience with my habit of constantly referring to the landscape of Italy as if that were the measure of the beauty of every other. Yet I am still more afraid that I cannot apologise for it, and must leave it in its culpable nakedness. It is an idle habit; but the reader will long since have discovered that this was an idle journey and that I give my impressions as they came to me. It came to me, then, that in all this view there was something transalpine, with a greater smartness and freshness and much less elegance and languor. This impression was occasionally deepened by the appearance, on the long eminence of which I speak, of a village, a church, a château, that seemed to look down at the plain from over the ruined wall. The perpetual vines, the bright-faced flat-roofed houses, covered with tiles, the softness and sweetness of the light and air, recalled the prosier portions of the Lombard plain. Toulouse itself has a little of this Italian expression, but not enough to give a colour to its dark, dirty, crooked streets, which are irregular without being eccentric, and which, if it were not for the superb church of Saint-Sernin, would be quite destitute of monuments.

I have already alluded to the way in which the names of certain places impose themselves on the mind, and I must add that of Toulouse to the list of expressive appellations. It certainly evokes a vision—suggests something highly *méridional*. But the city, it must be confessed, is less pictorial than the word, in spite of the Place du Capitole, in spite of the quay of the Garonne, in spite of the curious cloister of the old museum. What justifies the images that are latent in the word is not the aspect, but the history, of the town. The hotel to which the well-advised traveller will repair stands in a corner of the Place du Capitole, which is the heart and centre of Toulouse, and which bears a vague and inexpensive resemblance to Piazza Castello at Turin. The Capitol, with a wide modern face, occupies one side, and, like the palace at Turin, looks across at a high arcade, under which the hotels, the principal shops, and the lounging citizens are gathered. The shops, are probably better than the Turinese, but the people are not so good. Stunted, shabby, rather vitiated looking, they have none of the personal richness of the sturdy Piedmontese; and I will take this occasion to remark that in the course of a journey of several weeks in the French provinces I rarely encountered a well-dressed male. Can it be possible that republics are unfavourable to a certain attention to one's boots and one's beard? I risk this somewhat futile inquiry because the proportion of neat coats and trousers seemed to be about the same in France and in my native land. It was notably lower than in England and in Italy, and even warranted the supposition that most good provincials have their chin shaven and their boots blacked but once a week. I hasten to add, lest my observation should appear to be of a sadly superficial character, that the manners and conversation of these gentlemen bore (whenever I had occasion to appreciate them) no relation to the state of their chin and their boots. They were almost always marked by an extreme amenity. At Toulouse there was the strongest temptation to speak to people simply for the entertainment of hearing them reply with that curious, that fascinating accent of the Languedoc, which appears to abound in final consonants and leads the Toulousians to say *bien-g* and *maison-g* like Englishmen learning French. It is as if they talked with their teeth rather than with their tongue. I find in my note-book a phrase in regard to Toulouse which is perhaps a little ill-natured, but which I will transcribe as it stands: "The oddity is that the place should be both animated and dull. A big, brown-skinned population, clattering about in a flat, tortuous town, which produces nothing whatever that I can discover. Except the church of Saint-Sernin and the fine old court of the Hôtel d'Assézat, Toulouse has no architecture; the houses are for the most part of brick, of a greyish-red colour, and have no particular style. The brickwork of the place is in fact very poor—inferior to that of the North Italian towns and quite wanting in the wealth of tone which this homely material takes on in general in the climates of dampness and greenness." And then my note-book goes on to narrate a little visit to the Capitol, which was soon made, as the building was in course of repair and half the rooms were closed.

CHAPTER XX. TOULOUSE. THE CAPITOL

THE history of Toulouse is detestable, saturated with blood and perfidy; and the ancient custom of the Floral Games, grafted upon all sorts of internecine traditions, seems, with its false pastoralism, its mock chivalry, its display of fine feelings, to set off rather than to mitigate these horrors. The society was founded in the fourteenth century, and it has held annual meetings ever since—meetings at which poems in the fine old *langue d'oc* are declaimed and a blushing laureate is chosen. This business takes place in the Capitol, before the chief magistrate of the town, who is known as the *capitoul*, and of all the pretty women as well—a class very numerous at Toulouse. It is unusual to present a finer person than that of the portress who pretended to show me the apartments in which the Floral Games are held; a big, brown, expansive woman, still in the prime of life, with a speaking eye, an extraordinary assurance, and a pair of magenta stockings, which were inserted into the neatest and most polished little black sabots, and which, as she clattered up the stairs before me, lavishly displaying them, made her look like the heroine of an *opéra-bouffe*. Her talk was all in *n*'s, *g*'s and *d*'s, and in mute *e*'s strongly accented, as *autré, théâtré, splendidé*—the last being an epithet she applied to everything the Capitol contained, and especially to a horrible picture representing the famous Clémence Isaure, the reputed foundress of the poetical contest, presiding on one of these occasions. I wondered whether

Clémence Isaure had been anything like this terrible Toulousaine of to-day, who would have been a capital figure-head for a floral game. The lady in whose honour the picture I have just mentioned was painted is a somewhat mythical personage, and she is not to be found in the "Biographie Universelle." She is, however, a very graceful myth; and if she never existed, her statue at least does—a shapeless effigy transferred to the Capitol from the so-called tomb of Clémence in the old church of La Daurade. The great hall in which the Floral Games are held was encumbered with scaffoldings, and I was unable to admire the long series of busts of the bards who have won prizes and the portraits of all the capitouls of Toulouse. As a compensation I was introduced to a big bookcase filled with the poems that have been crowned since the days of the troubadours (a portentous collection), and the big butcher's knife with which, according to the legend, Henry, Duke of Montmorency, who had conspired against the great cardinal with Gaston of Orleans and Mary de'Medici, was, in 1632, beheaded on this spot by the order of Richelieu. With these objects the interest of the

Toulouse: the Capitol

Capitol was exhausted. The building indeed has not the grandeur of its name, which is a sort of promise that the visitor will find some sensible embodiment of the old Roman tradition that once nourished in this part of France. It is inferior in impressiveness to the other three famous Capitols of the modern world—that of Rome (if I may call the present structure modern) and those of Washington and Albany!

The only Roman remains at Toulouse are to be found in the museum—a very interesting establishment, which I was condemned to see as imperfectly as I had seen the Capitol. It was being rearranged; and the gallery of paintings, which is the least interesting feature, was the only part that was not upside-down. The pictures are mainly of the modern French school, and I remember nothing but a powerful though disagreeable specimen of Henner, who paints the human body, and paints it so well, with a brush dipped in blackness; and, placed among the paintings, a bronze replica of the charming young David of Mercié. These things have been set out in the church of an old monastery, long since suppressed, and the rest of the collection occupies the cloisters. These are two in number—a small one, which you enter first from the street, and a very vast and elegant one beyond it, which, with its light gothic arches and slim columns (of the fourteenth century), its broad walk, its little garden with old tombs and statues in the centre, is by far the most picturesque, the most sketchable, spot in Toulouse. It must be doubly so when the Roman busts, inscriptions, slabs, and sarcophagi are ranged along the walls; it must indeed (to compare small things with great, and as the judicious Murray remarks) bear a certain resemblance to the Campo Santo at Pisa. But these things are absent now; the cloister is a litter of confusion, and its treasures have been stowed away confusedly in sundry inaccessible rooms. The custodian attempted to console me by telling me that when they are exhibited again it will be on a scientific basis and with an order and regularity of which they were formerly innocent. But I was not consoled. I wanted simply the spectacle, the picture, and I didn't care in the least for the classification. Old Roman fragments exposed to light in the open air, under a southern sky, in a quadrangle round a garden, have an immortal charm simply in their general effect; and the charm is all the greater when the soil of the very place has yielded them up.

CHAPTER XXI. TOULOUSE. SAINT-SERNIN

MY real consolation was an hour I spent in Saint-Sernin, one of the noblest churches in southern France, and easily the first among those of Toulouse. This great structure, a masterpiece of twelfth-century romanesque and dedicated to Saint Saturninus—the Toulousains have abbreviated—is, I think, alone worth a journey to Toulouse. What makes it so is the extraordinary seriousness of its interior; no other term occurs to me as expressing so well the character of its clear grey nave. As a general thing, I favour little the fashion of attributing moral qualities to buildings; I shrink from talking about tender cornices and sincere campanili; but one feels that one can scarce get on without imputing some sort of morality to Saint-Sernin. As it stands to-day, the church has been completely restored by Viollet-le-Duc. The exterior is of brick, and has little charm save that of a tower of four rows of arches, narrowing together as they ascend. The nave is of great length and height, the barrel-roof of stone, the effect of the round arches and pillars in the triforium especially fine. There are two low aisles on either side. The choir is very deep and narrow; it seems to close together, and looks as if it were meant for intensely earnest rites. The transepts are most noble, especially the arches of the second tier. The whole church is narrow for its length and is singularly complete and homogeneous. As I say all this I feel that I quite fail to give an impression of its manly gravity, its strong proportions, or of the lonesome look of its renovated stones as I sat there while the October twilight gathered. It is a real work of art, a high conception. The crypt, into which I was eventually led captive by an importunate sacristan, is quite another affair, though indeed I suppose it may also be spoken of as a work of art. It is a rich museum of relics, and contains the head of Saint Thomas Aquinas wrapped up in a napkin and exhibited in a glass case. The sacristan took a lamp and guided me about, presenting me to one saintly remnant after another. The impression was grotesque, but some of the objects were contained in curious old cases of beaten silver and brass: these things at least, which looked as if they had been transmitted from the early church, were venerable. There was, however, a kind of wholesale sanctity about the place which overshot the mark; it pretends to be one of the holiest spots in the world. The effect is spoiled by the way the sacristans hang about and offer to take you into it for ten sous—I was accosted by two and escaped from another—and by the familiar manner in which you pop in and out. This episode rather broke the charm of Saint-Sernin, so that I took my departure and went in search of the cathedral. It was scarcely worth finding, and struck me as an odd, dislocated fragment. The front consists only of a portal beside which a tall brick tower of a later period has been erected. The nave was wrapped in dimness, with a few scattered lamps. I could only distinguish an immense vault, like a high cavern, without aisles. Here and there in the gloom was a kneeling figure; the whole place was mysterious and lopsided. The choir was curtained off; it appeared not to correspond with the nave—that is, not to have the same axis. The only other ecclesiastical impression I gathered at Toulouse came to me in the church of La Daurade, of which the front, on the quay by the Garonne, was closed with scaffoldings; so that one entered it from behind, where it is completely masked by houses, through a door which has at first no traceable connection with it. It is a vast, high, modernised, heavily decorated church, dimly lighted at all times, I should suppose, and enriched by the shades of evening at the time I looked into it. I perceived that it consisted mainly of a large square, beneath a dome, in the centre of which a single person—a lady—was praying with the utmost absorption. The manner of access to the church interposed such an obstacle to the outer profanities that I had a sense of intruding and presently withdrew, carrying with me a picture of the vast, still interior, the gilded roof gleaming in the twilight, and the solitary worshipper. What was she praying for, and was she not almost afraid to remain there alone?

Toulouse

For the rest, the picturesque at Toulouse consists principally of the walk beside the Garonne, which is spanned, to the faubourg of Saint-Cyprien, by a stout brick bridge. This hapless suburb, the baseness of whose site is noticeable, lay for days under the water at the time of the last inundations. The Garonne had almost mounted to the roofs of the houses, and the place continues to present a blighted, frightened look. Two or three persons with whom I had some conversation spoke of that time as a memory of horror. I have not done with my Italian comparisons; I shall never have done with them. I am therefore free to say that in the way in which Toulouse looks out on the Garonne there was something that reminded me vaguely of the way in which Pisa looks out on the Arno. The red-faced houses—all of brick—along the quay have a mixture of brightness and shabbiness, as well as the fashion of the open *loggia* in the top-storey. The river, with another bridge or two, might be the Arno, and the buildings on the other side of it—a hospital, a suppressed convent—dip their feet into it with real southern cynicism. I have spoken of the old Hôtel d'Assézat as the best house at Toulouse; with the exception of the cloister of the museum, it is the only "bit" I remember. It has fallen from the state of a noble residence of the sixteenth century to that of a warehouse and a set of offices; but a certain dignity lingers in its melancholy court, which is divided from the street by a gateway that is still imposing and in which a clambering vine and a red Virginia-creeper were suspended to the rusty walls of brick and stone.

The most interesting house at Toulouse is far from being the most striking. At the door of No. 50 Rue des Filatiers, a featureless, solid structure, was found hanging, one autumn evening, the body of the young Marc-Antoine Calas, whose ill-inspired suicide was to be the first act of a tragedy so horrible. The fanaticism aroused in the townsfolk by this incident; the execution by torture of Jean Calas, accused as a Protestant of having hanged his son, who had gone over to the Church of Rome; the ruin of the family; the claustration of the daughters; the flight of the widow to Switzerland; her introduction to Voltaire; the excited zeal of that incomparable partisan and the passionate persistence with which, from year to year, he pursued a reversal of judgment till at last he obtained it and devoted the tribunal of Toulouse to execration and the name of the victims to lasting wonder and pity—these things form part of one of the most interesting and touching episodes of the social history of the eighteenth century. The story has the fatal progression, the dark rigour, of one of the tragic dramas of the Greeks. Jean Calas, advanced in life, blameless, bewildered, protesting his innocence, had been broken on the wheel; and the sight of his decent dwelling, which brought home to me all that had been suffered there, spoiled for me, for half an hour, the impression of Toulouse.

CHAPTER XXII. CARCASSONNE

I SPENT but a few hours at Carcassonne; but those hours had a rounded felicity, and I cannot do better than transcribe from my note-book the little record made at the moment. Vitiated as it may be by crudity and incoherency, it has at any rate the freshness of a great emotion. This is the best quality that a reader may hope to extract from a narrative in which "useful information" and technical lore even of the most general sort are completely absent. For Carcassonne is moving, beyond a doubt; and the traveller who in the course of a little tour in France may have felt himself urged, in melancholy moments, to say that on the whole the disappointments are as numerous as the satisfactions, must admit that there can be nothing better than this.

The country after you leave Toulouse continues to be charming; the more so that it merges its flatness in the distant Cévennes on one side, and on the other, far away on your right, in the richer range of the Pyrenees. Olives and cypresses, pergolas and vines, terraces on the roofs of houses, soft, iridescent mountains, a warm yellow light—what more could the difficult tourist want? He left his luggage at the station, warily determined to look at the inn before committing himself to it. It was so evident (even to a cursory glance) that it might easily have been much better, that he simply took his way to the town, with the whole of a superb afternoon before him. When I say the town, I mean the towns; there being two at Carcassonne, perfectly distinct, and each with excellent claims to the title. They have settled the matter between them, however, and the elder, the shrine of pilgrimage, to which the other is but a stepping-stone, or even, as I may say, a humble door-mat, takes the name of the Cité. You see nothing of the Cité from the station; it is masked by the agglomeration of the *ville-basse*, which is relatively (but only relatively) new. A wonderful avenue of acacias leads to it from the station—leads past it, rather, and conducts you to a little high-backed bridge over the Aude, beyond which, detached and erect, a distinct mediæval silhouette, the Cité presents itself. Like a rival shop on the invidious side of a street, it has "no connection" with the establishment across the way, although the two places are united (if old Carcassonne may be said to be united to anything) by a vague little rustic faubourg. Perched on its solid pedestal, the perfect detachment of the Cité is what first strikes you. To take leave, without delay, of the *ville-basse*, I may say that the splendid acacias I have mentioned flung a summerish dusk over the place, in which a few scattered remains of stout walls and big bastions looked venerable and picturesque.

Carcassonne

A little boulevard winds round the town, planted with trees and garnished with more benches than I ever saw provided by a soft-hearted municipality. This precinct had a warm, lazy, dusty, southern look, as if the people sat out-of-doors a great deal and wandered about in the stillness of summer nights. The figure of the elder town at these hours must be ghostly enough on its neighbouring hill. Even by day it has the air of a vignette of Gustave Doré, a couplet of Victor Hugo. It is almost too perfect—as if it were an enormous model placed on a big green table at a museum. A steep, paved way, grass-grown like all roads where vehicles never pass, stretches up to it in the sun. It has a double enceinte, complete outer walls and complete inner (these, elaborately fortified, are the more curious); and this congregation of ramparts, towers, bastions, battlements, barbicans, is as fantastic and romantic as you please. The approach I mention here leads to the gate that looks toward Toulouse—the Porte de l'Aude. There is a second, on the other side, called, I believe, the Porte Narbonnaise, a magnificent gate, flanked with towers thick and tall, defended by elaborate outworks; and these two apertures alone admit you to the place—putting aside a small sally-port, protected by a great bastion, on the quarter that looks toward the Pyrenees.

As a votary, always, in the first instance, of a general impression, I walked all round the outer enceinte—a process on the very face of it entertaining. I took to the right of the Porte de l'Aude, without entering it, where the old moat has been filled in. The filling-in of the moat has created a grassy level at the foot of the big grey towers, which, rising at frequent intervals, stretch their stiff curtain of stone from point to point: the curtain drops without a fold upon the quiet grass, which was dotted here and there with a humble native dozing away the golden afternoon. The natives of the elder Carcassonne are all humble; for the core of the Cité has shrunken and decayed, and there is little life among the ruins. A few tenacious labourers who work in the neighbouring fields or in the *ville-basse*, and sundry octogenarians of both sexes, who are dying where they have lived and contribute much to the pictorial effect—these are the principal inhabitants. The process of converting the place from an irresponsible old town into a conscious "specimen" has of course been attended with eliminations; the population has, as a general thing, been restored away. I should lose no time in saying that restoration is the great mark of the Cité. M. Viollet-le-Duc has worked his will upon it, put it into perfect order, revived the fortifications in every detail. I do not pretend to judge the performance, carried out on a scale and in a spirit which really impose themselves on the imagination. Few architects have had such a chance, and M. Viollet-le-Duc must have been the envy of the whole restoring fraternity. The image of a more crumbling Carcassonne rises in the mind, and there is no doubt that forty years ago the place was more affecting. On the other hand, as we see it to-day it is a wonderful evocation; and if there is a great deal of new in the old, there is plenty of old in the new. The repaired crenellations, the inserted patches of the walls of the outer circle, sufficiently express this commixture. My walk brought me into full view of the Pyrenees, which, now that the sun had begun to sink and the shadows to grow long, had a wonderful violet glow. The platform at the base of the walls has a greater width on this side, and it made the scene more complete. Two or three old crones had crawled out of the Porte Narbonnaise to examine the advancing visitor; and a very ancient peasant, lying there with his back against a tower, was tending half a dozen lean sheep. A poor man in a very old blouse, crippled and with crutches lying beside him, had been brought out and placed on a stool, where he enjoyed the afternoon as best he might. He looked so ill and so patient that I spoke to him; found that his legs were paralysed and he was quite helpless. He had formerly been seven years in the army, and had made the campaign of Mexico with Bazaine. Born in the old Cité, he had come back there to end his days. It seemed strange, as he sat there with those romantic walls behind him and the great picture of the Pyrenees in front, to think that he had been across the seas to the far-away new world, had made part of a famous expedition, and was now a cripple at the gate of the mediæval city where he had played as a child. All this struck me as a great deal of history for so modest a figure—a poor little figure that could only just unclose its palm for a small silver coin.

Carcassonne

He was not the only acquaintance I made at Carcassonne. I had not pursued my circuit of the walls much farther when I encountered a person of quite another type, of whom I asked some question which had just then presented itself, and who proved to be the very genius of the spot. He was a sociable son of the *ville-basse*, a gentleman, and, as I afterwards learned, an employé at the prefecture—a person, in short, much esteemed at Carcassonne. (I may say all this, as he will never read these pages.) He had been ill for a month, and in the company of his little dog was taking his first airing; in his own phrase, he was *amoureux-fou de la Cité*—he could lose no time in coming back to it. He talked of it indeed as a lover, and, giving me for half an hour the advantage of his company, showed me all the points of the place. (I speak here always of the outer enceinte; you penetrate to the inner—which is the specialty of Carcassonne and the great curiosity—only by application at the lodge of the regular custodian, a remarkable functionary, who, half an hour later, when I had been introduced to him by my friend the amateur, marched me over the fortifications with a tremendous accompaniment of dates and technical terms.) My companion pointed out to me in particular the traces of different periods in the structure of the walls. There is a portentous amount of history embedded in them, beginning with Romans and Visigoths; here and there are marks of old breaches hastily repaired. We passed into the town— into that part of it not included in the citadel. It is the queerest and most fragmentary little place in the world, as everything save the fortifications is being suffered to crumble away in order that the spirit of M. Viollet-le-Duc alone may pervade it and it may subsist simply as a magnificent shell. As the leases of the wretched little houses fall in, the ground is cleared of them; and a mumbling old woman approached me in the course of my circuit, inviting me to condole with her on the disappearance of so many of the hovels which in the last few hundred years (since the collapse of Carcassonne as a stronghold) had attached themselves to the base of the walls, in the space between the two circles. These habitations, constructed of materials taken from the ruins, nestled there snugly enough. This intermediate space had therefore become a kind of street, which has crumbled in turn, as the fortress has grown up again. There are other streets beside, very diminutive and vague, where you pick your way over heaps of rubbish and become conscious of unexpected faces looking at you out of windows as detached as the cherubic heads. The most definite thing in the place was the little café, where the waiters, I think, must be the ghosts of the old Visigoths; the most definite, that is, after the little château and the little cathedral. Everything in the Cité is little; you can walk round the walls in twenty minutes. On the drawbridge of the château, which, with a picturesque old face, flanking towers, and a dry moat, is to-day simply a bare *caserne*, lounged half a dozen soldiers, unusually small. Nothing could be more odd than to see these objects enclosed in a receptacle which has much of the appearance of an enormous toy. The Cité and its population vaguely reminded me of an immense Noah's ark.

CHAPTER XXIII. CARCASSONNE

CARCASSONE dates from the Roman occupation of Gaul. The place commanded one of the great roads into Spain, and in the fourth century Romans and Franks ousted each other from such a point of vantage. In the year 436 Theodoric King of the Visigoths superseded both these parties; and it was during his occupation that the inner enceinte was raised upon the ruins of the Roman fortifications. Most of the Visigoth towers that are still erect are seated upon Roman substructions which appear to have been formed hastily, probably at the moment of the Frankish invasion. The authors of these solid defences, though occasionally disturbed, held Carcassonne and the neighbouring country, in which they had established their kingdom of Septimania, till the year 713, when they were expelled by the Moors of Spain, who ushered in an unillumined period of four centuries, of which no traces remain. These facts I derive from a source no more recondite than a pamphlet by M. Viollet-le-Duc—a very luminous description of the fortifications, which you may buy from the accomplished custodian. The writer makes a jump to the year 1209, when Carcassonne, then forming part of the realm of the viscounts of Béziers and infected by the Albigensian heresy, was besieged, in the name of the Pope, by the terrible Simon de Montfort and his army of crusaders. Simon was accustomed to success, and the town succumbed in the course of a fortnight. Thirty-one years later, having passed into the hands of the King of France, it was again besieged by the young Raymond de Trincavel, the last of the viscounts of Béziers; and of this siege M. Viollet-le-Duc gives a long and minute account, which the visitor who has a head for such things may follow, with the brochure in hand, on the fortifications themselves. The young Raymond de Trincavel, baffled and repulsed, retired at the end of twenty-four days. Saint Louis and Philip the Bold, in the thirteenth century, multiplied the defences of Carcassonne, which was one of the bulwarks of their kingdom on the Spanish quarter; and from this time forth, being regarded as impregnable, the place had nothing to fear. It was not even attacked; and when in 1355 Edward the Black Prince marched into it, the inhabitants had opened the gates to the conqueror before whom all Languedoc was prostrate. I am not one of those who, as I said just now, have a head for such things, and having extracted these few facts, had made all the use of M. Viollet-le-Duc's pamphlet of which I was capable.

I have mentioned that my obliging friend the *amoureux-fou* handed me over to the doorkeeper of the citadel. I should add that I was at first committed to the wife of this functionary, a stout peasant-woman, who took a key down from a nail, conducted me to a postern door, and ushered me into the presence of her husband. Having just begun his rounds with a party of four persons, he was not many steps in advance. I added myself perforce to this party, which was not brilliantly composed, except that two of its members were gendarmes in full toggery, who announced in the course of our tour that they had been stationed for a year at Carcassonne and had never before had the curiosity to come up to the Cité. There was something brilliant certainly in that. The *gardien* was an extraordinarily typical little Frenchman, who struck me even more forcibly than the wonders of the inner enceinte; and as I am bound to assume, at whatever cost to my literary vanity, that there is not the slightest danger of his reading these remarks, I may treat him as public property. With his diminutive stature and his perpendicular spirit, his flushed face, expressive protuberant eyes, high peremptory voice, extreme volubility, lucidity and neatness of utterance, he reminded me of the gentry who figure in the revolutions of his native land. If he was not a fierce little Jacobin, he ought to have been, for I am sure there were many men of his pattern on the Committee of Public Safety. He knew absolutely what he was about, understood the place thoroughly, and constantly reminded his audience of what he himself had done in the way of excavations and reparations. He described himself as the brother of the architect of the work actually going forward (that which has been done since the death of M. Viollet-le-Duc, I suppose he meant), and this fact was more illustrative than all the others. It reminded me, as one is reminded at every turn, of the democratic conditions of French life: a man of the people, with a wife *en bonnet*, extremely intelligent, full of special knowledge, and yet remaining essentially of the people and showing his intelligence with a kind of ferocity, of defiance. Such a personage helps one to understand the red radicalism of France, the revolutions, the barricades, the sinister passion for theories. (I do not, of course, take upon myself to say that the individual I describe—who can know nothing of the liberties I am taking with him—is actually devoted to these ideals; I only mean that many such devotees must have his qualities.) In just the *nuance* that I have tried to indicate here it is a terrible pattern of man. Permeated in a high degree by civilisation, it is yet untouched by the desire which one finds in the Englishman, in proportion as he rises in the world, to approximate to the figure of the gentleman. On the other hand, a *netteté*, a faculty of exposition, such as the English gentleman is rarely either blessed or cursed with.

Carcassonne

This brilliant, this suggestive warden of Carcassonne marched us about for an hour, haranguing, explaining, illustrating as he went; it was a complete little lecture, such as might have been delivered at the Lowell Institute, on the manner in which a first-rate *place forte* used to be attacked and defended. Our peregrinations made it very clear that Carcassonne was impregnable; it is impossible to imagine without having seen them such refinements of immurement, such ingenuities of resistance. We passed along the battlements and *chemins de ronde*, ascended and descended towers, crawled under arches, peered out of loopholes, lowered ourselves into dungeons, halted in all sorts of tight places while the purpose of something or other was described to us. It was very curious, very interesting; above all it was very pictorial, and involved perpetual peeps into the little crooked, crumbling, sunny, grassy, empty Cité. In places, as you stand upon it, the great towered and embattled enceinte produces an illusion; it looks as if it were still equipped and defended. One vivid challenge, at any rate, it flings down before you; it calls upon you to make up your mind on the matter of restoration. For myself I have no hesitation; I prefer in every case the ruined, however ruined, to the reconstructed, however splendid. What is left is more precious than what is added; the one is history, the other is fiction; and I like the former the better of the two—it is so much more romantic. One is positive, so far as it goes; the other fills up the void with things more dead than the void itself, inasmuch as they have never had life. After that I am free to say that the restoration of Carcassonne is a splendid achievement. The little custodian dismissed us at last, after having, as usual, inducted us into the inevitable repository of photographs. These photographs are a great nuisance all over the Midi. They are exceedingly bad for the most part; and the worst—those in the form of the hideous little *album-panorama*—are thrust upon you at every turn. They are a kind of tax that you must pay; the best way is to pay to be let off. It was not to be denied that there was a relief in separating from our accomplished guide, whose manner of imparting information reminded me of the energetic process by which I had seen mineral waters bottled. All this while the afternoon had grown more lovely; the sunset had deepened, the horizon of hills grown purple; the mass of the Canigou became more delicate, yet more distinct. The day had so far faded that the interior of the little cathedral was wrapped in twilight, into which the glowing windows projected something of their colour. This church has high beauty and value, but I will spare the reader a presentation of details which I myself had no opportunity to master. It consists of a romanesque nave, of the end of the eleventh century, and a Gothic choir and transepts of the beginning of the fourteenth; and, shut up in its citadel like a precious casket in a cabinet, it seems—or seemed at that hour—to have a sort of double sanctity. After leaving it and passing out of the two circles of walls, I treated myself, in the most infatuated manner, to another walk round the Cité. It is certainly this general impression that is most striking—the impression from outside, where the whole place detaches itself at once from the landscape. In the warm southern dusk it looked more than ever like a city in a fairy tale. To make the thing perfect, a white young moon, in its first quarter, came out and hung just over the dark silhouette. It was hard to come away—to incommode one's self for anything so vulgar as a railway train; I would gladly have spent the evening in revolving round the walls of Carcassonne. But I had in a measure engaged to proceed to Narbonne, and there was a certain magic in that name which gave me strength—Narbonne, the richest city in Roman Gaul.

CHAPTER XXIV. NARBONNE

AT Narbonne I took up my abode at the house of a *serrurier mécanicien*, and was very thankful for the accommodation. It was my misfortune to arrive at this ancient city late at night, on the eve of market-day; and market-day at Narbonne is a very serious affair. The inns, on this occasion, are stuffed with wine-dealers; for the country round about, dedicated almost exclusively to Bacchus, has hitherto escaped the phylloxera. This deadly enemy of the grape is encamped over the Midi in a hundred places; blighted vineyards and ruined proprietors being quite the order of the day. The signs of distress are more frequent as you advance into Provence, many of the vines being laid under water in the hope of washing the plague away. There are healthy regions still, however, and the vintners find plenty to do at Narbonne.

Narbonne

The traffic in wine appeared to be the sole thought of the Narbonnais; every one I spoke to had something to say about the harvest of gold that bloomed under its influence. "C'est inoui, monsieur, l'argent qu'il y a dans ce pays. Des gens à qui la vente de leur vin rapporte jusqu'à 500,000 francs par an." That little speech addressed to me by a gentleman at the inn gives the note of these revelations. It must be said that there was little in the appearance either of the town or of its population to suggest the possession of such treasures. Narbonne is a *sale petite ville* in all the force of the term, and my first impression on arriving there was an extreme regret that I had not remained for the night at the lovely Carcassonne. My journey from that delectable spot lasted a couple of hours and was performed in darkness—a darkness not so dense, however, but that I was able to make out, as we passed it, the great figure of Béziers, whose ancient roofs and towers, clustered on a goodly hill-top, looked as fantastic as you please. I know not what appearance Béziers may present by day, but by night it has quite the grand air. On issuing from the station at Narbonne I found that the only vehicle in waiting was a kind of bastard tramcar, a thing shaped as if it had been meant to go upon rails; that is, equipped with small wheels, placed beneath it, and with a platform at either end, but destined to rattle over the stones like the most vulgar of omnibuses. To complete the oddity of this conveyance, it was under the supervision, not of a conductor, but of a conductress. A fair young woman with a pouch suspended from her girdle had command of the platform; and as soon as the car was full she jolted us into the town through clouds of the thickest dust I ever have swallowed. I have had occasion to speak of the activity of women in France—of the way they are always in the ascendant; and here was a signal example of their general utility. The young lady I have mentioned conveyed her whole company to the wretched little Hôtel de France, where it is to be hoped that some of them found a lodging. For myself, I was informed that the place was crowded from cellar to attic, and that its inmates were sleeping three or four in a room. At Carcassonne I should have had a bad bed, but at Narbonne, apparently, I was to have no bed at all. I passed an hour or two of flat suspense while fate settled the question of whether I should go on to Perpignan, return to Béziers, or still discover a modest couch at Narbonne. I shall not have suffered in vain, however, if my example serves to deter other travellers from alighting unannounced at that city on a Wednesday evening. The retreat to Béziers, not attempted in time, proved impossible, and I was assured that at Perpignan, which I should not reach till midnight, the affluence of wine-dealers was not less than at Narbonne. I interviewed every hostess in the town, and got no satisfaction but distracted shrugs. Finally, at an advanced hour, one of the servants of the Hôtel de France, where I had attempted to dine, came to me in triumph to proclaim that he had secured for me a charming apartment in a *maison bourgeoise*. I took possession of it gratefully, in spite of its having an entrance like a stable and being pervaded by an odour compared with which that of a stable would have been delicious. As I have mentioned, my landlord was a locksmith, and he had strange machines which rumbled and whirred in the rooms below my own. Nevertheless I slept, and I dreamed of Carcassonne. It was better to do that than to dream of the Hôtel de France.

Narbonne

I was obliged to cultivate relations with the cuisine of this establishment. Nothing could have been more *méridional*; indeed, both the dirty little inn and Narbonne at large seemed to me to have the infirmities of the south without its usual graces. Narrow, noisy, shabby, belittered and encumbered, filled with clatter and chatter, the Hôtel de France would have been described in perfection by Alphonse Daudet. For what struck me above all in it was the note of the Midi as he has represented it—the sound of universal talk. The landlord sat at supper with sundry friends in a kind of glass cage, with a genial indifference to arriving guests; the waiters tumbled over the loose luggage in the hall; the travellers who had been turned away leaned gloomily against door-posts; and the landlady, surrounded by confusion, unconscious of responsibility, and animated only by the spirit of conversation, bandied high-voiced compliments with the *voyageurs de commerce*. At ten o'clock in the morning there was a table d'hôte for breakfast—a wonderful repast, which overflowed into every room and pervaded the whole establishment. I sat down with a hundred hungry marketers, fat, brown, greasy men, with a good deal of the rich soil of Languedoc adhering to their hands and their boots. I mention the latter articles because they almost put them on the table. It was very hot, and there were swarms of flies; the viands had the strongest odour; there was in particular a horrible mixture known as *gras-double*, a light grey, glutinous, nauseating mess, which my companions devoured in large quantities. A man opposite to me had the dirtiest fingers I ever saw; a collection of fingers which in England would have excluded him from a farmers' ordinary. The conversation was mainly bucolic; though a part of it, I remember, at the table at which I sat, consisted of a discussion as to whether or no the maid-servant were *sage*—a discussion which went on under the nose of this young lady, as she carried about the dreadful *gras-double*, and to which she contributed the most convincing blushes. It was thoroughly *méridional*.

In going to Narbonne I had of course counted upon Roman remains; but when I went forth in search of them I perceived that I had hoped too fondly. There is really nothing in the place to speak of; that is, on the day of my visit there was nothing but the market, which was in complete possession. "This intricate, curious, but lifeless town," Murray calls it; yet to me it appeared overflowing with life. Its streets are mere crooked, dirty lanes, bordered with perfectly insignificant houses; but they were filled with the same clatter and chatter that I had found at the hotel. The market was held partly in the little square of the hôtel de ville, a structure which a flattering woodcut in the Guide-Joanne had given me a desire to behold. The reality was not impressive, the old colour of the front having been completely restored away. Such interest as it superficially possesses it derives from a fine mediæval tower which rises beside it with turrets at the angles—always a picturesque thing. The rest of the market was held in another *place*, still shabbier than the first, which lies beyond the canal. The Canal du Midi flows through the town, and, spanned at this point by a small suspension-bridge, presented a certain sketchability. On the farther side were the vendors and chafferers—old women under awnings and big umbrellas, rickety tables piled high with fruit, white caps and brown faces, blouses, sabots, donkeys. Beneath this picture was another—a long row of washerwomen, on their knees on the edge of the canal, pounding and wringing the dirty linen of Narbonne—no great quantity, to judge by the costume of the people. Innumerable rusty men, scattered all over the place, were buying and selling wine, straddling about in pairs, in groups, with their hands in their pockets, and packed together at the doors of the cafés. They were mostly fat and brown and unshaven; they ground their teeth as they talked; they were very *méridionaux*.

Narbonne

The only two lions at Narbonne are the cathedral and the museum, the latter of which is quartered in the hôtel de ville. The cathedral, closely shut in by houses and with the west front undergoing repairs, is singular in two respects. It consists exclusively of a choir, which is of the end of the thirteenth century and the beginning of the next, and of great magnificence. There is absolutely nothing else. This choir, of extraordinary elevation, forms the whole church. I sat there a good while; there was no other visitor. I had taken a great dislike to poor little Narbonne, which struck me as sordid and overheated, and this place seemed to extend to me, as in the Middle Ages, the privilege of sanctuary. It is a very solemn corner. The other peculiarity of the cathedral is that, externally, it bristles with battlements, having anciently formed part of the defences of the *archevêché*, which is beside it and which connects it with the hôtel de ville. This combination of the church and the fortress is very curious, and during the Middle Ages was not without its value. The palace of the former archbishops of Narbonne (the hôtel de ville of to-day forms part of it) was both an asylum and an arsenal during the hideous wars by which all Languedoc was ravaged in the thirteenth century. The whole mass of buildings is jammed together in a manner that from certain points of view makes it far from apparent which feature is which. The museum occupies several chambers at the top of the hôtel de ville, and is not an imposing collection. It was closed, but I induced the portress to let me in—a silent, cadaverous person, in a black coif, like a *béguine*, who sat knitting in one of the windows while I went the rounds. The number of Roman fragments is small, and their quality is not the finest; I must add that this impression was hastily gathered. There is, indeed, a work of art in one of the rooms which creates a presumption in favour of the place—the portrait (rather a good one) of a citizen of Narbonne, whose name I forget, who is described as having devoted all his time and his intelligence to collecting the objects by which the visitor is surrounded. This excellent man was a connoisseur, and the visitor is doubtless often an ignoramus.

CHAPTER XXV. MONTPELLIER

"Cette, with its glistening houses white,

Curves with the curving beach away

To where the lighthouse beacons bright,

Far in the bay."

THAT stanza of Matthew Arnold's, which I happened to remember, gave a certain importance to the half-hour I spent in the buffet of the station at Cette while I waited for the train to Montpellier. I had left Narbonne in the afternoon, and by the time I reached Cette the darkness had descended. I therefore missed the sight of the glistening houses, and had to console myself with that of the beacon in the bay, as well as with a *bouillon* of which I partook at the buffet aforesaid; for, since the morning, I had not ventured to return to the table d'hôte at Narbonne. The Hôtel Nevet at Montpellier, which I reached an hour later, has an ancient renown all over the south of France— advertises itself, I believe, as *le plus vastedu midi*. It seemed to me the model of a good provincial inn; a big rambling, creaking establishment, with brown, labyrinthine corridors, a queer old open-air vestibule, into which the diligence, in the *bon temps*, used to penetrate, and an hospitality more expressive than that of the new caravansaries. It dates from the days when Montpellier was still accounted a fine winter residence for people with weak lungs; and this rather melancholy tradition, together with the former celebrity of the school of medicine still existing there, but from which the glory has departed, helps to account for its combination of high antiquity and vast proportions. The old hotels were usually more concentrated; but the school of medicine passed for one of the attractions of Montpellier. Long before Mentone was discovered or Colorado invented, British invalids travelled down through France in the post-chaise or the public coach, to spend their winters in the wonderful place which boasted both a climate and a faculty. The air is mild, no doubt, but there are refinements of mildness which were not then suspected, and which in a more analytic age have carried the annual wave far beyond Montpellier. The place is charming, all the same; and it served the purpose of John Locke, who made a long stay there, between 1675 and 1679, and became acquainted with a noble fellow-visitor, Lord Pembroke, to whom he dedicated the famous Essay. There are places that please without your being able to say wherefore, and Montpellier is one of the number. It has some charming views, from the great promenade of the Peyrou; but its position is not strikingly fine. Beyond this it contains a good museum and the long façades of its school, but these are its only definite treasures. Its cathedral struck me as quite the weakest I had seen, and I remember no other monument that made up for it. The place has neither the gaiety of a modern nor the solemnity of an ancient town, and it is agreeable as certain women are agreeable who are neither beautiful nor clever. An Italian would remark that it is sympathetic; a German would admit that it is *gemüthlich*. I spent two days there, mostly in the rain, and even under these circumstances I carried away a kindly impression. I think the Hôtel Nevet had something to do with it, and the sentiment of relief with which, in a quiet, even a luxurious, room that looked out on a garden, I reflected that I had washed my hands of Narbonne. The phylloxera has destroyed the vines in the country that surrounds Montpellier, and at that moment I was capable of rejoicing in the thought that I should not breakfast with vintners.

The gem of the place is the Musée Fabre, one of the best collections of paintings in a provincial city. François Fabre, a native of Montpellier, died there in 1837, after having spent a considerable part of his life in Italy, where he had collected a good many valuable pictures and some very poor ones, the latter class including several from his own hand. He was the hero of a remarkable episode, having succeeded no less a person than Vittorio Alfieri in the affections of no less a person than Louise de Stolberg, Countess of Albany, widow of no less a person than Charles Edward Stuart, the second pretender to the British crown. Surely no woman ever was associated sentimentally with three figures more diverse—a disqualified sovereign, an Italian dramatist, and a bad French painter. The productions of M. Fabre, who followed in the steps of David, bear the stamp of a cold mediocrity; there is not much to be said even for the portrait of the genial countess (her life has been written by M. Saint-Réné-Taillandier, who depicts her as delightful), which hangs in Florence, in the gallery of the Uffizzi, and makes a pendant to a likeness of Alfieri by the same author. Stendhal, in his "Mémoires d'un Touriste," says that this work of art represents her as a cook who has pretty hands. I am delighted to having an opportunity of quoting Stendhal, whose two volumes of the "Mémoires d'un Touriste" every traveller in France should carry in his portmanteau. I have had this opportunity more than once, for I have met him at Tours, at Nantes, at Bourges; and everywhere he is suggestive. But he has the defect that he is never pictorial, that he never by any chance makes an image, and that his style is perversely colourless for a man so fond of contemplation. His taste is often singularly false; it is the taste of the early years of the present century, the period that produced clocks surmounted with sentimental "subjects." Stendhal does not admire these clocks, but he almost does. He admires Domenichino and Guercino, he prizes the Bolognese school of painters because they "spoke to the soul." He is a votary of the new classic, is fond of tall, square, regular buildings, and thinks Nantes, for instance, full of the "air noble." It was a pleasure to me to reflect that five-and-forty years ago he had alighted in that city, at the very inn in which I spent a night and which looks down on the Place Graslin and the theatre. The hotel that was the best in 1837 appears to be the best to-day. On the subject of Touraine Stendhal is extremely refreshing; he finds the scenery meagre and much overrated, and proclaims his opinion with perfect frankness. He does, however, scant justice to the banks of the Loire; his want of appreciation of the picturesque—want of the sketcher's sense—causes him to miss half the charm of a landscape which is nothing if not "quiet," as a painter would say, and of which the felicities reveal themselves only to waiting eyes. He even despises the Indre, the river of Madame Sand. The "Mémoires d'un Touriste" are written in the character of a commercial traveller, and the author has nothing to say about Chenonceaux or Chambord, or indeed about any of the châteaux of that part of France; his system being to talk only of the large towns, where he may be supposed to find a market for his goods. It was his ambition to pass for an ironmonger. But in the large towns he is usually excellent company, though as discursive as Sterne and strangely indifferent, for a man of imagination, to those superficial aspects of things which the poor pages now before the reader are mainly an attempt to render. It is his conviction that Alfieri, at Florence, bored the Countess of Albany terribly; and he adds that the famous Gallophobe died of jealousy of the little painter from Montpellier. The Countess of Albany left her property to Fabre; and I suppose some of the pieces in the museum of his native town used to hang in the sunny saloons of that fine old palace on the Arno which is still pointed out to the stranger in Florence as the residence of Alfieri.

Montpellier

The institution has had other benefactors, notably a certain M. Bruyas, who has enriched it with an extraordinary number of portraits of himself. As these, however, are by different hands, some of them distinguished, we may suppose that it was less the model than the artists to whom M. Bruyas wished to give publicity. Easily first are two large specimens of David Teniers, which are incomparable for brilliancy and a glowing perfection of execution. I have a weakness for this singular genius, who combined the delicate with the grovelling, and I have rarely seen richer examples. Scarcely less valuable is a Gerard Dow which hangs near them, though it must rank lower, as having kept less of its freshness. This Gerard Dow did me good, for a master is a master, whatever he may paint. It represents a woman paring carrots, while a boy before her exhibits a mouse-trap in which he has caught a frightened victim. The goodwife has spread a cloth on the top of a big barrel which serves her as a table, and on this brown, greasy napkin, of which the texture is wonderfully rendered, lie the raw vegetables she is preparing for domestic consumption. Beside the barrel is a large caldron lined with copper, with a rim of brass. The way these things are painted brings tears to the eyes; but they give the measure, of the Musée Fabre, where two specimens of Teniers and a Gerard Dow are the jewels. The Italian pictures are of small value; but there is a work by Sir Joshua Reynolds, said to be the only one in France—an infant Samuel in prayer, apparently a repetition of the picture in England which inspired the little plaster image, disseminated in Protestant lands, that we used to admire in our childhood. Sir Joshua, somehow, was an eminently Protestant painter; no one can forget that, who in the National Gallery in London has looked at the picture in which he represents several young ladies as nymphs, voluminously draped, hanging garlands over a statue—a picture suffused indefinably with the Anglican spirit and exasperating to a member of one of the Latin races. It is an odd chance therefore that has led him into that part of France where Protestants have been least *bien vus*. This is the country of the dragonnades of Louis XIV. and of the pastors of the desert. From the garden of the Peyrou, at Montpellier, you may see the hills of the Cévennes, to which they of the religion fled for safety and out of which they were hunted and harried.

I have only to add, in regard to the Musée Fabre, that it contains the portrait of its founder—a little, pursy, fat-faced, elderly man, whose countenance contains few indications of the power that makes distinguished victims. He is, however, just such a personage as the mind's eye sees walking on the terrace of the Peyrou of an October afternoon in the early years of the century; a plump figure in a chocolate-coloured coat and a *culotte* that exhibits a good leg—a culotte provided with a watch-fob from which a heavy seal is suspended. This Peyrou (to come to it at last) is a wonderful place, especially to be found in a little provincial city. France is certainly the country of towns that aim at completeness; more than in other lands they contain stately features as a matter of course. We should never have ceased to hear about the Peyrou if fortune had placed it at a Shrewsbury or a Buffalo. It is true that the place enjoys a certain celebrity at home, which it amply deserves, moreover; for nothing could be more impressive and monumental. It consists of an "elevated platform," as Murray says—an immense terrace laid out, in the highest part of the town, as a garden, and commanding in all directions a view which in clear weather must be of the finest. I strolled there in the intervals of showers, and saw only the nearer beauties—a great pompous arch of triumph in honour of Louis XIV. (which is not, properly speaking, in the garden, but faces it, straddling across the *place* by which you approach it from the town), an equestrian statue of that monarch set aloft in the middle of the terrace, and a very exalted and complicated fountain, which forms a background to the picture. This fountain gushes from a kind of hydraulic temple, or *château d'eau*, to which you ascend by broad flights of steps, and which is fed by a splendid aqueduct, stretched in the most ornamental and unexpected manner across the neighbouring valley. All this work dates from the middle of the last century. The combination of features—the triumphal arch, or gate; the wide fair terrace, with its beautiful view; the statue of the grand monarch; the big architectural fountain, which would not surprise one at Rome, but does surprise one at Montpellier; and to complete the effect, the extraordinary aqueduct, charmingly fore-shortened—all this is worthy of a capital, of a little court-city. The whole place, with its repeated steps, its balustrades, its massive and plentiful stonework, is full of the air of the last century—*sent bien son dix-huitième siècle*; none the less so, I am afraid, that, as I read in my faithful Murray, after the revocation of the Edict of Nantes the block, the stake, the wheel had been erected here for the benefit of the desperate Camisards.

CHAPTER XXVI. THE PONT DU GARD

IT was a pleasure to feel one's self in Provence again—the land where the silver-grey earth is impregnated with the light of the sky. To celebrate the event, as soon as I arrived at Nîmes I engaged a calèche to convey me to the Pont du Gard. The day was yet young and was exceptionally fair; it appeared well, for a longish drive, to take advantage, without delay, of such security. After I had left the town I became more intimate with that Provençal charm which I had already enjoyed from the window of the train, and which glowed in the sweet sunshine and the white rocks and lurked in the smoke puffs of the little olives. The olive-trees in Provence are half the landscape. They are neither so tall, so stout, nor so richly contorted as you have seen them beyond the Alps; but this mild colourless bloom seems the very texture of the country. The road from Nîmes, for a distance of fifteen miles, is superb; broad enough for an army and as white and firm as a dinner-table. It stretches away over undulations which have a kind of rhythmic value, and in the curves it makes through the wide, free country, where there is never a hedge or a wall and the detail is always exquisite, there is something majestic, almost processional. Some twenty minutes before I reached the little inn that marks the termination of the drive my vehicle met with an accident which just missed being serious, and which engaged the attention of a gentleman who, followed by his groom and mounted on a strikingly handsome horse, happened to ride up at the moment. This young man, who, with his good looks and charming manner, might have stepped out of a novel of Octave Feuillet, gave me some very intelligent advice in reference to one of my horses that had been injured, and was so good as to accompany me to the inn, with the resources of which he was acquainted, to see that his recommendations were carried out. The result of our interview was that he invited me to come and look at a small but ancient château in the neighbourhood, which he had the happiness—not the greatest in the world, he intimated—to inhabit, and at which I engaged to present myself after I should have spent an hour at the Pont du Gard. For the moment, when we separated, I gave all my attention to that great structure. You are very near it before you see it; the ravine it spans suddenly opens and exhibits the picture. The scene at this point grows extremely beautiful. The ravine is the valley of the Garden, which the road from Nîmes has followed some time without taking account of it, but which, exactly at the right distance from the aqueduct, deepens and expands and puts on those characteristics which are best suited to give it effect.

The Pont du Gard

The gorge becomes romantic, still and solitary, and, with its white rocks and wild shrubbery, hangs over the clear-coloured river, in whose slow course there is, here and there, a deeper pool. Over the valley, from side to side and ever so high in the air, stretch the three tiers of the tremendous bridge. They are unspeakably imposing, and nothing could well be more Roman. The hugeness, the solidity, the unexpectedness, the monumental rectitude of the whole thing leave you nothing to say—at the time—and make you stand gazing. You simply feel that it is noble and perfect, that it has the quality of greatness. A road, branching from the highway, descends to the level of the river and passes under one of the arches. This road has a wide margin of grass and loose stones, which slopes upward into the bank of the ravine. You may sit here as long as you please, staring up at the light, strong piers; the spot is sufficiently "wild," though two or three stone benches have been erected on it. I remained there an hour and got a complete impression; the place was perfectly soundless and, for the time at least, lonely; the splendid afternoon had begun to fade, and there was a fascination in the object I had come to see. It came to pass that at the same time I discovered in it a certain stupidity, a vague brutality. That element is rarely absent from great Roman work, which is wanting in the nice adaptation of the means to the end. The means are always exaggerated; the end is so much more than attained. The Roman rigour was apt to overshoot the mark, and I suppose a race which could do nothing small is as defective as a race that can do nothing great. Of this

Roman rigour the Pont du Gard is an admirable example. It would be a great injustice, however, not to insist upon its beauty—a kind of manly beauty, that of an object constructed not to please but to serve, and impressive simply from the scale on which it carries out this intention. The number of arches in each tier is different; they are smaller and more numerous as they ascend. The preservation of the thing is extraordinary; nothing has crumbled or collapsed; every feature remains, and the huge blocks of stone, of a brownish-yellow (as if they had been baked by the Provençal sun for eighteen centuries), pile themselves, without mortar or cement, as evenly as the day they were laid together. All this to carry the water of a couple of springs to a little provincial city! The conduit on the top has retained its shape and traces of the cement with which it was lined. When the vague twilight began to gather, the lonely valley seemed to fill itself with the shadow of the Roman name, as if the mighty empire were still as erect as the supports of the aqueduct; and it was open to a solitary tourist, sitting there sentimental, to believe that no people has ever been, or will ever be, as great as that, measured, as we measure the greatness of an individual, by the push they gave to what they undertook. The Pont du Gard is one of the three or four deepest impressions they have left; it speaks of them in a manner with which they might have been satisfied.

I feel as if it were scarcely discreet to indicate the whereabouts of the château of the obliging young man I had met on the way from Nîmes; I must content myself with saying that it nestled in an enchanting valley— *dans le fond*, as they say in France—and that I took my course thither on foot after leaving the Pont du Gard. I find it noted in my journal as "an adorable little corner." The principal feature of the place is a couple of very ancient towers, brownish-yellow in hue, and mantled in scarlet Virginia-creeper. One of these towers, reputed to be of Saracenic origin, is isolated, and is only the more effective; the other is incorporated in the house, which is delightfully fragmentary and irregular. It had got to be late by this time, and the lonely *castel* looked crepuscular and mysterious. An old housekeeper was sent for, who showed me the rambling interior; and then the young man took me into a dim old drawing-room, which had no less than four chimney-pieces, all unlighted, and gave me a refection of fruit and sweet wine. When

I praised the wine and asked him what it was, he said simply "C'est du vin de ma mère!" Throughout my little journey I had never yet felt myself so far from Paris; and this was a sensation I enjoyed more than my host, who was an involuntary exile, consoling himself with laying out a *manège* which he showed me as I walked away. His civility was great, and I was greatly touched by it. On my way back to the little inn where I had left my vehicle I passed the Pont du Gard and took another look at it. Its great arches made windows for the evening sky, and the rocky ravine, with its dusky cedars and shining river, was lonelier than before. At the inn I swallowed, or tried to swallow, a glass of horrible wine with my coachman; after which, with my reconstructed team, I drove back to Nîmes in the moonlight. It only added a more solitary whiteness to the constant sheen of the Provençal landscape.

CHAPTER XXVII. AIGUES-MORTES

THE weather the next day was equally fair, so that it seemed an imprudence not to make sure of Aigues-Mortes. Nîmes itself could wait; at a pinch I could attend to Nîmes in the rain. It was my belief that Aigues-Mortes was a little gem, and it is natural to desire that gems should have an opportunity to sparkle. This is an excursion of but a few hours, and there is a little friendly, familiar, dawdling train that will convey you, in time for a noonday breakfast, to the small dead town where the blessed Saint Louis twice embarked for the Crusades. You may get back to Nîmes for dinner; the run—or rather the walk, for the train doesn't run—is of about an hour. I found the little journey charming and looked out of the carriage window, on my right, at the distant Cévennes, covered with tones of amber and blue, and, all around, at vineyards red with the touch of October. The grapes were gone, but the plants had a colour of their own.

Within a certain distance of Aigues-Mortes they give place to wide salt-marshes, traversed by two canals; and over this expanse the train rumbles slowly upon a narrow causeway, failing for some time, though you know you are near the object of your curiosity, to bring you to sight of anything but the horizon. Suddenly it appears, the towered and embattled mass, lying so low that the crest of its defences seems to rise straight out of the ground; and it is not till the train stops close before them that you are able to take the full measure of its walls.

Aigues-Mortes stands on the edge of a wide *étang*, or shallow inlet of the sea, the farther side of which is divided by a narrow band of coast from the Gulf of Lyons. Next after Carcassonne, to which it forms an admirable *pendant*, it is the most perfect thing of the kind in France. It has a rival in the person of Avignon, but the ramparts of Avignon are much less effective. Like Carcassonne, it is completely surrounded with its old fortifications; and if they are far simpler in character (there is but one circle), they are quite as well preserved. The moat has been filled up, and the site of the town might be figured by a billiard-table without pockets. On this absolute level, covered with coarse grass, Aigues-Mortes presents quite the appearance of the walled town that a school-boy draws upon his slate or that we see in the background of early Flemish pictures—a simple parallelogram, of a contour almost absurdly bare, broken at intervals by angular towers and square holes. Such, literally speaking, is this delightful little city, which needs to be seen to tell its full story. It is extraordinarily pictorial, and if it is a very small sister of Carcassonne, it has at least the essential features of the family. Indeed, it is even more like an image and less like a reality than Carcassonne; for by position and prospect it seems even more detached from the life of the present day. It is true that Aigues-Mortes does a little business; it sees certain bags of salt piled into barges which stand in a canal beside it, and which carry their cargo into actual places. But nothing could well be more drowsy and desultory than this industry as I saw it practised, with the aid of two or three brown peasants and under the eye of a solitary douanier, who strolled on the little quay beneath the western wall. "C'est bien plaisant, c'est bien paisible," said this worthy man, with whom I had some conversation; and pleasant and peaceful is the place indeed, though the former of these epithets may suggest an element of gaiety in which Aigues-Mortes is deficient. The sand, the salt, the dull sea-view, surround it with a bright, quiet melancholy. There are fifteen towers and nine gates, five of which are on the southern side, overlooking the water. I walked all round the place three times (it doesn't take long), but lingered most under the southern wall, where the afternoon light slept in the dreamiest, sweetest way. I sat down on an old stone and looked away to the desolate salt-marshes and the still, shining surface of the *étang*; and, as I did so, reflected that this was a queer little out-of-the-world corner to have been chosen, in the great dominions of either monarch, for that pompous interview which took place, in 1538, between Francis I. and Charles V. It was also not easy to perceive how Louis IX., when in 1248 and 1270 he started for the Holy Land, set his army afloat in such very undeveloped channels. An hour later I purchased in the town a little pamphlet by M. Marius Topin, who undertakes to explain this latter anomaly and to show that there is water enough in the port, as we may call it by courtesy, to have sustained a fleet of crusaders. I was unable to trace the channel that he points out, but was glad to believe that, as he contends, the sea has not retreated from the town since the thirteenth century. It was comfortable to think that things are not so changed as that. M. Topin indicates that the other French ports of the Mediterranean were not then *disponibles*, and that Aigues-Mortes was the most eligible spot for an embarkation.

Behind the straight walls and the quiet gates the little town has not crumbled like the Cité of Carcassonne. It can hardly be said to be alive; but if it is dead it has been very neatly embalmed. The hand of the restorer rests on it constantly; but this artist has not, as at Carcassonne, had miracles to accomplish. The interior is very still and empty, with small stony, whitewashed streets tenanted by a stray dog, a stray cat, a stray old woman. In the middle is a little *place*, with two or three cafés decorated by wide awnings—a little *place* of which the principal feature is a very bad bronze statue of Saint Louis by Pradier. It is almost as bad as the breakfast I had at the inn that bears the name of that pious monarch. You may walk round the enceinte of Aigues-Mortes both outside and in; but you may not, as at Carcassonne, make a portion of this circuit on the *chemin de ronde*, the little projecting footway attached to the inner face of the battlements. This footway, wide enough only for a single pedestrian, is in the best order, and near each of the gates a flight of steps leads up to it; but a locked gate at the top of the steps makes access impossible, or at least unlawful. Aigues-Mortes, however, has its citadel, an immense tower, larger than any of the others, a little detached and standing at the north-west angle of the town. I called upon the *casernier*—the custodian of the walls—and in his absence I was conducted through this big Tour de Constance by his wife, a very mild, meek woman, yellow with the traces of fever and ague—a scourge which, as might be expected in a town whose name denotes "dead waters," enters freely at the nine gates. The Tour de Constance is of extraordinary girth and solidity, divided into three superposed circular chambers, with very fine vaults, which are lighted by embrasures of prodigious depth, converging to windows little larger than loopholes. The place served for years as a prison to many of the Protestants of the south whom the revocation of the Edict of Nantes had exposed to atrocious penalties, and the annals of these dreadful chambers in the first half of the last century were written in tears and blood. Some of the recorded cases of long confinement there make one marvel afresh at what man has inflicted and endured. In a country in which a policy of extermination was to be put into practice this horrible tower was an obvious resource. From the battlements at the top, which is surmounted by an old disused lighthouse, you see the little compact rectangular town, which looks hardly bigger than a garden-patch, mapped out beneath you, and follow the plain configuration of its defences. You take possession of it, and you feel that you will remember it always.

CHAPTER XXVIII. NÎMES

AFTER this I was free to look about me at Nîmes, and I did so with such attention as the place appeared to require. At the risk of seeming too easily and too frequently disappointed, I will say that it required rather less than I had been prepared to give. It is a town of three or four fine features rather than a town with, as I may say, a general figure. In general Nîmes is poor; its only treasures are its Roman remains, which are of the first order. The new French fashions prevail in many of its streets; the old houses are paltry, and the good houses are new; while beside my hotel rose a big spick-and-span church, which had the oddest air of having been intended for Brooklyn or Cleveland. It is true that this church looked out on a square completely French—a square of a fine modern disposition, flanked on one side by a classical *palais de justice* embellished with trees and parapets and occupied in the centre with a group of allegorical statues such as one encounters only in the cities of France, the chief of these being a colossal figure by Pradier representing Nîmes. An English, an American town which should have such a monument, such a square as this would be a place of great pretensions; but, like so many little *villes de province* in the country of which I write, Nîmes is easily ornamental. What nobler element can there be than the Roman baths at the foot of Mont Cavalier and the delightful old garden that surrounds them? All that quarter of Nîmes has every reason to be proud of itself; it has been revealed to the world at large by copious photography. A clear, abundant stream gushes from the foot of a high hill (covered with trees and laid out in paths), and is distributed into basins which sufficiently refer themselves to the period that gave them birth—the period that has left its stamp on that pompous Peyrou which we admired at Montpellier. Here are the same terraces and steps and balustrades, and a system of waterworks less impressive perhaps, but very ingenious and charming. The whole place is a mixture of old Rome and of the French eighteenth century; for the remains of the antique baths are in a measure incorporated in the modern fountains. In a corner of this umbrageous precinct stands a small Roman ruin, which is known as a temple of Diana, but was more apparently a *nymphæum*, and appears to have had a graceful connection with the adjacent baths. I learn from Murray that this little temple, of the period of Augustus, "was reduced to its present state of ruin in 1577;" the moment at which the townspeople, threatened with a siege by the troops of the Crown, partly demolished it lest it should serve as a cover to the enemy. The remains are very fragmentary, but they serve to show that the place was lovely. I spent half an hour in it on a perfect Sunday morning (it is enclosed by a high *grille*, carefully tended, and has a warden of its own), and with the help of my imagination tried to reconstruct a little the aspect of things in the Gallo-Roman days. I do wrong perhaps to say that I *tried*; from a flight so deliberate I should have shrunk. But there was a certain contagion of antiquity in the air; and among the ruins of baths and temples, in the very spot where the aqueduct that crosses the Gardon in the wondrous manner I had seen discharged itself, the picture of a splendid paganism seemed vaguely to glow. Roman baths—Roman baths; those words alone were a scene. Everything was changed: I was strolling in a *jardin français*; the bosky slope of the Mont Cavalier (a very modest mountain), hanging over the place, is crowned with a shapeless tower, which is as likely to be of mediæval as of antique origin; and yet, as I leaned on the parapet of one of the fountains, where a flight of curved steps (a hemicycle, as the French say) descended into a basin full of dark, cool recesses, where the slabs of the Roman foundations gleam through the clear green water—as in this attitude I surrendered myself to contemplation and reverie, it seemed to me that I touched for a moment the ancient world. Such moments are illuminating, and the light of this one mingles, in my memory, with the dusky greenness of the Jardin de la Fontaine.

Nîmes

The fountain proper—the source of all these distributed waters—is the prettiest thing in the world, a reduced copy of Vaucluse. It gushes up at the foot of the Mont Cavalier, at a point where that eminence rises with a certain cliff-like effect, and, like other springs in the same circumstances, appears to issue from the rock with a sort of quivering stillness. I trudged up the Mont Cavalier—it is a matter of five minutes—and having committed this cockneyism, enhanced it presently by another. I ascended the stupid Tour Magne, the mysterious structure I mentioned a moment ago. The only feature of this dateless tube, except the inevitable collection of photographs to which you are introduced by the doorkeeper, is the view you enjoy from its summit. This view is of course remarkably fine, but I am ashamed to say I have not the smallest recollection of it; for while I looked into the brilliant spaces of the air I seemed still to see only what I saw in the depths of the Roman baths—the image, disastrously confused and vague, of a vanished world. This world, however, has left at Nîmes a far more considerable memento than a few old stones covered with water-moss. The Roman arena is the rival of those of Verona and of Arles; at a respectful distance it emulates the Colosseum.

It is a small Colosseum, if I may be allowed the expression, and is in much better preservation than the great circus at Rome. This is especially true of the external walls, with their arches, pillars, cornices. I must add that one should not speak of preservation, in regard to the arena at Nîmes, without speaking also of repair. After the great ruin ceased to be despoiled it began to be protected, and most of its wounds have been dressed with new material. These matters concern the archæologist; and I felt here, as I felt afterwards at Arles, that one of the profane, in the presence of such a monument, can only admire and hold his tongue. The great impression, on the whole, is an impression of wonder that so much should have survived. What remains at Nîmes, after all dilapidation is estimated, is astounding. I spent an hour in the Arènes on that same sweet Sunday morning, as I came back from the Roman baths, and saw that the corridors, the vaults, the staircases, the external casing, are still virtually there. Many of these parts are wanting in the Colosseum, whose sublimity of size, however, can afford to dispense with detail. The seats at Nîmes, like those at Verona, have been largely renewed; not that this mattered much, as I lounged on the cool surface of one of them and admired the mighty concavity of the place and the elliptical sky-line, broken by uneven blocks and forming the rim of the monstrous cup—a cup that had been filled with horrors. And yet I made my reflections: I said to myself that though a Roman arena is one of the most impressive of the works of man, it has a touch of that same stupidity which I ventured to discover in the Pont du Gard. It is brutal; it is monotonous; it is not at all exquisite. The Arènes at Nîmes were arranged for a bull-fight—a form of recreation that, as I was informed, is much *dans les habitudes Nîmoises*, and very common throughout Provence, where (still according to my information) it is the usual pastime of a Sunday afternoon. At Arles and Nîmes it has a characteristic setting, but in the villages the patrons of the game make a circle of carts and barrels, on which the spectators perch themselves. I was surprised at the prevalence in mild Provence of the Iberian vice, and hardly know whether it makes the custom more respectable that at Nîmes and Arles the thing is shabbily and imperfectly done. The bulls are rarely killed, and indeed often are bulls only in the Irish sense of the term—being domestic and motherly cows. Such an entertainment of course does not supply to the arena that element of the exquisite which I spoke of as wanting. The exquisite at Nîmes is mainly represented by the famous Maison Carrée. The first impression you receive from this delicate little building, as you stand before it, is that you have already seen it many times. Photographs, engravings, models, medals, have placed it definitely in your eye, so that from the sentiment with which you regard it curiosity and surprise are almost completely, and perhaps deplorably, absent. Admiration remains, however—admiration of a familiar and even slightly patronising kind. The Maison Carrée does not overwhelm you; you can conceive it. It is not one of the great sensations of antique art; but it is perfectly felicitous, and, in spite of having been put to all sorts of incongruous uses, marvellously preserved. Its slender columns, its delicate proportions, its charming compactness, seem to bring one nearer to the century that built it than the great superpositions of arenas and bridges, and give it the interest that vibrates from one age to another when the note of taste is struck. If anything were needed to make this little toy-temple a happy production, the service would be rendered by the second-rate boulevard that conducts to it, adorned with inferior cafés and tobacco-shops. Here, in a respectable recess, surrounded by vulgar habitations and with the theatre, of a classic pretension, opposite, stands the small "square house," so called because it is much longer than it is broad. I saw it first in the evening, in the vague moonlight, which made it look as if it were cast in bronze. Stendhal says, justly, that it has the shape of a playing-card, and he expresses his admiration for it by the singular wish that an "exact copy" of it should be erected in Paris. He even goes so far as to say that in the year 1880 this tribute will have been rendered to its charms; nothing would be more simple, to his mind, than to "have" in that city "le Panthéon de Rome, quelques temples de Grèce." Stendhal found it amusing to write in the character of a *commis-voyageur*, and sometimes it occurs to his reader that he really was one.

CHAPTER XXIX. TARASCON

ON my way from Nîmes to Arles I spent three hours at Tarascon; chiefly for the love of Alphonse Daudet, who has written nothing more genial than "Les Aventures Prodigieuses de Tartarin," and the story of the "siege" of the bright, dead little town (a mythic siege by the Prussians) in the "Contes du Lundi." In the introduction which, for the new edition of his works, he has lately supplied to "Tartarin," the author of this extravagant but kindly satire gives some account of the displeasure with which he has been visited by the ticklish Tarasconnais. Daudet relates that in his attempt to shed a humorous light upon some of the more vivid phases of the Provençal character he selected Tarascon at a venture; not because the temperament of its natives is more vainglorious than that of their neighbours, or their rebellion against the "despotism of fact" more marked, but simply because he had to name a particular Provençal city. Tartarin is a hunter of lions and charmer of women, a true "*produit du midi*," as Daudet says, a character of the most extravagant, genial comedy. He is a minimised Don Quixote, with much less dignity but with equal good faith; and the story of his exploits is a little masterpiece of the free fantastic. The Tarasconnais, however, declined to take the joke, and opened the vials of their wrath upon the mocking child of Nîmes, who would have been better employed, they doubtless thought, in showing up the infirmities of his own family. I am bound to add that when I passed through Tarascon they did not appear to be in the least out of humour. Nothing could have been brighter, easier, more suggestive of amiable indifference, than the picture it presented to my mind. It lies quietly beside the Rhone, looking across at Beaucaire, which seems very distant and independent, and tacitly consenting to let the castle of the good King René of Anjou, which projects very boldly into the river, pass for its most interesting feature. The other features are, primarily, a sort of vivid sleepiness in the aspect of the place, as if the September noon (it had lingered on into October) lasted longer there than elsewhere; certain low arcades which make the streets look grey and exhibit empty vistas; and a very curious and beautiful walk beside the Rhone, denominated the Chaussée—a long and narrow causeway, densely shaded by two rows of magnificent old trees planted in its embankment and rendered doubly effective at the moment I passed over it by a little train of collegians who had been taken out for mild exercise by a pair of young priests. Lastly one may say that a striking element of Tarascon, as of any town that lies on the Rhone, is simply the Rhone itself; the big brown flood, of uncertain temper, which has never taken time to forget that it is a child of the mountain and the glacier, and that such an origin carries with it great privileges. Later, at Avignon, I observed it in the exercise of these privileges, chief among which was that of frightening the good people of the old papal city half out of their wits.

Tarascon

The château of King René serves to-day as the prison of a district, and the traveller who wishes to look into it must obtain his permission at the Mairie of Tarascon. If he have had a certain experience of French manners, his application will be accompanied with the forms of a considerable obsequiosity, and in this case his request will be granted as civilly as it has been made. The castle has more of the air of a severely feudal fortress than I should suppose the period of its construction (the first half of the fifteenth century) would have warranted; being tremendously bare and perpendicular, and constructed for comfort only in the sense that it was arranged for defence. It is a square and simple mass, composed of small yellow stones and perched on a pedestal of rock which easily commands the river. The building has the usual circular towers at the corners and a heavy cornice at the top, and immense stretches of sun-scorched wall relieved at wide intervals by small windows, heavily cross-barred. It has, above all, an extreme steepness of aspect; I cannot express it otherwise. The walls are as sheer and inhospitable as precipices. The castle has kept its large moat, which is now a hollow filled with wild plants. To this tall fortress the good René retired in the middle of the fifteenth century, finding it apparently the most substantial thing left him in a dominion which had included Naples and Sicily, Lorraine and Anjou. He had been a much-tried monarch and the sport of a various fortune, fighting half his life for thrones he didn't care for, and exalted only to be quickly cast down. Provence was the country of his affection, and the memory of his troubles did not prevent him from holding a joyous court at Tarascon and at Aix. He finished the castle at Tarascon, which had been begun earlier in the century—finished it, I suppose, for consistency's sake, in the manner in which it had originally been designed rather than in accordance with the artistic tastes that formed the consolation of his old age. He was a painter, a writer, a dramatist, a modern dilettante, addicted to private theatricals. There is something very attractive in the image that he has imprinted on the page of history. He was both clever and kind, and many reverses and much suffering had not embittered him nor quenched his faculty of enjoyment. He was fond of his sweet Provence, and his sweet Provence has been grateful; it has woven a light tissue of legend around the memory of the good King René.

I strolled over his dusky habitation—it must have taken all his good humour to light it up—at the heels of the custodian, who showed me the usual number of castle-properties: a deep, well-like court; a collection of winding staircases and vaulted chambers, the embrasures of whose windows and the recesses of whose doorways reveal a tremendous thickness of wall. These things constitute the general identity of old castles; and when one has wandered through a good many, with due discretion of step and protrusion of head, one ceases very much to distinguish and remember, and contents one's self with consigning them to the honourable limbo of the romantic. I must add that this reflection did not in the least deter me from crossing the bridge which connects Tarascon with Beaucaire, in order to examine the old fortress whose ruins adorn the latter city. It stands on a foundation of rock much higher than that of Tarascon, and looks over with a melancholy expression at its better-conditioned brother. Its position is magnificent and its outline very gallant. I was well rewarded for my pilgrimage; for if the castle of Beaucaire is only a fragment, the whole place, with its position and its views, is an ineffaceable picture. It was the stronghold of the Montmorencys, and its last tenant was that rash Duke François whom Richelieu, seizing every occasion to trample on a great noble, caused to be beheaded at Toulouse, where we saw, in the Capitol, the butcher's knife with which the cardinal pruned the crown of France of its thorns. The castle, after the death of this victim, was virtually demolished. Its site, which nature to-day has taken again to herself, has an extraordinary charm. The mass of rock that it formerly covered rises high above the town and is as precipitous as the side of the Rhone. A tall, rusty iron gate admits you from a quiet corner of Beaucaire to a wild tangled garden covering the side of the hill—for the whole place forms the public promenade of the townsfolk—a garden without flowers, with little steep, rough paths that wind under a plantation of small, scrubby stone-pines. Above this is the grassy platform of the castle, enclosed on one side only (toward the river) by a large fragment of wall and a very massive dungeon. There are benches placed in the lee of the wall, and others on the edge of the platform, where one may enjoy a view, beyond the river, of certain peeled and scorched undulations. A sweet desolation, an everlasting peace, seemed to hang in the air. A very old man (a fragment, like the castle itself) emerged from some crumbling corner to do me the honours—a very gentle, obsequious, tottering, toothless, grateful old man. He beguiled me into an ascent of the solitary tower, from which you may look down on the big sallow river and glance at diminished Tarascon and the barefaced, bald-headed hills behind it. It may appear that I insist too much upon the nudity of the Provençal horizon—too much considering that I have spoken of the prospect from the heights of Beaucaire as lovely. But it is an exquisite bareness; it seems to exist for the purpose of allowing one to follow the delicate lines of the hills and touch with the eyes, as it were, the smallest inflections of the landscape. It makes the whole thing wonderfully bright and pure.

Tarascon

Beaucaire used to be the scene of a famous fair, the great fair of the south of France. It has gone the way of most fairs, even in France, where these delightful exhibitions hold their own much better than might be supposed. It is still held in the month of July; but the bourgeoises of Tarascon send to the Magasin du Louvre for their smart dresses, and the principal glory of the scene is its long tradition. Even now, however, it ought to be the prettiest of all fairs, for it takes place in, a charming wood which lies just beneath the castle, beside the Rhone. The booths, the barracks, the platforms of the mountebanks, the bright-coloured crowd, diffused through this midsummer shade and spotted here and there with the rich Provençal sunshine, must be of the most pictorial effect. It is highly probable too that it offers a large collection of pretty faces; for even in the few hours that I spent at Tarascon I discovered symptoms of the purity of feature for which the women of the *pays d'Arles* are renowned. The Arlesian head-dress was visible in the streets; and this delightful coiffure is so associated with a charming facial oval, a dark mild eye, a straight Greek nose, and a mouth worthy of all the rest, that it conveys a presumption of beauty which gives the wearer time either to escape or to please you. I have read somewhere, however, that Tarascon is supposed to produce handsome men, as Arles is known to deal in handsome women. It may be that I should have found the Tarasconnais very fine fellows if I had encountered enough specimens to justify an induction. But there are very few males in the streets, and the place presented no appearance of activity. Here and there the black coif of an old woman or of a young girl was framed by a low doorway; but for the rest, as I have said, Tarascon was mostly involved in a siesta. There was not a creature in the little church of Saint Martha, which I made a point of visiting before I returned to the station, and which, with its fine romanesque side-portal and its pointed and crocketed gothic spire, is as curious as it need be in view of its tradition. It stands in a quiet corner where the grass grows between the small cobble-stones, and you pass beneath a deep archway to reach it. The tradition relates that Saint Martha tamed with her own hands and attached to her girdle a dreadful dragon who was known as the Tarasque and is reported to have given his name to the city on whose site (amid the rocks which form the base of the château) he had his cavern. The dragon perhaps is the symbol of a ravening paganism dispelled by the eloquence of a sweet evangelist. The bones of the interesting saint, at all events, were found, in the eleventh century, in a cave beneath the spot on which her altar now stands. I know not what had become of the bones of the dragon.

CHAPTER XXX. ARLES

THERE are two shabby old inns at Arles which compete closely for your custom. I mean by this that if you elect to go to the Hôtel du Forum, the Hôtel du Nord, which is placed exactly beside it (at a right angle), watches your arrival with ill-concealed disapproval; and if you take the chances of its neighbour, the Hôtel du Forum seems to glare at you invidiously from all its windows and doors. I forget which of these establishments I selected; whichever it was, I wished very much that it had been the other. The two stand together on the Place des Hommes, a little public square of Arles which somehow quite misses its effect. As a city, indeed, Arles quite misses its effect in every way; and if it is a charming place, as I think it is, I can hardly tell the reason why. The straight-nosed Arlésiennes account for it in some degree; and the remainder may be charged to the ruins of the arena and the theatre. Beyond this, I remember with affection the ill-proportioned little Place des Hommes; not at all monumental, and given over to puddles and to shabby cafés. I recall with tenderness the tortuous and featureless streets, which looked liked the streets of a village and were paved with villainous little sharp stones, making all exercise penitential. Consecrated by association is even a tiresome walk that I took the evening I arrived, with the purpose of obtaining a view of the Rhone. I had been to Arles before, years ago, and it seemed to me that I remembered finding on the banks of the stream some sort of picture. I think that on the evening on which I speak there was a watery moon, which it seemed to me would light up the past as well as the present. But I found no picture, and I scarcely found the Rhone at all. I lost my way, and there was not a creature in the streets to whom I could appeal. Nothing could be more provincial than the situation of Arles at ten o'clock at night. At last I arrived at a kind of embankment where I could see the great mud-coloured stream slipping along in the soundless darkness. It had come on to rain, I know not what had happened to the moon, and the whole place was anything but gay. It was not what I had looked for; what I had looked for was in the irrecoverable past. I groped my way back to the inn over the infernal *cailloux*, feeling like a discomfited Dogberry. I remember now that this hotel was the one (whichever that may be) which has the fragment of a Gallo-Roman portico inserted into one of its angles. I had chosen it for the sake of this exceptional ornament. It was damp and dark, and the floors felt gritty to the feet; it was an establishment at which the dreadful *gras-double* might have appeared at the table d'hôte, as it had done at Narbonne. Nevertheless I was glad to get back to it; and nevertheless too—and this is the moral of my simple anecdote—my pointless little walk (I don't speak of the pavement) suffuses itself, as I look back upon it, with a romantic tone. And in relation to the inn I suppose I had better mention that I am well aware of the inconsistency of a person who dislikes the modern caravansary and yet grumbles when he finds a hotel of the superannuated sort. One ought to choose, it would seem, and make the best of either alternative. The two old taverns at Arles are quite unimproved; such as they must have been in the infancy of the modern world, when Stendhal passed that way and the lumbering diligence deposited him in the Place des Hommes, such in every detail they are to-day. *Vieilles auberges de France*, one ought to enjoy their gritty floors and greasy window-panes. Let it be put on record therefore that I have been, I won't say less comfortable, but at least less happy, at better inns.

To be really historic, I should have mentioned that before going to look for the Rhone I had spent part of the evening on the opposite side of the little place, and that I indulged in this recreation for two definite reasons. One of these was that I had an opportunity of gossiping at a café with a conversable young Englishman whom I had met in the afternoon at Tarascon and more remotely, in other years, in London; the other was that there sat enthroned behind the counter a splendid mature Arlésienne, whom my companion and I agreed that it was a rare privilege to contemplate. There is no rule of good manners or morals which makes it improper, at a café, to fix one's eyes upon the *dame de comptoir*; the lady is, in the nature of things, a part of your *consummation*. We were therefore free to admire without restriction the handsomest person I had ever seen give change for a five-franc piece. She was a large quiet woman, who would never see forty again; of an intensely feminine type, yet wonderfully rich and robust, and full of a certain physical nobleness. Though she was not really old, she was antique; and she was very grave, even a little sad. She had the dignity of a Roman empress, and she handled coppers as if they had been stamped with the head of Cæsar. I have seen washerwomen in the Trastevere who were perhaps as handsome as she; but even the head-dress of the Roman contadina contributes less to the dignity of the person born to wear it than the sweet and stately Arlesian cap, which sits at once aloft and on the back of the head; which is accompanied with a wide black bow covering a considerable part of the crown; and which, finally, accommodates itself indescribably well to the manner in which the tresses of the front are pushed behind the ears.

Arles: the Theatre

This admirable dispenser of lumps of sugar has distracted me a little, for I am still not sufficiently historical. Before going to the café I had dined, and before dining I had found time to go and look at the arena. Then it was that I discovered that Arles has no general physiognomy and, except the delightful little church of Saint Trophimus, no architecture, and that the rugosities of its dirty lanes affect the feet like knife-blades. It was not then, on the other hand, that I saw the arena best. The second day of my stay at Arles I devoted to a pilgrimage to the strange old hill town of Les Baux, the mediæval Pompeii, of which I shall give myself the pleasure of speaking. The evening of that day, however (my friend and I returned in time for a late dinner), I wandered among the Roman remains of the place by the light of a magnificent moon and gathered an impression which has lost little of its silvery glow. The moon of the evening before had been aqueous and erratic; but if on the present occasion it was guilty of any irregularity, the worst it did was only to linger beyond its time in the heavens in order to let us look at things comfortably. The effect was admirable; it brought back the impression of the way, in Rome itself, on evenings like that, the moonshine rests upon broken shafts and slabs of antique pavement. As we sat in the theatre looking at the two lone columns that survive—part of the decoration of the back of the stage—and at the fragments of ruin around them, we might have been in the Roman Forum. The arena at Arles, with its great magnitude, is less complete than that of Nîmes; it has suffered even more the assaults of time and the children of time, and it has been less repaired. The seats are almost wholly wanting; but the external walls, minus the topmost tier of arches, are massively, ruggedly complete; and the vaulted corridors seem as solid as the day they were built. The whole thing is superbly vast and as monumental, for a place of light amusement—what is called in America a "variety-show"—as it entered only into the Roman mind to make such establishments. The *podium* is much higher than at Nîmes, and many of the great white slabs that faced it have been recovered and put into their places. The proconsular box has been more or less reconstructed, and the great converging passages of approach to it are still majestically distinct; so that, as I sat there in the moon-charmed stillness, leaning my elbows on the battered parapet of the ring, it was not impossible to listen to the murmurs and shudders, the thick voice of the circus, that died away fifteen hundred years ago.

The theatre has a voice as well, but it lingers on the ear of time with a different music. The Roman theatre at Arles seemed to me one of the most charming and touching ruins I had ever beheld; I took a particular fancy to it. It is less than a skeleton—the arena may be called a skeleton—for it consists only of half a dozen bones. The traces of the row of columns which formed the scene—the permanent back-scene—remain; two marble pillars—I just mentioned them—are upright, with a fragment of their entablature. Before them is the vacant space which was filled by the stage, with the line of the proscenium distinct, marked by a deep groove impressed upon slabs of stone, which looks as if the bottom of a high screen had been intended to fit into it. The semicircle formed by the seats—half a cup—rises opposite; some of the rows are distinctly marked. The floor, from the bottom of the stage, in the shape of an arc of which the chord is formed by the line of the orchestra, is covered by slabs of coloured marble—red, yellow and green—which, though terribly battered and cracked to-day, give one an idea of the elegance of the interior. Everything shows that it was on a great scale: the large sweep of its enclosing walls, the massive corridors that passed behind the auditorium and of which we can still perfectly take the measure. The way in which every seat commanded the stage is a lesson to the architects of our epochs, as also the immense size of the place is a proof of extraordinary power of voice on the part of the Roman actors. It was after we had spent half an hour in the moonshine at the arena that we came on to this more ghostly and more exquisite ruin. The principal entrance was locked, but we effected an easy *escalade*, scaled a low parapet, and descended into the place behind the scenes. It was as light as day, and the solitude was complete. The two slim columns, as we sat on the broken benches, stood there like a pair of silent actors. What I called touching just now was the thought that here the human voice, the utterance of a great language, had been supreme. The air was full of intonations and cadences;

not of the echo of smashing blows, of riven armour, of howling victims and roaring beasts. The spot is, in short, one of the sweetest legacies of the ancient world; and there seems no profanation in the fact that by day it is open to the good people of Arles, who use it to pass, by no means in great numbers, from one part of the town to the other; treading the old marble floor and brushing, if need be, the empty benches. This familiarity does not kill the place again; it makes it, on the contrary, live a little—makes the present and the past touch each other.

CHAPTER XXXI. ARLES. THE MUSEUM

THE third lion of Arles has nothing to do with the ancient world, but only with the old one. The church of Saint Trophimus, whose wonderful romanesque porch is the principal ornament of the principal *place*—a *place* otherwise distinguished by the presence of a slim and tapering obelisk in the middle, as well as by that of the hôtel de ville and the museum—the interesting church of Saint Trophimus swears a little, as the French say, with the peculiar character of Arles. It is very remarkable, but I would rather it were in another place. Arles is delightfully pagan, and Saint Trophimus, with its apostolic sculptures, is rather a false note. These sculptures are equally remarkable for their primitive vigour and for the perfect preservation in which they have come down to us. The deep recess of a round-arched porch of the twelfth century is covered with quaint figures which have not lost a nose or a finger. An angular Byzantine-looking Christ sits in a diamond-shaped frame at the summit of the arch, surrounded by little angels, by great apostles, by winged beasts, by a hundred sacred symbols and grotesque ornaments. It is a dense embroidery of sculpture, black with time, but as uninjured as if it had been kept under glass. One good mark for the French Revolution! Of the interior of the church, which has a nave of the twelfth century and a choir three hundred years more recent, I chiefly remember the odd feature that the romanesque aisles are so narrow that you literally—or almost—squeeze through them. You do so with some eagerness, for your natural purpose is to pass out to the cloister. This cloister, as distinguished and as perfect as the porch, has a great deal of charm.

Its four sides, which are not of the same period (the earliest and best are of the twelfth century), have an elaborate arcade, supported on delicate pairs of columns, the capitals of which show an extraordinary variety of device and ornament. At the corners of the quadrangle these columns take the form of curious human figures. The whole thing is a gem of lightness and preservation and is often cited for its beauty; but—if it doesn't sound too profane—I prefer, especially at Arles, the ruins of the Roman theatre. The antique element is too precious to be mingled with anything less rare. This truth was very present to my mind during a ramble of a couple of hours that I took just before leaving the place; and the glowing beauty of the morning gave the last touch to the impression. I spent half an hour at the Museum; then I took another look at the Roman theatre; after which I walked a little out of the town to the Aliscamps, the old Elysian Fields, the meagre remnant of the old pagan place of sepulture, which was afterwards used by the Christians, but has been for ages deserted and now consists only of a melancholy avenue of cypresses lined with a succession of ancient sarcophagi, empty, mossy and mutilated. An iron-foundry, or some horrible establishment which is conditioned upon tall chimneys and a noise of hammering and banging, has been established near at hand; but the cypresses shut it out well enough, and this small patch of Elysium is a very romantic corner.

The door of the Museum stands ajar, and a vigilant custodian, with the usual batch of photographs on his mind, peeps out at you disapprovingly while you linger opposite, before the charming portal of Saint Trophimus, which you may look at for nothing. When you succumb to the silent influence of his eye and go over to visit his collection, you find yourself in a desecrated church, in which a variety of ancient objects disinterred in Arlesian soil have been arranged without any pomp. The best of these, I believe, were found in the ruins of the theatre. Some of the most curious of them are early Christian sarcophagi, exactly on the pagan model, but covered with rude yet vigorously wrought images of the apostles and with illustrations of scriptural history. Beauty of the highest kind, either of conception or of execution, is absent from most of the Roman fragments, which belong to the taste of a late period and a provincial civilisation. But a gulf divides them from the bristling little imagery of the Christian sarcophagi, in which, at the same time, one detects a vague emulation of the rich examples by which their authors were surrounded. There is a certain element of style in all the pagan things; there is not a hint of it in the early Christian relics, among which, according to M. Joanne, of the Guide, are to be found more fine sarcophagi than in any collection but that of St. John Lateran. In two or three of the Roman fragments there is a noticeable distinction; principally in a charming bust of a boy, quite perfect, with those salient eyes that one sees in antique portraits, and to which the absence of vision in the marble mask gives a look, often very touching, as of a baffled effort to see; also in the head of a woman, found in the ruins of the theatre, who, alas! has lost her nose and whose noble, simple contour, barring this deficiency, recalls the great manner of the Venus of Milo. There are various rich architectural fragments which indicate that that edifice was a very splendid affair. This little Museum at Arles, in short, is the most Roman thing I know of out of Rome.

CHAPTER XXXII. LES BAUX

I FIND that I declared one evening, in a little journal I was keeping at that time, that I was weary of writing (I was probably very sleepy), but that it was essential I should make some note of my visit to Les Baux. I must have gone to sleep as soon as I had recorded this necessity, for I search my small diary in vain for any account of that enchanting spot. I have nothing but my memory to consult—a memory which is fairly good in regard to a general impression, but is terribly infirm in the matter of details and items. We knew in advance, my companion and I, that Les Baux was a pearl of picturesqueness; for had we not read as much in the handbook of Murray, who has the testimony of an English nobleman as to its attractions? We also knew that it lay some miles from Arles, on the crest of the Alpilles, the craggy little mountains which, as I stood on the breezy platform of Beaucaire, formed to my eye a charming, if somewhat remote, background to Tarascon; this assurance having been given us by the landlady of the inn at Arles, of whom we hired a rather lumbering conveyance. The weather was not promising, but it proved a good day for the mediæval Pompeii; a grey, melancholy, moist, but rainless, or almost rainless day, with nothing in the sky to flout, as the poet says, the dejected and pulverised past. The drive itself was charming, for there is an inexhaustible sweetness in the grey-green landscape of Provence. It is never absolutely flat and yet is never really ambitious, and is full both of entertainment and repose. It is in constant undulation, and the bareness of the soil lends itself easily to outline and profile. When I say the bareness I mean the absence of woods and hedges. It blooms with heath and scented shrubs and stunted olive, and the white rock shining through the scattered herbage has a brightness which answers to the brightness of the sky. Of course it needs the sunshine, for all southern countries look a little false under the ground-glass of incipient bad weather. This was the case on the day of my pilgrimage to Les Baux. Nevertheless I was glad to keep going, as I was to arrive; and as I went it seemed to me that true happiness would consist in wandering through such a land on foot, on September afternoons, when one might stretch one's self on the warm ground in some shady hollow and listen to the hum of bees and the whistle of melancholy shepherds; for in Provence the shepherds whistle to their flocks. I saw two or three of them, in the course of this drive to Les Baux, meandering about, looking behind and calling upon the sheep in this way to follow, which the sheep always did, very promptly, with ovine unanimity. Nothing is more picturesque than to see a slow shepherd threading his way down one of the winding paths on a hillside, with his flock close behind him, necessarily expanded, yet keeping just at his heels, bending and twisting as it goes and looking rather like the tail of a dingy comet.

Les Baux

About four miles from Arles, as you drive northward towards the Alpilles, of which Alphonse Daudet has spoken so often and, as he might say, so intimately, stand on a hill that overlooks the road the very considerable ruins of the abbey of Montmajour, one of the innumerable remnants of a feudal and ecclesiastical (as well as an architectural) past that one encounters in the south of France; remnants which, it must be confessed, tend to introduce a certain confusion and satiety into the passive mind of the tourist. Montmajour, however, is very impressive and interesting; the only trouble with it is that, unless you have stopped and returned to Arles, you see it in memory over the head of Les Baux, which is a much more absorbing picture. A part of the mass of buildings (the monastery) dates only from the last century; and the stiff architecture of that period does not lend itself very gracefully to desolation: it looks too much as if it had been burnt down the year before. The monastery was demolished during the Revolution, and it injures a little the effect of the very much more ancient fragments that are connected with it. The whole place is on a great scale; it was a rich and splendid abbey. The church, a vast basilica of the eleventh century and of the noblest proportions, is virtually intact; I mean as regards its essentials, for the details have completely vanished. The huge solid shell is full of expression; it looks as if it had been hollowed out by the sincerity of early faith, and it opens into a cloister as impressive as itself. Wherever one goes, in France, one meets, looking backward a little, the spectre of the great Revolution; and one meets it always in the shape of the destruction of something beautiful and precious. To make us forgive it at all, how much it must also have destroyed that was more hateful than itself! Beneath the church of Montmajour is a most extraordinary crypt, almost as big as the edifice above it and making a complete subterranean temple, surrounded with a circular gallery, or deambulatory, which expands at intervals into five square chapels. There are other things, of which I have but a confused memory: a great fortified keep; a queer little primitive chapel hollowed out of the rock beneath these later structures and recommended to the visitor's attention as the confessional of Saint Trophimus, who shares with so many worthies the glory of being the first apostle of the Gauls. Then there is a strange, small church, of the dimmest antiquity, standing at a distance from the other buildings. I remember that after we had let ourselves down a good many steepish places to visit crypts and confessionals, we walked across a field to this archaic cruciform edifice and went thence to a point farther down the road, where our carriage was awaiting us. The chapel of the Holy Cross, as it is called, is classed among the historic monuments of France; and I read in a queer, rambling, ill-written book which I picked at Avignon, and in which the author, M. Louis de Laincel, has buried a great deal of curious information on the subject of Provence under a style inspiring little confidence, that the "délicieuse chapelle de Sainte-Croix" is a "véritable bijou artistique." He speaks of "a piece of lace in stone" which runs from one end of the building to the other, but of which I am obliged to confess that I have no recollection. I retain, however, a sufficiently clear impression of the little superannuated temple, with its four apses and its perceptible odour of antiquity—the odour of the eleventh century.

The ruins of Les Baux remain quite indistinguishable even when you are directly beneath them, at the foot of the charming little Alpilles, which mass themselves with a kind of delicate ruggedness. Rock and ruin have been so welded together by the confusions of time that as you approach it from behind—that is, from the direction of Arles—the place presents simply a general air of cragginess. Nothing can be prettier than the crags of Provence; they are beautifully modelled, as painters say, and they have a delightful silvery colour. The road winds round the foot of the hills on the top of which Les Baux is planted, and passes into another valley, from which the approach to the town is many degrees less precipitous and may be comfortably made in a carriage. Of course the deeply inquiring traveller will alight as promptly as possible, for the pleasure of climbing into this queerest of cities on foot is not the least part of the entertainment of going there. Then you appreciate its extraordinary position, its picturesqueness, its steepness, its desolation and decay. It hangs—that is, what remains of it—to the slanting summit of the mountain. Nothing would be more natural than for the whole place to roll down into the valley. A part of it has done so—for it is not unjust to suppose that in the process of decay the crumbled particles have sought the lower level, while the remainder still clings to its magnificent perch.

If I called Les Baux a city, just above, it was not that I was stretching a point in favour of the small spot which to-day contains but a few dozen inhabitants. The history of the place is as extraordinary as its situation. It was not only a city, but a state; not only a state, but an empire; and on the crest of its little mountain called itself sovereign of a territory, or at least of scattered towns and counties, with which its present aspect is grotesquely out of relation. The lords of Les Baux, in a word, were great feudal proprietors;

and there was a time during which the island of Sardinia, to say nothing of places nearer home, such as Arles and Marseilles, paid them homage. The chronicle of this old Provençal house has been written, in a style somewhat unctuous and flowery, by M. Jules Canonge. I purchased the little book—a modest pamphlet—at the establishment of the good sisters, just beside the church, in one of the highest parts of Les Baux. The sisters have a school for the hardy little Baussenques, whom I heard piping their lessons while I waited in the cold *parloir* for one of the ladies to come and speak to me. Nothing could have been more perfect than the manner of this excellent woman when she arrived; yet her small religious house seemed a very out-of-the-way corner of the world. It was spotlessly neat, and the rooms looked as if they had lately been papered and painted: in this respect, at the mediæval Pompeii, they were rather a discord. They were, at any rate, the newest, freshest thing at Les Baux. I remember going round to the church after I had left the good sisters, and to a little quiet terrace which stands in front of it, ornamented with a few small trees and bordered with a wall, breast-high, over which you look down steep hillsides, off into the air and all about the neighbouring country. I remember saying to myself that this little terrace was one of those felicitous nooks which the tourist of taste keeps in his mind as a picture. The church was small and brown and dark, with a certain rustic richness. All this, however, is no general description of Les Baux.

Les Baux

I am unable to give any coherent account of the place, for the simple reason that it is a mere confusion of ruin. It has not been preserved in lava like Pompeii, and its streets and houses, its ramparts and castle, have become fragmentary not through the sudden destruction, but through the gradual withdrawal, of a population. It is not an extinguished, but a deserted city; more deserted far than even Carcassonne and Aigues-Mortes, where I found so much entertainment in the grass-grown element. It is of very small extent, and even in the days of its greatness, when its lords entitled themselves counts of Cephalonia and Neophantis, kings of Arles and Vienne, princes of Achaia and emperors of Constantinople—even at this flourishing period, when, as M. Jules Canonge remarks, "they were able to depress the balance in which the fate of peoples and kings is weighed," the plucky little city contained at the most no more than thirty-six hundred souls. Yet its lords (who, however, as I have said, were able to present a long list of subject towns, most of them, though a few are renowned, unknown to fame) were seneschals and captains-general of Piedmont and Lombardy, grand admirals of the kingdom of Naples, and its ladies were sought in marriage by half the first princes in Europe. A considerable part of the little narrative of M. Canonge is taken up with the great alliances of the House of Baux, whose fortunes, matrimonial and other, he traces from the eleventh century down to the sixteenth. The empty shells of a considerable number of old houses, many of which must have been superb, the lines of certain steep little streets, the foundations of a castle, and ever so many splendid views, are all that remains to-day of these great titles. To such a list I may add a dozen very polite and sympathetic people who emerged from the interstices of the desultory little town to gaze at the two foreigners who had driven over from Arles and whose horses were being baited at the modest inn. The resources of this establishment we did not venture otherwise to test, in spite of the seductive fact that the sign over the door was in the Provençal tongue. This little group included the baker, a rather melancholy young man, in high boots and a cloak, with whom and his companions we had a good deal of conversation. The Baussenques of to-day struck me as a very mild and agreeable race, with a good deal of the natural amenity which, on occasions like this one, the traveller who is waiting for his horses to be put in or his dinner to be prepared observes in the charming people who lend themselves to conversation in the hill-towns of Tuscany. The spot where our entertainers at Les Baux congregated was naturally the most inhabited portion of the town; as I say, there were at least a dozen human figures within sight. Presently we wandered away from them, scaled the higher places, seated ourselves among the ruins of the castle, and looked down from the cliff overhanging that portion of the road which I have mentioned as approaching Les Baux from behind. I was unable to trace the configuration of the castle as plainly as the writers who have described it in the guide-books, and I am ashamed to say that I did not even perceive the three great figures of stone (the three Marys, as they are called; the two Marys of Scripture, with Martha) which constitute one of the curiosities of the place and of which M. Jules

Canonge speaks with almost hyperbolical admiration. A brisk shower, lasting some ten minutes, led us to take refuge in a cavity of mysterious origin, where the melancholy baker presently discovered us, having had the *bonne pensée* of coming up for us with an umbrella which certainly belonged, in former ages, to one of the Stéphanettes or Berangères commemorated by M. Canonge. His oven, I am afraid, was cold so long as our visit lasted. When the rain was over we wandered down to the little disencumbered space before the inn, through a small labyrinth of obliterated things. They took the form of narrow, precipitous streets bordered by empty houses with gaping windows and absent doors, through which we had glimpses of sculptured chimney-pieces and fragments of stately arch and vault. Some of the houses are still inhabited, but most of them are open to the air and weather. Some of them have completely collapsed; others present to the street a front which enables one to judge of the physiognomy of Les Baux in the days of its importance. This importance had pretty well passed away in the early part of the sixteenth century, when the place ceased to be an independent principality. It became—by bequest of one of its lords, Bernardin des Baux, a great captain of his time—part of the appanage of the kings of France, by whom it was placed under the protection of Arles, which had formerly occupied with regard to it a different position. I know not whether the Arlesians neglected their trust, but the extinction of the sturdy little stronghold is too complete not to have begun long ago. Its memories are buried under its ponderous stones. As we drove away from it in the gloaming my friend and I agreed that the two or three hours we had spent there were among the happiest impressions of a pair of tourists very curious of the picturesque. We almost forgot that we were bound to regret that the shortened day left us no time to drive five miles farther, above a pass in the little mountains—it had beckoned to us in the morning, when we came in sight of it, almost irresistibly—to see the Roman arch and mausoleum of Saint Remy. To compass this larger excursion (including the visit to Les Baux) you must start from Arles very early in the morning; but I can imagine no more delightful day.

CHAPTER XXXIII. AVIGNON

I HAD been twice at Avignon before, and yet I was not satisfied. I probably am satisfied now; nevertheless I enjoyed my third visit. I shall not soon forget the first, on which a particular emotion set an indelible stamp. I was creeping northward, in 1870, after four months spent, for the first time, in Italy. It was the middle of January, and I had found myself unexpectedly forced to return to England for the rest of the winter. It was an insufferable disappointment; I was wretched and broken-hearted. Italy appeared to me at that time so much better than anything else in the world, that to rise from table in the middle of the feast was a prospect of being hungry for the rest of my days. I had heard a great deal of praise of the south of France; but the south of France was a poor consolation. In this state of mind I arrived at Avignon, which under a bright, hard winter sun was tingling—fairly spinning—with the *mistral.* I find in my journal of the other day a reference to the acuteness of my reluctance in January 1870. France, after Italy, appeared in the language of the latter country *poco simpatica*; and I thought it necessary, for reasons now inconceivable, to read the *Figaro,* which was filled with descriptions of the horrible Troppmann, the murderer of the *famille* Kink. Troppmann, Kink, *le crime de Pantin*—the very names that figured in this episode seemed to wave me back. Had I abandoned the sonorous south to associate with vocables so base?

It was very cold the other day at Avignon, for though there was no mistral, it was raining as it rains in Provence, and the dampness had a terrible chill in it. As I sat by my fire late at night—for in genial Avignon, in October, I had to have a fire—it came back to me that eleven years before I had at that same hour sat by a fire in that same room and, writing to a friend to whom I was not afraid to appear extravagant, had made a vow that at some happier period of the future I would avenge myself on the *ci-devant* city of the Popes by taking it in a contrary sense. I suppose that I redeemed my vow on the occasion of my second visit better than on my third; for then I was on my way to Italy, and that vengeance, of course, was complete. The only drawback was that I was in such a hurry to get to Ventimiglia (where the Italian custom-house was to be the sign of my triumph), that I scarcely took time to make it clear to myself at Avignon that this was better than reading the *Figaro*. I hurried on almost too fast to enjoy the consciousness of moving southward. On this last occasion I was unfortunately destitute of that happy faith. Avignon was my southernmost limit, after which I was to turn round and proceed back to England. But in the interval I had been a great deal in Italy, and that made all the difference.

Avignon

I had plenty of time to think of this, for the rain kept me practically housed for the first twenty-four hours. It had been raining in these regions for a month, and people had begun to look askance at the Rhone, though as yet the volume of the river was not exorbitant. The only excursion possible, while the torrent descended, was a kind of horizontal dive, accompanied with infinite splashing, to the little *musée* of the town, which is within a moderate walk of the hotel. I had a memory of it from my first visit; it had appeared to me more pictorial than its pictures. I found that recollection had flattered it a little, and that it is neither better nor worse than most provincial museums. It has the usual musty chill in the air, the usual grass-grown forecourt, in which a few lumpish Roman fragments are disposed, the usual red tiles on the floor and the usual specimens of the more livid schools on the walls. I rang up the *gardien*, who arrived with a bunch of keys, wiping his mouth; he unlocked doors for me, opened shutters, and while (to my distress, as if the things had been worth lingering over) he shuffled about after me, he announced the names of the pictures before which I stopped in a voice that reverberated through the melancholy halls and seemed to make the authorship shameful when it was obscure and grotesque when it pretended to be great. Then there were intervals of silence, while I stared absent-mindedly, at haphazard, at some indistinguishable canvas and the only sound was the downpour of the rain on the skylights. The museum of Avignon derives a certain dignity from its Roman fragments. The town has no Roman monuments to show; in this respect, beside its brilliant neighbours, Arles and Nîmes, it is a blank. But a great many small objects have been found in its soil—pottery, glass, bronzes, lamps, vessels and ornaments of gold and silver. The glass is especially charming—small vessels of the most delicate shape and substance, many of them perfectly preserved. These diminutive, intimate things bring one near to the old Roman life; they seems like pearls strung upon the slender thread that swings across the gulf of time. A little glass cup that Roman lips have touched says more to us than the great vessel of an arena. There are two small silver *casseroles*, with chiselled handles, in the museum of Avignon, that struck me as among the most charming survivals of antiquity.

Avignon the Palace of the Popes

I did wrong, just above, to speak of my attack on this establishment as the only recreation I took that first wet day; for I remember a terribly moist visit to the former palace of the Popes, which could have taken place only in the same tempestuous hours. It is true that I scarcely know why I should have gone out to see the Papal palace in the rain, for I had been over it twice before, and even then had not found the interest of the place so complete as it ought to be; the fact nevertheless remains that this last occasion is much associated with an umbrella, which was not superfluous even in some of the chambers and corridors of the gigantic pile. It had already seemed to me the dreariest of all historical buildings, and my final visit confirmed the impression. The place is as intricate as it is vast, and as desolate as it is dirty. The imagination has, for some reason or other, to make more than the effort usual in such cases to restore and repeople it. The fact indeed is simply that the palace has been so incalculably abused and altered. The alterations have been so numerous that, though I have duly conned the enumerations, supplied in guide-books, of the principal perversions, I do not pretend to carry any of them in my head. The huge bare mass, without ornament, without grace, despoiled of its battlements and defaced with sordid modern windows, covering the Rocher des Doms and looking down over the Rhone and the broken bridge of Saint-Bénazet (which stops in such a sketchable manner in mid-stream), and across at the lonely tower of Philippe le Bel and the ruined wall of Villeneuve, makes at a distance, in spite of its poverty, a great figure, the effect of which is carried out by the tower of the church beside it (crowned though the latter be, in a top-heavy fashion, with an immense modern image of the Virgin) and by the thick, dark foliage of the garden laid out on a still higher portion of the eminence. This garden recalls faintly and a trifle perversely the grounds of the Pincian at Rome. I know not whether it is the shadow of the Papal name, present in both places, combined with a vague analogy between the churches—which, approached in each case by a flight of steps, seemed to defend the precinct—but each time I have seen the Promenade des Doms it has carried my thoughts to the wider and loftier terrace from which you look away at the Tiber and Saint Peter's.

Avignon: the Palace of the Popes

As you stand before the Papal palace, and especially as you enter it, you are struck with its being a very dull monument. History enough was enacted here: the great schism lasted from 1305 to 1370, during which seven Popes, all Frenchmen, carried on the court of Avignon on principles that have not commended themselves to the esteem of posterity. But history has been whitewashed away, and the scandals of that period have mingled with the dust of dilapidations and repairs. The building has for many years been occupied as a barrack for regiments of the line, and the main characteristics of a barrack—an extreme nudity and a very queer smell—prevail throughout its endless compartments. Nothing could have been more cruelly dismal than the appearance it presented at the time of this third visit of mine. A regiment, changing quarters, had departed the day before, and another was expected to arrive (from Algeria) on the morrow. The place had been left in the befouled and belittered condition which marks the passage of the military after they have broken camp, and it would offer but a melancholy welcome to the regiment that was about to take possession. Enormous windows had been left carelessly open all over the building, and the rain and wind were beating into empty rooms and passages, making draughts which purified, perhaps, but which scarcely cheered. For an arrival it was horrible. A handful of soldiers had remained behind. In one of the big vaulted rooms several of them were lying on their wretched beds, in the dim light, in the cold, in the damp, with the bleak bare walls before them and their overcoats, spread over them, pulled up to their noses. I pitied them immensely, though they may have felt less wretched than they looked. I thought not of the old profligacies and crimes, not of the funnel-shaped torture-chamber (which, after exciting the shudder of generations, has been ascertained now, I believe, to have been a mediæval bakehouse), not of the tower of the *glacière* and the horrors perpetrated here in the Revolution, but of the military burden of young France. One wonders how young France endures it, and one is forced to believe that the French conscript has, in addition to his notorious good-humour, greater toughness than is commonly supposed by those who consider only the more relaxing influences of French civilisation. I hope he finds occasional compensation for such moments as I saw those damp young peasants passing on the mattresses of their hideous barrack, without anything around to remind them that they were in the most civilised of countries. The only traces of former splendour now visible in the Papal pile are the walls and vaults of two small chapels, painted in fresco, so battered and effaced as to be scarcely distinguishable, by Simone Memmi. It offers of course a peculiarly good field for restoration, and I believe the Government intend to take it in hand. I mention this fact without a sigh, for they cannot well make it less interesting than it is at present.

CHAPTER XXXIV. VILLENEUVE-LÈS-AVIGNON

FORTUNATELY it did not rain every day (though I believe it was raining everywhere else in the department); otherwise I should not have been able to go to Villeneuve and to Vaucluse. The afternoon indeed was lovely when I walked over the interminable bridge that spans the two arms of the Rhone, divided here by a considerable island, and directed my course, like a solitary horseman—on foot, to the lonely tower which forms one of the outworks of Villeneuve-lès-Avignon. The picturesque, half-deserted little town lies a couple of miles farther up the river. The immense round towers of its old citadel and the long stretches of ruined wall covering the slope on which it lies are the most striking features of the nearer view, as you look from Avignon across the Rhone. I spent a couple of hours in visiting these objects, and there was a kind of pictorial sweetness in the episode; but I have not many details to relate. The isolated tower I just mentioned has much in common with the detached donjon of Montmajour, which I had looked at in going to Les Baux and to which I paid my respects in speaking of that excursion. Also the work of Philippe le Bel (built in 1307), it is amazingly big and stubborn, and formed the opposite limit of the broken bridge whose first arches (on the side of Avignon) alone remain to give a measure of the occasional volume of the Rhone. Half an hour's walk brought me to Villeneuve, which lies away from the river, looking like a big village half depopulated and occupied for the most part by dogs and cats, old women and small children; these last, in general, remarkably pretty, in the manner of the children of Provence. You pass through the place, which seems in a singular degree vague and unconscious, and come to the rounded hill on which the ruined abbey lifts its yellow walls— the Benedictine abbey of Saint-André, at once a church, a monastery, and a fortress. A large part of the crumbling enceinte disposes itself over the hill; but for the rest, all that has preserved any traceable cohesion is a considerable portion of the citadel. The defence of the place appears to have been entrusted largely to the huge round towers that flank the old gate; one of which, the more complete, the ancient warden (having first inducted me into his own dusky little apartment and presented me with a great bunch of lavender) enabled me to examine in detail. I would almost have dispensed with the privilege, for I think I have already mentioned that an acquaintance with many feudal interiors has wrought a sad confusion in my mind. The image of the outside always remains distinct; I keep it apart from other images of the same sort; it makes, a picture sufficiently ineffaceable. But the guard-rooms, winding staircases, loopholes, prisons, repeat themselves and intermingle; they have a wearisome family likeness. There are always black passages and corners, and walls twenty feet thick; and there is always some high place to climb up to for the sake of a "magnificent" view. The views, too, are apt to run together. These dense gate-towers of Philippe le Bel struck me, however, as peculiarly wicked and grim. Their capacity is of the largest, and they contain ever so many devilish little dungeons, lighted by the narrowest slit in the prodigious wall, where it comes over one with a good deal of vividness and still more horror that wretched human beings once lay there rotting in the dark. The dungeons of Villeneuve made a particular impression on me—greater than any except those of Loches, which must surely be the most gruesome in Europe. I hasten to add that every dark hole at Villeneuve is called a dungeon; and I believe it is well established that in this manner, in almost all old castles and towers, the sensibilities of the modern tourist are unscrupulously played upon. There were plenty of black holes in the Middle Ages that were not dungeons, but household receptacles of various kinds; and many a tear dropped in pity for the groaning captive has really been addressed to the spirits of the larder and the faggot-nook. For all this, there are some very bad corners in the towers of Villeneuve, so that I was not wide of the mark when I began to think again, as I had often thought before, of the stoutness of the human composition in the Middle Ages and the tranquillity of nerve of people to whom the groaning captive and the blackness of a "living tomb" were familiar ideas which did not at all interfere with their happiness or their sanity. Our modern nerves, our irritable sympathies, our easy discomforts and fears, make one think (in some relations) less respectfully of human nature. Unless indeed it be true, as I have heard it maintained, that in the

Villeneuve-lès-Avignon

Middle Ages every one did go mad—every one *was* mad. The theory that this was a period of general dementia is not altogether untenable.

Within the old walls of its immense abbey the town of Villeneuve has built itself a rough faubourg; the fragments with which the soil was covered having been, i suppose, a quarry of material. There are no streets; the small, shabby houses, almost hovels, straggle at random over the uneven ground. The only important feature is a convent of cloistered nuns, who have a large garden (always within the walls) behind their house, and whose doleful establishment you look down into, or down at simply, from the battlements of the citadel. One or two of the nuns were passing in and out of the house; they wore grey robes with a bright red cape. I thought their situation most provincial. I came away and wandered a little over the base of the hill, outside the walls. Small white stones cropped through the grass, over which low olive-trees were scattered. The afternoon had a yellow brightness. I sat down under one of the little trees, on the grass—the delicate grey branches were not much above my head—and rested and looked at Avignon across the Rhone. It was very soft, very still and pleasant, though I am not sure it was all I once should have expected of that combination of elements: an old city wall for a background, a canopy of olives, and for a couch the soil of Provence.

Avignon

When I came back to Avignon the twilight was already thick, but I walked up to the Rocher des Doms. Here I again had the benefit of that amiable moon which had already lighted up for me so many romantic scenes. She was full, and she rose over the Rhone and made it look in the distance like a silver serpent. I remember saying to myself at this moment that it would be a beautiful evening to walk round the walls of Avignon—the remarkable walls which challenge comparison with those of Carcassonne and Aigues-Mortes, and which it was my duty, as an observer of the picturesque, to examine with some attention. Presenting themselves to that silver sheen, they could not fail to be impressive. So, at least, I said to myself; but unfortunately I did not believe what I said. It is a melancholy fact that the walls of Avignon had never impressed me at all, and I had never taken the trouble to make the circuit. They are continuous and complete, but for some mysterious reason they fail of their effect. This is partly because they are very low, in some places almost absurdly so, being buried in new accumulations of soil and by the filling in of the moat up to their middle. Then they have been too well tended; they not only look at present very new, but look as if they had never been old. The fact that their extent is very much greater makes them more of a curiosity than those of Carcassonne; but this is exactly, at the same time, what is fatal to their pictorial unity. With their thirty-seven towers and seven gates, they lose themselves too much to make a picture that will compare with the admirable little vignette of Carcassonne. I may mention, now that I am speaking of the general mass of Avignon, that nothing is more curious than the way in which, viewed from a distance, it is all reduced to naught by the vast bulk of the palace of the Popes. From across the Rhone, or from the train as you leave the place, this great grey block is all Avignon; it seems to occupy the whole city, extensive, with its shrunken population, as the city is.

CHAPTER XXXV. VAUCLUSE

IT was the morning after this, I think (a certain Saturday), that when I came out of the Hôtel de l'Europe, which lies in shallow concavity just within the city gate that opens on the Rhone—came out to look at the sky from the little *place* before the inn and see how the weather promised for the obligatory excursion to Vaucluse—I found the whole town in a terrible taking. I say the whole town advisedly, for every inhabitant appeared to have taken up a position on the bank of the river, or on the uppermost parts of the promenade of the Doms, where a view of its course was to be obtained. It had risen surprisingly in the night, and the good people of Avignon had reason to know what a rise of the Rhone might signify. The town, in its lower portions, is quite at the mercy of the swollen waters; and it was mentioned to me that in 1856 the Hôtel de l'Europe, in its convenient hollow, was flooded up to within a few feet of the ceiling of the dining-room, where the long board which had served for so many a table d'hôte floated disreputably, with its legs in the air. On the present occasion the mountains of the Ardêche, where it had been raining for a month, had sent down torrents which, all that fine Friday night, by the light of the innocent-looking moon, poured themselves into the Rhone and its tributary the Durance. The river was enormous and continued to rise, and the sight was beautiful and horrible. The water in many places was already at the base of the city walls, the quay, with its parapet just emerging, being already covered. The country, seen from the Plateau des Doms, resembled a vast lake, with protrusions of trees, houses, bridges, gates. The people looked at it in silence, as I had seen people before—on the occasion of a rise of the Arno, at Pisa—appear to consider the prospect of an inundation. "Il monte; il monte toujours"—there was not much said but that. It was a general holiday, and there was an air of wishing to profit, for sociability's sake, by any interruption of the commonplace (the popular mind likes "a change," and the element of change mitigates the sense of disaster); but the affair was not otherwise a holiday. Suspense and anxiety were in the air, and it never is pleasant to be reminded of the helplessness of man. In the presence of a loosened river, with its ravaging, unconquerable volume, this impression is as strong as possible; and as I looked at the deluge which threatened to make an island of the Papal palace I perceived that the scourge of water is greater than the scourge of fire. A blaze may be quenched, but where could the flame be kindled that would arrest the quadrupled Rhone? For the population of Avignon a good deal was at stake, and I am almost ashamed to confess that in the midst of the public alarm I considered the situation from the point of view of the little projects of a sentimental tourist. Would the prospective inundation interfere with my visit to Vaucluse, or make it imprudent to linger twenty-four hours longer at Avignon? I must add that the tourist was not perhaps, after all, so sentimental. I have spoken of the pilgrimage to the shrine of Petrarch as obligatory, and that was, in fact, the light in which it presented itself to me; all the more that I had been twice at Avignon without undertaking it. This is why I was vexed at the Rhone.—if vexed I was—for representing as impracticable an excursion which I cared nothing about. How little I cared was manifest from my inaction on former occasions. I had a prejudice against Vaucluse, against Petrarch, even against the incomparable Laura. I was sure that the place was cockneyfied and threadbare, and I had never been able to take an interest in the poet and the lady. I was sure that I had known many women as charming and as handsome as she, about whom much less noise had been made; and I was convinced that her singer was factitious and literary, and that there are half a dozen stanzas in Wordsworth that speak more to the soul than the whole collection of his *fioriture*. This was the crude state of mind in which I determined to go, at any risk, to Vaucluse. Now that I think it over, I seem to remember that I had hoped, after all, that the submersion of the roads would forbid it. Since morning the clouds had gathered again, and by noon they were so heavy that there was every prospect of a torrent. It appeared absurd to choose such a time as this to visit a fountain—a fountain which would be indistinguishable in the general cataract.

Vaucluse

Nevertheless I took a vow, that if at noon the rain should not have begun to descend upon Avignon I would repair to the head-spring of the Sorgues. When the critical moment arrived the clouds were hanging over Avignon like distended water-bags, which only needed a prick to empty themselves. The prick was not given, however; all nature was too much occupied in following the aberrations of the Rhone to think of playing tricks elsewhere. Accordingly I started for the station in a spirit which, for a tourist who sometimes had prided himself on his unfailing supply of sentiment, was shockingly perfunctory.

"For tasks in hours of insight willed

May be in hours of gloom fulfilled."

I remembered these lines of Matthew Arnold (written, apparently, in an hour of gloom), and carried out the idea, as I went, by hoping that with the return of insight I should be glad to have seen Vaucluse. Light has descended upon me since then, and I declare that the excursion is in every way to be recommended. The place makes a great impression, quite apart from Petrarch and Laura.

There was no rain; there was only, all the afternoon, a mild, moist wind and a sky magnificently black; which made a *repoussoir* for the paler cliffs of the fountain. The road, by train, crosses a flat, expressionless country, towards the range of arid hills which lie to the east of Avignon, and which spring (says Murray) from the mass of the Mont-Ventoux. At Isle-sur-Sorgues, at the end of about an hour, the foreground becomes much more animated and the distance much more (or perhaps I should say much less) actual. I descended from the train and ascended to the top of an omnibus which was to convey me into the recesses of the hills. It had not been among my previsions that I should be indebted to a vehicle of that kind for an opportunity to commune with the spirit of Petrarch; and I had to borrow what consolation I could from the fact that at least I had the omnibus to myself. I was the only passenger; every one else was at Avignon watching the Rhone. I lost no time in perceiving that I could not have come to Vaucluse at a better moment. The Sorgues was almost as full as the Rhone, and of a colour much more romantic. Rushing along its narrowed channel under an avenue of fine *platanes* (it is confined between solid little embankments of stone), with the good wives of the village, on the brink, washing their linen in its contemptuous flood, it gave promise of high entertainment farther on.

The drive to Vaucluse is of about three-quarters of an hour; and though the river, as I say, was promising, the big pale hills, as the road winds into them, did not look as if their slopes of stone and shrub were a nestling-place for superior scenery. It is a part of the merit of Vaucluse indeed that it is as much as possible a surprise. The place has a right to its name, for the valley appears impenetrable until you get fairly into it. One perverse twist follows another until the omnibus suddenly deposits you in front of the "cabinet" of Petrarch. After that you have only to walk along the left bank of the river. The cabinet of Petrarch is to-day a hideous little *café*, bedizened, like a signboard, with extracts from the ingenious "Rime." The poet and his lady are of course the stock-in-trade of the little village, which has had for several generations the privilege of attracting young couples engaged in their wedding-tour and other votaries of the tender passion. The place has long been familiar, on festal Sundays, to the swains of Avignon and their attendant nymphs. The little fish of the Sorgues are much esteemed, and, eaten on the spot, they constitute, for the children of the once Papal city, the classic suburban dinner. Vaucluse has been turned to account, however, not only by sentiment, but by industry; the banks of the stream being disfigured by a pair of hideous mills for the manufacture of paper and of wool. In an enterprising and economical age the water-power of the Sorgues was too obvious a motive; and I must say that, as the torrent rushed past them, the wheels of the dirty little factories appeared to turn merrily enough. The footpath on the left bank, of which I just spoke, carries one fortunately quite out of sight of them, and out of sound as well, inasmuch as on the day of my visit the stream itself, which was in tremendous force, tended more and more, as one approached the fountain, to fill the valley with its own echoes. Its colour was magnificent, and the whole spectacle more like a corner of Switzerland than a nook in Provence. The protrusions of the mountain shut it in, and you penetrate to the bottom of the recess which they form. The Sorgues rushes and rushes; it is almost like Niagara after the jump of the cataract. There are dreadful little booths beside the path, for the sale of photographs and *immortelles*—I don't know what one is to do with the immortelles—where you are offered a brush dipped in tar to write your name withal on the rocks. Thousands of vulgar persons, of both sexes, and exclusively, it appeared, of the French nationality, had availed themselves of this implement, for every square inch of accessible stone was scored over with some human appellation. It is not only we in America, therefore, who besmirch our scenery; the practice exists, in a more organised form (like everything else in France), in the country of good taste. You leave the little booths and stalls behind; but the bescribbled crag, bristling with human vanity, keeps you company even when you stand face to face with the fountain. This happens when you find yourself at the foot of the enormous straight cliff out of which the river gushes. It rears itself to an extraordinary height—a huge forehead of bare stone—looking as if it were the half of a tremendous mound split open by volcanic action. The little valley, seeing it there, at a bend, stops suddenly and receives in its arms the magical spring. I call it magical on account of the mysterious manner in which it comes into the world, with the huge shoulder of the mountain rising over it as if to protect the secret. From under the mountain it silently rises, without visible movement, filling a small natural basin with the stillest blue water. The contrast between the stillness of this basin and the agitation of the water directly after it has overflowed, constitutes half the charm of Vaucluse. The violence of the stream when once it has been set loose on the rocks is as fascinating and indescribable as that of other cataracts; and the rocks in the bed of the Sorgues have been arranged by a master-hand. The setting of the phenomenon struck me as so simple and so fine—the vast sad cliff, covered with the afternoon light, still and solid for ever, while the liquid element rages and roars at its base—that I had no difficulty in understanding the celebrity of Vaucluse. I understood it, but I will not say that I understood Petrarch. He must have been very self-supporting, and Madonna Laura must indeed have been much to him.

Vaucluse

The aridity of the hills that shut in the valley is Vauclusecomplete, and the whole impression is best conveyed by that very expressive French epithet *morne*. There are the very fragmentary ruins of a castle (of one of the bishops of Cavaillon) on a high spur of the mountain, above the river; and there is another remnant of a feudal habitation on one of the more accessible ledges. Having half an hour to spare before my omnibus was to leave (I must beg the reader's pardon for this atrociously false note; call the vehicle a *diligence*, and for some undiscoverable reason the offence is minimised), I clambered up to this latter spot and sat among the rocks in the company of a few stunted olives. The Sorgues, beneath me, reaching the plain, flung itself crookedly across the meadows like an unrolled blue ribbon. I tried to think of the *amant de Laure*, for literature's sake; but I had no great success, and the most I could do was to say to myself that I must try again. Several months have elapsed since then, and I am ashamed to confess that the trial has not yet come off. The only very definite conviction I arrived at was that Vaucluse is indeed cockneyfied, but that I should have been a fool, all the same, not to come.

CHAPTER XXXVI. ORANGE

MOUNTED into my diligence at the door of the Hôtel de Pétrarque et de Laure, and we made our way back to Isle-sur-Sorgues in the fading light. This village, where at six o'clock every one appeared to have gone to bed, was fairly darkened by its high, dense plane-trees, under which the rushing river, on a level with its parapets, looked unnaturally, almost wickedly, blue. It was a glimpse which has left a picture in my mind: the little closed houses, the place empty and soundless in the autumn dusk but for the noise of waters, and in the middle, amid the blackness of the shade, the gleam of the swift, strange tide. At the station every one was talking of the inundation being in many places an accomplished fact, and, in particular, of the condition of the Durance at some point that I have forgotten. At Avignon, an hour later, I found the water in some of the streets. The sky cleared in the evening, the moon lighted up the submerged suburbs, and the population again collected in the high places to enjoy the spectacle. It exhibited a certain sameness, however, and by nine o'clock there was considerable animation in the Place Crillon, where there is nothing to be seen but the front of the theatre and of several cafés—in addition indeed to a statue of this celebrated brave, whose valour redeemed some of the numerous military disasters of the reign of Louis

XV. The next morning the lower quarters of the town were in a pitiful state: the situation seemed to me odious. To express my disapproval of it I lost no time in taking the train to Orange, which, with its other attractions, had the merit of not being seated on the Rhone. It was destiny to move northward; but even if I had been at liberty to follow a less unnatural course I should not then have undertaken it, inasmuch as the railway between Avignon and Marseilles was credibly reported to be (in places) under water. This was the case with almost everything but the line itself on the way to Orange. The day proved splendid, and its brilliancy only lighted up the desolation. Farmhouses and cottages were up to their middle in the yellow liquidity; haystacks looked like dull little islands; windows and doors gaped open, without faces; and interruption and flight were represented in the scene. It was brought home to me that the *populations rurales* have many different ways of suffering, and my heart glowed with a grateful sense of cockneyism. It was under the influence of this emotion that I alighted at Orange to visit a collection of eminently civil monuments.

Orange

The collection consists of but two objects, but these objects are so fine that I will let the word pass. One of them is a triumphal arch, supposedly of the period of Marcus Aurelius; the other is a fragment, magnificent in its ruin, of a Roman theatre. But for these fine Roman remains and for its name, Orange is a perfectly featureless little town, without the Rhone—which, as I have mentioned, is several miles distant—to help it to a physiognomy. It seems one of the oddest things that this obscure French borough—obscure, I mean, in our modern era, for the Gallo-Roman Arausio must have been, judging it by its arches and theatre, a place of some importance—should have given its name to the heirs-apparent of the throne of Holland and been borne by a king of England who had sovereign rights over it. During the Middle Ages it formed part of an independent principality; but in 1531 it fell, by the marriage of one of its princesses, who had inherited it, into the family of Nassau. I read in my indispensable Murray that it was made over to France by the treaty of Utrecht. The arch of triumph, which stands a little way out of the town, is rather a pretty than an imposing vestige of the Romans. If it had greater purity of style one might say of it that it belonged to the same family of monuments as the Maison Carrée at Nîmes. It has three passages—the middle much higher than the others—and a very elevated attic. The vaults of the passages are richly sculptured, and the whole structure is covered with friezes and military trophies. This sculpture is rather mixed; much of it is broken and defaced, and the rest seemed to me ugly, though its workmanship is praised. The arch is at once well preserved and much injured. Its general mass is there, and as Roman monuments go it is remarkably perfect; but it has suffered, in patches, from the extremity of restoration. It is not, on the whole, of absorbing interest. It has a charm, nevertheless, which comes partly from its soft, bright yellow colour, partly from a certain elegance of shape, of expression; and on that well-washed Sunday morning, with its brilliant tone, surrounded by its circle of thin poplars, with the green country lying beyond it and a low blue horizon showing through its empty portals, it made, very sufficiently, a picture that hangs itself to one of the lateral hooks of the memory. I can take down the modest composition and place it before me as I write. I see the shallow, shining puddles in the hard, fair French road; the pale blue sky, diluted by days of rain; the disgarnished autumnal fields; the mild sparkle of the low horizon; the solitary figure in sabots, with a bundle under its arm, advancing along the *chaussée*; and in the middle I see the little ochre-coloured trio of apertures, which, in spite of its antiquity, looks bright and gay, as everything must look in France of a fresh Sunday morning.

It is true that this was not exactly the appearance of the Roman theatre, which lies on the other side of the town; a fact that did not prevent me from making my way to it in less than five minutes, through a succession of little streets concerning which I have no observations to record. None of the Roman remains in the south of France are more impressive than this stupendous fragment. An enormous mound rises above the place, which was formerly occupied—I quote from Murray—first by a citadel of the Romans, then by a castle of the princes of Nassau, razed by Louis XIV. Facing this hill a mighty wall erects itself, thirty-six metres high and composed of massive blocks of dark brown stone simply laid one on the other; the whole naked, rugged surface of which suggests a natural cliff (say of the Vaucluse order) rather than an effort of human or even of Roman labour. It is the biggest thing at Orange—it is bigger than all Orange put together—and its permanent massiveness makes light of the shrunken city. The face it presents to the town—the top of it garnished with two rows of brackets perforated with holes to receive the staves of the *velarium*—bears the traces of more than one tier of ornamental arches; though how these flat arches were applied, or incrusted, upon the wall, I do not profess to explain. You pass through a diminutive postern—which seems in proportion about as high as the entrance of a rabbit-hutch—into the lodge of the custodian, who introduces you to the interior of the theatre. Here the mass of the hill affronts you, which the ingenious Romans treated simply as the material of their auditorium. They inserted their stone seats, in a semicircle, in the slope of the hill, and planted their colossal wall opposite to it. This wall, from the inside, is, if possible, even more imposing. It formed the back of the stage, the permanent scene, and its enormous face was coated with marble. It contains three doors, the middle one being the highest and having above it, far aloft, a deep niche apparently intended for an imperial statue. A few of the benches remain on the hillside, which, however, is mainly a confusion of fragments. There is part of a corridor built into the hill, high up, and on the crest are the remnants of the demolished castle. The whole place is a kind of wilderness of ruin; there are scarcely any details; the great feature is the overtopping wall. This wall being the back of the scene, the space left between it and the chord of the semicircle (of the auditorium) which formed the proscenium is rather less than one would have supposed. In other words, the stage was very shallow, and appears to have been arranged for a number of performers placed in a line like a company of soldiers. There stands the silent skeleton, however, as impressive by what it leaves you to guess and wonder about as by what it tells you. It has not the sweetness, the softness of melancholy, of the theatre at Aries; but it is more extraordinary, and one can imagine only tremendous tragedies being enacted there—

"Presenting Thebes' or Pelops' line."

Orange

At either end of the stage, coming forward, is an immense wing—immense in height, I mean, as it reaches to the top of the scenic wall; the other dimensions are not remarkable. The division to the right, *as you* face the stage, is pointed out as the green-room; its portentous altitude and the open arches at the top give it the air of a well. The compartment on the left is exactly similar, save that it opens into the traces of other chambers, said to be those of a hippodrome adjacent to the theatre. Various fragments are visible which refer themselves plausibly to such an establishment; the greater axis of the hippodrome would appear to have been on a line with the triumphal arch. This is all I saw, and all there was to see, of Orange, which had a very rustic, bucolic aspect, and where I was not even called upon to demand breakfast at the hotel. The entrance of this resort might have been that of a stable of the Roman days.

CHAPTER XXXVII. MACON

I HAVE been trying to remember whether I fasted all the way to Macon, which I reached at an advanced hour of the evening, and think I must have done so except for the purchase of a box of nougat at Montélimart (the place is famous for the manufacture of this confection, which, at the station, is hawked at the windows of the train) and for a bouillon, very much later, at Lyons. The journey beside the Rhone—past Valence, past Tournon, past Vienne—would have been charming, on that luminous Sunday, but for two disagreeable accidents. The express from Marseilles, which I took at Orange, was full to overflowing; and the only refuge I could find was an inside angle in a carriage laden with Germans who had command of the windows, which they occupied as strongly as they have been known to occupy other strategical positions. I scarcely know, however, why I linger on this particular discomfort, for it was but a single item in a considerable list of grievances—grievances dispersed through six weeks of constant railway-travel in France. I have not touched upon them at an earlier stage of this chronicle, but my reserve is not owing to any sweetness of association. This form of locomotion, in the country of the amenities, is attended with a dozen discomforts; almost all the conditions of the business are detestable. They force the sentimental tourist again and again to ask himself whether, in consideration of such mortal annoyances, the game is worth the candle. Fortunately a railway journey is a good deal like a sea-voyage; its miseries fade from the mind as soon as you arrive. That is why I completed, to my great satisfaction, my little tour in France. Let this small effusion of ill-nature be my first and last tribute to the whole despotic *gare*: the deadly *salle d'attente*, the insufferable delays over one's luggage, the porterless platform, the overcrowded and illiberal train. How many a time did I permit myself the secret reflection that it is in perfidious Albion that they order this matter best! How many a time did the eager British mercenary, clad in velveteen and clinging to the door of the carriage as it glides into the station, revisit my invidious dreams! The paternal porter and the responsive hansom are among the best gifts of the English genius to the world. I hasten to add, faithful to my habit (so insufferable to some of my friends) of ever and again readjusting the balance after I have given it an honest tip, that the bouillon at Lyons, which I spoke of above, was, though by no means an idea bouillon, much better than any I could have obtained at an English railway-station. After I had imbibed it I sat in the train (which waited a long time at Lyons) and, by the light of one of the big lamps on the platform, read all sorts of disagreeable things in certain radical newspapers which I had bought at the bookstall. I gathered from these sheets that Lyons was in extreme commotion. The Rhone and the Saone, which form a girdle for the splendid town, were almost in the streets, as I could easily believe from what I had seen of the country after leaving Orange. The Rhone, all the way to Lyons, had been in all sorts of places where it had no business to be, and matters were naturally not improved by its confluence with the charming and copious stream which, at Macon, is said once to have given such a happy opportunity to the egotism of the capital. A visitor from Paris (the anecdote is very old), being asked on the quay of that city whether he didn't admire the Saone, replied good-naturedly that it was very pretty, but that in Paris they spelled it with the *ei*. This moment of general alarm at Lyons had been chosen by certain ingenious persons (I credit them perhaps with too sure a prevision of the rise of the rivers) for practising further upon the apprehensions of the public. A bombshell filled with dynamite had been thrown into a café, and various votaries of the comparatively innocuous *petit verre* had been wounded (I am not sure whether any one had been killed) by the irruption. Of course there had been arrests and incarcerations, and the *Intransigeant* and the *Rappel* were filled with the echoes of the explosion. The tone of these organs is rarely edifying, and it had never been less so than on this occasion. I wondered as I looked through them whether I was losing all my radicalism; and then I wondered whether, after all, I had any to lose. Even in so long a wait as that tiresome delay at Lyons I failed to settle the question, any more than I made up my mind as to the probable future of the militant democracy, or the ultimate form of a civilisation which should have blown up everything else. A few days later the water went down at Lyons; but the democracy has not gone down.

Macon

I remember vividly the remainder of that evening which I spent at Macon—remember it with a chattering of the teeth. I know not what had got into the place; the temperature, for the last day of October, was eccentric and incredible. These epithets may also be applied to the hotel itself—an extraordinary structure, all façade, which exposes an uncovered rear to the gaze of nature. There is a demonstrative, voluble landlady, who is of course part of the façade; but everything behind her is a trap for the winds, with chambers, corridors, staircases all exhibited to the sky as if the outer wall of the house had been lifted off. It would have been delightful for Florida, but it didn't do for Burgundy even on the eve of November 1, so that I suffered absurdly from the rigour of a season that had not yet begun. There was something in the air; I felt it the next day, even on the sunny quay of the Saone, where in spite of a fine southerly exposure I extracted little warmth from the reflection that Alphonse de Lamartine had often trodden the flags. Macon struck me, somehow, as suffering from a chronic numbness, and there was nothing exceptionally cheerful in the remarkable extension of the river. It was no longer a river—it had become a lake; and from my window, in the painted face of the inn, I saw that the opposite bank had been moved back, as it were, indefinitely. Unfortunately the various objects with which it was furnished had not been moved as well, the consequence of which was an extraordinary confusion in the relations of things. There were always poplars to be seen, but the poplar had become an aquatic plant. Such phenomena, however, at Macon attract but little attention, as the Saone, at certain seasons of the year, is nothing if not expansive. The people are as used to it as they appeared to be to the bronze statue of Lamartine, which is the principal monument of the *place*, and which, representing the poet in a frogged overcoat and top-boots, improvising in a high wind, struck me as even less casual in its attitude than monumental sculpture usually succeeds in being. It is true that in its present position I thought better of this work of art, which is from the hand of M. Falguière, than when I had seen it through the factitious medium of the Salon of 1876. I walked up the hill where the older part of Macon lies, in search of the natal house of the *amant d'Elvire*, the Petrarch whose Vaucluse was the bosom of the public. The Guide-Joanne quotes from "Les Confidences" a description of the birthplace of the poet, whose treatment of the locality is indeed poetical. It tallies strangely little with the reality, either as regards position or other features; and it may be said to be not an aid, but a direct obstacle, to a discovery of the house. A very humble edifice, in a small back street, is designated by a municipal tablet, set into its face, as the scene of Lamartine's advent into the world. He himself speaks of a vast and lofty structure, at the angle of a *place*, adorned with iron clamps, with a *porte haute et large* and many other peculiarities. The house with the tablet has two meagre storeys above the basement, and (at present, at least) an air of extreme shabbiness; the *place*, moreover, never can have been vast. Lamartine was accused of writing history incorrectly, and apparently he started wrong at first; it had never become clear to him where he was born. Or is the tablet wrong? If the house is small, the tablet is very big.

CHAPTER XXXVIII. BOURG-EN-BRESSE

THE foregoing reflections occur, in a cruder form, as it were, in my note-book, where I find this remark appended to them: "Don't take leave of Lamartine on that contemptuous note; it will be easy to think of something more sympathetic!" Those friends of mine, mentioned a little while since, who accuse me of always tipping back the balance, could not desire a paragraph more characteristic; but I wish to give no further evidence of such infirmities, and will therefore hurry away from the subject—hurry away in the train which, very early on a crisp, bright morning, conveyed me, by way of an excursion, to the ancient city of Bourg-en-Bresse. Shining in early light, the Saone was spread, like a smooth white tablecloth, over a considerable part of the flat country that I traversed. There is no provision made in this image for the long, transparent screens of thin-twigged trees which rose at intervals out of the watery plain; but as, in all the conditions, there seemed to be no provision for them in fact, I will let my metaphor go for what it is worth. My journey was (as I remember it) of about an hour and a half; but I passed no object of interest, as the phrase is, whatever. The phrase hardly applies even to Bourg itself, which is simply a town *quelconque*, as M. Zola would say. Small, peaceful, rustic, it stands in the midst of the great dairy-feeding plains of Bresse, of which fat county, sometime property of the house of Savoy, it was the modest capital. The blue masses of the Jura give it a creditable horizon, but the only nearer feature it can point to is its famous sepulchral church. This edifice lies at a fortunate distance from the town, which, though inoffensive, is of too common a stamp to consort with such a treasure. All I ever knew of the church of Brou I had gathered, years ago The Church of Broufrom Matthew Arnold's beautiful poem which bears its name. I remember thinking, in those years, that it was

The Church of Brou

impossible verses could be more touching than these; and as I stood before the object of my pilgrimage, in the gay French light (though the place was so dull), I recalled the spot where I had first read them and where I had read them again and yet again, wondering whether it would ever be my fortune to visit the church of Brou. The spot in question was an armchair in a window which looked out on some cows in a field; and whenever I glanced at the cows it came over me—I scarcely know why—that I should probably never behold the structure reared by the Duchess Margaret. Some of our visions never come to pass; but we must be just—others do. "So sleep, for ever sleep, O princely pair!" I remembered that line of Matthew Arnold's, and the stanza about the Duchess Margaret coming to watch the builders on her palfrey white. Then there came to me something in regard to the moon shining on winter nights through the cold clere-storey. The tone of the place at that hour was not at all lunar; it was cold and bright, but with the chill of an autumn morning; yet this, even with the fact of the unexpected remoteness of the church from the Jura added to it, did not prevent me from feeling that I looked at a monument in the production of which—or at least in the effect of which on the tourist-mind of to-day—Matthew Arnold had been much concerned. By a pardonable licence he has placed it a few miles nearer to the forests of the Jura than it stands at present. It is very true that, though the mountains in the sixteenth century can hardly have been in a different position, the plain which separates the church from them may have been bedecked with woods. The visitor to-day cannot help wondering why the beautiful building, with its splendid works of art, is dropped down in that particular spot, which looks so accidental and arbitrary. But there are reasons for most things, and there were reasons why the church of Brou should be at Brou, which is a vague little suburb of a vague little town.

The responsibility rests, at any rate, upon the Duchess Margaret—Margaret of Austria, daughter of the Emperor Maximilian and his wife Mary of Burgundy, daughter of Charles the Bold. This lady has a high name in history, having been regent of the Netherlands in behalf of her nephew, the Emperor Charles V., of whose early education she had had the care. She married in 1501 Philibert the Handsome, Duke of Savoy, to whom the province of Bresse belonged, and who died two years later. She had been betrothed, as a child, to Charles VIII. of France, and was kept for some time at the French court—that of her prospective father-in-law, Louis XI.; but she was eventually repudiated, in order that her *fiancé* might marry Anne of Brittany—an alliance so magnificently political that we almost condone the offence to a sensitive princess. Margaret did not want for husbands, however, inasmuch as before her marriage to Philibert she had been united to John of Castile, son of Ferdinand V., King of Aragon—an episode terminated by the death of the Spanish prince within a year. She was twenty-two years regent of the Netherlands and died, at fifty-one, in 1530. She might have been, had she chosen, the wife of Henry VII. of England. She was one of the signers of the League of Cambray against the Venetian Republic, and was a most politic, accomplished, and judicious princess. She undertook to build the church of Brou as a mausoleum for her second husband and herself, in fulfilment of a vow made by Margaret of Bourbon, mother of Philibert, who died before she could redeem her pledge and who bequeathed the duty to her son. He died shortly afterwards, and his widow assumed the pious task. According to Murray, she entrusted the erection of the church to "Maistre Loys von Berghem," and the sculpture to "Maistre Conrad." The author of a superstitious but carefully The Church of Brouprepared little Notice which I bought at Bourg calls the architect and sculptor (at once) Jehan de Paris, author (*sic*) of the tomb of Francis II.

The Church of Brou

of Brittany, to which we gave some attention at Nantes, and which the writer of my pamphlet ascribes only subordinately to Michel Colomb. The church, which is not of great size, is in the last and most flamboyant phase of gothic and in admirable preservation; the west front, before which a quaint old sun-dial is laid out on the ground—a circle of numbers marked in stone, like those on a clock-face, let into the earth—is covered with delicate ornament. The great feature, however (the nave is perfectly bare and wonderfully new-looking, though the warden, a stolid yet sharp old peasant in a blouse, who looked more as if his line were chaffering over turnips than showing off works of art, told me that it has never been touched and that its freshness is simply the quality of the stone)—the great feature is the admirable choir, in the midst of which the three monuments have bloomed under the chisel like exotic plants in a conservatory. I saw the place to small advantage, for the stained glass of the windows, which are fine, was under repair, and much of it was masked with planks.

187

In the centre lies Philibert-le-Bel, a figure of white marble on a great slab of black, in his robes and his armour, with two boy-angels holding a tablet at his head, and two more at his feet. On either side of him is another cherub; one guarding his helmet, the other his stiff gauntlets. The attitudes of these charming children, whose faces are all bent upon him in pity, have the prettiest tenderness and respect. The table on which he lies is supported by elaborate columns adorned with niches containing little images and with every other imaginable elegance; and beneath it he is represented in that other form so common in the tombs of the Renaissance—a man naked and dying, with none of the state and splendour of the image above. One of these figures embodies the duke, the other simply the mortal; and there is something very strange and striking in the effect of the latter, seen dimly and with difficulty through the intervals of the rich supports of the upper slab. The monument of Margaret herself is on the left, all in white marble tormented into a multitude of exquisite patterns, the last extravagance of a gothic which had gone so far that nothing was left it but to return upon itself. Unlike her husband, who has only the high roof of the church above him, she lies under a canopy supported and covered by a wilderness of embroidery—flowers, devices, initials, arabesques, statuettes. Watched over by cherubs, she is also in her robes and ermine, with a greyhound sleeping at her feet (her husband, at his, has a waking lion); and the artist has not, it is to be presumed, represented her as more beautiful than she was. She looks indeed like the regent of a turbulent realm. Beneath her couch is stretched another figure—a less brilliant Margaret, wrapped in her shroud, with her long hair over her shoulders. Round the tomb is the battered iron railing placed there originally, with the mysterious motto of the duchess worked into the top—*fortune infortune fort une*. The other two monuments are protected by barriers of the same pattern. That of Margaret of Bourbon, Philibert's mother, stands on the right of the choir; and I suppose its greatest distinction is that it should have been erected to a mother-in-law. It is but little less florid and sumptuous than the others; it has, however, no second recumbent figure. On the other hand, the statuettes that surround the base of the tomb are of even more exquisite workmanship: they represent weeping women, in long mantles and hoods, which latter hang forward over the small face of the figure, giving the artist a chance to carve the features within this hollow of drapery—an extraordinary play of skill. There is a high, white marble shrine of the Virgin, as extraordinary as all the rest (a series of compartments representing the various scenes of her life, with the Assumption in the middle); and there is a magnificent series of stalls, which are simply the intricate embroidery of the tombs translated into polished oak. All these things are splendid, ingenious, elaborate, precious; it is goldsmith's work on a monumental scale, and the general effect is none the less beautiful and solemn because it is so rich. But the monuments of the church of Brou are not the noblest that one may see; the great tombs of Verona are finer, and various other early Italian work. These things are not insincere, as Ruskin would say; but they are pretentious, and they are not positively *naïfs*. I should mention that the walls of the choir are embroidered in places with Margaret's tantalising device, which—partly perhaps because it is tantalising—is so very decorative, as they say in London. I know not whether she was acquainted with this epithet, but she had anticipated one of the fashions most characteristic of our age.

The Church of Brou

One asks one's self how all this decoration, this luxury of fair and chiselled marble, survived the French Revolution. An hour of liberty in the choir of Brou would have been a carnival for the image-breakers. The well-fed Bressois are surely a good-natured people. I call them well-fed both on general and on particular grounds. Their province has the most savoury aroma, and I found an opportunity to test its reputation. I walked back into the town from the church (there was really nothing to be seen by the way), and as the hour of the midday breakfast had struck, directed my steps to the inn. The table d'hôte was going on, and a gracious, bustling, talkative landlady welcomed me. I had an excellent repast—the best repast possible—which consisted simply of boiled eggs and bread and butter. It was the quality of these simple ingredients that made the occasion memorable. The eggs were so good that I am ashamed to say how many of them I consumed. "La plus belle fille du monde," as the French proverb says, "ne peut donner que ce qu'elle a;" and it might seem that an egg which has succeeded in being fresh has done all that can reasonably be expected of it. But there was a bloom of punctuality, so to speak, about these eggs of Bourg, as if it had been the intention of the very hens themselves that they should be promptly served. "Nous sommes en Bresse, et le beurre n'est pas mauvais," the landlady said with a sort of dry coquetry, as she placed this article before me. It was the poetry of butter, and I ate a pound or two of it; after which I came away with a strange mixture of impressions of late gothic sculpture and thick *tartines*. I came away through the town, where, on a little green promenade, facing the hotel, is a bronze statue of Bichat the physiologist, who was a Bressois. I mention it not on account of its merit (though, as statues go, I don't remember that it is bad), but because I learned from it—my ignorance, doubtless, did me little honour—that Bichat had died at thirty years of age, and this revelation was almost agitating. To have done so much in so short a life was to be truly great. This reflection, which looks deplorably trite as I write it here, had the effect of eloquence as I uttered it for my own benefit on the bare little mall at Bourg.

CHAPTER XXXIX. BEAUNE

ON my return to Macon I found myself fairly face to face with the fact that my tour was near its end. Dijon had been marked by fate as its farthest limit, and Dijon was close at hand. After that I was to drop the tourist and re-enter Paris as much as possible like a Parisian. Out of Paris the Parisian never loiters, and therefore it would be impossible for me to stop between Dijon and the capital. But I might be a tourist a few hours longer by stopping somewhere between Macon and Dijon. The question was where I should spend these hours. Where better, I asked myself (for reasons not now entirely clear to me), than at Beaune? On my way to this town I passed the stretch of the Côte d'Or, which, covered with a mellow autumn haze, with the sunshine shimmering through, looked indeed like a golden slope. One regards with a kind of awe the region in which the famous *crûs* of Burgundy (Vougeot, Chambertin, Nuits, Beaune) are, I was going to say, manufactured. Adieu, paniers; vendanges sont faites! The vintage was over; the shrunken russet fibres alone clung to their ugly stick. The horizon on the left of the road had a charm, however; there is something picturesque in the big, comfortable shoulders of the Côte. That delicate critic M. Emile Montégut, in a charming record of travel through this region published some years ago, praises Shakespeare for having talked (in "Lear") of "waterish Burgundy." Vinous Burgundy would surely be more to the point. I stopped at Beaune in pursuit of the picturesque, but I might almost have seen the little I discovered without stopping. It is a drowsy Burgundian town, very old and ripe, with crooked streets, vistas always oblique, and steep, moss covered roofs. The principal lion is the Hôpital-Saint-Esprit, or the Hôtel-Dieu simply, as they call it there, founded in 1443 by Nicholas Rollin, Chancellor of Burgundy. It is administered by the sisterhood of the Holy Ghost, and is one of the most venerable and stately of hospitals. The face it presents to the street is simple, but striking—a plain, windowless wall, surmounted by a vast slate roof, of almost mountainous steepness. Astride this roof sits a tall, slate-covered spire, from which, as I arrived, the prettiest chimes I ever heard (worse luck to them, as I will presently explain) were ringing. Over the door is a high, quaint canopy, without supports, with its vault painted blue and covered with gilded stars. (This, and indeed the whole building, have lately been restored, and its antiquity is quite of the spick-and-span order. But it is very delightful.) The treasure of the place is a precious picture—a Last Judgment, attributed equally to John van Eyck and Roger van der Weyden—given to the hospital in the fifteenth century by Nicholas Rollin aforesaid.

I learned, however, to my dismay, from a sympathising but inexorable concierge, that what remained to me of the time I had to spend at Beaune, between trains—I had rashly wasted half an hour of it in breakfasting at the station—was the one hour of the day (that of the dinner of the nuns; the picture is in their refectory) during which the treasure could not be shown. The purpose of the musical chimes to which I had so artlessly listened was to usher in this fruitless interval. The regulation was absolute, and my disappointment relative, as I have been happy to reflect since I "looked up" the picture. Crowe and Cavalcaselle assign it without hesitation to Roger van der Weyden, and give a weak little drawing of it in their "Flemish Painters." I learn from them also—what I was ignorant of—that Nicholas Rollin,

Chancellor of Burgundy and founder of the establishment at Beaune, was the original of the worthy kneeling before the Virgin in the magnificent John van Eyck of the Salon Carré. All I could see was the court of the hospital and two or three rooms. The court, with its tall roofs, its pointed gables and spires, its wooden galleries, its ancient well, with an elaborate superstructure of wrought iron, is one of those places into which a sketcher ought to be let loose. It looked Flemish or English rather than French, and a splendid tidiness pervaded it. The porter took me into two rooms on the ground-floor, into which the sketcher should also be allowed to penetrate, for they made irresistible pictures. One of them, of great proportions, painted in elaborate "subjects" like a ball-room of the seventeenth century, was filled with the beds of patients, all draped in curtains of dark red cloth, the traditional uniform of these eleemosynary couches. Among them the sisters moved about in their robes of white flannel with big white linen hoods. The other room was a strange, immense apartment, lately restored with much splendour. It was of great length and height, had a painted and gilded barrel-roof, and one end of it—the one I was introduced to—appeared to serve as a chapel, as two white-robed sisters were on their knees before an altar. This was divided by red curtains from the larger part; but the porter lifted one of the curtains and showed me that the rest of it, a long, imposing vista, served as a ward lined with little red-draped beds. "C'est l'heure de la lecture," remarked my guide; and a group of convalescents—all the patients I saw were women— were gathered in the centre around a nun, the points of whose white hood nodded a little above them and whose gentle voice came to us faintly, with a little echo, down the high perspective. I know not what the good sister was reading—a dull book, I am afraid—but there was so much colour and such a fine, rich air of tradition about the whole place that it seemed to me I would have risked listening to her. I turned away, however, with that sense of defeat which is always irritating to the appreciative tourist, and pottered about Beaune rather vaguely for the rest of my hour: looked at the statue of Gaspard Monge, the mathematician, in the little *place* (there is no *place* in France too little to contain an effigy to a glorious son); at the fine old porch— completely despoiled at the Revolution—of the principal church; and even at the meagre treasures of a courageous but melancholy little museum, which has been arranged—part of it being the gift of a local collector—in a small hôtel de ville. I carried away from Beaune the impression of something mildly autumnal—something rusty yet kindly, like the taste of a sweet russet pear.

CHAPTER XL. DIJON

IT was very well that my little tour was to terminate at Dijon, for I found, rather to my chagrin, that there was not a great deal, from the pictorial point of view, to be done with Dijon. It was no great matter, for I held my proposition to have been by this time abundantly demonstrated—the proposition with which I started: that if Paris is France, France is by no means Paris. If Dijon was a good deal of a disappointment, I felt therefore that I could afford it. It was time for me to reflect, also, that for my disappointments, as a general thing, I had only myself to thank. They had too often been the consequence of arbitrary preconceptions produced by influences of which I had lost the trace. At any rate, I will say plumply that the ancient capital of Burgundy is wanting in character; it is not up to the mark. It is old and narrow and crooked, and it has been left pretty well to itself: but it is not high and overhanging; it is not, to the eye, what the Burgundian capital should be. It has some tortuous vistas, some mossy roofs, some bulging fronts, some grey-faced hotels, which look as if in former centuries—in the last, for instance, during the time of that delightful Président de Brosses whose Letters from Italy throw an interesting sidelight on Dijon—they had witnessed a considerable amount of good living. But there is nothing else. I speak as a man who, for some reason which he doesn't remember now, did not pay a visit to the celebrated Puits de Moïse, an ancient cistern embellished with a sculptured figure of the Hebrew lawgiver.

The ancient palace of the dukes of Burgundy, long since converted into an hôtel de ville, presents to a wide, clean court, paved with washed-looking stones, and to a small semicircular *place*, opposite, which looks as if it had tried to be symmetrical and had failed, a façade and two wings characterised by the stiffness, but not by the grand air, of the early part of the eighteenth century. It contains, however, a large and rich museum—a museum really worthy of a capital. The gem of this collection is the great banqueting hall of the old palace, one of the few features of the place that has not been essentially altered. Of great height, roofed with the old beams and cornices, it exhibits, filling one end, a colossal gothic chimney-piece with a fireplace large enough to roast, not an ox, but a herd of oxen. In the middle of this striking hall, the walls of which are covered with objects more or less precious, have been placed the tombs of Philippe-le-Hardi and Jean-sans-Peur. These monuments, very splendid in their general effect, have a limited interest. The limitation comes from the fact that we see them to-day in a transplanted and mutilated condition. Placed originally in a church which has disappeared from the face of the earth, demolished and dispersed at the Revolution, they have been reconstructed and restored out of fragments recovered and pieced together. The piecing has been beautifully done; it is covered with gilt and with brilliant paint; the whole result is most artistic. But the spell of the old mortuary figures is broken, and it will never work again. Meanwhile the monuments are immensely decorative.

Dijon

I think the thing that pleased me best at Dijon was the little old Parc, a charming public garden, about a mile from the town, to which I walked by a long, straight autumnal avenue. It is a *jardin français* of the last century—a dear old place, with little blue-green perspectives and alleys and *rond-points*, in which everything balances. I went there late in the afternoon, without meeting a creature, though I had hoped I should meet the Président de Brosses. At the end of it was a little river that looked like a canal, and on the farther bank was an old-fashioned villa, close to the water, with a little French garden of its own. On the hither side was a bench, on which I seated myself, lingering a good while; for this was just the sort of place I like. It was the farthermost point of my little tour. I thought that over, as I sat there, on the eve of taking the express to Paris; and as the light faded in the Parc the vision of some of the things I had enjoyed became more distinct.

FOOTNOTES:

[a] 1884.

[b] "Promenades pittoresques en Touraine." Tours: 1869.

THE SACRED FOUNT

I

IT was an occasion, I felt—the prospect of a large party—to look out at the station for others, possible friends and even possible enemies, who might be going. Such premonitions, it was true, bred fears when they failed to breed hopes, though it was to be added that there were sometimes, in the case, rather happy ambiguities. One was glowered at, in the compartment, by people who on the morrow, after breakfast, were to prove charming; one was spoken to first by people whose sociability was subsequently to show as bleak; and one built with confidence on others who were never to reappear at all— who were only going to Birmingham. As soon as I saw Gilbert Long, some way up the platform, however, I knew him as an element. It was not so much that the wish was father to the thought as that I remembered having already more than once met him at Newmarch. He was a friend of the house—he wouldn't be going to Birmingham. I so little expected him, at the same time, to recognise me that I stopped short of the carriage near which he stood—I looked for a seat that wouldn't make us neighbours.

I had met him at Newmarch only—a place of a charm so special as to create rather a bond among its guests; but he had always, in the interval, so failed to know me that I could only hold him as stupid unless I held him as impertinent. He was stupid in fact, and in that character had no business at Newmarch; but he had also, no doubt, his system, which he applied without discernment. I wondered, while I saw my things put into my corner, what Newmarch could see in him—for it always had to see something before it made a sign. His good looks, which were striking, perhaps paid his way—his six feet and more of stature, his low-growing, tight-curling hair, his big, bare, blooming face. He was a fine piece of human furniture—he made a small party seem more numerous. This, at least, was the impression of him that had revived before I stepped out again to the platform, and it armed me only at first with surprise when I saw him come down to me as if for a greeting. If he had decided at last to treat me as an acquaintance made, it was none the less a case for letting him come all the way. That, accordingly, was what he did, and with so clear a conscience, I hasten to add, that at the end of a minute we were talking together quite as with the tradition of prompt intimacy. He was good-looking enough, I now again saw, but not such a model of it as I had seemed to remember; on the other hand his manners had distinctly gained in ease. He referred to our previous encounters and common contacts—he was glad I was going; he peeped into my compartment and thought it better than his own. He called a porter, the next minute, to shift his things, and while his attention was so taken I made out some of the rest of the contingent, who were finding or had already found places.

This lasted till Long came back with his porter, as well as with a lady unknown to me and to whom he had apparently mentioned that our carriage would pleasantly accommodate her. The porter carried in fact her dressing-bag, which he put upon a seat and the bestowal of which left the lady presently free to turn to me with a reproach: "I don't think it very nice of you not to speak to me." I stared, then caught at her identity through her voice; after which I reflected that she might easily have thought me the same sort of ass as I had thought Long. For she was simply, it appeared, Grace Brissenden. We had, the three of us, the carriage to ourselves, and we journeyed together for more than an hour, during which, in my corner, I had my companions opposite. We began at first by talking a little, and then as the train—a fast one—ran straight and proportionately bellowed, we gave up the effort to compete with its music. Meantime, however, we had exchanged with each other a fact or two to turn over in silence. Brissenden was coming later— not, indeed, that that was such a fact. But his wife was informed—she knew about the numerous others; she had mentioned, while we waited, people and things: that Obert, R.A., was somewhere in the train, that her husband was to bring on Lady John, and that Mrs. Froome and Lord Lutley were in the wondrous new fashion—and their servants too, like a single household— starting, travelling, arriving together. It came back to me as I sat there that when she mentioned Lady John as in charge of Brissenden the other member of our trio had expressed interest and surprise—expressed it so as to have made her reply with a smile: "Didn't you really know?" This passage had taken place on the platform while, availing ourselves of our last minute, we hung about our door.

"Why in the world *should* I know?"

To which, with good nature, she had simply returned: "Oh, it's only that I thought you always did!" And they both had looked at me a little oddly, as if appealing from each other. "What in the world does she mean?" Long might have seemed to ask; while Mrs. Brissenden conveyed with light profundity: "*You* know why he should as well as I, don't you?" In point of fact I didn't in the least; and what afterwards struck me much more as the beginning of my anecdote was a word dropped by Long after someone had come up to speak to her. I had then given him his cue by alluding to my original failure to place her. What in the world, in the year or two, had happened to her? She had changed so extraordinarily for the better. How could a woman who had been plain so long become pretty so late?

It was just what he had been wondering. "I didn't place her at first myself. She had to speak to me. But I hadn't seen her since her marriage, which was—wasn't it?—four or five years ago. She's amazing for her age."

"What then *is* her age?"

"Oh—two or three-and-forty."

"She's prodigious for that. But can it be so great?"

"Isn't it easy to count?" he asked. "Don't you remember, when poor Briss married her, how immensely she was older? What was it they called it?—a case of child-stealing. Everyone made jokes. Briss isn't yet thirty." No, I bethought myself, he wouldn't be; but I hadn't remembered the difference as so great. What I had mainly remembered was that she had been rather ugly. At present she was rather handsome. Long, however, as to this, didn't agree. "I'm bound to say I don't quite call it beauty."

"Oh, I only speak of it as relative. She looks so well—and somehow so 'fine.' Why else shouldn't we have recognised her?"

"Why indeed? But it isn't a thing with which beauty has to do." He had made the matter out with an acuteness for which I shouldn't have given him credit. "What has happened to her is simply that—well, that nothing has."

"Nothing has happened? But, my dear man, she has been married. That's supposed to be something."

"Yes, but she has been married so little and so stupidly. It must be desperately dull to be married to poor Briss. His comparative youth doesn't, after all, make more of him. He's nothing but what he is. Her clock has simply stopped. She looks no older—that's all."

"Ah, and a jolly good thing too, when you start where she did. But I take your discrimination," I added, "as just. The only thing is that if a woman doesn't grow older she may be said to grow younger; and if she grows younger she may be supposed to grow prettier. That's all—except, of course, that it strikes me as charming also for Brissenden himself. *He* had the face, I seem to recall, of a baby; so that if his wife did flaunt her fifty years——!"

"Oh," Long broke in, "it wouldn't have mattered to him if she had. That's the awfulness, don't you see? of the married state. People have to get used to each other's charms as well as to their faults. He wouldn't have noticed. It's only you and I who do, and the charm of it is for *us*."

"What a lucky thing then," I laughed, "that, with Brissenden so out of it and relegated to the time-table's obscure hereafter, it should be you and I who enjoy her!" I had been struck in what he said with more things than I could take up, and I think I must have looked at him, while he talked, with a slight return of my first mystification. He talked as I had never heard him—less and less like the heavy Adonis who had so often "cut" me; and while he did so I was proportionately more conscious of the change in him. He noticed in fact after a little the vague confusion of my gaze and asked me—with complete good nature—why I stared at him so hard. I sufficiently disembroiled myself to reply that I could only be fascinated by the way he made his points; to which he—with the same sociability—made answer that he, on the contrary, more than suspected me, clever and critical as I was, of amusement at his artless prattle. He stuck none the less to his idea that what we had been discussing was lost on Brissenden. "Ah, then I hope," I said, "that at least Lady John isn't!"

"Oh, Lady John——!" And he turned away as if there were either too much or too little to say about her.

I found myself engaged again with Mrs. Briss while he was occupied with a newspaper-boy—and engaged, oddly, in very much the free view of him that he and I had just taken of herself. She put it to me frankly that she had never seen a man so improved: a confidence that I met with alacrity, as it showed me that, under the same impression, I had not been astray. She had only, it seemed, on seeing him, made him out with a great effort. I took in this confession, but I repaid it. "He hinted to me that he had not known you more easily."

"More easily than you did? Oh, nobody does that; and, to be quite honest, I've got used to it and don't mind. People talk of our changing every seven years, but they make me feel as if I changed every seven minutes. What will you have, at any rate, and how can I help it? It's the grind of life, the wear and tear of time and misfortune. And, you know, I'm ninety-three."

"How young you must feel," I answered, "to care to talk of your age! I envy you, for nothing would induce me to let you know mine. You look, you see, just twenty-five."

It evidently too, what I said, gave her pleasure—a pleasure that she caught and held. "Well, you can't say I dress it."

"No, you dress, I make out, ninety-three. If you *would* only dress twenty-five you'd look fifteen."

"Fifteen in a schoolroom charade!" She laughed at this happily enough. "Your compliment to my taste is odd. I know, at all events," she went on, "what's the difference in Mr. Long."

"Be so good then, for my relief, as to name it."

"Well, a very clever woman has for some time past——"

"Taken"—this beginning was of course enough—"a particular interest in him? Do you mean Lady John?" I inquired; and, as she evidently did, I rather demurred. "Do you call Lady John a very clever woman?"

"Surely. That's why I kindly arranged that, as she was to take, I happened to learn, the next train, Guy should come with her."

"You arranged it?" I wondered. "She's not so clever as you then."

"Because you feel that *she* wouldn't, or couldn't? No doubt she wouldn't have made the same point of it—for more than one reason. Poor Guy hasn't pretensions—has nothing but his youth and his beauty. But that's precisely why I'm sorry for him and try whenever I can to give him a lift. Lady John's company *is*, you see, a lift."

"You mean it has so unmistakably been one to Long?"

"Yes—it has positively given him a mind and a tongue. *That's* what has come over him."

"Then," I said, "it's a most extraordinary case—such as one really has never met."

"Oh, but," she objected, "it happens."

"Ah, so very seldom! Yes—I've positively never met it. Are you very sure," I insisted, "that Lady John is the influence?"

"I don't mean to say, of course," she replied, "that he looks fluttered if you mention her, that he doesn't in fact look as blank as a pickpocket. But that proves nothing—or rather, as they're known to be always together, and she from morning till night as pointed as a hat-pin, it proves just what one sees. One simply takes it in."

I turned the picture round. "They're scarcely together when she's together with Brissenden."

"Ah, that's only once in a way. It's a thing that from time to time such people—don't you know?—make a particular point of: they cultivate, to cover their game, the appearance of other little friendships. It puts outsiders off the scent, and the real thing meanwhile goes on. Besides, you yourself acknowledge the effect. If she hasn't made him clever, what has she made him? She has given him, steadily, more and more intellect."

"Well, you may be right," I laughed, "though you speak as if it were cod-liver oil. Does she administer it, as a daily dose, by the spoonful? or only as a drop at a time? Does he take it in his food? Is he supposed to know? The difficulty for me is simply that if I've seen the handsome grow ugly and the ugly handsome, the fat grow thin and the thin fat, the short grow long and the long short; if I've even, likewise, seen the clever, as I've too fondly, at least, supposed them, grow stupid: so have I *not* seen—no, not once in all my days—the stupid grow clever."

It was a question, none the less, on which she could perfectly stand up. "All I can say is then that you'll have, the next day or two, an interesting new experience."

"It *will* be interesting," I declared while I thought—"and all the more if I make out for myself that Lady John *is* the agent."

"You'll make it out if you talk to her—that is, I mean, if you make *her* talk. You'll see how she *can*."

"She keeps her wit then," I asked, "in spite of all she pumps into others?"

"Oh, she has enough for two!"

"I'm immensely struck with yours," I replied, "as well as with your generosity. I've seldom seen a woman take so handsome a view of another."

"It's because I like to be kind!" she said with the best faith in the world; to which I could only return, as we entered the train, that it was a kindness Lady John would doubtless appreciate. Long rejoined us, and we ran, as I have said, our course; which, as I have also noted, seemed short to me in the light of such a blaze of suggestion. To each of my companions—and the fact stuck out of them—something unprecedented had happened.

II

THE day was as fine and the scene as fair at Newmarch as the party was numerous and various; and my memory associates with the rest of the long afternoon many renewals of acquaintance and much sitting and strolling, for snatches of talk, in the long shade of great trees and through the straight walks of old gardens. A couple of hours thus passed, and fresh accessions enriched the picture. There were persons I was curious of—of Lady John, for instance, of whom I promised myself an early view; but we were apt to be carried away in currents that reflected new images and sufficiently beguiled impatience. I recover, all the same, a full sequence of impressions, each of which, I afterwards saw, had been appointed to help all the others. If my anecdote, as I have mentioned, had begun, at Paddington, at a particular moment, it gathered substance step by step and without missing a link. The links, in fact, should I count them all, would make too long a chain. They formed, nevertheless, the happiest little chapter of accidents, though a series of which I can scarce give more than the general effect.

One of the first accidents was that, before dinner, I met Ford Obert wandering a little apart with Mrs. Server, and that, as they were known to me as agreeable acquaintances, I should have faced them with confidence had I not immediately drawn from their sequestered air the fear of interrupting them. Mrs. Server was always lovely and Obert always expert; the latter straightway pulled up, however, making me as welcome as if their converse had dropped. She was extraordinarily pretty, markedly responsive, conspicuously charming, but he gave me a look that really seemed to say: "Don't—there's a good fellow—leave me any longer alone with her!" I had met her at Newmarch before—it was indeed only so that I had met her—and I knew how she was valued there. I also knew that an aversion to pretty women—numbers of whom he had preserved for a grateful posterity—was his sign neither as man nor as artist; the effect of all of which was to make me ask myself what she could have been doing to him. Making love, possibly—yet from that he would scarce have appealed. She wouldn't, on the other hand, have given him her company only to be inhuman. I joined them, at all events, learning from Mrs. Server that she had come by a train previous to my own; and we made a slow trio till, at a turn of the prospect, we came upon another group. It consisted of Mrs. Froome and Lord Lutley and of Gilbert Long and Lady John—mingled and confounded, as might be said, not assorted according to tradition. Long and Mrs. Froome came first, I recollect, together, and his lordship turned away from Lady John on seeing me rather directly approach her. She had become for me, on the spot, as interesting as, while we travelled, I had found my two friends in the train. As the source of the flow of "intellect" that had transmuted our young man, she had every claim to an earnest attention; and I should soon have been ready to pronounce that she rewarded it as richly as usual. She was indeed, as Mrs. Briss had said, as pointed as a hat-pin, and I bore in mind that lady's injunction to look in her for the answer to our riddle.

The riddle, I may mention, sounded afresh to my ear in Gilbert Long's gay voice; it hovered there—before me, beside, behind me, as we all paused—in his light, restless step, a nervous animation that seemed to multiply his presence. He became really, for the moment, under this impression, the thing I was most conscious of; I heard him, I felt him even while I exchanged greetings with the sorceress by whose wand he had been touched. To be touched myself was doubtless not quite what I wanted; yet I wanted, distinctly, a glimpse; so that, with the smart welcome Lady John gave me, I might certainly have felt that I was on the way to get it. The note of Long's predominance deepened during these minutes in a manner I can't describe, and I continued to feel that though we pretended to talk it was to him only we listened. He had us all in hand; he controlled for the moment all our attention and our relations. He was in short, as a consequence of our attitude, in possession of the scene to a tune he couldn't have dreamed of a year or two before—inasmuch as at that period he could have figured at no such eminence without making a fool of himself. And the great thing was that if his eminence was now so perfectly graced he yet knew less than any of us what was the matter with him. He was unconscious of how he had "come out"—which was exactly what sharpened my wonder. Lady John, on her side, was thoroughly conscious, and I had a fancy that she looked at me to measure how far *I* was. I cared, naturally, not in the least what she guessed; her interest for me was all in the operation of her influence. I am afraid I watched to catch it in the act—watched her with a curiosity of which she might well have become aware.

What an intimacy, what an intensity of relation, I said to myself, so successful a process implied! It was of course familiar enough that when people were so deeply in love they rubbed off on each other—that a great pressure of soul to soul usually left on either side a sufficient show of tell-tale traces. But for Long to have been so stamped as I found him, how the pliant wax must have been prepared and the seal of passion applied! What an affection the woman working such a change in him must have managed to create as a preface to her influence! With what a sense of her charm she must have paved the way for it! Strangely enough, however—it was even rather irritating—there was nothing more than usual in Lady John to assist my view of the height at which the pair so evoked must move. These things—the way other people could feel about each other, the power not one's self, in the given instance, that made for passion—were of course at best the mystery of mysteries; still, there were cases in which fancy, sounding the depths or the shallows, could at least drop the lead. Lady John, perceptibly, was no such case; imagination, in her presence, was but the weak wing of the insect that bumps against the glass. She was pretty, prompt, hard, and, in a way that was special to her, a mistress at once of "culture" and of slang. She was like a hat—with one of Mrs. Briss's hat-pins—askew on the bust of Virgil. Her ornamental information—as strong as a coat of furniture-polish—almost knocked you down. What I felt in her now more than ever was that, having a reputation for "point" to keep up, she was always under arms, with absences and anxieties like those of a celebrity at a public dinner. She thought too much of her "speech"—of how soon it would have to come. It was none the less wonderful, however, that, as Grace Brissenden had said, she should still find herself with intellect to spare—have lavished herself by precept and example on Long and yet have remained for each other interlocutor as fresh as the clown bounding into the ring. She cracked, for my benefit, as many jokes and turned as many somersaults as might have been expected; after which I thought it fair to let her off. We all faced again to the house, for dressing and dinner were in sight.

I found myself once more, as we moved, with Mrs. Server, and I remember rejoicing that, sympathetic as she showed herself, she didn't think it necessary to be, like Lady John, always "ready." She was delightfully handsome—handsomer than ever; slim, fair, fine, with charming pale eyes and splendid auburn hair. I said to myself that I hadn't done her justice; she hadn't organised her forces, was a little helpless and vague, but there was ease for the weary in her happy nature and her peculiar grace. These last were articles on which, five minutes later, before the house, where we still had a margin, I was moved to challenge Ford Obert.

"What was the matter just now—when, though you were so fortunately occupied, you yet seemed to call me to the rescue?"

"Oh," he laughed, "I was only occupied in being frightened!"

"But at what?"

"Well, at a sort of sense that she wanted to make love to me."

I reflected. "Mrs. Server? Does Mrs. Server make love?"

"It seemed to me," my friend replied, "that she began on it to *you* as soon as she got hold of you. Weren't you aware?"

I debated afresh; I didn't know that I had been. "Not to the point of terror. She's so gentle and so appealing. Even if she took one in hand with violence, moreover," I added, "I don't see why terror—given so charming a person—should be the result. It's flattering."

"Ah, you're brave," said Obert.

"I didn't know you were ever timid. How can you be, in your profession? Doesn't it come back to me, for that matter, that—only the other year—you painted her?"

"Yes, I faced her to that extent. But she's different now."

I scarcely made it out. "In what way different? She's as charming as ever."

209

As if even for his own satisfaction my friend seemed to think a little. "Well, her affections were not then, I imagine, at her disposal. I judge that that's what it must have been. They were fixed—with intensity; and it made the difference with *me*. Her imagination had, for the time, rested its wing. At present it's ready for flight—it seeks a fresh perch. It's trying. Take care."

"Oh, I don't flatter myself," I laughed, "that I've only to hold out my hand! At any rate," I went on, "*I* sha'n't call for help."

He seemed to think again. "I don't know. You'll see."

"If I do I shall see a great deal more than I now suspect." He wanted to get off to dress, but I still held him. "Isn't she wonderfully lovely?"

"Oh!" he simply exclaimed.

"Isn't she as lovely as she seems?"

But he had already broken away. "What has that to do with it?"

"What has anything, then?"

"She's too beastly unhappy."

"But isn't that just one's advantage?"

"No. It's uncanny." And he escaped.

The question had at all events brought us indoors and so far up our staircase as to where it branched towards Obert's room. I followed it to my corridor, with which other occasions had made me acquainted, and I reached the door on which I expected to find my card of designation. This door, however, was open, so as to show me, in momentary possession of the room, a gentleman, unknown to me, who, in unguided quest of his quarters, appeared to have arrived from the other end of the passage. He had just seen, as the property of another, my unpacked things, with which he immediately connected me. He moreover, to my surprise, on my entering, sounded my name, in response to which I could only at first remain blank. It was in fact not till I had begun to help him place himself that, correcting my blankness, I knew him for Guy Brissenden. He had been put by himself, for some reason, in the bachelor wing and, exploring at hazard, had mistaken the signs. By the time we found his servant and his lodging I had reflected on the oddity of my having been as stupid about the husband as I had been about the wife. He had escaped my notice since our arrival, but I had, as a much older man, met him—the hero of his odd union—at some earlier time. Like his wife, none the less, he had now struck me as a stranger, and it was not till, in his room, I stood a little face to face with him that I made out the wonderful reason.

The wonderful reason was that I was *not* a much older man; Guy Brissenden, at any rate, was not a much younger. It was he who was old—it was he who was older—it was he who was oldest. That was so disconcertingly what he had become. It was in short what he would have been had he been as old as he looked. He looked almost anything—he looked quite sixty. I made it out again at dinner, where, from a distance, but opposite, I had him in sight. Nothing could have been stranger than the way that, fatigued, fixed, settled, he seemed to have piled up the years. They were there without having had time to arrive. It was as if he had discovered some miraculous short cut to the common doom. He had grown old, in fine, as people you see after an interval sometimes strike you as having grown rich—too quickly for the honest, or at least for the straight, way. He had cheated or inherited or speculated. It took me but a minute then to add him to my little gallery—the small collection, I mean, represented by his wife and by Gilbert Long, as well as in some degree doubtless also by Lady John: the museum of those who put to me with such intensity the question of what had happened to them. His wife, on the same side, was not out of my range, and now, largely exposed, lighted, jewelled, and enjoying moreover visibly the sense of these things—his wife, upon my honour, as I soon remarked to the lady next me, his wife (it was too prodigious!) looked about twenty.

"Yes—isn't it funny?" said the lady next me.

It was so funny that it set me thinking afresh and that, with the interest of it, which became a positive excitement, I had to keep myself in hand in order not too publicly to explain, not to break out right and left with my reflections. I don't know why—it was a sense instinctive and unreasoned, but I felt from the first that if I was on the scent of something ultimate I had

211

better waste neither my wonder nor my wisdom. I *was* on the scent—that I was sure of; and yet even after I was sure I should still have been at a loss to put my enigma itself into words. I was just conscious, vaguely, of being on the track of a law, a law that would fit, that would strike me as governing the delicate phenomena—delicate though so marked—that my imagination found itself playing with. A part of the amusement they yielded came, I daresay, from my exaggerating them—grouping them into a larger mystery (and thereby a larger "law") than the facts, as observed, yet warranted; but that is the common fault of minds for which the vision of life is an obsession. The obsession pays, if one will; but to pay it has to borrow. After dinner, but while the men were still in the room, I had some talk again with Long, of whom I inquired if he had been so placed as to see "poor Briss."

He appeared to wonder, and poor Briss, with our shifting of seats, was now at a distance. "I think so—but I didn't particularly notice. What's the matter with poor Briss?"

"That's exactly what I thought you might be able to tell me. But if nothing, in him, strikes you——!"

He met my eyes a moment—then glanced about. "Where is he?"

"Behind you; only don't turn round to look, for he knows——" But I dropped, having caught something directed toward me in Brissenden's face. My interlocutor remained blank, simply asking me, after an instant, what it was he knew. On this I said what I meant. "He knows we've noticed."

Long wondered again. "Ah, but I *haven't*!" He spoke with some sharpness.

"He knows," I continued, noting the sharpness too, "what's the matter with him."

"Then what the devil is it?"

I waited a little, having for the moment an idea on my hands. "Do you see him often?"

Long disengaged the ash from his cigarette. "No. Why should I?"

Distinctly, he was uneasy—though as yet perhaps but vaguely—at what I might be coming to. That was precisely my idea, and if I pitied him a little for my pressure my idea was yet what most possessed me. "Do you mean there's nothing in him that strikes you?"

On this, unmistakably, he looked at me hard. "'Strikes' me—in that boy? Nothing in him, that I know of, ever struck me in my life. He's not an object of the smallest interest to me!"

I felt that if I insisted I should really stir up the old Long, the stolid coxcomb, capable of rudeness, with whose redemption, reabsorption, supersession—one scarcely knew what to call it—I had been so happily impressed. "Oh, of course, if you haven't noticed, you haven't, and the matter I was going to speak of will have no point. You won't know what I mean." With which I paused long enough to let his curiosity operate if his denial had been sincere. But it hadn't. His curiosity never operated. He only exclaimed, more indulgently, that he didn't know what I was talking about; and I recognised after a little that if I had made him, without intention, uncomfortable, this was exactly a proof of his being what Mrs. Briss, at the station, had called cleverer, and what I had so much remarked while, in the garden before dinner, he held our small company. Nobody, nothing could, in the time of his inanity, have made him turn a hair. It was the mark of his aggrandisement. But I spared him—so far as was consistent with my wish for absolute certainty; changed the subject, spoke of other things, took pains to sound disconnectedly, and only after reference to several of the other ladies, the name over which we had just felt friction. "Mrs. Brissenden's quite fabulous."

He appeared to have strayed, in our interval, far. "'Fabulous'?"

"Why, for the figure that, by candle-light and in cloth-of-silver and diamonds, she is still able to make."

"Oh dear, yes!" He showed as relieved to be able to see what I meant. "She has grown so very much less plain."

But that wasn't at all what I meant. "Ah," I said, "you put it the other way at Paddington—which was much more the right one."

He had quite forgotten. "How then did I put it?"

As he had done before, I got rid of my ash. "She hasn't grown very much less plain. She has only grown very much less old."

"Ah, well," he laughed, but as if his interest had quickly dropped, "youth is—comparatively speaking—beauty."

"Oh, not always. Look at poor Briss himself."

"Well, if you like better, beauty is youth."

"Not always, either," I returned. "Certainly only when it *is* beauty. To see how little it may be either, look," I repeated, "at poor Briss."

"I thought you told me just now not to!" He rose at last in his impatience.

"Well, at present you can."

I also got up, the other men at the same moment moved, and the subject of our reference stood in view. This indeed was but briefly, for, as if to examine a picture behind him, the personage in question suddenly turned his back. Long, however, had had time to take him in and then to decide. "I've looked. What then?"

"You don't see anything?"

"Nothing."

"Not what everyone else must?"

"No, confound you!"

I already felt that, to be so tortuous, he must have had a reason, and the search for his reason was what, from this moment, drew me on. I had in fact half guessed it as we stood there. But this only made me the more explanatory. "It isn't really, however, that Brissenden has grown less lovely—it's only that he has grown less young."

To which my friend, as we quitted the room, replied simply: "Oh!"

The effect I have mentioned was, none the less, too absurd. The poor youth's back, before us, still as if consciously presented, confessed to the burden of time. "How old," I continued, "did we make out this afternoon that he would be?"

"That who would?"

"Why, poor Briss."

He fairly pulled up in our march. "Have you got him on the brain?"

"Don't I seem to remember, my dear man, that it was you yourself who knew? He's thirty at the most. He can't possibly be more. And there he is: as fine, as swaddled, as royal a mummy, to the eye, as one would wish to see. Don't pretend! But it's all right." I laughed as I took myself up. "I must talk to Lady John."

I did talk to her, but I must come to it. What is most to the point just here is an observation or two that, in the smoking-room, before going to bed, I exchanged with Ford Obert. I forbore, as I have hinted, to show all I saw, but it was lawfully open to me to judge of what other people did; and I had had before dinner my little proof that, on occasion, Obert could see as much as most. Yet I said nothing more to him for the present about Mrs. Server. The Brissendens were new to him, and his experience of every sort of facial accident, of human sign, made him just the touchstone I wanted. Nothing, naturally, was easier than to turn him on the question of the fair and the foul, type and character, weal and woe, among our fellow-visitors; so that my mention of the air of disparity in the couple I have just named came in its order and produced its effect. This effect was that of my seeing—which was all I required—that if the disparity was marked for him this expert observer could yet read it quite the wrong way. Why had so fine a young creature married a man three times her age? He was of course astounded when I told him the young creature was much nearer three times Brissenden's, and this led to some interesting talk between us as to the consequences, in general, of such association on such terms. The particular case before us, I easily granted, sinned by over-emphasis, but it was a fair, though a gross, illustration of what almost always occurred when twenty and forty, when thirty and sixty, mated or mingled, lived together in intimacy. Intimacy of course had to be postulated. Then either the high number or the low always got the upper hand, and it was usually the high that succeeded. It seemed, in other words, more possible to go back than to keep still, to grow young than to remain so. If Brissenden had been of his wife's age and his wife of Brissenden's, it would thus be he who must have redescended the hill, it would be she who would have been pushed over the brow. There was really a touching truth in it, the stuff of—what did people call such things?—an apologue or a parable. "One of the pair," I said, "has to pay for the other. What ensues is a miracle, and miracles are expensive. What's a greater one than to have your youth twice over? It's a second wind, another 'go'—which isn't the sort of thing life mostly treats us to. Mrs. Briss had to get her new blood, her extra allowance of time and bloom, somewhere; and from whom could she so conveniently extract them as from Guy himself? She *has*, by an extraordinary feat of legerdemain, extracted them; and he, on his side, to supply her, has had to tap the sacred fount. But the sacred fount is like the greedy man's description of the turkey as an 'awkward' dinner dish. It may be sometimes too much for a single share, but it's not enough to go round."

Obert was at all events sufficiently struck with my view to throw out a question on it. "So that, paying to his last drop, Mr. Briss, as you call him, can only die of the business?"

"Oh, not yet, I hope. But before *her*—yes: long."

He was much amused. "How you polish them off!"

"I only talk," I returned, "as you paint; not a bit worse! But one must indeed wonder," I conceded, "how the poor wretches feel."

"You mean whether Brissenden likes it?"

I made up my mind on the spot. "If he loves her he must. That is if he loves her passionately, sublimely." I saw it all. "It's in fact just because he does so love her that the miracle, for her, is wrought."

"Well," my friend reflected, "for taking a miracle coolly——!"

"She hasn't her equal? Yes, she does take it. She just quietly, but just selfishly, profits by it."

"And doesn't see then how her victim loses?"

"No. She can't. The perception, if she had it, would be painful and terrible—might even be fatal to the process. So she hasn't it. She passes round it. It takes all her flood of life to meet her own chance. She has only a wonderful sense of success and well-being. The *other* consciousness——"

"Is all for the other party?"

"The author of the sacrifice."

"Then how beautifully 'poor Briss,'" my companion said, "must have it!"

I had already assured myself. He had gone to bed, and my fancy followed him. "Oh, he has it so that, though he goes, in his passion, about with her, he dares scarcely show his face." And I made a final induction. "The agents of the sacrifice are uncomfortable, I gather, when they suspect or fear that you see."

My friend was charmed with my ingenuity. "How you've worked it out!"

"Well, I feel as if I were on the way to something."

He looked surprised. "Something still more?"

"Something still more." I had an impulse to tell him I scarce knew what. But I kept it under. "I seem to snuff up——"

"*Quoi donc?*"

"The sense of a discovery to be made."

"And of what?"

"I'll tell you to-morrow. Good-night."

III

I did on the morrow several things, but the first was not to redeem that vow. It was to address myself straight to Grace Brissenden. "I must let you know that, in spite of your guarantee, it doesn't go at all—oh, but not at all! I've tried Lady John, as you enjoined, and I can't but feel that she leaves us very much where we were." Then, as my listener seemed not quite to remember where we had been, I came to her help. "You said yesterday at Paddington, to explain the change in Gilbert Long—don't you recall?—that that woman, plying him with her genius and giving him of her best, is clever enough for two. She's not clever enough then, it strikes me, for three—or at any rate for four. I confess I don't see it. Does she really dazzle *you*?"

My friend had caught up. "Oh, you've a standard of wit!"

"No, I've only a sense of reality—a sense not at all satisfied by the theory of such an influence as Lady John's."

She wondered. "Such a one as whose else then?"

"Ah, that's for us still to find out! Of course this can't be easy; for as the appearance is inevitably a kind of betrayal, it's in somebody's interest to conceal it."

This Mrs. Brissenden grasped. "Oh, you mean in the lady's?"

"In the lady's most. But also in Long's own, if he's really tender of the lady—which is precisely what our theory posits."

My companion, once roused, was all there. "I see. You call the appearance a kind of betrayal because it points to the relation behind it."

"Precisely."

"And the relation—to do that sort of thing—must be necessarily so awfully intimate."

"*Intimissima*."

"And kept therefore in the background exactly in that proportion."

"Exactly in that proportion."

"Very well then," said Mrs. Brissenden, "doesn't Mr. Long's tenderness of Lady John quite fall in with what I mentioned to you?"

I remembered what she had mentioned to me. "His making her come down with poor Briss?"

"Nothing less."

"And is that all you go upon?"

"That and lots more."

I thought a minute—but I had been abundantly thinking. "I know what you mean by 'lots.' Is Brissenden in it?"

"Dear no—poor Briss! He wouldn't like that. *I* saw the manœuvre, but Guy didn't. And you must have noticed how he stuck to her all last evening."

"How Gilbert Long stuck to Lady John? Oh yes, I noticed. They were like Lord Lutley and Mrs. Froome. But is that what one can call being tender of her?"

My companion weighed it. "He must speak to her *sometimes*. I'm glad you admit, at any rate," she continued, "that it does take what you so prettily call some woman's secretly giving him of her best to account for him."

"Oh, that I admit with all my heart—or at least with all my head. Only, Lady John has none of the signs——"

"Of being the beneficent woman? What then *are* they—the signs—to be so plain?" I was not yet quite ready to say, however; on which she added: "It proves nothing, you know, that *you* don't like her."

"No. It would prove more if she didn't like *me*, which—fatuous fool as you may find me—I verily believe she does. If she hated me it would be, you see, for my ruthless analysis of her secret. She *has* no secret. She would like awfully to have—and she would like almost as much to be believed to have. Last evening, after dinner, she could feel perhaps for a while that she *was* believed. But it won't do. There's nothing in it. You asked me just now," I pursued, "what the signs of such a secret would naturally be. Well, bethink yourself a moment of what the secret itself must naturally be."

Oh, she looked as if she knew all about *that*! "Awfully charming— mustn't it?—to act upon a person, through an affection, so deeply."

"Yes—it can certainly be no vulgar flirtation." I felt a little like a teacher encouraging an apt pupil; but I could only go on with the lesson. "Whoever she is, she gives all she has. She keeps nothing back—nothing for herself."

"I see—because *he* takes everything. He just cleans her out." She looked at me—pleased at last really to understand—with the best conscience in the world. "Who *is* the lady then?"

But I could answer as yet only by a question. "How can she possibly be a woman who gives absolutely nothing whatever; who scrapes and saves and hoards; who keeps every crumb for herself? The whole show's there—to minister to Lady John's vanity and advertise the business—behind her smart shop-window. You can see it, as much as you like, and even amuse yourself with pricing it. But she never parts with an article. If poor Long depended on *her*——"

"Well, what?" She was really interested.

"Why, he'd be the same poor Long as ever. He would go as he used to go—naked and unashamed. No," I wound up, "he deals—turned out as we now see him—at another establishment."

"I'll grant it," said Mrs. Brissenden, "if you'll only name me the place."

Ah, I could still but laugh and resume! "He doesn't screen Lady John— she doesn't screen herself—with your husband or with anybody. It's she who's herself the screen! And pleased as she is at being so clever, and at being thought so, she doesn't even know it. She doesn't so much as suspect it. She's an unmitigated fool about it. 'Of course Mr. Long's clever, because he's in love with me and sits at my feet, and don't you see how clever *I* am? Don't you hear what good things I say—wait a little, I'm going to say another in about three minutes; and how, if you'll only give him time too, he comes out with them after me? They don't perhaps sound so good, but you see where he has got them. I'm so brilliant, in fine, that the men who admire me have only to imitate me, which, you observe, they strikingly do.' Something like that is all her philosophy."

My friend turned it over. "You do sound like her, you know. Yet how, if a woman's stupid——"

"Can she have made a man clever? She can't. She can't at least have begun it. What we shall know the real person by, in the case that you and I are studying, is that the man himself will have made her what she has become. She will have done just what Lady John has not done—she will have put up the shutters and closed the shop. She will have parted, for her friend, with her wit."

"So that she may be regarded as reduced to idiocy?"

"Well—so I can only see it."

"And that if we look, therefore, for the right idiot——"

"We shall find the right woman—our friend's mystic Egeria? Yes, we shall be at least approaching the truth. We shall 'burn,' as they say in hide-and-seek." I of course kept to the point that the idiot would have to *be* the right one. *Any* idiot wouldn't be to the purpose. If it was enough that a woman was a fool the search might become hopeless even in a house that would have passed but ill for a fool's paradise. We were on one of the shaded terraces, to which, here and there, a tall window stood open. The picture without was all morning and August, and within all clear dimness and rich gleams. We stopped once or twice, raking the gloom for lights, and it was at some such moment that Mrs. Brissenden asked me if I then regarded Gilbert Long as now exalted to the position of the most brilliant of our companions. "The cleverest man of the party?"—it pulled me up a little. "Hardly that, perhaps—for don't you see the proofs I'm myself giving you? But say he *is*"—I considered—"the cleverest but one." The next moment I had seen what she meant. "In that case the thing we're looking for ought logically to be the person, of the opposite sex, giving us the maximum sense of depletion for his benefit? The biggest fool, you suggest, *must*, consistently, be the right one? Yes again; it would so seem. But that's not really, you see, the short cut it sounds. The biggest fool is what we want, but the question is to discover who *is* the biggest."

"I'm glad then *I* feel so safe!" Mrs. Brissenden laughed.

"Oh, you're not the biggest!" I handsomely conceded. "Besides, as I say, there must be the other evidence—the evidence of relations."

We had gone on, with this, a few steps, but my companion again checked me, while her nod toward a window gave my attention a lead. "Won't *that*, as it happens, then do?" We could just see, from where we stood, a corner of one of the rooms. It was occupied by a seated couple, a lady whose face was in sight and a gentleman whose identity was attested by his back, a back somehow replete for us, at the moment, with a guilty significance. There *was* the evidence of relations. That we had suddenly caught Long in the act of presenting his receptacle at the sacred fount seemed announced by the tone in which Mrs. Brissenden named the other party—"Mme. de Dreuil!" We looked at each other, I was aware, with some elation; but our triumph was brief. The Comtesse de Dreuil, we quickly felt—an American married to a Frenchman—wasn't at all the thing. She was almost as much "all there" as Lady John. She was only another screen, and we perceived, for that matter, the next minute, that Lady John was also present. Another step had placed us within range of her; the picture revealed in the rich dusk of the room was a group of three. From that moment, unanimously, we gave up Lady John, and as we continued our stroll my friend brought out her despair. "Then he has nothing *but* screens? The need for so many does suggest a fire!" And in spite of discouragement she sounded, interrogatively, one after the other, the names of those ladies the perfection of whose presence of mind might, when considered, pass as questionable. We soon, however, felt our process to be, practically, a trifle invidious. Not one of the persons named could, at any rate—to do them all justice—affect us as an intellectual ruin. It was natural therefore for Mrs. Brissenden to conclude with scepticism. "She may exist— and exist as you require her; but what, after all, proves that she's here? She mayn't have come down with him. Does it necessarily follow that they always go about together?"

I was ready to declare that it necessarily followed. I had my idea, and I didn't see why I shouldn't bring it out. "It's my belief that he no more goes away without her than you go away without poor Briss."

She surveyed me in splendid serenity. "But what have we in common?"

"With the parties to an abandoned flirtation? Well, you've in common your mutual attachment and the fact that you're thoroughly happy together."

"Ah," she good-humouredly answered, "we don't flirt!"

"Well, at all events, you don't separate. He doesn't really suffer you out of his sight, and, to circulate in the society you adorn, you don't leave him at home."

"Why shouldn't I?" she asked, looking at me, I thought, just a trifle harder.

"It isn't a question of why you shouldn't—it's a question of whether you do. You don't—do you? That's all."

She thought it over as if for the first time. "It seems to me I often leave him when I don't want him."

"Oh, when you don't want him—yes. But when don't you want him? You want him when you want to be right, and you want to be right when you mix in a scene like this. I mean," I continued for my private amusement, "when you want to be happy. Happiness, you know, is, to a lady in the full tide of social success, even more becoming than a new French frock. You have the advantage, for your beauty, of being admirably married. You bloom in your husband's presence. I don't say he need always be at your elbow; I simply say that you're most completely yourself when he's not far off. If there were nothing else there would be the help given you by your quiet confidence in his lawful passion."

"I'm bound to say," Mrs. Brissenden replied, "that such help is consistent with his not having spoken to me since we parted, yesterday, to come down here by different trains. We haven't so much as met since our arrival. My finding him so indispensable is consistent with my not having so much as looked at him. Indispensable, please, for what?"

"For your not being without him."

"What then do I do *with* him?"

I hesitated—there were so many ways of putting it; but I gave them all up. "Ah, I think it will be only *he* who can tell you! My point is that you've the instinct—playing in you, on either side, with all the ease of experience—of what you are to each other. All I mean is that it's the instinct that Long and *his* good friend must have. They too perhaps haven't spoken to each other. But where he comes she does, and where she comes he does. That's why I know she's among us."

"It's wonderful what you know!" Mrs. Brissenden again laughed. "How can you think of them as enjoying the facilities of people in *our* situation?"

"Of people married and therefore logically in presence? I don't," I was able to reply, "speak of their facilities as the same, and I recognise every limit to their freedom. But I maintain, none the less, that so far as they *can* go, they do go. It's a relation, and they work the relation: the relation, exquisite surely, of knowing they help each other to shine. Why are they not, therefore, like you and Brissenden? What I make out is that when they do shine one will find—though only after a hunt, I admit, as you see—they must both have been involved. Feeling their need, and consummately expert, they will have managed, have arranged."

She took it in with her present odd mixture of the receptive and the derisive. "Arranged what?"

"Oh, ask *her*!"

"I would if I could find her!" After which, for a moment, my interlocutress again considered. "But I thought it was just your contention that *she* doesn't shine. If it's Lady John's perfect repair that puts that sort of thing out of the question, your image, it seems to me, breaks down."

It did a little, I saw, but I gave it a tilt up. "Not at all. It's a case of shining as Brissenden shines." I wondered if I might go further—then risked it. "By sacrifice."

I perceived at once that I needn't fear: her conscience was too good—she was only amused. "Sacrifice, for mercy's sake, of what?"

"Well—for mercy's sake—of his time."

"His time?" She stared. "Hasn't he all the time he wants?"

"My dear lady," I smiled, "he hasn't all the time *you* want!"

But she evidently had not a glimmering of what I meant. "Don't I make things of an ease, don't I make life of a charm, for him?"

I'm afraid I laughed out. "That's perhaps exactly it! It's what Gilbert Long does for *his* victim—makes things, makes life, of an ease and a charm."

She stopped yet again, really wondering at me now. "Then it's the woman, simply, who's happiest?"

"Because Brissenden's the man who is? Precisely!"

On which for a minute, without her going on, we looked at each other. "Do you really mean that if you only knew *me* as I am, it would come to you in the same way to hunt for my confederate? I mean if he weren't made obvious, you know, by his being my husband."

I turned this over. "If you were only in flirtation—as you reminded me just now that you're not? Surely!" I declared. "I should arrive at him, perfectly, after all eliminations, on the principle of looking for the greatest happiness——"

"Of the smallest number? Well, he may be a small number," she indulgently sighed, "but he's wholly content! Look at him now there," she added the next moment, "and judge." We had resumed our walk and turned

225

the corner of the house, a movement that brought us into view of a couple just round the angle of the terrace, a couple who, like ourselves, must have paused in a sociable stroll. The lady, with her back to us, leaned a little on the balustrade and looked at the gardens; the gentleman close to her, with the same support, offered us the face of Guy Brissenden, as recognisable at a distance as the numbered card of a "turn"—the black figure upon white—at a music-hall. On seeing us he said a word to his companion, who quickly jerked round. Then his wife exclaimed to me—only with more sharpness—as she had exclaimed at Mme. de Dreuil: "By all that's lovely—May Server!" I took it, on the spot, for a kind of "Eureka!" but without catching my friend's idea. I was only aware at first that this idea left me as unconvinced as when the other possibilities had passed before us. Wasn't it simply the result of this lady's being the only one we had happened not to eliminate? She had not even occurred to us. She was pretty enough perhaps for any magic, but she hadn't the other signs. I didn't believe, somehow—certainly not on such short notice—either in her happiness or in her flatness. There was a vague suggestion, of a sort, in our having found her there with Brissenden: there would have been a pertinence, to our curiosity, or at least to mine, in this juxtaposition of the two persons who paid, as I had amused myself with calling it, so heroically; yet I had only to have it marked for me (to see them, that is, side by side,) in order to feel how little—at any rate superficially—the graceful, natural, charming woman ranged herself with the superannuated youth.

She had said a word to him at sight of us, in answer to his own, and in a minute or two they had met us. This had given me time for more than one reflection. It had also given Mrs. Brissenden time to insist to me on her identification, which I could see she would be much less quick to drop than in the former cases. "We have her," she murmured; "we have her; it's *she!*" It was by her insistence in fact that my thought was quickened. It even felt a kind of chill—an odd revulsion—at the touch of her eagerness. Singular perhaps that only then—yet quite certainly then—the curiosity to which I had so freely surrendered myself began to strike me as wanting in taste. It was reflected in Mrs. Brissenden quite by my fault, and I can't say just what cause for shame, after so much talk of our search and our scent, I found in our awakened and confirmed keenness. Why in the world hadn't I found it before? My scruple, in short, was a thing of the instant; it was in a positive flash that the amusing question was stamped for me as none of my business. One of the reflections I have just mentioned was that I had not had a happy hand in making it so completely Mrs. Brissenden's. Another was, however, that nothing, fortunately, that had happened between us really signified. For what had so suddenly overtaken me was the consciousness of this anomaly: that I was at the same time as disgusted as if I had exposed Mrs. Server and absolutely convinced that I had yet *not* exposed her.

While, after the others had greeted us and we stood in vague talk, I caught afresh the effect of their juxtaposition, I grasped, with a private joy that was quite extravagant—as so beyond the needed mark—at the reassurance it offered. This reassurance sprang straight from a special source. Brissenden's secret was so aware of itself as to be always on the defensive. Shy and suspicious, it was as much on the defensive at present as I had felt it to be—so far as I was concerned—the night before. What was there accordingly in Mrs. Server—frank and fragrant in the morning air—to correspond to any such consciousness? Nothing whatever—not a symptom. Whatever secrets she might have had, she had not *that* one; she was not in the same box; the sacred fount, in her, was not threatened with exhaustion. We all soon re-entered the house together, but Mrs. Brissenden, during the few minutes that followed, managed to possess herself of the subject of her denunciation. She put me off with Guy, and I couldn't help feeling it as a sign of her concentration. She warmed to the question just as I had thrown it over; and I asked myself rather ruefully what on earth I had been thinking of. I hadn't in the least had it in mind to "compromise" an individual; but an individual would be compromised if I didn't now take care.

IV

I have said that I did many things on this wonderful day, but perhaps the simplest way to describe the rest of them is as a sustained attempt to avert that disaster. I succeeded, by vigilance, in preventing my late companion from carrying Mrs. Server off: I had no wish to see her studied—by anyone but myself at least—in the light of my theory. I felt by this time that I understood my theory, but I was not obliged to believe that Mrs. Brissenden did. I am afraid I must frankly confess that I called deception to my aid; to separate the two ladies I gave the more initiated a look in which I invited her to read volumes. This look, or rather the look she returned, comes back to me as the first note of a tolerably tight, tense little drama, a little drama of which our remaining hours at Newmarch were the all too ample stage. She understood me, as I meant, that she had better leave me to get at the truth—owing me some obligation, as she did, for so much of it as I had already communicated. This step was of course a tacit pledge that she should have the rest from me later on. I knew of some pictures in one of the rooms that had not been lighted the previous evening, and I made these my pretext for the effect I desired. I asked Mrs. Server if she wouldn't come and see them with me, admitting at the same time that I could scarce expect her to forgive me for my share in the invasion of the quiet corner in which poor Briss had evidently managed so to interest her.

"Oh, yes," she replied as we went our way, "he *had* managed to interest me. Isn't he curiously interesting? But I hadn't," she continued on my being too struck with her question for an immediate answer—"I hadn't managed to interest *him*. Of course you know why!" she laughed. "No one interests him but Lady John, and he could think of nothing, while I kept him there, but of how soon he could return to her."

These remarks—of which I give rather the sense than the form, for they were a little scattered and troubled, and I helped them out and pieced them together—these remarks had for me, I was to find, unexpected suggestions, not all of which was I prepared on the spot to take up. "And is Lady John interested in our friend?"

"Not, I suppose, given her situation, so much as he would perhaps desire. You don't know what her situation *is?*" she went on while I doubtless appeared to be sunk in innocence. "Isn't it rather marked that there's only one person she's interested in?"

"One person?" I was thoroughly at sea.

But we had reached with it the great pictured saloon with which I had proposed to assist her to renew acquaintance and in which two visitors had anticipated us. "Why, here he is!" she exclaimed as we paused, for admiration, in the doorway. The high frescoed ceiling arched over a floor so highly polished that it seemed to reflect the faded pastels set, in rococo borders, in the walls and constituting the distinction of the place. Our companions, examining together one of the portraits and turning their backs, were at the opposite end, and one of them was Gilbert Long.

I immediately named the other. "Do you mean Ford Obert?"

She gave me, with a laugh, one of her beautiful looks. "Yes!"

It was answer enough for the moment, and the manner of it showed me to what legend she was committed. I asked myself, while the two men faced about to meet us, why she was committed to it, and I further considered that if Grace Brissenden, against every appearance, was right, there would now be something for me to see. Which of the two—the agent or the object of the sacrifice—would take most precautions? I kept my companion purposely, for a little while, on our side of the room, leaving the others, interested in their observations, to take their time to join us. It gave me occasion to wonder if the question mightn't be cleared up on the spot. There *was* no question, I had compunctiously made up my mind, for Mrs. Server; but now I should see the proof of that conclusion. The proof of it would be, between her and her imputed lover, the absence of anything that was not perfectly natural. Mrs. Server, with her eyes raised to the painted dome, with response charmed almost to solemnity in her exquisite face, struck me at this moment, I had to concede, as more than ever a person to have a lover imputed. The place, save for its pictures of later date, a triumph of the florid decoration of two centuries ago, evidently met her special taste, and a kind of profane piety had dropped on her, drizzling down, in the cold light, in silver, in crystal, in faint, mixed delicacies of colour, almost as on a pilgrim at a shrine. I don't know what it was in her—save, that is, the positive pitch of delicacy in her beauty—that made her, so impressed and presented, indescribably touching. She was like an awestruck child; she might have been herself—all Greuze tints, all pale pinks and blues and pearly whites and candid eyes—an old dead pastel under glass.

She was not too reduced to this state, however, not to take, soon enough, her own precaution—if a precaution it was to be deemed. I was acutely conscious that the naturalness to which I have just alluded would be, for either party, the only precaution worth speaking of. We moved slowly round the room, pausing here and there for curiosity; during which time the two men remained where we had found them. She had begun at last to watch them and had proposed that we should see in what they were so absorbed; but I checked her in the movement, raising my hand in a friendly admonition to wait. We waited then, face to face, looking at each other as if to catch a strain of music. This was what I had intended, for it had just come to me that one of the voices was in the air and that it had imposed close attention. The distinguished painter listened while—to all appearance—Gilbert Long did, in the presence of the picture, the explaining. Ford Obert moved, after a little, but not so as to interrupt—only so as to show me his face in a recall of what had passed between us the night before in the smoking-room. I turned my eyes from Mrs. Server's; I allowed myself to commune a little, across the shining space, with those of our fellow-auditor. The occasion had thus for a minute the oddest little air of an aesthetic lecture prompted by accidental, but immense, suggestions and delivered by Gilbert Long.

I couldn't, at the distance, with my companion, quite follow it, but Obert was clearly patient enough to betray that he was struck. His impression was at any rate doubtless his share of surprise at Long's gift of talk. This was what his eyes indeed most seemed to throw over to me—"What an unexpected demon of a critic!" It was extraordinarily interesting—I don't mean the special drift of Long's eloquence, which I couldn't, as I say, catch; but the phenomenon of his, of all people, dealing in that article. It put before me the question of whether, in these strange relations that I believed I had thus got my glimpse of, the action of the person "sacrificed" mightn't be quite out of proportion to the resources of that person. It was as if these elements might really multiply in the transfer made of them; as if the borrower practically found himself—or herself—in possession of a greater sum than the known property of the creditor. The surrender, in this way, added, by pure beauty, to the thing surrendered. We all know the French adage about that *plus belle fille du monde* who can give but what she has; yet if Mrs. Server, for instance, *had* been the heroine of this particular connection, the communication of her intelligence to her friend would quite have falsified it. She would have given much more than she had.

When Long had finished his demonstration and his charged voice had dropped, we crossed to claim acquaintance with the work that had inspired him. The place had not been completely new to Mrs. Server any more than to myself, and the impression now made on her was but the intenser vibration of a chord already stirred; nevertheless I was struck with her saying, as a result of more remembrance than I had attributed to her "Oh yes,—the man with the mask in his hand!" On our joining the others I expressed regret at our having turned up too late for the ideas that, on a theme so promising, they would have been sure to produce, and Obert, quite agreeing that we had lost a treat, said frankly, in reference to Long, but addressing himself more especially to Mrs. Server: "He's perfectly amazing, you know—he's perfectly amazing!"

I observed that as a consequence of this Long looked neither at Mrs. Server nor at Obert; he looked only at me, and with quite a penetrable shade of shyness. Then again a strange thing happened, a stranger thing even than my quick sense, the previous afternoon at the station, that he was a changed man. It was as if he were still more changed—had altered as much since the evening before as during the so much longer interval of which I had originally to take account. He had altered almost like Grace Brissenden—he looked fairly distinguished. I said to myself that, without his stature and certain signs in his dress, I should probably not have placed him. Engrossed an instant with this view and with not losing touch of the uneasiness that I conceived I had fastened on him, I became aware only after she had spoken that Mrs. Server had gaily and gracefully asked of Obert why in the world so clever a man should *not* have been clever. "Obert," I accordingly took upon myself to remark, "had evidently laboured under some extraordinary delusion. He must literally have doubted if Long *was* clever."

"Fancy!" Mrs. Server explained with a charming smile at Long, who, still looking pleasantly competent and not too fatuous, amiably returned it.

"They're natural, they're natural," I privately reflected; "that is, he's natural to *her*, but he's not so to me." And as if seeing depths in this, and to try it, I appealed to him. "Do, my dear man, let us have it again. It's the picture, of all pictures, that most needs an interpreter. *Don't* we want," I asked of Mrs. Server, "to know what it means?" The figure represented is a young man in black—a quaint, tight black dress, fashioned in years long past; with a pale, lean, livid face and a stare, from eyes without eyebrows, like that of some whitened old-world clown. In his hand he holds an object that strikes the spectator at first simply as some obscure, some ambiguous work of art, but that on a second view becomes a representation of a human face, modelled and coloured, in wax, in enamelled metal, in some substance not human. The object thus appears a complete mask, such as might have been fantastically fitted and worn.

"Yes, what in the world does it mean?" Mrs. Server replied. "One could call it—though that doesn't get one much further—the Mask of Death."

"Why so?" I demanded while we all again looked at the picture. "Isn't it much rather the Mask of Life? It's the man's own face that's Death. The other one, blooming and beautiful——"

"Ah, but with an awful grimace!" Mrs. Server broke in.

"The other one, blooming and beautiful," I repeated, "is Life, and he's going to put it on; unless indeed he has just taken it off."

"He's dreadful, he's awful—that's what I mean," said Mrs. Server. "But what does Mr. Long think?"

"The artificial face, on the other hand," I went on, as Long now said nothing, "is extremely studied and, when you carefully look at it, charmingly pretty. I don't see the grimace."

"I don't see anything else!" Mrs. Server good-humouredly insisted. "And what does Mr. Obert think?"

He kept his eyes on her a moment before replying. "He thinks it looks like a lovely lady."

"That grinning mask? What lovely lady?"

"It does," I declared to him, really seeing what he meant—"it does look remarkably like Mrs. Server."

She laughed, but forgivingly. "I'm immensely obliged. You deserve," she continued to me, "that I should say the gentleman's own face is the image of a certain other gentleman's."

"It isn't the image of yours," Obert said to me, fitting the cap, "but it's a funny thing that it should really recall to one some face among us here, on this occasion—I mean some face in our party—that I can't think of." We had our eyes again on the ominous figure. "We've seen him yesterday—we've seen him already this morning." Obert, oddly enough, still couldn't catch it. "Who the deuce is it?"

"I know," I returned after a moment—our friend's reference having again, in a flash, become illuminating. "But nothing would induce me to tell."

"If *I* were the flattered individual," Long observed, speaking for the first time, "I've an idea that you'd give me the benefit of the compliment. Therefore it's probably not me."

"Oh, it's not you in the least," Mrs. Server blandly took upon herself to observe. "This face is so bad——"

"And mine is so good?" our companion laughed. "Thank you for saving me!"

I watched them look at each other, for there had been as yet between them no complete exchange. Yes, they were natural. I couldn't have made it out that they were not. But there was something, all the same, that I wanted to know, and I put it immediately to Long. "Why do you bring against me such an accusation?"

He met the question—singularly enough—as if his readiness had suddenly deserted him. "I don't know!"—and he turned off to another picture.

It left the three of us all the more confronted with the conundrum launched by Obert, and Mrs. Server's curiosity remained. "*Do* name," she said to me, "the flattered individual."

"No, it's a responsibility I leave to Obert."

But he was clearly still at fault; he was like a man desiring, but unable, to sneeze. "I see the fellow—yet I don't. Never mind." He turned away too. "He'll come to me."

"The resemblance," said Long, on this, at a distance from us and not turning, "the resemblance, which I shouldn't think would puzzle anyone, is simply to 'poor Briss'!"

"Oh, of course!"—and Obert gave a jump round.

"Ah—I do see it," Mrs. Server conceded with her head on one side, but as if speaking rather for harmony.

I didn't believe she saw it, but that only made her the more natural; which was also the air she had on going to join Long, in his new contemplation, after I had admitted that it was of Brissenden I myself had thought. Obert and I remained together in the presence of the Man with the Mask, and, the others being out of earshot, he reminded me that I had promised him the night before in the smoking-room to give him to-day the knowledge I had then withheld. If I had announced that I was on the track of a discovery, pray had I made it yet, and what was it, at any rate, that I proposed to discover? I felt now, in truth, more uncomfortable than I had expected in being kept to my obligation, and I beat about the bush a little till, instead of meeting it, I was able to put the natural question: "What wonderful things was Long just saying to you?"

"Oh, characteristic ones enough—whimsical, fanciful, funny. The things he says, you know."

It was indeed a fresh view. "They strike you as characteristic?"

"Of the man himself and his type of mind? Surely. Don't *you*? He talks to talk, but he's really amusing."

I was watching our companions. "Indeed he is—extraordinarily amusing." It was highly interesting to me to hear at last of Long's "type of mind." "See how amusing he is at the present moment to Mrs. Server."

Obert took this in; she was convulsed, in the extravagance always so pretty as to be pardonable, with laughter, and she even looked over at us as if to intimate with her shining, lingering eyes that we wouldn't be surprised at her transports if we suspected what her entertainer, whom she had never known for such a humourist, was saying. Instead of going to find out, all the same, we remained another minute together. It was for me, now, I could see, that Obert had his best attention. "What's the matter with them?"

It startled me almost as much as if he had asked me what was the matter with myself—for that something *was*, under this head, I was by this time unable to ignore. Not twenty minutes had elapsed since our meeting with Mrs. Server on the terrace had determined Grace Brissenden's elation, but it was a fact that my nervousness had taken an extraordinary stride. I had perhaps not till this instant been fully aware of it—it was really brought out by the way Obert looked at me as if he fancied he had heard me shake. Mrs. Server might be natural, and Gilbert Long might be, but I should not preserve that calm unless I pulled myself well together. I made the effort, facing my sharp interlocutor; and I think it was at this point that I fully measured my dismay. I had grown—that was what was the matter with me—precipitately, preposterously anxious. Instead of dropping, the discomfort produced in me by Mrs. Brissenden had deepened to agitation, and this in spite of the fact that in the brief interval nothing worse, nothing but what was right, had happened. Had I myself suddenly fallen so much in love with Mrs. Server that the care for her reputation had become with me an obsession? It was of no use saying I simply pitied her: what did I pity her for if she wasn't in danger? She *was* in danger: that rushed over me at present—rushed over me while I tried to look easy and delayed to answer my friend. She *was* in danger—if only because she had caught and held the search-light of Obert's attention. I took up his inquiry. "The matter with them? I don't know anything but that they're young and handsome and happy—children, as who should say, of the world; children of leisure and pleasure and privilege."

Obert's eyes went back to them. "Do you remember what I said to you about her yesterday afternoon? She darts from flower to flower, but she clings, for the time, to each. You've been feeling, I judge, the force of my remark."

"Oh, she didn't at all 'dart,'" I replied, "just now at me. I darted, much rather, at *her*."

"Long didn't, then," Obert said, still with his eyes on them.

I had to wait a moment. "Do you mean he struck you as avoiding her?"

He in turn considered. "He struck me as having noticed with what intensity, ever since we came down, she has kept alighting. She inaugurated it, the instant she arrived, with *me*, and every man of us has had his turn. I dare say it's only fair, certainly, that Long should have."

"He's lucky to get it, the brute! She's as charming as she can possibly be."

"That's it, precisely; and it's what no woman ought to be—as charming as she possibly can!—more than once or twice in her life. This lady is so every blessed minute, and to every blessed male. It's as if she were too awfully afraid one wouldn't take it in. If she but knew how one does! However," my friend continued, "you'll recollect that we differed about her yesterday—and what does it signify? One should of course bear lightly on anything so light. But I stick to it that she's different."

I pondered. "Different from whom?"

"Different from herself—as she was when I painted her. There's something the matter with her."

"Ah, then, it's for me to ask *you* what. I don't myself, you see, perceive it."

He made for a little no answer, and we were both indeed by this time taken up with the withdrawal of the two other members of our group. They moved away together across the shining floor, pausing, looking up at the painted vault, saying the inevitable things—bringing off their retreat, in short, in the best order. It struck me somehow as a retreat, and yet I insisted to myself, once more, on its being perfectly natural. At the high door, which stood open, they stopped a moment and looked back at us—looked frankly, sociably, as if in consciousness of our sympathetic attention. Mrs. Server waved, as in temporary farewell, a free explanatory hand at me; she seemed to explain that she was now trying somebody else. Obert moreover added *his* explanation. "That's the way she collars us."

"Oh, Long doesn't mind," I said. "But what's the way she strikes you as different?"

"From what she was when she sat to me? Well, a part of it is that she can't keep still. She was as still then as if she had been paid for it. Now she's all over the place." But he came back to something else. "I like your talking, my dear man, of what you 'don't perceive.' I've yet to find out what that remarkable quantity is. What you do perceive has at all events given me so much to think about that it doubtless ought to serve me for the present. I feel I ought to let you know that you've made me also perceive the Brissendens." I of course remembered what I had said to him, but it was just this that now touched my uneasiness, and I only echoed the name, a little blankly, with the instinct of gaining time. "You put me on them wonderfully," Obert continued, "though of course I've kept your idea to myself. All the same it sheds a great light."

I could again but feebly repeat it. "A great light?"

"As to what may go on even between others still. It's a jolly idea—a torch in the darkness; and do you know what I've done with it? I've held it up, I don't mind telling you, to just the question of the change, since this interests you, in Mrs. Server. If you've got your mystery I'll be hanged if I won't have mine. If you've got your Brissendens I shall see what I can do

237

with *her*. You've given me an analogy, and I declare I find it dazzling. I don't see the end of what may be done with it. If Brissenden's paying for his wife, for her amazing second bloom, who's paying for Mrs. Server? Isn't *that*—what do the newspapers call it?—the missing word? Isn't it perhaps in fact just what you told me last night you were on the track of? But don't add now," he went on, more and more amused with his divination, "don't add now that the man's obviously Gilbert Long—for I won't be put off with anything of the sort. She collared him much too markedly. The real man must be one she doesn't markedly collar."

"But I thought that what you a moment ago made out was that she so markedly collars all of us." This was my immediate reply to Obert's blaze of ingenuity, but I none the less saw more things in it than I could reply to. I saw, at any rate, and saw with relief, that if he should look on the principle suggested to him by the case of the Brissendens, there would be no danger at all of his finding it. If, accordingly, I was nervous for Mrs. Server, all I had to do was to keep him on this false scent. Since it was not she who was paid for, but she who possibly paid, his fancy might harmlessly divert him till the party should disperse. At the same time, in the midst of these reflections, the question of the "change" in her, which he was in so much better a position than I to measure, couldn't help having for me its portent, and the sense of that was, no doubt, in my next words. "What makes you think that what you speak of was what I had in my head?"

"Well, the way, simply, that the shoe fits. She's absolutely not the same person I painted. It's exactly like Mrs. Brissenden's having been for you yesterday not the same person you had last seen bearing her name."

"Very good," I returned, "though I didn't in the least mean to set you digging so hard. However, dig on your side, by all means, while I dig on mine. All I ask of you is complete discretion."

"Ah, naturally!"

"We ought to remember," I pursued, even at the risk of showing as too sententious, "that success in such an inquiry may perhaps be more embarrassing than failure. To nose about for a relation that a lady has her reasons for keeping secret——"

"Is made not only quite inoffensive, I hold"—he immediately took me up—"but positively honourable, by being confined to psychologic evidence."

I wondered a little. "Honourable to whom?"

"Why, to the investigator. Resting on the *kind* of signs that the game takes account of when fairly played—resting on psychologic signs alone, it's a high application of intelligence. What's ignoble is the detective and the keyhole."

"I see," I after a moment admitted. "I did have, last night, my scruples, but you warm me up. Yet I confess also," I still added, "that if I do muster the courage of my curiosity, it's a little because I feel even yet, as I think you also must, altogether destitute of a material clue. If I had a material clue I should feel ashamed: the fact would be deterrent. I start, for my part, at any rate, quite in the dark—or in a darkness lighted, at best, by what you have called the torch of my analogy. The analogy too," I wound up, "may very well be only half a help. It was easy to find poor Briss, because poor Briss is here, and it's always easy, moreover, to find a husband. But say Mrs. Server's poor Briss—or his equivalent, whoever it may be—*isn't* here."

We had begun to walk away with this, but my companion pulled up at the door of the room. "I'm sure he is. She tells me he's near."

"'Tells' you?" I challenged it, but I uncomfortably reflected that it was just what I had myself told Mrs. Brissenden.

"She wouldn't be as she is if he weren't. Her being as she is is the sign of it. He wasn't present—that is he wasn't present in her life at all—when I painted her; and the difference we're impressed with is exactly the proof that he is now."

My difficulty in profiting by the relief he had so unconsciously afforded me resided of course in my not feeling free to show for quite as impressed as he was. I hadn't really made out at all what he was impressed *with*, and I should only have spoiled everything by inviting him to be definite. This was a little of a worry, for I should have liked to know; but on the other hand I felt my track at present effactually covered. "Well, then, grant he's one of us. There are more than a dozen of us—a dozen even with you and me and Brissenden counted out. The hitch is that we're nowhere without a primary lead. As to Brissenden there *was* the lead."

"You mean as afforded by his wife's bloated state, which was a signal——?"

"Precisely: for the search for something or other that would help to explain it. Given his wife's bloated state, his own shrunken one was what was to have been predicated. I knew definitely, in other words, what to look for."

"Whereas we don't know here?"

"Mrs. Server's state, unfortunately," I replied, "is not bloated."

He laughed at my "unfortunately," though recognising that I spoke merely from the point of view of lucidity, and presently remarked that he had his own idea. He didn't say what it was, and I didn't ask, intimating thereby that I held it to be in this manner we were playing the game; but I indulgently questioned it in the light of its not yet having assisted him. He answered that the minutes we had just passed were what had made the difference; it had sprung from the strong effect produced on him after she came in with me. "It's but now I really see her. She did and said nothing special, nothing striking or extraordinary; but that didn't matter—it never does: one saw how she *is*. She's nothing but *that*."

"Nothing but what?"

"She's all *in* it," he insisted. "Or it's all in *her*. It comes to the same thing."

"Of course it's all in her," I said as impatiently as I could, though his attestation—for I wholly trusted his perception—left me so much in his debt. "That's what we start with, isn't it? It leaves us as far as ever from what we must arrive at."

But he was too interested in his idea to heed my question. He was wrapped in the "psychologic" glow. "I *have* her!"

"Ah, but it's a question of having *him*!"

He looked at me on this as if I had brought him back to a mere detail, and after an instant the light went out of his face. "So it is. I leave it to you. I don't care." His drop had the usual suddenness of the drops of the artistic temperament. "Look for the last man," he nevertheless, but with more detachment, added. "I daresay it would be he."

"The last? In what sense the last?"

"Well, the last sort of creature who could be believed of her."

"Oh," I rejoined as we went on, "the great bar to that is that such a sort of creature as the last won't *be* here!"

He hesitated. "So much the better. I give him, at any rate, wherever he is, up to you."

"Thank you," I returned, "for the beauty of the present! You do see, then, that our psychologic glow doesn't, after all, prevent the thing——"

"From being none of one's business? Yes. Poor little woman!" He seemed somehow satisfied; he threw it all up. "It isn't any of one's business, is it?"

"Why, that's what I was telling you," I impatiently exclaimed, "that *I* feel!"

<u>V</u>

THE first thing that happened to me after parting with him was to find myself again engaged with Mrs. Brissenden, still full of the quick conviction with which I had left her. "It *is* she—quite unmistakably, you know. I don't see how I can have been so stupid as not to make it out. I haven't your cleverness, of course, till my nose is rubbed into a thing. But when it *is*—!" She celebrated her humility in a laugh that was proud. "The two are off together."

"Off where?"

"I don't know where, but I saw them a few minutes ago most distinctly 'slope.' They've gone for a quiet, unwatched hour, poor dears, out into the park or the gardens. When one knows it, it's all there. But what's that vulgar song?—'You've got to know it first!' It strikes me, if you don't mind my telling you so, that the way *you* get hold of things is positively uncanny. I mean as regards what first marked her for you."

"But, my dear lady," I protested, "nothing at all first marked her for me. She *isn't* marked for me, first or last. It was only you who so jumped at her."

My interlocutress stared, and I had at this moment, I remember, an almost intolerable sense of her fatuity and cruelty. They were all unconscious, but they were, at that stage, none the less irritating. Her fine bosom heaved, her blue eyes expanded with her successful, her simplified egotism. I couldn't, in short, I found, bear her being so keen about Mrs. Server while she was so stupid about poor Briss. She seemed to recall to me nobly the fact that *she* hadn't a lover. No, she was only eating poor Briss up inch by inch, but she hadn't a lover. "I don't," I insisted, "see in Mrs. Server any of the right signs."

She looked almost indignant. "Even after your telling me that you see in Lady John only the wrong ones?"

"Ah, but there are other women here than Mrs. Server and Lady John."

"Certainly. But didn't we, a moment ago, think of them all and dismiss them? If Lady John's out of the question, how can Mrs. Server possibly *not* be in it? We want a fool——"

"Ah, *do* we?" I interruptingly wailed.

"Why, exactly by your own theory, in which you've so much interested me! It was you who struck off the idea."

"That we want a fool?" I felt myself turning gloomy enough. "Do we really want anyone at all?"

She gave me, in momentary silence, a strange smile. "Ah, you want to take it back now? You're sorry you spoke. My dear man, you may be——" but that didn't hinder the fact, in short, that I had kindled near me a fine, if modest and timid, intelligence. There did remain the truth of our friend's striking development, to which I had called her attention. Regretting my rashness didn't make the prodigy less. "You'll lead me to believe, if you back out, that there's suddenly someone you want to protect. Weak man," she exclaimed with an assurance from which, I confess, I was to take alarm, "something has happened to you since we separated! Weak man," she repeated with dreadful gaiety, "you've been squared!"

I literally blushed for her. "Squared?"

"Does it inconveniently happen that you find you're in love with her yourself?"

"Well," I replied on quick reflection, "do, if you like, call it that; for you see what a motive it gives me for being, in such a matter as this wonderful one that you and I happened to find ourselves for a moment making so free with, absolutely sure about her. I *am* absolutely sure. There! She won't do. And for your postulate that she's at the present moment in some sequestered spot in Long's company, suffer me without delay to correct it. It won't hold water. If you'll go into the library, through which I have just passed, you'll find her there in the company of the Comte de Dreuil."

Mrs. Briss stared again. "Already? She *was*, at any rate, with Mr. Long, and she told me on my meeting them that they had just come from the pastels."

"Exactly. They met there—she and I having gone together; and they retired together under my eyes. They must have parted, clearly, the moment after."

She took it all in, turned it all over. "Then what does that prove but that they're afraid to be seen?"

"Ah, they're *not* afraid, since both you and I saw them!"

"Oh, only just long enough for them to publish themselves as not avoiding each other. All the same, you know," she said, "they do."

"Do avoid each other? How is your belief in that," I asked, "consistent with your belief that they parade together in the park?"

"They ignore each other in public; they foregather in private."

"Ah, but they *don't*—since, as I tell you, she's even while we talk the centre of the mystic circle of the twaddle of M. de Dreuil; chained to a stake if you *can* be. Besides," I wound up, "it's not only that she's not the 'right fool'—it's simply that she's not a fool at all. We want the woman who has been rendered most inane. But this lady hasn't been rendered so in any degree. She's the reverse of inane. She's in full possession."

"In full possession of what?"

"Why, of herself."

"Like Lady John?"

I had unfortunately to discriminate here. "No, not like Lady John."

"Like whom then?"

"Like anyone. Like me; like you; like Brissenden. Don't I satisfy you?" I asked in a moment.

She only looked at me a little, handsome and hard. "If you wished to satisfy me so easily you shouldn't have made such a point of working me up. I daresay I, after all, however," she added, "notice more things than you."

"As for instance?"

"Well, May Server last evening. I was not quite conscious at the time that I did, but when one has had the 'tip' one looks back and sees things in a new light."

It was doubtless because my friend irritated me more and more that I met this with a sharpness possibly excessive. "She's perfectly natural. What I saw was a test. And so is he."

But she gave me no heed. "If there hadn't been so many people I should have noticed of myself after dinner that there was something the matter with her. I should have seen what it was. She was all over the place."

She expressed it as the poor lady's other critic had done, but this didn't shut my mouth. "Ah, then, in spite of the people, you did notice. What do you mean by 'all over the place'?"

"She couldn't keep still. She was different from the woman one had last seen. She used to be so calm—as if she were always sitting for her portrait. Wasn't she in fact always being painted in a pink frock and one row of pearls, always staring out at you in exhibitions, as if she were saying 'Here they are again'? Last night she was on the rush."

"The rush? Oh!"

"Yes, positively—from one man to another. She was on the pounce. She talked to ten in succession, making up to them in the most extraordinary way and leaving them still more crazily. She's as nervous as a cat. Put it to any man here, and see if he doesn't tell you."

"I should think it quite unpleasant to put it to any man here," I returned; "and I should have been sure you would have thought it the same. I spoke to you in the deepest confidence."

245

Mrs. Brissenden's look at me was for a moment of the least accommodating; then it changed to an intelligent smile. "How you *are* protecting her! But don't cry out," she added, "before you're hurt. Since your confidence has distinguished me—though I don't quite see why—you may be sure I haven't breathed. So I all the more resent your making me a scene on the extraordinary ground that I've observed as well as yourself. Perhaps what you don't like is that my observation may be turned on *you*. I confess it is."

It was difficult to bear being put in the wrong by her, but I made an effort that I believe was not unsuccessful to recover my good humour. "It's not in the least to your observation that I object, it's to the extravagant inferences you draw from it. Of course, however, I admit I always want to protect the innocent. What does she gain, on your theory, by her rushing and pouncing? Had she pounced on Brissenden when we met him with her? Are you so very sure he hadn't pounced on *her*? They had, at all events, to me, quite the air of people settled; she was not, it was clear, at that moment meditating a change. It was we, if you remember, who had absolutely to pull them apart."

"Is it your idea to make out," Mrs. Brissenden inquired in answer to this, "that she has suddenly had the happy thought of a passion for my husband?"

A new possibility, as she spoke, came to me with a whirr of wings, and I half expressed it. "She may have a sympathy."

My interlocutress gazed at space. "You mean she may be sorry for him? On what ground?"

I had gone too far indeed; but I got off as I could. "You neglect him so! But what is she, at any rate," I went on, "nervous—as nervous as you describe her—*about*?"

"About her danger; the contingency of its being fixed upon them—an intimacy so thoroughgoing that they can scarcely afford to let it be seen even as a mere acquaintance. Think of the circumstances—*her* personal ones, I mean, and admit that it wouldn't do. It would be too bad a case. There's everything to make it so. They must live on pins and needles. Anything proved would go tremendously hard for her."

"In spite of which you're surprised that I 'protect' her?"

It was a question, however, that my companion could meet. "From people in general, no. From me in particular, yes."

In justice to Mrs. Brissenden I thought a moment. "Well, then, let us be fair all round. That you don't, as you say, breathe is a discretion I appreciate; all the more that a little inquiry, tactfully pursued, would enable you to judge whether any independent suspicion does attach. A little loose collateral evidence *might* be picked up; and your scorning to handle it is no more than I should, after all, have expected of you."

"Thank you for 'after all'!" My companion tossed her head. "I know for myself what I scorn to handle. Quite apart from that there's another matter. You must have noticed yourself that when people are so much liked——"

"There's a kind of general, amiable consensus of blindness? Yes—one can think of cases. Popularity shelters and hallows—has the effect of making a good-natured world agree not to see."

My friend seemed pleased that I so sufficiently understood. "This evidently has been a case then in which it has not only agreed not to see, but agreed not even to look. It has agreed in fact to look straight the other way. They say there's no smoke without fire, but it appears there may be fire without smoke. I'm satisfied, at all events, that one wouldn't in connection with these two find the least little puff. Isn't that just what makes the magnificence of their success—the success that reduces us to playing over them with mere moonshine?" She thought of it; seemed fairly to envy it. "I've never *seen* such luck!"

"A rare case of the beauty of impunity *as* impunity?" I laughed. "Such a case puts a price on passions otherwise to be deprecated? I'm glad indeed you admit we're 'reduced.' We *are* reduced. But what I meant to say just now was that if you'll continue to join in the genial conspiracy while I do the same—each of us making an exception only for the other—I'll pledge myself absolutely to the straight course. If before we separate I've seen reason to change my mind, I'll loyally let you know."

"What good will that do me," she asked, "if you *don't* change your mind? You won't change it if you shut your eyes to her."

"Ah, I feel I can't do that now. I *am* interested. The proof of that is," I pursued, "that I appeal to you for another impression of your own. I still don't see the logic of her general importunity."

"The logic is simply that she has a terror of appearing to encourage anyone in particular."

"Why then isn't it in her own interest, for the sake of the screen, just to *do* that? The appearance of someone in particular would be exactly the opposite of the appearance of Long. Your own admission is that that's *his* line with Lady John."

Mrs. Brissenden took her view. "Oh, she doesn't want to do anything so like the real thing. And, as for what he does, they don't feel in the same way. He's not nervous."

"Then why does he go in for a screen?"

"I mean"—she readily modified it—"that he's not so nervous as May. He hasn't the same reasons for panic. A man never has. Besides, there's not so much in Mr. Long to show——"

"What, by my notion, has taken place? Why not, if it was precisely by the change in him that my notion was inspired? Any change in *her* I know comparatively little about."

We hovered so near the case of Mr. and Mrs. Brissenden that it positively excited me, and all the more for her sustained unconsciousness. "Oh, the man's not aware of his own change. He doesn't see it as we do. It's all to his advantage."

"But *we* see it to his advantage. How should that prevent?"

"We see it to the advantage of his mind and his talk, but not to that of——"

"Well, what?" I pressed as she pulled up.

She was thinking how to name such mysteries. "His delicacy. His consideration. His thought *for* her. He would think for her if he weren't selfish. But he *is* selfish—too much so to spare her, to be generous, to realise. It's only, after all," she sagely went on, feeding me again, as I winced to feel, with profundity of my own sort, "it's only an excessive case, a case that in him happens to show as what the doctors call 'fine,' of what goes on whenever two persons are so much mixed up. One of them always gets more out of it than the other. One of them—you know the saying—gives the lips, the other gives the cheek."

"It's the deepest of all truths. Yet the cheek profits too," I more prudently argued.

"It profits most. It takes and keeps and uses all the lips give. The cheek, accordingly," she continued to point out, "is Mr. Long's. The lips are what we began by looking for. We've found them. They're drained—they're dry, the lips. Mr. Long finds his improvement natural and beautiful. He revels in it. He takes it for granted. He's sublime."

It kept me for a minute staring at her. "So—do you know?—are *you*!"

She received this wholly as a tribute to her acuteness, and was therefore proportionately gracious. "That's only because it's catching. You've *made* me sublime. You found me dense. You've affected me quite as Mrs. Server has affected Mr. Long. I don't pretend I show it," she added, "quite as much as he does."

"Because that would entail *my* showing it as much as, by your contention, *she* does? Well, I confess," I declared, "I do feel remarkably like that pair of lips. I feel drained—I feel dry!" Her answer to this, with another toss of her head, was extravagant enough to mean forgiveness—was that I was impertinent, and her action in support of her charge was to move away from me, taking her course again to the terrace, easily accessible from the room in which we had been talking. She passed out of the window that opened to the ground, and I watched her while, in the brighter light, she put up her pink parasol. She walked a few paces, as if to look about her for a change of company, and by this time had reached a flight of steps that descended to a lower level. On observing that here, in the act to go down, she suddenly paused, I knew she had been checked by something seen below and that this was what made her turn the next moment to give me a look. I took it as an invitation to rejoin her, and I perceived when I had done so what had led her to appeal to me. We commanded from the point in question one of the shady slopes of the park and in particular a spreading beech, the trunk of which had been inclosed with a rustic circular bench, a convenience that appeared to have offered, for the moment, a sense of leafy luxury to a lady in pale blue. She leaned back, her figure presented in profile and her head a little averted as if for talk with some one on the other side of her, someone so placed as to be lost to our view.

"There!" triumphed Mrs. Brissenden again—for the lady was unmistakably Mrs. Server. Amusement was inevitable—the fact showed her as so correctly described by the words to which I had twice had to listen. She seemed really all over the place. "I thought you said," my companion remarked, "that you had left her tucked away somewhere with M. de Dreuil."

"Well," I returned after consideration, "that is obviously M. de Dreuil."

"Are you so sure? I don't make out the person," my friend continued—"I only see she's not alone. I understood you moreover that you had lately left them in the house."

"They *were* in the house, but there was nothing to keep them from coming out. They've had plenty of time while we've talked; they must have passed down by some of the other steps. Perhaps also," I added, "it's another man."

But by this time she was satisfied. "It's *he*!"

"Gilbert Long? I thought you just said," I observed, "that you can make nobody out."

We watched together, but the distance was considerable, and the second figure continued to be screened. "It *must* be he," Mrs. Brissenden resumed with impatience, "since it was with him I so distinctly saw her."

"Let me once more hold you to the fact," I answered, "that she had, to my knowledge, succumbed to M. de Dreuil afterwards. The moments have fled, you see, in our fascinating discussion, and various things, on your theory of her pounce, have come and gone. Don't I moreover make out a brown shoe, in a white gaiter, protruding from the other side of her dress? It must be Lord Lutley."

Mrs. Brissenden looked and mused. "A brown shoe in a white gaiter?" At this moment Mrs. Server moved, and the next—as if it were time for another pounce—she had got up. We could, however, still distinguish but a shoulder and an out-stretched leg of her gentleman, who, on her movement, appeared, as in protest, to have affirmed by an emphatic shift of his seat his preference for their remaining as they were. This carried him further round the tree. We thus lost him, but she stood there while we waited, evidently exhorting him; after a minute of which she came away as in confidence that he would follow. During this process, with a face more visible, she had looked as charming as a pretty woman almost always does in rising eloquent before the apathetic male. She hadn't yet noticed us, but something in her attitude and manner particularly spoke to me. There were implications in it to which I couldn't be blind, and I felt how my neighbour also would have caught them and been confirmed in her certitude. In fact I felt the breath of her confirmation in another elated "There!"—in a "Look at her *now*!" Incontestably, while not yet aware of us, Mrs. Server confessed with every turn of her head to a part in a relation. It stuck out of her, her part in a relation; it hung before us, her part in a relation; it was large to us beyond the breadth of the glade. And since, off her guard, she so let us have it, with whom in the world could the relation—so much of one as that—be but with Gilbert Long? The question was not settled till she had come on some distance; then the producer of our tension, emerging and coming after her, offered himself to our united, to our confounded, anxiety once more as poor Briss.

That we should have been confounded was doubtless but a proof of the impression—the singular assurance of intimacy borne toward us on the soft summer air—that we had, however delusively, received. I should myself have been as ready as my neighbour to say "Whoever he is, they're in deep!"—and on grounds, moreover, quite as recklessly, as fantastically constructive as hers. There was nothing to explain our impression but the fact of our already having seen them figure together, and of this we needed breathing-time to give them the natural benefit. It was not indeed as an absolute benefit for either that Grace Brissenden's tone marked our recognition. "Dear Guy *again*?"—but she had recovered herself enough to laugh. "I should have thought he had had more than his turn!" She had recovered herself in fact much more than I; for somehow, from this instant, convinced as she had been and turning everything to her conviction, I found myself dealing, in thought, with still larger material. It was odd what a difference was made for me by the renewed sight of dear Guy. I didn't of course analyse this sense at the time; that was still to come. Our friends meanwhile had noticed us, and something clearly passed between them—it almost produced, for an instant, a visible arrest in their advance—on the question of their having perhaps been for some time exposed.

They came on, however, and I waved them from afar a greeting, to which Mrs. Server alone replied. Distances were great at Newmarch and landscape-gardening on the grand scale; it would take them still some minutes to reach our place of vantage or to arrive within sound of speech. There was accordingly nothing marked in our turning away and strolling back to the house. We had been so intent that we confessed by this movement to a quick impulse to disown it. Yet it was remarkable that, before we went in, Mrs. Brissenden should have struck me afresh as having got all she wanted. Her recovery from our surprise was already so complete that her high lucidity now alone reigned. "You don't require, I suppose, anything more than *that*?"

"Well, I don't quite see, I'm bound to say, just where even 'that' comes in." It incommoded me singularly little, at the point to which I had jumped, that this statement was the exact reverse of the truth. Where it came in was what I happened to be in the very act of seeing—seeing to the exclusion of almost everything else. It was sufficient that I might perhaps feel myself to have done at last with Mrs. Brissenden. I desired, at all events, quite as if this benefit were assured me, to leave her the honours of the last word.

She was finely enough prepared to take them. "Why, this invention of using my husband——!" She fairly gasped at having to explain.

"Of 'using' him?"

"Trailing him across the scent as she does all of you, one after the other. Excuse my comparing you to so many red herrings. You each have your turn; only *his* seems repeated, poor dear, till he's quite worn out with it."

I kept for a little this image in my eye. "I can see of course that his whole situation must be something of a strain for him; for I've not forgotten what you told me yesterday of his service with Lady John. To have to work in such a way for two of them at once"—it couldn't help, I admitted, being a tax on a fellow. Besides, when one came to think of it, the same man couldn't be *two* red herrings. To show as Mrs. Server's would directly impair his power to show as Lady John's. It would seem, in short, a matter for his patronesses to have out together.

Mrs. Brissenden betrayed, on this, some annoyance at my levity. "Oh, the cases are not the same, for with Lady John it amuses him: he thinks he knows."

"Knows what?"

"What she wants him for. He doesn't know"—she kept it wonderfully clear—"that she really doesn't want him for anything; for anything except, of course"—this came as a droll second thought—"himself."

"And he doesn't know, either"—I tried to remain at her level—"that Mrs. Server does."

"No," she assented, "he doesn't know what it's her idea to do with him."

"He doesn't know, in fine," I cheerfully pursued, "the truth about anything. And of course, by your agreement with me, he's not to learn it."

She recognised her agreement with me, yet looked as if she had reserved a certain measure of freedom. Then she handsomely gave up even that. "I certainly don't want him to become conscious."

"It's his unconsciousness," I declared, "that saves him."

"Yes, even from himself."

"We must accordingly feed it." In the house, with intention, we parted company; but there was something that, before this, I felt it due to my claim of consistency to bring out. "It wasn't, at all events, Gilbert Long behind the tree!"

My triumph, however, beneath the sponge she was prepared to pass again over much of our experience, was short-lived. "Of course it wasn't. We shouldn't have been treated to the scene if it *had* been. What could she possibly have put poor Briss there for but just to show it wasn't?"

VI

I saw other things, many things, after this, but I had already so much matter for reflection that I saw them almost in spite of myself. The difficulty with me was in the momentum already acquired by the act—as well as, doubtless, by the general habit—of observation. I remember indeed that on separating from Mrs. Brissenden I took a lively resolve to get rid of my ridiculous obsession. It was absurd to have consented to such immersion, intellectually speaking, in the affairs of other people. One had always affairs of one's own, and I was positively neglecting mine. Such, for a while, was my foremost reflection; after which, in their order or out of it, came an inevitable train of others. One of the first of these was that, frankly, my affairs were by this time pretty well used to my neglect. There were connections enough in which it had never failed. A whole cluster of such connections, effectually displacing the centre of interest, now surrounded me, and I was—though always but intellectually—drawn into their circle. I did my best for the rest of the day to turn my back on them, but with the prompt result of feeling that I meddled with them almost more in thinking them over in isolation than in hovering personally about them. Reflection was the real intensity; reflection, as to poor Mrs. Server in particular, was an indiscreet opening of doors. She became vivid in the light of the so limited vision of her that I already possessed—try positively as I would not further to extend it. It was something not to ask another question, to keep constantly away both from Mrs. Brissenden and from Ford Obert, whom I had rashly invited to a degree of participation; it was something to talk as hard as possible with other persons and on other subjects, to mingle in groups much more superficial than they supposed themselves, to give ear to broader jokes, to discuss more tangible mysteries.

The day, as it developed, was large and hot, an unstinted splendour of summer; excursions, exercise, organised amusement were things admirably spared us; life became a mere arrested ramble or stimulated lounge, and we profited to the full by the noble freedom of Newmarch, that overarching ease which in nothing was so marked as in the tolerance of talk. The air of the place itself, in such conditions, left one's powers with a sense of play; if one wanted something to play at one simply played at being there. I did this myself, with the aid, in especial, of two or three solitary strolls, unaccompanied dips, of half an hour a-piece, into outlying parts of the house and the grounds. I must add that while I resorted to such measures not to see I only fixed what I *had* seen, what I did see, the more in my mind. One of these things had been the way that, at luncheon, Gilbert Long, watching the chance given him by the loose order in which we moved to it, slipped, to the visible defeat of somebody else, into the chair of conspicuity beside clever Lady John. A second was that Mrs. Server then occupied a place as remote as possible from this couple, but not from Guy Brissenden, who had found means to seat himself next her while my notice was engaged by the others. What I was at the same time supremely struck with could doubtless only be Mrs. Server's bright ubiquity, as it had at last come to seem to me, and that of the companions she had recruited for the occasion. Attended constantly by a different gentleman, she was in the range of my vision wherever I turned—she kept repeating her picture in settings separated by such intervals that I wondered at the celerity with which she proceeded from spot to spot. She was never discernibly out of breath, though the associate of her ecstasy at the given moment might have been taken as being; and I kept getting afresh the impression which, the day before, had so promptly followed my arrival, the odd impression, as of something the matter with each party, that I had gathered, in the grounds, from the sight of her advance upon me with Obert. I had by this time of course made out—and it was absurd to shut my eyes to it—what *that* particular something, at least, was. It was that Obert had quickly perceived something to be the matter with *her*, and that she, on her side, had become aware of his discovery.

I wondered hereupon if the discovery were inevitable for each gentleman in succession, and if this were their reason for changing so often. Did everyone leave her, like Obert, with an uneasy impression of her, and were these impressions now passed about with private hilarity or profundity, though without having reached me save from the source I have named? I affected myself as constantly catching her eye, as if she wished to call my attention to the fact of who was with her and who was not. I had kept my distance since our episode with the pastels, and yet nothing could more come home to me than that I had really not, since then, been absent from her. We met without talk, but not, thanks to these pointed looks, without contact. I daresay that, for that matter, my cogitations—for I must have bristled with them—would have made me as stiff a puzzle to interpretative minds as I had suffered other phenomena to become to my own. I daresay I wandered with a tell-tale restlessness of which the practical detachment might well have mystified those who hadn't suspicions. Whenever I caught Mrs. Server's eye it was really to wonder how many suspicions *she* had. I came upon her in great dim chambers, and I came upon her before sweeps of view. I came upon her once more with the Comte de Dreuil, with Lord Lutley, with Ford Obert, with almost every other man in the house, and with several of these, as if there had not been enough for so many turns, two or three times over. Only at no moment, whatever the favouring frame, did I come upon her with Gilbert Long. It was of course an anomaly that, as an easy accident, I was not again myself set in the favouring frame. That I consistently escaped being might indeed have been the meaning most marked in our mute recognitions.

Discretion, then, I finally felt, played an odd part when it simply left one more attached, morally, to one's prey. What was most evident to me by five o'clock in the afternoon was that I was too preoccupied not to find it the best wisdom to accept my mood. It was all very well to run away; there would be no effectual running away but to have my things quickly packed and catch, if possible, a train for town. On the spot I had to *be* on it; and it began to dawn before me that there was something quite other I possibly might do with Mrs. Server than endeavour ineffectually to forget her. What was none of one's business might change its name should importunity take the form of utility. In resisted observation that was vivid thought, in inevitable thought that was vivid observation, through a succession, in short, of phases in which I shall not pretend to distinguish one of these elements from the other, I found myself cherishing the fruit of the seed dropped equally by Ford Obert and by Mrs. Briss. What was the matter with *me?*—so much as that I had ended by asking myself; and the answer had come as an unmistakable return of the anxiety produced in me by my first seeing that I had fairly let Grace Brissenden loose. My original protest against the flash of inspiration in which she had fixed responsibility on Mrs. Server had been in fact, I now saw, but the scared presentiment of something in store for myself. This scare, to express it sharply, had verily not left me from that moment; and if I had been already then anxious it was because I had felt myself foredoomed to be sure the poor lady herself would be. Why I should have minded this, should have been anxious at her anxiety and scared at her scare, was a question troubling me too little on the spot for me to suffer it to trouble me, as a painter of my state, in this place. It is sufficient that when so much of the afternoon had waned as to bring signs of the service of tea in the open air, I knew how far I was gone in pity for her. For I had at last had to take in what my two interlocutors had given me. Their impression, coinciding and, as one might say, disinterested, couldn't, after a little, fail in some degree to impose itself. It had its value. Mrs. Server *was* "nervous."

It little mattered to me now that Mrs. Briss had put it to me—that I had even whimsically put it to myself—that I was perhaps in love with her. That was as good a name as another for an interest springing up in an hour, and was moreover a decent working hypothesis. The sentiment had not indeed asserted itself at "first sight," though it might have taken its place remarkably well among the phenomena of what is known as second. The real fact was, none the less, that I was quite too sorry for her to be anything except sorry. This odd feeling was something that I may as well say I shall not even now attempt to account for—partly, it is true, because my recital of the rest of what I was to see in no small measure does so. It was a force that I at this stage simply found I had already succumbed to. If it was not the result of what I had granted to myself was the matter with her, then it was rather the very cause of my making that concession. It was a different thing from my first prompt impulse to shield her. I had already shielded her—fought for her so far as I could or as the case immediately required. My own sense of how I was affected had practically cleared up, in short, in the presence of this deeper vision of her. My divinations and inductions had finally brought home to me that in the whole huge, brilliant, crowded place I was the only person save one who was in anything that could be called a relation to her. The other person's relation was concealed, and mine, so far as she herself was concerned, was unexpressed—so that I suppose what most, at the juncture in question, stirred within me was the wonder of how I might successfully express it. I felt that so long as I didn't express it I should be haunted with the idea of something infinitely touching and tragic in her loneliness—possibly in her torment, in her terror. If she was "nervous" to the tune I had come to recognise, it could only be because she had grounds. And what might her grounds more naturally be than that, arranged and arrayed, disguised and decorated, pursuing in vain, through our careless company, her search for the right shade of apparent security, she felt herself none the less all the while the restless victim of fear and failure?

Once my imagination had seen her in this light the touches it could add to the picture might be trusted to be telling. Further observation was to convince me of their truth, but while I waited for it with my apprehension that it would come in spite of me I easily multiplied and lavished them. I made out above all what she would most be trying to hide. It was not, so to speak, the guarded primary fact—it could only be, wretched woman, that produced, that disastrous, treacherous consequence of the fact which her faculties would exhibit, and most of all the snapped cord of her faculty of talk. Guy Brissenden had, at the worst, his compromised face and figure to show and to shroud—if he were really, that is, as much aware of them as one had suspected. She had her whole compromised machinery of thought and speech, and if these signs were not, like his, external, that made her case but the harder, for she had to create, with intelligence rapidly ebbing, with wit half gone, the illusion of an unimpaired estate. She was like some unhappy lady robbed of her best jewels—obliged so to dispose and distribute the minor trinkets that had escaped as still to give the impression of a rich *écrin*. Was not that embarrassment, if one analysed a little, at the bottom of her having been all day, in the vulgar phrase and as the three of us had too cruelly noted, all over the place? *Was* indeed, for that matter, this observation confined to us, or had it at last been irrepressibly determined on the part of the company at large? This was a question, I hasten to add, that I would not now for the world have put to the test. I felt I should have known how to escape had any rumour of wonder at Mrs. Server's ways been finally conveyed to me. I might from this moment have, as much as I liked, my own sense of it, but I was definitely conscious of a sort of loyalty to her that would have rendered me blank before others: though not indeed that—oh, at last, quite the contrary!—it would have forbidden me to watch and watch. I positively dreaded the accident of my being asked by one of the men if I knew how everyone was talking about her. If everyone was talking about her, I wanted positively not to know. But nobody was, probably—they scarcely could be as yet. Without suggestive collateral evidence there would be nobody in the house so conscientiously infernal as Mrs. Brissenden, Obert and I.

Newmarch had always, in our time, carried itself as the great asylum of the finer wit, more or less expressly giving out that, as invoking hospitality or other countenance, none of the stupid, none even of the votaries of the grossly obvious, need apply; but I could luckily at present reflect that its measurements in this direction had not always been my own, and that, moreover, whatever precision they possessed, human blandness, even in such happy halls, had not been quite abolished. There was a sound law in virtue of which one could always—alike in privileged and unprivileged circles—rest more on people's density than on their penetrability. Wasn't it their density too that would be practically nearest their good nature? Whatever her successive partners of a moment might have noticed, they wouldn't have discovered in her reason for dropping them quickly a principle of fear that they might notice her failure articulately to keep up. My own actual vision, which had developed with such affluence, was that, in a given case, she could keep up but for a few minutes and was therefore obliged to bring the contact to an end before exposure. I had consistently mastered her predicament: she had at once to cultivate contacts, so that people shouldn't guess her real concentration, and to make them a literal touch and go, so that they shouldn't suspect the enfeeblement of her mind. It was obviously still worth everything to her that she was so charming. I had theorised with Mrs. Brissenden on her supposititious inanity, but the explanation of such cynicism in either of us could only be a sensibility to the truth that attractions so great might float her even a long time after intelligence pure and simple should have collapsed.

Was not my present uneasiness, none the less, a private curiosity to ascertain just how much or how little of that element she had saved from the wreck? She dodged, doubled, managed, broke off, clutching occasions, yet doubtless risking dumbnesses, vaguenesses and other betrayals, depending on attitudes, motions, expressions, a material personality, in fine, in which a plain woman would have found nothing but failure; and peace therefore might rule the scene on every hypothesis but that of her getting, to put it crudely, worse. How I remember saying to myself that if she didn't get better she surely *must* get worse!—being aware that I referred on the one side to her occult surrender and on the other to its awful penalty. It became present to me that she possibly might recover if anything should happen that would pull her up, turn her into some other channel. If, however, that consideration didn't detain me longer the fact may stand as a sign of how little I believed in any check. Gilbert Long might die, but not the intensity he had inspired. The analogy with the situation of the Brissendens here, I further considered, broke down; I at any rate rather positively welcomed the view that the sacrificed party to *that* union might really find the arrest of his decline, if not the renewal of his youth, in the loss of his wife. Would this lady indeed, as an effect of *his* death, begin to wrinkle and shrivel? It would sound brutal to say that this was what I should have preferred to hold, were it not that I in fact felt forced to recognise the slightness of such a chance. She would have loved his youth, and have made it her own, in death as in life, and he would have quitted the world, in truth, only the more effectually to leave it to her. Mrs. Server's quandary—which was now all I cared for—was exactly in her own certitude of every absence of issue. But I need give little more evidence of how it had set me thinking.

As much as anything else, perhaps, it was the fear of what one of the men might say to me that made me for an hour or two, at this crisis, continuously shy. Nobody, doubtless, would have said anything worse than that she was more of a flirt than ever, that they had all compared notes and would accordingly be interested in some hint of another, possibly a deeper, experience. It would have been almost as embarrassing to have to tell them how little experience I had had in fact as to have had to tell them how much I had had in fancy—all the more that I had as yet only my thin idea of the line of feeling in her that had led her so to spare me. Tea on the terraces represented, meanwhile, among us, so much neglect of everything else that my meditations remained for some time as unobserved as I could desire. I was not, moreover, heeding much where they carried me, and became aware of what I owed them only on at last finding myself anticipated as the occupant of an arbour into which I had strolled. Then I saw I had reached a remote part of the great gardens, and that for some of my friends also secluded thought had inducements; though it was not, I hasten to add, that either of the pair I here encountered appeared to be striking out in any very original direction. Lady John and Guy Brissenden, in the arbour, were thinking secludedly together; they were together, that is, because they were scarce a foot apart, and they were thinking, I inferred, because they were doing nothing else. Silence, by every symptom, had definitely settled on them, and whatever it was I interrupted had no resemblance to talk. Nothing—in the general air of evidence—had more struck me than that what Lady John's famous intellect seemed to draw most from Brissenden's presence was the liberty to rest. Yet it shook off this languor as soon as she saw me; it threw itself straight into the field; it went, I could see, through all the motions required of it by her ladyship's fallacious philosophy. I could mark these emotions, and what determined them, as behind clear glass.

I found, on my side, a rare intellectual joy, the oddest secret exultation, in feeling her begin instantly to play the part I had attributed to her in the irreducible drama. She broke out in a manner that could only have had for its purpose to represent to me that mere weak amiability had committed her to such a predicament. It was to humour her friend's husband that she had strayed so far, for she was somehow sorry for him, and—good creature as we all knew her—had, on principle, a kind little way of her own with silly infatuations. His *was* silly, but it was unmistakable, and she had for some time been finding it, in short, a case for a special tact. That he bored her to death I might have gathered by the way they sat there, and she could trust me to believe—couldn't she?—that she was only musing as to how she might most humanely get rid of him. She would lead him safely back to the fold if I would give her time. She seemed to ask it all, oddly, of *me*, to take me remarkably into her confidence, to refer me, for a specimen of his behaviour, to his signal abandonment of his wife the day before, his having waited over, to come down, for the train in which poor *she* was to travel. It was at all events, I felt, one of the consequences of having caught on to so much that I by this time found myself catching on to everything. I read into Lady John's wonderful manner—which quite clamoured, moreover, for an interpretation—all that was implied in the lesson I had extracted from other portions of the business. It was distinctly poor she who gave me the lead, and it was not less definite that she put it to me that I should render her a service either by remaining with them or by inventing something that would lure her persecutor away. She desired him, even at the cost of her being left alone, distracted from his pursuit.

Poor he, in his quarter, I hasten to add, contributed to my picking out this embroidery nothing more helpful than a sustained detachment. He said as little as possible, seemed heedless of what was otherwise said, and only gave me on his own account a look or two of dim suggestiveness. Yet it was these looks that most told with me, and what they, for their part, conveyed was a plea that directly contradicted Lady John's. I understood him that it was he who was bored, he who had been pursued, he for whom perversity had become a dreadful menace, he, in fine, who pleaded for my intervention. He was so willing to trust me to relieve him of his companion that I think he would simply have bolted without deferring to me if I had not taken my precautions against it. I had, as it happened, another momentary use for him than this: I wished on the one hand not to lose him and on the other not to lose Lady John, though I had quickly enough guessed this brilliant woman's real preference, of which it in fact soon became my lively wish to see the proof. The union of these two was too artificial for me not already to have connected with it the service it might render, in her ladyship's view, to that undetected cultivation, on her part, of a sentiment for Gilbert Long which, through his feigned response to it, fitted so completely to the other pieces in my collection. To see all this was at the time, I remember, to be as inhumanly amused as if one had found one could create something. I had created nothing but a clue or two to the larger comprehension I still needed, yet I positively found myself overtaken by a mild artistic glow. What had occurred was that, for my full demonstration, I needed Long, and that, by the same stroke, I became sure I should certainly get him by temporising a little.

Lady John was in love with him and had kicked up, to save her credit, the dust of a fictive relation with another man—the relation one of mere artifice and the man one in her encouragement of whom nobody would believe. Yet she was also discoverably divided between her prudence and her vanity, for if it was difficult to make poor Briss figure at all vividly as an insistent satellite, the thankless tact she had to employ gave her exactly, she argued, the right to be refreshingly fanned with an occasional flap of the flag under which she had, as she ridiculously fancied, truly conquered. If she was where I found her because her escort had dragged her there, she had made the best of it through the hope of assistance from another quarter. She had held out on the possibility that Mr. Long—whom one *could* without absurdity sit in an arbour with—might have had some happy divination of her plight. He had had such divinations before—thanks to a condition in him that made sensibility abnormal—and the least a wretched woman could do when betrayed by the excess of nature's bounty was to play admirer against admirer and be "talked about" on her own terms. She would just this once have admitted it, I was to gather, to be an occasion for pleading guilty—oh, so harmlessly!—to a consciousness of the gentleman mutely named between us. Well, the "proof" I just alluded to was that I had not sat with my friends five minutes before Gilbert Long turned up.

I saw in a moment how neatly my being there with them played *his* game; I became in this fashion a witness for him that he could almost as little leave Lady John alone as—well, as other people could. It may perfectly have been the pleasure of this reflection that again made him free and gay—produced in him, in any case, a different shade of manner from that with which, before luncheon, as the consequence perhaps of a vague *flair* for my possible penetration, I had suspected him of edging away from me. Not since my encounter with him at Paddington the afternoon before had I had so to recognise him as the transfigured talker. To see Lady John with him was to have little enough doubt of *her* recognitions, just as this spectacle also dotted each "i" in my conviction of his venial—I can only call it that—duplicity. I made up my mind on the spot that it had been no part of his plan to practise on her, and that the worst he could have been accused of was a good-natured acceptance, more apparent than real, for his own purposes, of her theory—

which she from time to time let peep out—that they would have liked each other better if they hadn't been each, alas! so good. He profited by the happy accident of having pleased a person so much in evidence, and indeed it was tolerably clear to me that neither party was duped. Lady John didn't want a lover; this would have been, as people say, a larger order than, given the other complications of her existence, she could meet; but she wanted, in a high degree, the appearance of carrying on a passion that imposed alike fearless realisations and conscious renouncements, and this circumstance fully fell in with the convenience and the special situation of her friend. Her vanity rejoiced, so far as she dared to let it nibble, and the mysteries she practised, the dissimulations she elaborated, the general danger of detection in which she flattered herself that she publicly walked, were after all so much grist to the mill of that appetite.

By just so much, however, as it could never come up between them that there was another woman in Gilbert's history, by just so much would it on the other hand have been an articulate axiom that as many of the poor Brisses of the world as she might care to accommodate would be welcome to figure in her own. This personage, under that deeper induction, I suddenly became aware that I also greatly pitied—pitied almost as much as I pitied Mrs. Server; and my pity had doubtless something to do with the fact that, after I had proposed to him that we should adjourn together and we had, on his prompt, even though slightly dry response, placed the invidious arbour at a certain distance, I passed my hand into his arm. There were things I wanted of him, and the first was that he should let me show him I could be kind to him. I had made of the circumstance of tea at the house a pretext for our leaving the others, each of whom I felt as rather showily calling my attention to their good old ground for not wishing to rejoin the crowd. As to what Brissenden wished I had made up my mind; I had made up my mind as to the subject of his thoughts while they wandered, during his detention, from Lady John; and if the next of my wishes was to enter into his desire, I had decided on giving it effect by the time we reached the shortest of the vistas at the end of which the house reared a brave front.

VII

I stayed him there while I put it to him that he would probably in fact prefer to go back.

"You're not going then yourself?"

"No, I don't particularly want tea; and I may as well now confess to you that I'm taking a lonely, unsociable walk. I don't enjoy such occasions as these," I said, "unless I from time to time get off by myself somewhere long enough to tell myself how much I do enjoy them. That's what I was cultivating solitude for when I happened just now to come upon you. When I found you there with Lady John there was nothing for me but to make the best of it; but I'm glad of this chance to assure you that, every appearance to the contrary notwithstanding, I wasn't prowling about in search of you."

"Well," my companion frankly replied, "I'm glad you turned up. I wasn't especially amusing myself."

"Oh, I think I know how little!"

He fixed me a moment with his pathetic old face, and I knew more than ever that I was sorry for him. I was quite extraordinarily sorry, and I wondered whether I mightn't without offence or indiscretion really let him see it. It was to this end I had held him and wanted a little to keep him, and I was reassured as I felt him, though I had now released him, linger instead of leaving me. I had made him uneasy last night, and a new reason or two for my doing so had possibly even since then come up; yet these things also would depend on the way he might take them. The look with which he at present faced me seemed to hint that he would take them as I hoped, and there was no curtness, but on the contrary the dawn of a dim sense that I might possibly aid him, in the tone with which he came half-way. "You 'know'?"

"Ah," I laughed, "I know everything!"

He didn't laugh; I hadn't seen him laugh, at Newmarch, once; he was continuously, portentously grave, and I at present remembered how the effect of this had told for me at luncheon, contrasted as it was with that of Mrs. Server's desperate, exquisite levity. "You know I decidedly have too much of that dreadful old woman?"

There was a sound in the question that would have made me, to my own sense, start, though I as quickly hoped I had not done so to Brissenden's. I couldn't have persuaded myself, however, that I had escaped showing him the flush of my effort to show nothing. I had taken his disgusted allusion as to Mrs. Brissenden, and the action of that was upsetting. But nothing, fortunately, was psychologically more interesting than to grasp the next moment the truth of his reference. It was only the fact of his himself looking so much older than Lady John that had blinded me for an instant to the propriety of his not thinking her as young. She wasn't young as *he* had a right to call people, and I felt a glow—also, I feared, too visible—as soon as I had seen whom he meant. His meaning Lady John did me somehow so much good that I believed it would have done me still more to hear him call her a harridan or a Jezebel. It was none of my business; how little was anything, when it came to that, my business!—yet indefinably, unutterably, I felt assuaged for him and comforted. I verily believe it hung in the balance a minute or two that in my impulse to draw him out, so that I might give him my sympathy, I was prepared to risk overturning the edifice of my precautions. I luckily, as it happened, did nothing of the sort; I contrived to breathe consolingly on his secret without betraying an intention. There was almost no one in the place save two or three of the very youngest women whom he wouldn't have had a right to call old. Lady John was a hag, then; Mrs. Server herself was more than on the turn; Gilbert Long was fat and forty; and I cast about for some light in which I could show that I—*à plus forte raison*—was a pantaloon. "Of course you can't quite see the fun of it, and it really isn't fair to you. You struck me as much more in your element," I ventured to add, "when, this morning, more than once, I chanced to observe you led captive by Mrs. Server."

"Oh, that's a different affair," he answered with an accent that promised a growth of confidence.

"Mrs. Server's an old woman," I continued, "but she can't seem to a fellow like you as old as Lady John. She has at any rate more charm; though perhaps not," I added, "quite so much talk."

On this he said an extraordinary thing, which all but made me start again. "Oh, she hasn't any *talk*!"

I took, as quickly as possible, refuge in a surprised demurrer. "Not *any*?"

"None to speak of."

I let all my wonder come. "But wasn't she chattering to you at luncheon?" It forced him to meet my eyes at greater length, and I could already see that my experiment—for insidiously and pardonably such I wished to make it— was on the way to succeed. I had been right then, and I knew where I stood. He couldn't have been "drawn" on his wife, and he couldn't have been drawn, in the least directly, on himself, but as he could thus easily be on Lady John, so likewise he could on other women, or on the particular one, at least, who mattered to me. I felt I really knew what I was about, for to draw him on Mrs. Server was in truth to draw him indirectly on himself. It was indeed perhaps because I had by this time in a measure expressed, in terms however general, the interest with which he inspired me, that I now found myself free to shift the ground of my indiscretion. I only wanted him to know that on the question of Mrs. Server I was prepared to go as far with him as he should care to move. How it came to me now that he was *the* absolutely safe person in the house to talk of her with! "I was too far away from you to hear," I had gone on; "and I could only judge of her flow of conversation from the animated expression of her face. It was extraordinarily animated. But that, I admit," I added, "strikes one always as a sort of *parti pris* with her. She's never *not* extraordinarily animated."

"She has no flow of conversation whatever," said Guy Brissenden.

I considered. "Really?"

He seemed to look at me quite without uneasiness now. "Why, haven't you seen for yourself——?"

"How the case stands with her on that head? Do you mean haven't I talked with her? Well, scarcely; for it's a fact that every man in the house *but* I strikes me as having been deluged with that privilege: if indeed," I laughed, "her absence of topics suffers it to be either a privilege or a deluge! She affects me, in any case, as determined to have nothing to do with me. She walks all the rest of you about; she gives you each your turn; me only she skips, she systematically ignores. I'm half consoled for it, however," I wound up, "by seeing what short innings any individual of you has. You personally strike me as having had the longest."

Brissenden appeared to wonder where I was coming out, yet not as if he feared it. There was even a particular place, if I could but guess it, where he would have liked me to come. "Oh, she's extremely charming. But of course she's strikingly odd."

"Odd?—really?"

"Why, in the sense, I mean, that I thought you suggested you've noticed."

"That of extravagant vivacity? Oh, I've had to notice it at a distance, without knowing what it represents."

He just hesitated. "You haven't any idea at all what it represents?"

"How should I have," I smiled, "when she never comes near me? I've thought *that*, as I tell you, marked. What does her avoidance of *me* represent? Has she happened, with you, to throw any light on it?"

"I think," said Brissenden after another moment, "that she's rather afraid of you."

I could only be surprised. "The most harmless man in the house?"

"*Are* you really?" he asked—and there was a touch of the comic in hearing him put it with his inveterate gravity.

"If you take me for anything else," I replied, "I doubt if you'll find anyone to back you."

My companion, on this, looked away for a little, turned about, fixed his eyes on the house, seemed, as with a drop of interest, on the point of leaving me. But instead of leaving me he brought out the next moment: "I don't want anyone to back me. I don't care. I didn't mean just now," he continued, "that Mrs. Server has said to me anything against you, or that she fears you because she dislikes you. She only told me she thought you disliked *her*."

It gave me a kind of shock. "A creature so beautiful, and so—so———"

"So what?" he asked as I found myself checked by my desire to come to her aid.

"Well, so brilliantly happy."

I had all his attention again. "Is that what she *is*?"

"Then don't you, with your opportunities, know?" I was conscious of rather an inspiration, a part of which was to be jocose. "What are you trying," I laughed, "to get out of me?"

It struck me luckily that, though he remained as proof against gaiety as ever, he was, thanks to his preoccupation, not disagreeably affected by my tone. "Of course if you've no idea, I can get nothing."

"No idea of what?"

Then it was that I at last got it straight. "Well, of what's the matter with her."

"Is there anything particular? If there *is*," I went on, "there's something that I've got out of *you*!"

"How so, if you don't know what it is?"

"Do you mean if you yourself don't?" But without detaining him on this, "Of what in especial do the signs," I asked, "consist?"

"Well, of everyone's thinking so—that there's something or other."

This again struck me, but it struck me too much. "Oh, everyone's a fool!"

He saw, in his queer wan way, how it had done so. "Then you *have* your own idea?"

I daresay my smile at him, while I waited, showed a discomfort. "Do you mean people are talking about her?"

But he waited himself. "Haven't they shown you——?"

"No, no one has spoken. Moreover I wouldn't have let them."

"Then there you *are*!" Brissenden exclaimed. "If you've kept them off, it must be because you differ with them."

"I shan't be sure of that," I returned, "till I know what they think! However, I repeat," I added, "that I shouldn't even then care. I don't mind admitting that she much interests me."

"There you are, there you are!" he said again.

"That's all that's the matter with her so far as *I'm* concerned. You see, at any rate, how little it need make her afraid of me. She's lovely and she's gentle and she's happy."

My friend kept his eyes on me. "What is there to interest you so in that? Isn't it a description that applies here to a dozen other women? You can't say, you know, that you're interested in *them*, for you just spoke of them as so many fools."

There was a certain surprise for me in so much acuteness, which, however, doubtless admonished me as to the need of presence of mind. "I wasn't thinking of the ladies—I was thinking of the men."

"That's amiable to *me*," he said with his gentle gloom.

"Oh, my dear Brissenden, I except 'you.'"

"And why should you?"

I felt a trifle pushed. "I'll tell you some other time. And among the ladies I except Mrs. Brissenden, with whom, as you may have noticed, I've been having much talk."

"And will you tell me some other time about that too?" On which, as I but amicably shook my head for no, he had his first dimness of pleasantry. "I'll get it then from my wife."

"Never. She won't tell you."

"She has passed you her word? That won't alter the fact that she tells me everything."

He really said it in a way that made me take refuge for an instant in looking at my watch. "Are you going back to tea? If you are, I'll, in spite of my desire to roam, walk twenty steps with you." I had already again put my hand into his arm, and we strolled for a little till I threw off that I was sure Mrs. Server was waiting for him. To this he replied that if I wished to get rid of him he was as willing to take that as anything else for granted—an observation that I, on my side, answered with an inquiry, though an inquiry that had nothing to do with it. "Do you also tell everything to Mrs. Brissenden?"

It brought him up shorter than I had expected. "Do you ask me that in order that I shan't speak to her of this?"

I showed myself at a loss. "Of 'this'——?"

"Why, of what we've made out——"

"About Mrs. Server, you and I? You must act as to that, my dear fellow, quite on your own discretion. All the more that what on earth *have* we made out? I assure you I haven't a secret to confide to you about her, except that I've never seen a person more unquenchably radiant."

He almost jumped at it. "Well, that's just it!"

"But just what?"

"Why, what they're all talking about. That she *is* so awfully radiant. That she's so tremendously happy. It's the question," he explained, "of what in the world she has to make her so."

I winced a little, but tried not to show it. "My dear man, how do *I* know?"

"She *thinks* you know," he after a moment answered.

I could only stare. "Mrs. Server thinks I know what makes her happy?" I the more easily represented such a conviction as monstrous in that it truly had its surprise for me.

But Brissenden now was all with his own thought. "She *isn't* happy."

"You mean that that's what's the matter with her under her appearance——? Then what makes the appearance so extraordinary?"

"Why, exactly what I mention—that one doesn't see anything whatever in her to correspond to it."

I hesitated. "Do you mean in her circumstances?"

"Yes—or in her character. Her circumstances are nothing wonderful. She has none too much money; she has had three children and lost them; and nobody that belongs to her appears ever to have been particularly nice to her."

I turned it over. "How you *do* get on with her!"

"Do you call it getting on with her to be the more bewildered the more I see her?"

"Isn't to say you're bewildered only, on the whole, to say you're charmed? That always—doesn't it?—describes more or less any engrossed relation with a lovely lady."

"Well, I'm not sure I'm so charmed." He spoke as if he had thought this particular question over for himself; he had his way of being lucid without brightness. "I'm not at all easily charmed, you know," he the next moment added; "and I'm not a fellow who goes about much after women."

"Ah, that I never supposed! Why in the world *should* you? It's the last thing!" I laughed. "But isn't this—quite (what shall one call it?) innocently—rather a peculiar case?"

My question produced in him a little gesture of elation—a gesture emphasised by a snap of his forefinger and thumb. "I knew you knew it was special! I knew you've been thinking about it!"

"You certainly," I replied with assurance, "have, during the last five minutes, made me do so with some sharpness. I don't pretend that I don't now recognise that there *must* be something the matter. I only desire—not unnaturally—that there *should* be, to put me in the right for having thought, if, as you're so sure, such a freedom as that can be brought home to me. If Mrs. Server is beautiful and gentle and strange," I speciously went on, "what are those things but an attraction?"

I saw how he had them, whatever they were, before him as he slowly shook his head. "They're not an attraction. They're too queer."

I caught in an instant my way to fall in with him; and not the less that I by this time felt myself committed, up to the intellectual eyes, to ascertaining just *how* queer the person under discussion might be. "Oh, of course I'm not speaking of her as a party to a silly flirtation, or an object of any sort of trivial pursuit. But there are so many different ways of being taken."

"For a fellow like you. But not for a fellow like me. For me there's only one."

"To be, you mean, in love?"

He put it a little differently. "Well, to be thoroughly pleased."

"Ah, that's doubtless the best way and the firm ground. And you mean you're *not* thoroughly pleased with Mrs. Server?"

"No—and yet I want to be kind to her. Therefore what's the matter?"

"Oh, if it's what's the matter with *you* you ask me, that extends the question. If you want to be kind to her, you get on with her, as we were saying, quite enough for my argument. And isn't the matter also, after all," I demanded, "that you simply feel she desires you to be kind?"

"She does that." And he looked at me as with the sense of drawing from me, for his relief, some greater help than I was as yet conscious of the courage to offer. "It *is* that she desires me. She likes it. And the extraordinary thing is that *I* like it."

"And why in the world shouldn't you?"

"Because she terrifies me. She has something to hide."

"But, my dear man," I asked with a gaiety singularly out of relation to the small secret thrill produced in me by these words—"my dear man, what woman who's worth anything hasn't?"

"Yes, but there are different ways. What *she* tries for is this false appearance of happiness."

I weighed it. "But isn't that the best thing?"

"It's terrible to have to keep it up."

"Ah, but if you don't *for* her? If it all comes on herself?"

"It doesn't," Guy Brissenden presently said. "I do—'for' her—help to keep it up." And then, still unexpectedly to me, came out the rest of his confession. "I want to—I try to; that's what I mean by being kind to her, and by the gratitude with which she takes it. One feels that one doesn't want her to break down."

It was on this—from the poignant touch in it—that I at last felt I had burnt my ships and didn't care how much I showed I was with him. "Oh, but she won't. You must keep her going."

He stood a little with a thumb in each pocket of his trousers, and his melancholy eyes ranging far over my head—over the tops of the highest trees. "Who am *I* to keep people going?"

"Why, you're just the man. Aren't you happy?"

He still ranged the tree-tops. "Yes."

"Well, then, you belong to the useful class. You've the wherewithal to give. It's the happy people who should help the others."

He had, in the same attitude, another pause. "It's easy for *you* to talk!"

"Because I'm not happy?"

It made him bring his eyes again down to me. "I think you're a little so now at my expense."

I shook my head reassuringly. "It doesn't cost you anything if—as I confess to it now—I do to some extent understand."

"That's more, then, than—after talking of it this way with you—I feel that *I* do!"

He had brought that out with a sudden sigh, turning away to go on; so that we took a few steps more. "You've nothing to trouble about," I then freely remarked, "but that you *are* as kind as the case requires and that you do help. I daresay that you'll find her even now on the terrace looking out for you." I patted his back, as we went a little further, but as I still preferred to stay away from the house I presently stopped again. "Don't fall below your chance. *Noblesse oblige.* We'll pull her through."

"You say 'we,'" he returned, "but you do keep out of it!"

"Why should you wish me to interfere with you?" I asked. "I wouldn't keep out of it if she wanted me as much as she wants you. That, by your own admission, is exactly what she doesn't."

"Well, then," said Brissenden, "I'll make her go for you. I think I want your assistance quite as much as she can want mine."

"Oh," I protested for this, "I've really given you already every ounce of mine I can squeeze out. And you know for yourself far more than I do."

"No, I don't!"—with which he became quite sharp; "for you know *how* you know it—which I've not a notion of. It's just what I think," he continued, facing me again, "you ought to tell me."

"I'm a little in doubt of what you're talking of, but I suppose you to allude to the oddity of my being so much interested without my having been more informed."

"You've got some clue," Brissenden said; "and a clue is what I myself want."

"Then get it," I laughed, "from Mrs. Server!"

He wondered. "Does she know?"

I had still, after all, to dodge a little. "Know what?"

"Why, that you've found out what she has to hide."

"You're perfectly free to ask her. I wonder even that you haven't done so yet."

"Well," he said with the finest stroke of unconsciousness he had yet shown me—"well, I suppose it's because I'm afraid of her."

"But not too much afraid," I risked suggesting, "to be hoping at this moment that you'll find her if you go back to where most of our party is gathered. You're not going for tea—you're going for Mrs. Server: just of whom it was, as I say, you were thinking while you sat there with Lady John. So what is it you so greatly fear?"

It was as if I could see through his dim face a sort of gratitude for my making all this out to him. "I don't know that it's anything that she may do to *me*." He could make it out in a manner for himself. "It's as if something might happen to her. It's what I told you—that she may break down. If you ask me how, or in what," he continued, "how can I tell you? In whatever it is that she's trying to do. I don't understand it." Then he wound up with a sigh that, in spite of its softness, he imperfectly stifled. "But it's something or other!"

"What would it be, then," I asked, "but what you speak of as what I've 'found out'? The effort you distinguish in her is the effort of concealment—vain, as I gather it strikes you both, so far as *I*, in my supernatural acuteness, am concerned."

Following this with the final ease to which my encouragement directly ministered, he yet gave me, before he had quite arrived, a queer sidelong glance. "Wouldn't it really be better if you were to tell me? I don't ask her myself, you see. I don't put things to her in that way."

"Oh, no—I've shown you how I do see. That's a part of your admirable consideration. But I must repeat that nothing would induce me to tell you."

His poor old face fairly pleaded. "But I want so to know."

"Ah, there it is!" I almost triumphantly laughed.

"There what is?"

"Why, everything. What I've divined, between you and Mrs. Server, as the tie. Your wanting so to know."

I felt as if he were now, intellectually speaking, plastic wax in my hand. "And her wanting me not to?"

"Wanting *me* not to," I smiled.

He puzzled it out. "And being willing, therefore——"

"That you—you only, for sympathy, for fellowship, for the wild wonder of it—*should* know? Well, for all those things, and in spite of what you call your fear, *try* her!" With which now at last I quitted him.

VIII

I'M afraid I can't quite say what, after that, I at first did, nor just how I immediately profited by our separation. I felt absurdly excited, though this indeed was what I had felt all day; there had been in fact deepening degrees of it ever since my first mystic throb after finding myself, the day before in our railway-carriage, shut up to an hour's contemplation and collation, as it were, of Gilbert Long and Mrs. Brissenden. I have noted how my first full contact with the changed state of these associates had caused the knell of the tranquil mind audibly to ring for me. I have spoken of my sharpened perception that something altogether out of the common had happened, independently, to each, and I could now certainly flatter myself that I hadn't missed a feature of the road I had thus been beguiled to travel. It was a road that had carried me far, and verily at this hour I *felt* far. I daresay that for a while after leaving poor Briss, after what I may indeed call launching him, this was what I predominantly felt. To be where I was, to whatever else it might lead, treated me by its help to the taste of success. It appeared then that the more things I fitted together the larger sense, every way, they made—a remark in which I found an extraordinary elation. It justified my indiscreet curiosity; it crowned my underhand process with beauty. The beauty perhaps was only for *me*—the beauty of having been right; it made at all events an element in which, while the long day softly dropped, I wandered and drifted and securely floated. This element bore me bravely up, and my private triumph struck me as all one with the charm of the moment and of the place.

There was a general shade in all the lower reaches—a fine clear dusk in garden and grove, a thin suffusion of twilight out of which the greater things, the high tree-tops and pinnacles, the long crests of motionless wood and chimnied roof, rose into golden air. The last calls of birds sounded extraordinarily loud; they were like the timed, serious splashes, in wide, still water, of divers not expecting to rise again. I scarce know what odd consciousness I had of roaming at close of day in the grounds of some castle of enchantment. I had positively encountered nothing to compare with this since the days of fairy-tales and of the childish imagination of the impossible. *Then* I used to circle round enchanted castles, for then I moved in a world in which the strange "came true." It was the coming true that was the proof of the enchantment, which, moreover, was naturally never so great as when such coming was, to such a degree and by the most romantic stroke of all, the fruit of one's own wizardry. I was positively—so had the wheel revolved—proud of my work. I had thought it all out, and to have thought it was, wonderfully, to have brought it. Yet I recall how I even then knew on the spot that there was something supreme I should have failed to bring unless I had happened suddenly to become aware of the very presence of the haunting principle, as it were, of my thought. This was the light in which Mrs. Server, walking alone now, apparently, in the grey wood and pausing at sight of me, showed herself in her clear dress at the end of a vista. It was exactly as if she had been there by the operation of my intelligence, or even by that—in a still happier way—of my feeling. My excitement, as I have called it, on seeing her, was assuredly emotion. Yet what *was* this feeling, really?—of which, at the point we had thus reached, I seemed to myself to have gathered from all things an invitation to render some account.

Well, I knew within the minute that I was moved by it as by an extraordinary tenderness; so that this is the name I must leave it to make the best of. It had already been my impression that I was sorry for her, but it was marked for me now that I was sorrier than I had reckoned. All her story seemed at once to look at me out of the fact of her present lonely prowl. I met it without demur, only wanting her to know that if I struck her as waylaying her in the wood, as waiting for her there at eventide with an idea, I shouldn't in the least defend myself from the charge. I can scarce clearly tell how many fine strange things I thought of during this brief crisis of her hesitation. I wanted in the first place to make it end, and while I moved a few steps toward her I felt almost as noiseless and guarded as if I were trapping a bird or stalking a fawn. My few steps brought me to a spot where another perspective crossed our own, so that they made together a verdurous circle with an evening sky above and great lengthening, arching recesses in which the twilight thickened. Oh, it was quite sufficiently the castle of enchantment, and when I noticed four old stone seats, massive and mossy and symmetrically placed,

I recognised not only the influence, in my adventure, of the grand style, but the familiar identity of this consecrated nook, which was so much of the type of all the bemused and remembered. We were in a beautiful old picture, we were in a beautiful old tale, and it wouldn't be the fault of Newmarch if some other green *carrefour*, not far off, didn't balance with this one and offer the alternative of niches, in the greenness, occupied by weather-stained statues on florid pedestals.

I sat straight down on the nearest of our benches, for this struck me as the best way to express the conception with which the sight of Mrs. Server filled me. It showed her that if I watched her I also waited for her, and that I was therefore not affected in any manner she really need deprecate. She had been too far off for me to distinguish her face, but her approach had faltered long enough to let me see that if she had not taken it as too late she would, to escape me, have found some pretext for turning off. It was just my seating myself that made the difference—it was my being so simple with her that brought her on. She came slowly and a little wearily down the vista, and her sad, shy advance, with the massed wood on either side of her, was like the reminiscence of a picture or the refrain of a ballad. What made the difference with *me*—if any difference had remained to be made—was the sense of this sharp cessation of her public extravagance. She had folded up her manner in her flounced parasol, which she seemed to drag after her as a sorry soldier his musket. It was present to me without a pang that this was the person I had sent poor Briss off to find—the person poor Briss would owe me so few thanks for his failure to have found. It was equally marked to me that, however detached and casual she might, at the first sight of me, have wished to show herself, it was to alight on poor Briss that she had come out, it was because he had not been at the house and might therefore, on his side, be wandering, that she had taken care to be unaccompanied. My demonstration was complete from the moment I thus had them in the act of seeking each other, and I was so pleased at having gathered them in that I cared little what else they had missed. I neither moved nor spoke till she had come quite near me, and as she also gave no sound the meaning of our silence seemed to stare straight out. It absolutely phrased there, in all the wonderful conditions, a relation already established; but the strange and beautiful thing was that as soon as we had recognised and accepted it this relation put us almost at our ease. "You must be weary of walking," I said at last, "and you see I've been keeping a seat for you."

I had finally got up, as a sign of welcome, but I had directly afterwards resumed my position, and it was an illustration of the terms on which we met that we neither of us seemed to mind her being meanwhile on her feet. She stood before me as if to take in—with her smile that had by this time sunk quite to dimness—more than we should, either of us, after all, be likely to be able to say. I even saw from this moment, I think, that, whatever she might understand, she would be able herself to say but little. She gave herself, in that minute, more than she doubtless knew—gave herself, I mean, to my intenser apprehension. She went through the form of expression, but what told me everything was the way the form of expression broke down. Her lovely grimace, the light of the previous hours, was as blurred as a bit of brushwork in water-colour spoiled by the upsetting of the artist's glass. She fixed me with it as she had fixed during the day forty persons, but it fluttered like a bird with a broken wing. She looked about and above, down each of our dusky avenues and up at our gilded tree-tops and our painted sky, where, at the moment, the passage of a flight of rooks made a clamour. She appeared to wish to produce some explanation of her solitude, but I was quickly enough sure that she would never find a presentable one. I only wanted to show her how little I required it. "I like a lonely walk," I went on, "at the end of a day full of people: it's always, to me, on such occasions, quite as if something has happened that the mind wants to catch and fix before the vividness fades. So I mope by myself an hour—I take stock of my impressions. But there's one thing I don't believe you know. This is the very first time, in such a place and at such an hour, that it has ever befallen me to come across a friend stricken with the same perversity and engaged in the same pursuit. Most people, don't you see?"—I kept it up as I could—"don't in the least know what has happened to them, and don't care to know. That's one way, and I don't deny it may be practically the best. But if one does care to know, that's another way. As soon as I saw you there at the end of the alley I said to myself, with quite a little thrill of elation, 'Ah, then it's *her* way too!' I wonder if you'll let me tell you," I floundered pleasantly on, "that I immediately liked you the better for it. It seemed to bring us more together. That's what I sat straight down here to show you. 'Yes,' I wished you to understand me as frankly saying, 'I *am*, as well as you, on the mope, or on the muse, or on whatever you call it, and this isn't half a bad corner for such a mood.' I can't tell you what a pleasure it is to me to see you do understand."

I kept it up, as I say, to reassure and soothe and steady her; there was nothing, however fantastic and born of the pressure of the moment, that I wouldn't have risked for that purpose. She was absolutely on my hands with her secret—I felt that from the way she stood and listened to me, silently showing herself relieved and pacified. It was marked that if I had hitherto seen her as "all over the place," she had yet nowhere seemed to me less so than at this furthermost point. But if, though only nearer to her secret and still not in possession, I felt as justified as I have already described myself, so it equally came to me that I was quite near enough, at the pass we had reached, for what I should have to take from it all. She was on my hands—it was she herself, poor creature, who was: this was the thing that just now loomed large, and the secret was a comparative detail. "I think you're very kind," she said for all answer to the speech I have reported, and the minute after this she had sunk down, in confessed collapse, to my bench, on which she sat and stared before her. The mere mechanism of her expression, the dangling paper lantern itself, was now all that was left in her face. She remained a little as if discouraged by the sight of the weariness that her surrender had let out. I hesitated, from just this fear of adding to it, to commiserate her for it more directly, and she spoke again before I had found anything to say. She brought back her attention indeed as if with an effort and from a distance. "What is it that has happened to you?"

"Oh," I laughed, "what is it that has happened to *you?*" My question had not been in the least intended for pressure, but it made her turn and look at me, and this, I quickly recognised, was all the answer the most pitiless curiosity could have desired—all the more, as well, that the intention in it had been no greater than in my words. Beautiful, abysmal, involuntary, her exquisite weakness simply opened up the depths it would have closed. It was in short a supremely unsuccessful attempt to say nothing. It said everything, and by the end of a minute my chatter—none the less out of place for being all audible—was hushed to positive awe by what it had conveyed. I saw as I had never seen before what consuming passion can make of the marked mortal on whom, with fixed beak and claws, it has settled as on a prey. She reminded me of a sponge wrung dry and with fine pores agape. Voided and scraped of everything, her shell was merely crushable. So it was brought home to me that the victim could be abased, and so it disengaged itself from these things that the abasement could be conscious. That was Mrs. Server's tragedy, that her consciousness survived—survived with a force that made it struggle and dissemble. This consciousness was all her secret—it was at any rate all mine. I promised myself roundly that I would henceforth keep clear of any other.

I none the less—from simply sitting with her there—gathered in the sense of more things than I could have named, each of which, as it came to me, made my compassion more tender. Who of us all could say that his fall might not be as deep?—or might not at least become so with equal opportunity. I for a while fairly forgot Mrs. Server, I fear, in the intimacy of this vision of the possibilities of our common nature. She became such a wasted and dishonoured symbol of them as might have put tears in one's eyes. When I presently returned to her—our session seeming to resolve itself into a mere mildness of silence—I saw how it was that whereas, in such cases in general, people might have given up much, the sort of person this poor lady was could only give up everything. She was the absolute wreck of her storm, accordingly, but to which the pale ghost of a special sensibility still clung, waving from the mast, with a bravery that went to the heart, the last tatter of its flag. There are impressions too fine for words, and I shall not attempt to say how it was that under the touch of this one I felt how nothing that concerned my companion could ever again be present to me but the fact itself of her admirable state. This was the source of her wan little glory, constituted even for her a small sublimity in the light of which mere minor identifications turned vulgar. I knew who *he* was now with a vengeance, because I had learnt precisely from that who *she* was; and nothing could have been sharper than the force with which it pressed upon me that I had really learnt more than I had bargained for. Nothing need have happened if I hadn't been so absurdly, so fatally meditative about poor Long—an accident that most people, wiser people, appeared on the whole to have steered sufficiently clear of. Compared with my actual sense, the sense with which I sat there, that other vision was gross, and grosser still the connection between the two.

Such were some of the reflections in which I indulged while her eyes—with their strange intermissions of darkness or of light: who could say which?—told me from time to time that she knew whatever I was thinking of to be for her virtual advantage. It was prodigious what, in the way of suppressed communication, passed in these wonderful minutes between us. Our relation could be at the best but an equal confession, and I remember saying to myself that if she had been as subtle as I—which she wasn't!—she too would have put it together that I had dreadfully talked about her. She would have traced in me my demonstration to Mrs. Briss that, whoever she was, she must logically have been idiotised. It was the special poignancy of her collapse that, so far at least as I was concerned, this was a ravage the extent of which she had ceased to try to conceal. She had been trying, and more or less succeeding, all day: the little drama of her public unrest had had, when one came to consider, no other argument. It had been terror that had directed her steps; the need constantly to show herself detached and free, followed by the sterner one not to show herself, by the same token, limp and empty. This had been the distinct, ferocious logic of her renewals and ruptures—the anxious mistrust of her wit, the haunting knowledge of the small distance it would take her at once, the consequent importance of her exactly timing herself, and the quick instinct of flight before the menace of discovery. She couldn't let society alone, because that would have constituted a symptom; yet, for fear of the appearance of a worse one, she could only mingle in it with a complex diplomacy. She was accordingly exposed on every side, and to be with her a while thus quietly was to read back into her behaviour the whole explanation, which was positively simple to me now. To take up again the vivid analogy, she had been sailing all day, though scarce able to keep afloat, under the flag of her old reputation for easy response. She had given to the breeze any sad scrap of a substitute, for the play of mind once supposed remarkable. The last of all the things her stillness said to me was that I could judge from so poor a show what had become of her conversability. What I did judge was that a frantic art had indeed been required to make her pretty silences pass, from one crisis to another, for pretty speeches. Half this art, doubtless, was the glittering deceit of her smile, the sublime, pathetic overdone geniality which represented so her share in any talk that, every other eloquence failing, there could only be nothing at all from the moment it abandoned its office. There *was* nothing at all. That was the truth; in accordance with which I finally—for everything it might mean to myself—put out my hand and bore ever so gently on her own. Her own rested listlessly on the stone of our seat. Of course, it had been an immense thing for her that she was, in spite of everything, so lovely.

All this was quite consistent with its eventually coming back to me that, though she took from me with appreciation what was expressed in the gesture I have noted, it was certainly in quest of a still deeper relief that she had again come forth. The more I considered her face—and most of all, so permittedly, in her passive, conscious presence—the more I was sure of this and the further I could go in the imagination of her beautiful duplicity. I ended by divining that if I was assuredly good for her, because the question of keeping up with me had so completely dropped, and if the service I so rendered her was not less distinct to her than to myself—I ended by divining that she had none the less her obscure vision of a still softer ease. Guy Brissenden had become in these few hours her positive need—a still greater need than I had lately amused myself with making out that he had found her. Each had, by their unprecedented plight, something for the other, some intimacy of unspeakable confidence, that no one else in the world could have for either. They had been feeling their way to it, but at the end of their fitful day they had grown confusedly, yet beneficently sure. The explanation here again was simple—they had the sense of a common fate. They hadn't to name it or to phrase it—possibly even couldn't had they tried; peace and support came to them, without that, in the simple revelation of each other. Oh, how I made it out that if it was indeed very well for the poor lady to feel thus in *my* company that her burden was lifted, my company would be after all but a rough substitute for Guy's! He was a still better friend, little as he could have told the reason; and if I could in this connection have put the words into her mouth, here follows something of the sense that I should have made them form.

"Yes, my dear man, I do understand you—quite perfectly now, and (by I know not what miracle) I've really done so to some extent from the first. Deep is the rest of feeling with you, in this way, that I'm watched, for the time, only as you watch me. It has all stopped, and *I* can stop. How can I make you understand what it is for me that there isn't at last a creature any more in sight, that the wood darkens about me, that the sounds drop and the relief goes on; what can it mean for you even that I've given myself up to not caring whether or no, amongst others, I'm missed and spoken of? It does help my strange case, in fine, as you see, to let you keep me here; but I should have found still more what I was in need of if I had only found, instead of you, him whom I had in mind. He is as much better than you as you are than everyone else." I finally felt, in a word, so qualified to attribute to my companion some such mute address as that, that it could only have, as the next consequence, a determining effect on me—an effect under the influence of which I spoke. "I parted with him, some way from here, some time ago. I had found him in one of the gardens with Lady John; after which we came away from her together. We strolled a little and talked, but I knew what he really wanted. He wanted to find you, and I told him he would probably do so at tea on the terrace. It was visibly with that idea—to return to the house—that he left me."

She looked at me for some time on this, taking it in, yet still afraid of it. "You found him with Lady John?" she at last asked, and with a note in her voice that made me see what—as there was a precaution I had neglected—she feared.

The perception of this, in its turn, operated with me for an instant almost as the rarest of temptations. I had puzzled out everything and put everything together; I was as morally confident and as intellectually triumphant as I have frankly here described myself; but there was no objective test to which I had yet exposed my theory. The chance to apply one—and it would be infallible—had suddenly cropped up. There would be excitement, amusement, discernment in it; it would be indeed but a more roundabout expression of interest and sympathy. It would, above all, pack the question I had for so many hours been occupied with into the compass of a needle-point. I was dazzled by my opportunity. She had had an uncertainty, in other words, as to whom I meant, and that it kept her for some seconds on the rack was a trifle compared to my chance. She would give herself away supremely if she showed she suspected me of placing my finger on the spot—if she understood the person I had not named to be nameable as Gilbert Long. What had created her peril, of course, was my naming Lady John. Well, how can I say in any sufficient way how much the extraordinary beauty of her eyes during this brevity of suspense had to do with the event? It had everything—for it was what caused me to be touched beyond even what I had already been, and I could literally bear no more of that. I therefore took no advantage, or took only the advantage I had spoken with the intention of taking. I laughed out doubtless too nervously, but it didn't compromise my tact. "Don't you know how she's perpetually pouncing on him?"

Still, however, I had not named him—which was what prolonged the tension. "Do you mean—a—do you mean——?" With which she broke off on a small weak titter and a still weaker exclamation. "There are so *many* gentlemen!"

There was something in it that might in other conditions have been as trivial as the giggle of a housemaid; but it had in fact for my ear the silver ring of poetry. I told her instantly whom I meant. "Poor Briss, you know," I said, "is always in her clutches."

Oh, how it let her off! And yet, no sooner had it done so and had I thereby tasted on the instant the sweetness of my wisdom, than I became aware of something much more extraordinary. It let her off—she showed me this for a minute, in spite of herself; but the next minute she showed me something quite different, which was, most wonderful of all, that she wished me to see her as not quite feeling why I should so much take for granted the person I *had* named. "Poor Briss?" her face and manner appeared suddenly to repeat—quite, moreover (and it was the drollest, saddest part), as if all our friends had stood about us to listen. Wherein did poor Briss so intimately concern her? What, pray, was my ground for such free reference to poor Briss? She quite repudiated poor Briss. She knew nothing at all about him, and the whole airy structure I had erected with his aid might have crumbled at the touch she thus administered if its solidity had depended only on that. I had a minute of surprise which, had it lasted another minute as surprise pure and simple, might almost as quickly have turned to something like chagrin. Fortunately it turned instead into something even more like enthusiasm than anything I had yet felt. The stroke *was* extraordinary, but extraordinary for its nobleness. I quickly saw in it, from the moment I had got my point of view, more fine things than ever. I saw for instance that, magnificently, she wished not to incriminate him. All that had passed between us had passed in silence, but it was a different matter for what might pass in sound. We looked at each other therefore with a strained smile over any question of identities. It was as if it had been one thing—to her confused, relaxed intensity—to give herself up to me, but quite another thing to give up somebody else.

And yet, superficially arrested as I was for the time, I directly afterwards recognised in this instinctive discrimination—the last, the expiring struggle of her native lucidity—a supremely convincing bit of evidence. It was still more convincing than if she had done any of the common things—stammered, changed colour, shown an apprehension of what the person named might have said to me. She had had it from me that he and I had talked about her, but there was nothing that she accepted the idea of his having been able to say. I saw—still more than this—that there was nothing to my purpose (since my purpose was to understand) that she would have had, as matters stood, coherence enough to impute to him. It was extremely curious to me to divine, just here, that she hadn't a glimmering of the real logic of Brissenden's happy effect on her nerves. It was the effect, as coming from him, that a beautiful delicacy forbade her as yet to give me her word for; and she was certainly herself in the stage of regarding it as an anomaly. Why, on the contrary, I might have wondered, shouldn't she have jumped at the chance, at the comfort, of seeing a preference trivial enough to be "worked" imputed to her? Why shouldn't she have been positively pleased that people might helpfully couple her name with that of the wrong man? Why, in short, in the language that Grace Brissenden and I had used together, was not that lady's husband the perfection of a red herring? Just because, I perceived, the relation that had established itself between them *was*, for its function, a real relation, the relation of a fellowship in resistance to doom.

Nothing could have been stranger than for *me* so to know it was while the stricken parties themselves were in ignorance; but nothing, at the same time, could have been, as I have since made out, more magnanimous than Mrs. Server's attitude. She moved, groping and panting, in the gathering dusk of her fate, but there were calculations she still could dimly make. One of these was that she must drag no one else in. I verily believe that, for that matter, she had scruples, poignant and exquisite, even about letting our friend himself see how much she liked to be with him. She wouldn't, at all events, let another see. I saw what I saw, I felt what I felt, but such things were exactly a sign that I could take care of myself. There was apparently, I was obliged to admit, but little apprehension in her of her unduly showing that *our* meeting had been anything of a blessing to her. There was no one indeed just then to be the wiser for it; I might perhaps else even have feared that she would have been influenced to treat the incident as closed. I had, for that matter, no wish to prolong it beyond her own convenience; it had already told me everything it could possibly tell. I thought I knew moreover what she would have got from it. I preferred, none the less, that we should separate by my own act; I wanted not to see her move in order to be free of me. So I stood up, to put her more at her ease, and it was while I remained before her that I tried to turn to her advantage what I had committed myself to about Brissenden.

"I had a fancy, at any rate, that he was looking for you—all the more that he didn't deny it."

She had not moved; she had let me take my hand from her own with as little sign as on her first feeling its touch. She only kept her eyes on me. "What made you have such a fancy?"

"What makes me ever have any?" I laughed. "My extraordinary interest in my fellow-creatures. I have more than most men. I've never really seen anyone with half so much. That breeds observation, and observation breeds ideas. Do you know what it has done?" I continued. "It has bred for me the idea that Brissenden's in love with you."

There was something in her eyes that struck me as betraying—and the appeal of it went to the heart—the constant dread that if entangled in talk she might show confusion. Nevertheless she brought out after a moment, as naturally and charmingly as possible: "How can that be when he's so strikingly in love with his wife?"

I gave her the benefit of the most apparent consideration. "Strikingly, you call it?"

"Why, I thought it was noticed—what he does for her."

"Well, of course she's extremely handsome—or at least extremely fresh and attractive. He *is* in love with her, no doubt, if you take it by the quarter, or by the year, like a yacht or a stable," I pushed on at random. "But isn't there such a state also as being in love by the day?"

She waited, and I guessed from the manner of it exactly why. It was the most obscure of intimations that she would have liked better that I shouldn't make her talk; but obscurity, by this time, offered me no more difficulties. The hint, none the less, a trifle disconcerted me, and, while I vaguely sought for some small provisional middle way between going and not going on, the oddest thing, as a fruit of my own delay, occurred. This was neither more nor less than the revival of her terrible little fixed smile. It came back as if with an audible click—as a gas-burner makes a pop when you light it. It told me visibly that from the moment she must talk she could talk only with its aid. The effect of its aid I indeed immediately perceived.

"How do I know?" she asked in answer to my question. "I've never *been* in love."

"Not even by the day?"

"Oh, a day's surely a long time."

"It is," I returned. "But I've none the less, more fortunately than you, been in love for a whole one." Then I continued, from an impulse of which I had just become conscious and that was clearly the result of the heart-breaking facial contortion—heart-breaking, that is, when one knew what I knew—by which she imagined herself to represent the pleasant give-and-take of society. This sense, for me, was a quick horror of forcing her, in such conditions, to talk at all. Poor Briss had mentioned to me, as an incident of his contact with her, his apprehension of her breaking down; and now, at a touch, I saw what he had meant. She *would* break down if I didn't look out. I found myself thus, from one minute to the other, as greatly dreading it for her, dreading it indeed for both of us, as I might have dreaded some physical accident or danger, her fall from an unmanageable horse or the crack beneath her of thin ice. It was impossible—that was the extraordinary impression—to come too much to her assistance. We had each of us all, in our way, hour after hour, been, as goodnaturedly as unwittingly, giving her a lift; yet what was the end of it but her still sitting there to assure me of a state of gratitude—that she couldn't even articulate—for every hint of a perch that might still be held out? What could only, therefore, in the connection, strike me as indicated was fairly to put into her mouth—if one might do so without showing too ungracefully as alarmed—the words one might have guessed her to wish to use were she able to use any. It was a small service of anticipation that I tried to render her with as little of an air as possible of being remedial. "I daresay you wonder," I remarked on these lines, "why, at all, I should have thrust Brissenden in."

"Oh, I *do* so wonder!" she replied with the refined but exaggerated glee that is a frequent form in high companies and light colloquies. I *did* help her—it was admirable to feel it. She liked my imposing on her no more complex a proposition. She liked my putting the thing to her so much better than she could have put it to me. But she immediately afterwards looked away as if—now that we *had* put it, and it didn't matter which of us best—we had nothing more to do with it. She gave me a hint of drops and inconsequences that might indeed have opened up abysses, and all the while she smiled and smiled. Yet whatever she did or failed of, as I even then observed to myself, how she remained lovely! One's pleasure in that helped one somehow not to break down on one's own side—since breaking down was in question—for commiseration. I didn't know what she might have hours of for the man—whoever he was—to whom her sacrifice had been made; but I doubted if for any other person she had ever been so beautiful as she was for me at these moments. To have kept her so, to have made her more so—how might that result of their relation not in fact have shone as a blinding light into the eyes of her lover? What would he have been bound to make out in her after all but her passion and her beauty? Wasn't it enough for such wonders as these to fill his consciousness? If they didn't fill mine—even though occupying so large a place in it—was that not only because I had not the direct benefit of them as the other party to the prodigy had it? They filled mine too, for that matter, just at this juncture, long enough for me to describe myself as rendered subject by them to a temporary loss of my thread. What *could* pass muster with her as an account of my reason for evoking the blighted identity of our friend? There came constantly into her aspect, I should say, the strangest alternatives, as I can only most conveniently call them, of presence and absence—something like intermissions of intensity, cessations and resumptions of life. They were like the slow flickers of a troubled flame, breathed upon and then left, burning up and burning down. She had really burnt down—I mean so far as her sense of things went—while I stood there.

I stood long enough to see that it didn't in the least signify whether or no I explained, and during this interval I found myself—to my surprise—in receipt of still better assistance than any I had to give. I had happened to turn, while I awkwardly enough, no doubt, rested and shifted, to the quarter from which Mrs. Server had arrived; and there, just at the end of the same vista, I gathered material for my proper reply. Her eyes at this moment were fixed elsewhere, and that gave me still a little more time, at the end of which my reference had all its point. "I supposed you to have Brissenden in your head," I said, "because it's evidently what he himself takes for granted. But let him tell you!" He was already close to us: missing her at the house, he had started again in search of her and had successfully followed. The effect on him of coming in sight of us had been for an instant to make him hang back as I had seen Mrs. Server hang. But he had then advanced just as she had done; I had waited for him to reach us; and now she saw him. She looked at him as she always looked at all of us, yet not at either of us as if we had lately been talking of him. If it was vacancy it was eloquent; if it was vigilance it was splendid. What was most curious, at all events, was that it was now poor Briss who was disconcerted. He had counted on finding her, but not on finding her with me, and I interpreted a certain ruefulness in him as the sign of a quick, uneasy sense that he must have been in question between us. I instantly felt that the right thing was to let him know he had been, and I mentioned to him, as a joke, that he had come just in time to save himself. We had been talking of him, and I wouldn't answer for what Mrs. Server had been going to say. He took it gravely, but he took everything so gravely that I saw no symptom in that. In fact, as he appeared at first careful not to meet my eyes, I saw for a minute or two no symptom in anything—in anything, at least, but the way in which, standing beside me and before Mrs. Server's bench, he received the conscious glare of her recognition without returning it and without indeed giving her a look. He looked all about—looked, as she herself had done after our meeting, at the charming place and its marks of the hour, at the rich twilight, deeper now in the avenues, and at the tree-tops and sky, more flushed now with colour. I found myself of a sudden quite as sorry for him as I had been for Mrs. Server, and I scarce know how it was suggested to me that during the short interval since our separation something had happened that made a difference in him. Was the difference a consciousness still more charged than I had left it? I couldn't exactly say, and the question really lost itself in what soon came uppermost for me—the desire, above all, to spare them both and to spare them equally.

The difficulty, however, was to spare them in some fashion that would not be more marked than continuing to observe them. To leave them together without a decent pretext would be marked; but this, I eagerly recognised, was none the less what most concerned me. Whatever they might see in it, there was by this time little enough doubt of how it would indicate for my own mind that the wheel had completely turned. That was the point to which I had been brought by the lapse of a few hours. I had verily travelled far since the sight of the pair on the terrace had given its arrest to my first talk with Mrs. Briss. I was obliged to admit to myself that nothing could very well have been more singular than some of my sequences. I had come round to the opposite pole of the protest my companion had then drawn from me—which was the pole of agreement with herself; and it hung sharply before me that I was pledged to confess to her my revolution. I couldn't now be in the presence of the two creatures I was in the very act of finally judging to be not a whit less stricken than I had originally imagined them—I couldn't do this and think with any complacency of the redemption of my pledge; for the process by which I had at last definitely inculpated Mrs. Server was precisely such a process of providential supervision as made me morally responsible, so to speak, for her, and thereby intensified my scruples. Well, my scruples had the last word—they were what determined me to look at my watch and profess that, whatever sense of a margin Brissenden and Mrs. Server might still enjoy, it behoved me not to forget that I took, on such great occasions, an hour to dress for dinner. It was a fairly crude cover for my retreat; perhaps indeed I should rather say that my retreat was practically naked and unadorned. It formulated their relation. I left them with the formula on their hands, both queerly staring at it, both uncertain what to do with it. For some passage that would soon be a correction of this, however, one might surely feel that one could trust them. I seemed to feel my trust justified, behind my back, before I had got twenty yards away. By the time I had done this, I must add, something further had befallen me. Poor Briss had met my eyes just previous to my flight, and it was then I satisfied myself of what had happened to him at the house. He had met his wife; she had in some way dealt with him; he had been with her, however briefly, alone; and the intimacy of their union had been afresh impressed upon him. Poor Briss, in fine, looked ten years older.

IX

I SHALL never forget the impressions of that evening, nor the way, in particular, the immediate effect of some of them was to merge the light of my extravagant perceptions in a glamour much more diffused. I remember feeling seriously warned, while dinner lasted, not to yield further to my idle habit of reading into mere human things an interest so much deeper than mere human things were in general prepared to supply. This especial hour, at Newmarch, had always a splendour that asked little of interpretation, that even carried itself, with an amiable arrogance, as indifferent to what the imagination could do for it. I think the imagination, in those halls of art and fortune, was almost inevitably accounted a poor matter; the whole place and its participants abounded so in pleasantness and picture, in all the felicities, for every sense, taken for granted there by the very basis of life, that even the sense most finely poetic, aspiring to extract the moral, could scarce have helped feeling itself treated to something of the snub that affects—when it does affect—the uninvited reporter in whose face a door is closed. I said to myself during dinner that these were scenes in which a transcendent intelligence had after all no application, and that, in short, any preposterous acuteness might easily suffer among them such a loss of dignity as overtakes the newspaperman kicked out. We existed, all of us together, to be handsome and happy, to be really what we looked—since we looked tremendously well; to be that and neither more nor less, so not discrediting by musty secrets and aggressive doubts our high privilege of harmony and taste. We were concerned only with what was bright and open, and the expression that became us all was, at worst, that of the shaded but gratified eye, the air of being forgivingly dazzled by too much lustre.

Mrs. Server, at table, was out of my range, but I wondered if, had she not been so, I shouldn't now have been moved to recognise in her fixed expressiveness nothing more than our common reciprocal tribute. Hadn't everyone my eyes could at present take in a fixed expressiveness? Was I not very possibly myself, on this ground of physiognomic congruity, more physiognomic than anyone else? I made my excellence, on the chance, go as far as it would to cover my temporary doubts. I saw Mrs. Brissenden, in another frock, naturally, and other jewels from those of the evening before; but she gave me, across the board, no more of a look than if she had quite done with me. It struck me that she felt she *had* done—that, as to the subject of our discussion, she deemed her case by this time so established as to offer comparatively little interest. I couldn't come to her to renew the discussion; I could only come to her to make my submission; and it doubtless appeared to her—to do her justice—more delicate not to triumph over me in advance. The profession of joy, however, reigned in her handsome face none the less largely for my not having the benefit of it. If I seem to falsify my generalisation by acknowledging that her husband, on the same side, made no more public profession of joy than usual, I am still justified by the fact that there was something in a manner decorative even in Brissenden's wonted gloom. He reminded me at this hour more than ever of some fine old Velasquez or other portrait—a presentation of ugliness and melancholy that might have been royal. There was as little of the common in his dry, distinguished patience as in the case I had made out for him. Blighted and ensconed, he looked at it over the rigid convention, his peculiar perfection of necktie, shirt-front and waistcoat, as some aged remnant of sovereignty at the opera looks over the ribbon of an order and the ledge of a box.

I must add, however, that in spite of my sense of his wife's indulgence I kept quite aware of the nearer approach, as course followed course, of my hour of reckoning with her—more and more saw the moment of the evening at which, frankly amused at last at having me in a cleft stick, she would draw me a little out of the throng. Of course, also, I was much occupied in asking myself to what degree I was prepared to be perjured. *Was* I ready to pretend that my candour was still unconvinced? And was I in this case only instinctively mustering my arguments? I was certainly as sorry that Mrs. Server was out of my view as if I proposed still to fight; and I really felt, so far as that went, as if there might be something to fight for after the lady on my left had given me a piece of news. I had asked her if she happened to know, as we couldn't see, who was next Mrs. Server, and, though unable to say at the moment, she made no scruple, after a short interval, of ascertaining with the last directness. The stretch forward in which she had indulged, or the information she had caused to be passed up to her while I was again engaged on my right, established that it was Lord Lutley who had brought the lovely lady in and that it was Mr. Long who was on her other side. These things indeed were not the finest point of my companion's communication, for I saw that what she felt I would be really interested in was the fact that Mr. Long had brought in Lady John, who was naturally, therefore, his other neighbour. Beyond Lady John was Mr. Obert, and beyond Mr. Obert Mrs. Froome, not, for a wonder, this time paired, as by the immemorial tradition, so fairly comical in its candour, with Lord Lutley. Wasn't it too funny, the kind of grandmotherly view of their relation shown in their always being put together? If I perhaps questioned whether "grandmotherly" were exactly the name for the view, what yet at least was definite in the light of this evening's arrangement was that there did occur occasions on which they were put apart. My friend of course disposed of this observation by the usual exception that "proved the rule"; but it was absurd how I had thrilled with her announcement, and our exchange of ideas meanwhile helped to carry me on.

My theory had not at all been framed to embrace the phenomenon thus presented; it had been precisely framed, on the contrary, to hang together with the observed inveteracy of escape, on the part of the two persons about whom it busied itself, from public juxtaposition of more than a moment. I was fairly upset by the need to consider at this late hour whether going in for a new theory or bracing myself for new facts would hold out to me the better refuge. It is perhaps not too much to say that I should scarce have been able to sit still at all but for the support afforded me by the oddity of the separation of Lord Lutley and Mrs. Froome; which, though resting on a general appearance directly opposed to that of my friends, offered somehow the relief of a suggestive analogy. What I could directly clutch at was that if the exception did prove the rule in the one case it might equally prove it in the other. If on a rare occasion one of these couples might be divided, so, by as uncommon a chance, the other might be joined; the only difference being in the gravity of the violated law. For which pair was the betrayal greatest? It was not till dinner was nearly ended and the ladies were about to withdraw that I recovered lucidity to make out how much more machinery would have had to be put into motion consistently to prevent, than once in a way to minimise, the disconcerting accident.

All accidents, I must add, were presently to lose themselves in the unexpectedness of my finding myself, before we left the dining-room, in easy talk with Gilbert Long—talk that was at least easy for *him*, whatever it might have struck me as necessarily destined to be for me. I felt as he approached me—for he did approach me—that it was somehow "important"; I was so aware that something in the state of my conscience would have prevented me from assuming conversation between us to be at this juncture possible. The state of my conscience was that I knew too much—that no one had really any business to know what I knew. If he suspected but the fiftieth part of it there was no simple spirit in which he could challenge me. It would have been simple of course to desire to knock me down, but that was barred by its being simple to excess. It wouldn't even have been enough for him merely to ground it on a sudden fancy. It fitted, in fine, with my cogitations that it was so significant for him to wish to speak to me that I didn't envy him his attempt at the particular shade of assurance required for carrying the thing off. He would have learned from Mrs. Server that I was not, as regarded them, at all as others were; and thus his idea, the fruit of that stimulation, could only be either to fathom, to felicitate, or—as it were—to destroy me. What was at the same time obvious was that no one of these attitudes would go quite of itself. The simple sight of him as he quitted his chair to take one nearer my own brought home to me in a flash—and much more than anything had yet done—the real existence in him of the condition it was my private madness (none the less private for Grace Brissenden's so limited glimpse of it,) to believe I had coherently stated. Is not this small touch perhaps the best example I can give of the intensity of amusement I had at last enabled my private madness to yield me? I found myself owing it, from this time on and for the rest of the evening, moments of the highest concentration.

Whatever there might have been for me of pain or doubt was washed straight out by the special sensation of seeing how "clever" poor Long not only would have to be, but confidently and actually *was*; inasmuch as this apprehension seemed to put me in possession of his cleverness, besides leaving me all my own. I made him welcome, I helped him to another cigarette, I felt above all that I should enjoy him; my response to his overture was, in other words, quickly enough to launch us. Yet I fear I can do little justice to the pleasant suppressed tumult of impression and reflection that, on my part, our ten minutes together produced. The elements that mingled in it scarce admit of discrimination. It was still more than previously a deep sense of being justified. My interlocutor was for those ten minutes immeasurably superior—superior, I mean, to himself—and he couldn't possibly have become so save through the relation I had so patiently tracked. He faced me there with another light than his own, spoke with another sound, thought with another ease and understood with another ear. I should put it that what came up between us was the mere things of the occasion, were it not for the fine point to which, in my view, the things of the occasion had been brought. While our eyes, at all events, on either side, met serenely, and our talk, dealing with the idea, dealing with the extraordinary special charm, of the social day now deepening to its end, touched our companions successively, touched the manner in which this one and that had happened to be predominantly a part of that charm; while such were our immediate conditions I wondered of course if he had not, just as consciously and essentially as I, quite another business in mind. It was not indeed that our allusion to the other business would not have been wholly undiscoverable by a third person.

So far as it took place it was of a "subtlety," as we used to say at Newmarch, in relation to which the common register of that pressure would have been, I fear, too old-fashioned a barometer. I had moreover the comfort—for it amounted to that—of perceiving after a little that we understood each other too well for our understanding really to have tolerated the interference of passion, such passion as would have been represented on his side by resentment of my intelligence and on my side by resentment of his. The high sport of such intelligence—between gentlemen, to the senses of any other than whom it must surely be closed—demanded and implied in its own intimate interest a certain amenity. Yes, accordingly, I had promptly got the answer that my wonder at his approach required: he had come to me for the high sport. He would formerly have been incapable of it, and he was beautifully capable of it now. It was precisely the kind of high sport—the play of perception, expression, sociability—in which Mrs. Server would a year or two before have borne as light a hand. I need scarcely add how little it would have found itself in that lady's present chords. He had said to me in our ten minutes everything amusing she couldn't have said. Yet if when our host gave us the sign to adjourn to the drawing-room so much as all this had grown so much clearer, I had still, figuratively speaking, a small nut or two left to crack. By the time we moved away together, however, these resistances had yielded. The answers had really only been waiting for the questions. The play of Long's mind struck me as more marked, since the morning, by the same amount, as it might have been called, as the march of poor Briss's age; and if I had, a while before, in the wood, had my explanation of this latter addition, so I had it now of the former—as to which I shall presently give it.

When music, in English society, as we know, is not an accompaniment to the voice, the voice can in general be counted on to assert its pleasant identity as an accompaniment to music; but at Newmarch we had been considerably schooled, and this evening, in the room in which most of us had assembled, an interesting pianist, who had given a concert the night before at the near county town and been brought over during the day to dine and sleep, would scarce have felt in any sensitive fibre that he was not having his way with us. It may just possibly have been an hallucination of my own, but while we sat together after dinner in a dispersed circle I could have worked it out that, as a company, we were considerably conscious of some experience, greater or smaller from one of us to the other, that had prepared us for the player's spell. Felicitously scattered and grouped, we might in almost any case have had the air of looking for a message from it—of an imagination to be flattered, nerves to be quieted, sensibilities to be soothed. The whole scene was as composed as if there were scarce one of us but had a secret thirst for the infinite to be quenched. And it was the infinite that, for the hour, the distinguished foreigner poured out to us, causing it to roll in wonderful waves of sound, almost of colour, over our receptive attitudes and faces. Each of us, I think, now wore the expression—or confessed at least to the suggestion—of some indescribable thought; which might well, it was true, have been nothing more unmentionable than the simple sense of how the posture of deference to this noble art has always a certain personal grace to contribute. We neglected nothing of it that could make our general effect ample, and whether or no we were kept quiet by the piano, we were at least admonished, to and fro, by our mutual visibility, which each of us clearly, desired to make a success. I have little doubt, furthermore, that to each of us was due, as the crown of our inimitable day, the imputation of having something quite of our own to think over.

We thought, accordingly—we continued to think, and I felt that, by the law of the occasion, there had as yet been for everyone no such sovereign warrant for an interest in the private affairs of everyone else. As a result of this influence all that at dinner had begun to fade away from me came back with a rush and hovered there with a vividness. I followed many trains and put together many pieces; but perhaps what I most did was to render a fresh justice to the marvel of our civilised state. The perfection of that, enjoyed as we enjoyed it, all made a margin, a series of concentric circles of rose-colour (shimmering away into the pleasant vague of everything else that didn't matter,) for the so salient little figure of Mrs. Server, still the controlling image for me, the real principle of composition, in this affluence of fine things. What, for my part, while I listened, I most made out was the beauty and the terror of conditions so highly organised that under their rule her small lonely fight with disintegration could go on without the betrayal of a gasp or a shriek, and with no worse tell-tale contortion of lip or brow than the vibration, on its golden stem, of that constantly renewed flower of amenity which my observation had so often and so mercilessly detached only to find again in its place. This flower nodded perceptibly enough in our deeply stirred air, but there was a peace, none the less, in feeling the spirit of the wearer to be temporarily at rest. There was for the time no gentleman on whom she need pounce, no lapse against which she need guard, no presumption she need create, nor any suspicion she need destroy. In this pause in her career it came over me that I should have liked to leave her; it would have prepared for me the pleasant after-consciousness that I had seen her pass, as I might say, in music out of sight.

But we were, alas! all too much there, too much tangled and involved for that; every actor in the play that had so unexpectedly insisted on constituting itself for me sat forth as with an intimation that they were not to be so easily disposed of. It was as if there were some last act to be performed before the curtain could fall. Would the definite dramatic signal for ringing the curtain down be then only—as a grand climax and *coup de théâtre*—the due attestation that poor Briss had succumbed to inexorable time and Mrs. Server given way under a cerebral lesion? Were the rest of us to disperse decorously by the simple action of the discovery that, on our pianist's striking his last note, with its consequence of permitted changes of attitude, Gilbert Long's victim had reached the point of final simplification and Grace Brissenden's the limit of age recorded of man? I could look at neither of these persons without a sharper sense of the contrast between the tragedy of their predicament and the comedy of the situation that did everything for them but suspect it. They had truly been arrayed and anointed, they had truly been isolated, for their sacrifice. I was sufficiently aware even then that if one hadn't known it one might have seen nothing; but I was not less aware that one couldn't know anything without seeing all; and so it was that, while our pianist played, my wandering vision played and played as well. It took in again, while it went from one of them to the other, the delicate light that each had shed on the other, and it made me wonder afresh what still more delicate support they themselves might not be in the very act of deriving from their dim community. It was for the glimmer of this support that I had left them together two or three hours before; yet I was obliged to recognise that, travel between them as my fancy might, it could detect nothing in the way of a consequent result. I caught no look from either that spoke to me of service rendered them; and I caught none, in particular, from one of them to the other, that I could read as a symptom of their having compared notes. The fellow-feeling of each for the lost light of the other remained for me but a tie supposititious—the full-blown flower of my theory. It would show here as another flower, equally mature, for me to have made out a similar dim community between Gilbert Long and Mrs. Brissenden—to be able to figure them as groping side by side, proportionately, towards a fellowship of light overtaken; but if I failed of this, for ideal symmetry, that seemed to rest on the general truth that joy brings people less together than sorrow.

So much for the course of my impressions while the music lasted—a course quite consistent with my being prepared for new combinations as soon as it was over. Promptly, when that happened, the bow was unbent; and the combination I first seized, amid motion and murmur and rustle, was that, once more, of poor Briss and Lady John, the latter of whom had already profited by the general reaction to endeavour to cultivate afresh the vainest of her sundry appearances. She had laid on him the same coercive hand to which I owed my having found him with her in the afternoon, but my intervention was now to operate with less ceremony. I chanced to be near enough to them for Brissenden, on seeing me, to fix his eyes on me in silence, but in a manner that could only bring me immediately nearer. Lady John never did anything in silence, but she greeted me as I came up to them with a fine false alarm. "No, indeed," she cried, "you shan't carry him off this time!"—and poor Briss disappeared, leaving us face to face, even while she breathed defiance. He had made no joke of it, and I had from him no other recognition; it was therefore a mere touch, yet it gave me a sensible hint that he had begun, as things were going, to depend upon me, that I already in a fashion figured to him—and on amazingly little evidence after all—as his natural protector, his providence, his effective omniscience. Like Mrs. Server herself, he was materially on my hands, and it was proper I should "do" for him. I wondered if he were really beginning to look to me to avert his inexorable fate. Well, if his inexorable fate was to be an unnameable climax, it had also its special phases, and one of these I *had* just averted. I followed him a moment with my eyes, and I then observed to Lady John that she decidedly took me for too simple a person. She had meanwhile also watched the direction taken by her liberated victim, and was the next instant prepared with a reply to my charge. "Because he has gone to talk with May Server? I don't quite see what you mean, for I believe him really to be in terror of her. Most of the men here *are*, you know, and I've really assured myself that he doesn't find her any less awful than the rest. He finds her the more so by just the very marked extra attention that you may have noticed she has given him."

"And does that now happen to be what he has so eagerly gone off to impress upon her?"

Lady John was so placed that she could continue to look at our friends, and I made out in her that she was not, in respect to them, without some slight elements of perplexity. These were even sufficient to make her temporarily neglect the defence of the breach I had made in her consistency. "If you mean by 'impressing upon' her speaking to her, he hasn't gone—you can see for yourself—to impress upon her anything; they have the most extraordinary way, which I've already observed, of sitting together without sound. I don't know," she laughed, "what's the matter with such people!"

"It proves in general," I admitted, "either some coldness or some warmth, and I quite understand that that's not the way *you* sit with your friends. You steer admirably clear of every extravagance. I don't see, at any rate, why Mrs. Server is a terror——"

But she had already taken me up. "If she doesn't chatter as *I* do?" She thought it over. "But she does—to everyone but Mr. Briss. I mean to every man she can pick up."

I emulated her reflection. "Do they complain of it to you?"

"They're more civil than you," she returned; "for if, when they flee before it, they bump up against me in their flight, they don't explain that by intimating that they're come from bad to worse. Besides, I see what they suffer."

"And do you hear it?"

"What they suffer? No, I've taken care not to suffer myself. I don't listen. It's none of my business."

"Is that a way of gently expressing," I ventured to ask, "that it's also none of mine?"

"It might be," she replied, "if I had, as you appear to, the imagination of atrocity. But I don't pretend to so much as conceive what's your business."

"I wonder if it isn't just now," I said after a moment, "to convict you of an attempt at duplicity that has not even had the saving grace of success! Was it for Brissenden himself that you spoke just now as if you believed him to wish to cling to you?"

"Well, I'm kind enough for anything," she goodnaturedly enough laughed. "But what," she asked more sharply, "are you trying to find out?"

Such an awful lot, the answer to this would politely have been, that I daresay the aptness of the question produced in my face a shade of embarrassment. I felt, however, the next moment that I needn't fear too much. What I, on approaching Lady John, had found myself moved to test, using her in it as a happy touchstone, was the degree of the surrounding, the latent, sense of things: an impulse confirmed by the manner in which she had momentarily circled about the phenomenon of Mrs. Server's avidity, about the mystery of the terms made with it by our friend. It was present to me that if I could catch, on the part of my interlocutress, anything of a straight scent, I might take that as the measure of a diffused danger. I mentally applied this term to the possibility of diffusion, because I suddenly found myself thinking with a kind of horror of any accident by which I might have to expose to the world, to defend against the world, to share with the world, that now so complex tangle of hypotheses that I have had for convenience to speak of as my theory. I could toss the ball myself, I could catch it and send it back, and familiarity had now made this exercise—in my own inner precincts— easy and safe. But the mere brush of Lady John's clumsier curiosity made me tremble for the impunity of my creation. If there had been, so to speak, a discernment, however feeble, of *my* discernment, it would have been irresistible to me to take this as the menace of some incalculable catastrophe or some public ugliness. It wasn't for me definitely to image the logical result of a verification by the sense of others of the matter of my vision; but the thing had only to hang before me as a chance for me to feel that I should utterly object to it, though I may appear to weaken this statement if I add that the opportunity to fix the degree of my actual companion's betrayed mystification was almost a spell. This, I conceive, was just by reason of what was at stake. How could I happily tell her what I was trying to find out?—tell her, that is, not too much for security and yet enough for relief? The best answer seemed a brave jump. I was conscious of a certain credit open with her in my appearance of intellectual sympathy.

"Well," I brought out at last, "I'm quite aching to ask you if you'll forgive me a great liberty, which I owe to your candid challenge my opportunity to name. Will you allow me to say frankly that I think you play a dangerous game with poor Briss, in whom I confess I'm interested? I don't of course speak of the least danger to yourself; but it's an injustice to any man to make use of him quite so flagrantly. You don't in the least flatter yourself that the poor fellow is in love with you—you wouldn't care a bit if he were. Yet you're willing to make him think you like him, so far as that may be necessary to explain your so frequently ingenious appropriation of him. He doesn't like you *too* much, as yet; doesn't even like you quite enough. But your potency may, after all, work on him, and then, as your interest is so obviously quite elsewhere, what will happen will be that you'll find, to your inconvenience, that you've gone too far. A man never likes a woman enough unless he likes her *more* than enough. Unfortunately it's what the inveterate ass is sure sooner or later to do."

Lady John looked just enough interested to look detached from most of the more vulgar liabilities to offence. "Do I understand that to be the pretty name by which you describe Mr. Briss?"

"He has his share of it, for I'm thinking of the idiots that we everyone of us are. I throw out a warning against a contingency."

"Are you providing for the contingency of his ceasing to care for his wife? If you are"—and Lady John's amusement took on a breadth—"you may be said to have a prudent mind and to be taking time by the forelock."

At this I pricked up my ears. "Do you mean because of his apparently incorruptible constancy?"

"I mean because the whole thing's so before one. She has him so in hand that they're neither of them in as much danger as would count for a mouse. It doesn't prevent his liking to dally by the way—for *she* dallies by the way, and he does everything she does. Haven't I observed her," Lady John continued, "dallying a little, so far as that goes, with *you*? You've the tact to tell me that he doesn't think me good enough, but I don't require, do I?—for such a purpose as his—to be very extraordinarily good. You may say that you wrap

307

it up immensely and try to sugar the dose! Well, all the same, give up, for a quiet life, the attempt to be a providence. You can't be a providence and not be a bore. A real providence *knows*; whereas you," said Lady John, making her point neatly, "have to find out—and to find out even by asking 'the likes of' *me*. Your fine speech meanwhile doesn't a bit tell me what."

It affected me again that she could get so near without getting nearer. True enough it was that I wanted to find out; and though I might expect, or fear, too much of her, I wondered at her only seeing this—at her not reading deeper. The peril of the public ugliness that haunted me rose or fell, at this moment, with my varying view of her density. Or rather, to be more exact, I already saw her as necessarily stupid because I saw her as extravagantly vain. What I see now of course is that I was on my own side almost stupidly hard with her—as I may also at that hour have been subject to her other vice. Didn't I perhaps, in proportion as I felt how little she saw, think awfully well of myself, as we said at Newmarch, for seeing so much more? It comes back to me that the sense thus established of my superior vision may perfectly have gone a little to my head. If it was a frenzied fallacy I was all to blame, but if it was anything else whatever it was naturally intoxicating. I really remember in fact that nothing so much as this confirmed presumption of my impunity had appeared to me to mark the fine quality of my state. I think there must fairly have been a pitch at which I was not sure that not to partake of that state was, on the part of others, the sign of a gregarious vulgarity; as if there were a positive advantage, an undiluted bliss, in the intensity of consciousness that I had reached. *I* alone was magnificently and absurdly aware—everyone else was benightedly out of it. So I reflected that there would be almost nothing I mightn't with safety mention to my present subject of practice as an acknowledgment that I was meddlesome. I could put no clue in her hand that her notorious acuteness would make of the smallest use to her. The most she could do would be to make it of use to myself, and the clue it seemed best to select was therefore a complete confession of guilt.

"You've a lucidity of your own in which I'm forced to recognise that the highest purity of motive looks shrivelled and black. You bring out accordingly what has made me thus beat about the bush. Have you really such a fund of indulgence for Gilbert Long as we most of us, I gather—though perhaps in our blindness—seem to see it stick out again that he supposes? *May* he fondly feel that he can continue to count on it? Or, if you object to my question in that form, is it not, frankly, to making his attitude—after all so thoroughly public—more convenient to each of you that (without perhaps quite measuring what you're about,) you've gone on sacrificing poor Briss? I call it sacrificing, you see, in spite of there having been as yet no such great harm done. And if you ask me again what business of mine such inquiries may represent, why, the best thing will doubtless be to say to you that, with a smaller dose of irrepressible irony in my composition than you have in yours, I can't make so light as you of my tendency to worry on behalf of those I care for. Let me finally hasten to add that I'm not now including in that category either of the two gentlemen I've named."

I freely concede, as I continue my record, that to follow me at all, at this point, gave proof on Lady John's part of a faculty that should have prevented my thinking of her as inordinately backward. "Then who in the world *are* these objects of your solicitude?"

I showed, over and above my hesitation, my regret for the need of it. "I'm afraid I can't tell you."

At this, not unnaturally, she fairly scoffed. "Asking me everything and telling me nothing, you nevertheless look to me to satisfy you? Do you mean," she pursued, "that you speak for persons whose interest is more legitimately founded than the interest you so flatteringly attribute to myself?"

"Well, yes—let them be so described! Can't you guess," I further risked, "who constitutes at least *one* of my preoccupations?"

The condescension of her consent to think marked itself handsomely enough. "Is it your idea to pretend to me that I'm keeping Grace Brissenden awake?" There was consistency enough in her wonder. "She has not been anything but nice to me; she's not a person whose path one crosses without finding it out; and I can't imagine what has got into her if any such grievance as that is what she has been pouring out to you in your apparently so deep confabulations."

This toss of the ball was one that, I saw quickly enough, even a taste for sport wouldn't justify my answering, and my logical interest lay moreover elsewhere. "Dear no! Mrs. Brissenden certainly feels her strength, and I should never presume to take under my charge any personal situation of hers. I had in my mind a very different identity."

Lady John, as if to be patient with me, looked about at our companions for a hint of it, wondering which of the ladies I might have been supposed to "care for" so much as to tolerate in her a preference for a rival; but the effect of this survey was, I the next instant observed, a drop of her attention from what I had been saying. Her eye had been caught by the sight of Gilbert Long within range of us, and then had been just visibly held by the fact that the person seated with him on one of the small sofas that almost of necessity made conversation intimate was the person whose name, just uttered between us, was, in default of the name she was in search of, still in the air. Gilbert Long and Mrs. Briss were in familiar colloquy—though I was aware, at the first flush, of nothing in this that should have made my interlocutress stare. That is I was aware of nothing but that I had simultaneously myself been moved to some increase of sharpness. What *could* I have known that should have caused me to wonder at the momentary existence of this particular conjunction of minds unless it were simply the fact that I hadn't seen it occur amid the many conjunctions I had already noticed—*plus* the fact that I had a few minutes before, in the interest of the full roundness of my theory, actually been missing it? These two persons had met in my presence at Paddington and had travelled together under my eyes; I had talked of Mrs. Briss with Long and of Long with Mrs. Briss; but the vivid picture that their social union forthwith presented stirred within me, though so strangely late in the day, it might have seemed, for such an emotion, more than enough freshness of impression. Yet—now that I did have it there—why should it be vivid, why stirring, why a picture at all? Was *any* temporary collocation, in a house so encouraging to sociability, out of the range of nature? Intensely prompt, I need scarcely say, were both my freshness and my perceived objections to it. The happiest objection, could I have taken time to phrase it, would doubtless have been that the particular effect of this juxtaposition—to my eyes at least—was a thing not to have been foreseen. The parties to it looked, certainly, as I felt that I hadn't prefigured them; though even this, for my reason, was not a description of their aspect. Much less was it a description for the intelligence of Lady John—to whom, however, after all, some formulation of what she dimly saw would not be so indispensable.

We briefly watched, at any rate, together, and as our eyes met again we moreover confessed that we had watched. And we could ostensibly have offered each other no explanation of that impulse save that we had been talking of those concerned as separate and that it was in consequence a little odd to find ourselves suddenly seeing them as one. For that was it—they *were* as one; as one, at all events, for *my* large reading. My large reading had meanwhile, for the convenience of the rest of my little talk with Lady John, to make itself as small as possible. I had an odd sense, till we fell apart again, as of keeping my finger rather stiffly fixed on a passage in a favourite author on which I had not previously lighted. I held the book out of sight and behind me; I spoke of things that were not at all in it—or not at all on that particular page; but my volume, none the less, was only waiting. What might be written there hummed already in my ears as a result of my mere glimpse. Had *they* also wonderfully begun to know? Had *she*, most wonderfully, and had they, in that case, prodigiously come together on it? This was a possibility into which my imagination could dip even deeper than into the depths over which it had conceived the other pair as hovering. These opposed couples balanced like bronze groups at the two ends of a chimney-piece, and the most I could say to myself in lucid deprecation of my thought was that I mustn't take them equally for granted merely *because* they balanced. Things in the real had a way of not balancing; it was all an affair, this fine symmetry, of artificial proportion. Yet even while I kept my eyes away from Mrs. Briss and Long it was vivid to me that, "composing" there beautifully, they could scarce help playing a part in my exhibition. The mind of man, furthermore—and my generalisation pressed hard, with a quick twist, on the supersubtlety as to which I had just been privately complacent—the mind of man doubtless didn't know from one minute to the other, under the appeal of phantasmagoric life, what it would profitably be at. It had struck me a few seconds before as vulgarly gross in Lady John that she was curious, or conscious, of so small a part; in spite of which I was already secretly wincing at the hint that these others had begun to find themselves less in the dark and perhaps even directly to exchange their glimmerings.

My personal privilege, on the basis of the full consciousness, had become, on the spot, in the turn of an eye, more than questionable, and I was really quite scared at the chance of having to face—of having to see *them* face— another recognition. What did this alarm imply but the complete reversal of my estimate of the value of perception? Mrs. Brissenden and Long had been hitherto magnificently without it, and I was responsible perhaps for having, in a mood practically much stupider than the stupidest of theirs, put them gratuitously and helplessly *on* it. To be without it was the most consistent, the most successful, because the most amiable, form of selfishness; and why should people admirably equipped for remaining so, people bright and insolent in their prior state, people in whom this state was to have been respected as a surface without a scratch is respected, be made to begin to vibrate, to crack and split, from within? Wasn't it enough for *me* to pay, vicariously, the tax on being absurd? Were we all to be landed, without an issue or a remedy, in a condition on which that tax would be generally levied? It was as if, abruptly, with a new emotion, I had wished to unthink every thought with which I had been occupied for twenty-four hours. Let me add, however, that even had this process been manageable I was aware of not proposing to begin it till I should have done with Lady John.

The time she took to meet my last remark is naturally not represented by this prolonged glance of mine at the amount of suggestion that just then happened to reach me from the other quarter. It at all events duly came out between us that Mrs. Server was the person I did have on my mind; and I remember that it had seemed to me at the end of a minute to matter comparatively little by which of us, after all, she was first designated. There is perhaps an oddity—which I must set down to my emotion of the moment— in my not now being able to say. I should have been hugely startled if the sight of Gilbert Long had appeared to make my companion suddenly think of her; and reminiscence of that shock is not one of those I have found myself storing up. What does abide with me is the memory of how, after a little, my apprehensions, of various kinds, dropped—most of all under the deepening conviction that Lady John was not a whit less agreeably superficial than I could even at the worst have desired. The point established for me was that, whereas she passed with herself and so many others as taking in everything, she had taken in nothing whatever that it was to my purpose she should not take. Vast, truly, was the world of observation, that we could both glean in it so actively without crossing each other's steps. There we stood close together, yet—save for the accident of a final dash, as I shall note—were at opposite ends of the field.

It's a matter as to which the truth sounds priggish, but I can't help it if—yes, positively—it affected me as hopelessly vulgar to have made any induction at all about our companions *but* those I have recorded, in such detail, on behalf of my own energy. It was better verily not to have touched them—which was the case of everyone else—than to have taken them up, with knowing gestures, only to do so little with them. That I felt the interest of May Server, that May Server felt the interest of poor Briss, and that my feeling incongruously presented itself as putting up, philosophically, with the inconvenience of the lady's—these were, in fine, circumstances to which she clearly attached ideas too commonplace for me to judge it useful to gather them in. She read all things, Lady John, heaven knows, in the light of the universal possibility of a "relation"; but most of the relations that she had up her sleeve could thrust themselves into my theory only to find themselves, the next minute, eliminated. They were of alien substance—insoluble in the whole. Gilbert Long had for her no connection, in my deeper sense, with Mrs. Server, nor Mrs. Server with Gilbert Long, nor the husband with the wife, nor the wife with the husband, nor I with either member of either pair, nor anyone with anything, nor anything with anyone. She was thus exactly where I wanted her to be, for, frankly, I became conscious, at this climax of my conclusion, that I a little wanted her to be where she had distinctly ended by betraying to me that her proper inspiration had placed her. If I have just said that my apprehensions, of various kinds, had finally and completely subsided, a more exact statement would perhaps have been that from the moment our eyes met over the show of our couple on the sofa, the question of any other calculable thing than *that* hint of a relation had simply known itself superseded. Reduced to its plainest terms, this sketch of an improved acquaintance between our comrades was designed to make Lady John think. It was designed to make me do no less, but we thought, inevitably, on different lines.

I have already so represented my successions of reflection as rapid that I may not appear to exceed in mentioning the amusement and philosophy with which I presently perceived it as unmistakable that she believed in the depth of her new sounding. It visibly went down for her much nearer to the bottom of the sea than any plumb I might be qualified to drop. Poor Briss was in love with his wife—that, when driven to the wall, she had had to recognise; but she had not had to recognise that his wife was in love with poor Briss. What was then to militate, on that lady's part, against a due consciousness, at the end of a splendid summer day, a day on which occasions had been so multiplied, of an impression of a special order? What was to prove that there was "nothing in it" when two persons sat looking so very exceptionally *much* as if there were everything in it, as if they were for the first time—thanks to finer opportunity—doing each other full justice? Mustn't it indeed at this juncture have come a little over my friend that Grace had lent herself with uncommon good nature, the previous afternoon, to the arrangement by which, on the way from town, her ladyship's reputation was to profit by no worse company, precisely, than poor Briss's? Mrs. Brissenden's own was obviously now free to profit by my companion's remembering—if the fact had reached her ears—that Mrs. Brissenden had meanwhile had Long for an escort. So much, at least, I saw Lady John as seeing, and my vision may be taken as representing the dash I have confessed myself as making from my end of our field. It offers us, to be exact, as jostling each other just sensibly—though *I* only might feel the bruise—in our business of picking up straws. Our view of the improved acquaintance was only a straw, but as I stooped to it I felt my head bump with my neighbour's. This might have made me ashamed of my eagerness, but, oddly enough, that effect was not to come. I felt in fact that, since we had even pulled against each other at the straw, I carried off, in turning away, the larger piece.

IT was in the moment of turning away that I somehow learned, without looking, that Mrs. Brissenden had also immediately moved. I wanted to look and yet had my reasons for not appearing to do it too quickly; in spite of which I found my friends, even after an interval, still distinguishable as separating for the avoidance of comment. Gilbert Long, rising directly after his associate, had already walked away, but this associate, lingering where she stood and meeting me with it, availed herself of the occasion to show that she wished to speak to me. Such was the idea she threw out on my forthwith going to her. "For a few minutes—presently."

"Do you mean alone? Shall I come with you?"

She hesitated long enough for me to judge her as a trifle surprised at my being so ready—as if indeed she had rather hoped I wouldn't be; which would have been an easy pretext to her to gain time. In fact, with a face not quite like the brave face she had at each step hitherto shown me, yet unlike in a fashion I should certainly not have been able to define on the spot; with an expression, in short, that struck me as taking refuge in a general reminder that not my convenience, but her own, was in question, she replied: "Oh, no— but before it's too late. A few minutes hence. Where shall you be?" she asked with a shade, as I imagined, of awkwardness. She had looked about as for symptoms of acceptance of the evening's end on the part of the ladies, but we could both see our hostess otherwise occupied. "We don't go up quite yet. In the morning," she added as with an afterthought, "I suppose you leave early."

I debated. "I haven't thought. And you?"

She looked at me straighter now. "I haven't thought either." Then she was silent, neither turning away nor coming to the point, as it seemed to me she might have done, of telling me what she had in her head. I even fancied that her momentary silence, combined with the way she faced me—as if that might speak for her—was meant for an assurance that, whatever train she should take in the morning, she would arrange that it shouldn't be, as it had been the day before, the same as mine. I really caught in her attitude a world of invidious reference to the little journey we had already made together. She had sympathies, she had proprieties that imposed themselves, and I was not to think that any little journey was to be thought of again in those conditions. It came over me that this might have been quite a matter discussed by her, discussed and settled, with her interlocutor on the sofa. It came over me that if, before our break-up for the night, I should happen also to have a minute's talk with that interlocutor, I would equally get from it the sense of an intention unfavourable to our departing in the same group. And I wondered if this, in that case, wouldn't affect me as marking a change back to Long's old manner—a forfeiture of the conditions, whatever view might be taken of them, that had made him, at Paddington, suddenly show himself as so possible and so pleasant. If *he* "changed back," wouldn't Grace Brissenden change by the same law? And if Grace Brissenden did, wouldn't her husband? Wouldn't the miracle take the form of the rejuvenation of that husband? Would it, still by the same token, take the form of *her* becoming very old, becoming if not as old as her husband, at least as old, as one might say, as herself? Would it take the form of her becoming dreadfully plain— plain with the plainness of mere stout maturity and artificial preservation? And if it took this form for the others, which would it take for May Server? Would she, at a bound as marked as theirs, recover her presence of mind and her lost equipment?

The kind of suspense that these rising questions produced for me suffered naturally no drop after Mrs. Briss had cut everything short by rustling voluminously away. She had something to say to me, and yet she hadn't; she had nothing to say, and yet I felt her to have already launched herself in a statement. There were other persons I had made uncomfortable without at all intending it, but she at least had not suffered from me, and I had no wish that she should; according to which she had no pressure to fear. My suspense, in spite of this, remained—indeed all the more sensibly that I had suddenly lost my discomfort on the subject of redeeming my pledge to her. It had somehow left me at a stroke, my dread of her calling me, as by our agreement, to submit in respect to what we had talked of as the identification of the woman. That call had been what I looked for from her after she had seen me break with Lady John; my first idea *then* could only be that I must come, as it were, to time. It was strange that, the next minute, I should find myself sure that I was, as I may put it, free; it was at all events indisputable that as I stood there watching her recede and fairly studying, in my preoccupation, her handsome affirmative back and the special sweep of her long dress—it was indisputable that, on some intimation I could, at the instant, recognise but not seize, my consciousness was aware of having performed a full revolution. If I was free, that was what I had been only so short a time before, what I had been as I drove, in London, to the station. Was this now a foreknowledge that, on the morrow, in driving away, I should feel myself restored to that blankness? The state lost was the state of exemption from intense obsessions, and the state recovered would therefore logically match it. If the foreknowledge had thus, as by the stir of the air from my friend's whisk of her train, descended upon me, my liberation was in a manner what I was already tasting. Yet how I also felt, with it, something of the threat of a chill to my curiosity! The taste of its being all over, that really sublime success of the strained vision in which I had been living for crowded hours—was this a taste that I was sure I should particularly enjoy? Marked enough it was, doubtless, that even in the stress of perceiving myself broken with I ruefully reflected on all the more, on the ever so much, I still wanted to know!

Well, something of this quantity, in any case, would come, since Mrs. Briss did want to speak to me. The suspense that remained with me, as I have indicated, was the special fresh one she had just produced. It fed, for a little, positively, on that survey of her fine retreating person to which I have confessed that my eyes attached themselves. These seconds were naturally few, and yet my memory gathers from them something that I can only compare, in its present effect, to the scent of a strange flower passed rapidly under my nose. I seem in other words to recall that I received in that brush the very liveliest impression that my whole adventure was to yield—the impression that is my reason for speaking of myself as having at the juncture in question "studied" Mrs. Brissenden's back. Study of a profound sort would appear needed in truth to account for it. It was as handsome and affirmative that she at once met and evaded my view, but was not the affirmation (as distinguished from the handsomeness, which was a matter of stature and mass,) fairly downright and defiant? Didn't what I saw strike me as saying straight *at* me, as far as possible, "I *am* young—I am and I *will* be; see, *see* if I'm not; there, there, there!"—with "there's" as insistent and rhythmical as the undulations of her fleeing presence, as the bejewelled nod of her averted brow? If her face had not been hidden, should I not precisely have found myself right in believing that it looked, exactly, for those instants, dreadfully older than it had ever yet had to? The answer ideally cynical would have been: "Oh, any woman of your resources can look young with her back turned! But you've had to turn it to make that proclamation." She passed out of the room proclaiming, and I did stand there a little defeated, even though with her word for another chance at her. Was this word one that she would keep? I had got off—yes, to a certainty. But so too had not she?

Naturally, at any rate, I didn't stay planted; and though it seemed long it was probably for no great time after this that I roamed in my impatience. I was divided between the discourtesy of wishing the ladies would go to bed and the apprehension that if they did too soon go I might yet lose everything. Was Mrs. Briss waiting for more privacy, or was she only waiting for a complete escape? Of course, even while I asked myself that, I had to remember how much I was taking for granted on her part in the way of conscious motive. Still, if she had not a motive for escaping, why had she not had one, five minutes before, for coming to the point with me? This inquiry kept me hovering where she might at any instant find me, but that was not inconsistent with my presently passing, like herself, into another room. The first one I entered—there were great chains of them at Newmarch—showed me once more, at the end opposite the door, the object that all day had been, present or absent, most in my eyes, and that there now could be no fallacy in my recognising. Mrs. Server's unquenchable little smile had never yet been so far from quenched as when it recognised, on its own side, that I had just had time to note how Ford Obert was, for a change, taking it in. These two friends of mine appeared to have moved together, after the music, to the corner in which I should not have felt it as misrepresenting the matter to say that I surprised them. They owed nothing of the harmony that held them—unlike my other couple—to the constraint of a common seat; a small glazed table, a receptacle for minute objects of price, extended itself between them as if it had offered itself as an occasion for their drawing toward it a pair of low chairs; but their union had nevertheless such an air of accepted duration as led it slightly to puzzle me. This would have been a reason the more for not interrupting it even had I not peculiarly wished to respect it. It was grist to my mill somehow that something or other had happened as a consequence of which Obert had lost the impulse to repeat to me his odd invitation to intervene. He gave me no notice as I passed; the notice was all from his companion. It constituted, I felt, on her part, precisely as much and precisely as little of an invitation as it had constituted at the moment—so promptly following our arrival—of my first seeing them linked; which is but another way of saying that nothing in Mrs. Server appeared to acknowledge a lapse. It was nearly midnight, but she was again under arms; everything conceivable— or perhaps rather inconceivable—had passed between us before dinner, but her face was exquisite again in its repudiation of any reference.

Any reference, I saw, would have been difficult to *me*, had I unluckily been forced to approach her. What would have made the rare delicacy of the problem was that blankness itself was the most direct reference of all. I had, however, as I passed her by, a comprehension as inward as that with which I had watched Mrs. Briss's retreat. "*What* shall I see when I next see you?" was what I had mutely asked of Mrs. Briss; but "God grant I don't see *you* again at all!" was the prayer sharply determined in my heart as I left Mrs. Server behind me. I left her behind me for ever, but the prayer has not been answered. I did see her again; I see her now; I shall see her always; I shall continue to feel at moments in my own facial muscles the deadly little ache of her heroic grin. With this, however, I was not then to reckon, and my simple philosophy of the moment could be but to get out of the room. The result of that movement was that, two minutes later, at another doorway, but opening this time into a great corridor, I found myself arrested by a combination that should really have counted for me as the least of my precious anomalies, but that— as accident happened to protect me—I watched, so long as I might, with intensity. I should in this connection describe my eyes as yet again engaging the less scrutable side of the human figure, were it not that poor Briss's back, now presented to me beside his wife's—for these were the elements of the combination—had hitherto seemed to me the most eloquent of his aspects. It was when he presented his face that he looked, each time, older; but it was when he showed you, from behind, the singular stoop of his shoulders, that he looked oldest.

They had just passed the door when I emerged, and they receded, at a slow pace and with a kind of confidential nearness, down the long avenue of the lobby. Her head was always high and her husband's always low, so that I couldn't be sure—it might have been only my fancy—that the contrast of this habit was more marked in them than usual. If I had known nothing about them I should have just unimaginatively said that talk was all on one side and attention all on the other. I, of course, for that matter, *did* know nothing about them; yet I recall how it came to me, as my extemporised shrewdness hung in their rear, that I mustn't think anything too grossly simple of what might be taking place between them. My position was, in spite of myself, that of my having mastered enough possibilities to choose from. If one of these might be—for her face, in spite of the backward cock of her head, was turned to him—that she was looking her time of life straight *at* him and yet making love to him with it as hard as ever she could, so another was that he had been already so thoroughly got back into hand that she had no need of asking favours, that she was more splendid than ever, and that, the same poor Briss as before his brief adventure, he was only feeling afresh in his soul, as a response to her, the gush of the sacred fount. Presumptuous choice as to these alternatives failed, on my part, in time, let me say, to flower; it rose before me in time that, whatever might be, for the exposed instant, the deep note of their encounter, only one thing concerned me in it: its being wholly their own business. So for that I liberally let it go, passing into the corridor, but proceeding in the opposite sense and aiming at an issue which I judged I should reach before they would turn in their walk. I had not, however, reached it before I caught the closing of the door furthest from me; at the sound of which I looked about to find the Brissendens gone. They had not remained for another turn, but had taken their course, evidently, back to the principal drawing-room, where, no less presumably, the procession of the ladies bedward was even then forming. Mrs. Briss would fall straight into it, and I *had* accordingly lost her. I hated to appear to pursue her, late in the day as it may appear to affirm that I put my dignity before my curiosity.

Free again, at all events, to wait or to wander, I lingered a minute where I had stopped—close to a wide window, as it happened, that, at this end of the passage, stood open to the warm darkness and overhung, from no great height, one of the terraces. The night was mild and rich, and though the lights within were, in deference to the temperature, not too numerous, I found the breath of the outer air a sudden corrective to the grossness of our lustre and the thickness of our medium, our general heavy humanity. I felt its taste sweet, and while I leaned for refreshment on the sill I thought of many things. One of those that passed before me was the way that Newmarch and its hospitalities were sacrificed, after all, and much more than smaller circles, to material frustrations. We were all so fine and formal, and the ladies in particular at once so little and so much clothed, so beflounced yet so denuded, that the summer stars called to us in vain. We had ignored them in our crystal cage, among our tinkling lamps; no more free really to alight than if we had been dashing in a locked railway-train across a lovely land. I remember asking myself if I mightn't still take a turn under them, and I remember that on appealing to my watch for its sanction I found midnight to have struck. That then was the end, and my only real alternatives were bed or the smoking-room. The difficulty with bed was that I was in no condition to sleep, and the difficulty about rejoining the men was that—definitely, yes—there was one of them I desired not again to see. I felt it with sharpness as I leaned on the sill; I felt it with sadness as I looked at the stars; I felt once more what I had felt on turning a final back five minutes before, so designedly, on Mrs. Server. I saw poor Briss as he had just moved away from me, and I knew, as I had known in the other case, that my troubled sense would fain feel I had practically done with him. It would be well, for aught I could do *for* him, that I should have seen the last of him. What remained with me from that vision of his pacing there with his wife was the conviction that his fate, whatever it was, held him fast. It wouldn't let him go, and all I could ask of it now was that it should let *me*. I *would* go—I was going; if I had not had to accept the interval of the night I should indeed already have gone. The admonitions of that moment—only confirmed, I hasten to add, by what was still to come—were that I should catch in the morning, with energy, an earlier train to town than anyone else was likely to take, and get off alone by it, bidding farewell for a long day to Newmarch. I should be in small haste to come back, for I should leave behind me my tangled theory, no loose thread of which need I ever again pick up, in no stray mesh of which need my foot again trip. It was on my way to the place, in fine, that my obsession had met me, and it was by retracing those steps that I should be able to get rid of it. Only I must break off sharp, must escape all reminders by forswearing all returns.

That was very well, but it would perhaps have been better still if I had gone straight to bed. In that case I *should* have broken off sharp—too sharp to become aware of something that kept me a minute longer at the window and that had the instant effect of making me wonder if, in the interest of observation, I mightn't snap down the electric light that, playing just behind me, must show where I stood. I resisted this impulse and, with the thought that my position was in no way compromising, chanced being myself observed. I presently saw moreover that I was really not in evidence: I could take in freely what I had at first not been sure of, the identity of the figure stationed just within my range, but just out of that of the light projected from my window. One of the men of our company had come out by himself for a stroll, and the man was Gilbert Long. He had paused, I made out, in his walk; his back was to the house, and, resting on the balustrade of the terrace with a cigarette in his lips, he had given way to a sense of the fragrant gloom. He moved so little that I was sure—making no turn that would have made me draw back; he only smoked slowly in his place and seemed as lost in thought as I was lost in my attention to him. I scarce knew what this told me; all I felt was that, however slight the incident and small the evidence, it essentially fitted in. It had for my imagination a value, for my theory a price, and it in fact constituted an impression under the influence of which this theory, just impatiently shaken off, perched again on my shoulders. It was of the deepest interest to me to see Long in such detachment, in such apparent concentration. These things marked and presented him more than any had yet done, and placed him more than any yet in relation to other matters. They showed him, I thought, as serious, his situation as grave. I couldn't have said what they proved, but I was as affected by them as if they proved everything. The proof simply acted from the instant the vision of him alone there in the warm darkness was caught. It was just with all that was in the business that he *was*, that he had fitfully needed to be, alone. Nervous and restless after separating, under my eyes, from Mrs. Briss, he had wandered off to the smoking-room, as yet empty; *he* didn't know what to do either, and was incapable of bed and of sleep. He had observed the communication of the smoking-room with the terrace and had come out into the air; this was what suited him, and, with pauses and meditations, much, possibly, by this time to turn over, he prolonged his soft vigil. But he at last moved, and I found myself startled. I gave up watching and retraced my course. I felt, none the less, fairly humiliated. It had taken but another turn of an eye to re-establish all my connections.

I had not, however, gone twenty steps before I met Ford Obert, who had entered the corridor from the other end and was, as he immediately let me know, on his way to the smoking-room.

"Is everyone then dispersing?"

"Some of the men, I think," he said, "are following me; others, I believe—wonderful creatures!—have gone to array themselves. Others still, doubtless, have gone to bed."

"And the ladies?"

"Oh, they've floated away—soared aloft; to high jinks—isn't that the idea?—in their own quarters. Don't they too, at these hours, practise sociabilities of sorts? They make, at any rate, here, an extraordinary picture on that great staircase."

I thought a moment. "I wish I had seen it. But I do see it. Yes—splendid. Is the place wholly cleared of them?"

"Save, it struck me, so far as they may have left some 'black plume as a token'——"

"Not, I trust," I returned, "of any 'lie' their 'soul hath spoken!' But not one of them lingers?"

He seemed to wonder. "'Lingers?' For what?"

"Oh, I don't know—in this house!"

He looked at our long vista, still lighted—appeared to feel with me our liberal ease, which implied that unseen powers waited on our good pleasure and sat up for us. There is nothing like it in fact, the liberal ease at Newmarch. Yet Obert reminded me—if I needed the reminder—that I mustn't after all presume on it. "Was one of them to linger for *you*?"

"Well, since you ask me, it was what I hoped. But since you answer for it that my hope has not been met, I bow to a superior propriety."

"You mean you'll come and smoke with me? Do then come."

"What, if I do," I asked with an idea, "will you give me?"

"I'm afraid I can promise you nothing more that *I* deal in than a bad cigarette."

"And what then," I went on, "will you take from me?"

He had met my eyes, and now looked at me a little with a smile that I thought just conscious. "Well, I'm afraid I *can't* take any more——"

"Of the sort of stuff," I laughed, "you've already had? Sorry stuff, perhaps—a poor thing but mine own! Such as it is, I only ask to keep it for myself, and that isn't what I meant. I meant what flower will you gather, what havoc will you play——?"

"Well?" he said as I hesitated.

"Among superstitions that I, after all, cherish. *Mon siège est fait*—a great glittering crystal palace. How many panes will you reward me for amiably sitting up with you by smashing?"

It might have been my mere fancy—but it *was* my fancy—that he looked at me a trifle harder. "How on earth can I tell what you're talking about?"

I waited a moment, then went on: "Did you happen to count them?"

"Count whom?"

"Why, the ladies as they filed up. Was the number there?"

He gave a jerk of impatience. "Go and see for yourself!"

Once more I just waited. "But suppose I should find Mrs. Server——?"

"Prowling there on the chance of you? Well—I thought she was what you wanted."

"Then," I returned, "you *could* tell what I was talking about!" For a moment after this we faced each other without more speech, but I presently continued: "You didn't really notice if any lady stayed behind?"

"I think you ask too much of me," he at last brought out. "Take care of your ladies, my dear man, yourself! Go," he repeated, "and see."

"Certainly—it's better; but I'll rejoin you in three minutes." And while he went his way to the smoking-room I proceeded without more delay to assure myself, performing in the opposite sense the journey I had made ten minutes before. It was extraordinary what the sight of Long alone in the outer darkness had done for me: my expression of it would have been that it had put me "on" again at the moment of my decidedly feeling myself off. I believed that if I hadn't seen him I could now have gone to bed without seeing Mrs. Briss; but my renewed impression had suddenly made the difference. If that was the way he struck me, how might not, if I could get at her, she? And she might, after all, in the privacy at last offered us by empty rooms, be waiting for me. I went through them all, however, only to find them empty indeed. In conformity with the large allowances of every sort that were the law of Newmarch, they were still open and lighted, so that if I had believed in Mrs. Briss's reappearance I might conveniently, on the spot, have given her five minutes more. I am not sure, for that matter, that I didn't. I remember at least wondering if I mightn't ring somewhere for a servant and cause a question to be sent up to her. I didn't ring, but I must have lingered a little on the chance of the arrival of servants to extinguish lights and see the house safe. They had not arrived, however, by the time I again felt that I must give up.

XI

I gave up by going, decidedly, to the smoking-room, where several men had gathered and where Obert, a little apart from them, was in charmed communion with the bookshelves. They are wonderful, everywhere, at Newmarch, the bookshelves, but he put a volume back as he saw me come in, and a moment later, when we were seated, I said to him again, as a recall of our previous passage, "Then you *could* tell what I was talking about!" And I added, to complete my reference, "Since you thought Mrs. Server was the person whom, when I stopped you, I was sorry to learn from you I had missed."

His momentary silence appeared to admit the connection I established. "Then you find you *have* missed her? She wasn't there for you?"

"There's no one 'there for me'; so that I fear that if you weren't, as it happens, here for me, my amusement would be quite at an end. I had, in fact," I continued, "already given it up as lost when I came upon you, a while since, in conversation with the lady we've named. At that, I confess, my prospects gave something of a flare. I said to myself that since *your* interest hadn't then wholly dropped, why, even at the worst, should mine? Yours *was* mine, wasn't it? for a little, this morning. Or was it mine that was yours? We exchanged, at any rate, some lively impressions. Only, before we had done, your effort dropped or your discretion intervened: you gave up, as none of your business, the question that had suddenly tempted us."

"And you gave it up too," said my friend.

"Yes, and it was on the idea that it was mine as little as yours that we separated."

"Well then?" He kept his eyes, with his head thrown back, on the warm bindings, admirable for old gilt and old colour, that covered the opposite wall.

"Well then, if I've correctly gathered that you're, in spite of our common renunciation, still interested, I confess to you that I am. I took my detachment too soon for granted. I haven't been detached. I'm not, hang me! detached now. And it's all because you were originally so suggestive."

"Originally?"

"Why, from the moment we met here yesterday—the moment of my first seeing you with Mrs. Server. The look you gave me then was really the beginning of everything. Everything"—and I spoke now with real conviction—"was traceably to spring from it."

"What do you mean," he asked, "by everything?"

"Well, this failure of detachment. What you said to me as we were going up yesterday afternoon to dress—what you said to me then is responsible for it. And since it comes to that," I pursued, "I make out for myself now that you're not detached either—unless, that is, simply detached from *me*. I had indeed a suspicion of that as I passed through the room there."

He smoked through another pause. "You've extraordinary notions of responsibility."

I watched him a moment, but he only stared at the books without looking round. Something in his voice had made me more certain, and my certainty made me laugh. "I see you *are* serious!"

But he went on quietly enough. "You've extraordinary notions of responsibility. I deny altogether mine."

"You *are* serious—you *are*!" I repeated with a gaiety that I meant as inoffensive and that I believe remained so. "But no matter. You're no worse than I."

"I'm clearly, by your own story, not half so bad. But, as you say, no matter. I don't care."

I ventured to keep it up. "Oh, don't you?"

His good nature was proof. "I don't care."

"Then why didn't you so much as look at me a while ago?"

"Didn't I look at you?"

"You know perfectly you didn't. Mrs. Server did—with her unutterable intensity; making me feel afresh, by the way, that I've never seen a woman compromise herself so little by proceedings so compromising. But though you saw her intensity, it never diverted you for an instant from your own."

He lighted before he answered this a fresh cigarette. "A man engaged in talk with a charming woman scarcely selects that occasion for winking at somebody else."

"You mean he contents himself with winking at *her*? My dear fellow, that wasn't enough for you yesterday, and it wouldn't have been enough for you this morning, among the impressions that led to our last talk. It was just the fact that you did wink, that you *had* winked, at me that wound me up."

"And what about the fact that you had winked at *me*? *Your* winks—come"—Obert laughed—"are portentous!"

"Oh, if we recriminate," I cheerfully said after a moment, "we agree."

"I'm not so sure," he returned, "that we agree."

"Ah, then, if we differ it's still more interesting. Because, you know, we didn't differ either yesterday or this morning."

Without hurry or flurry, but with a decent confusion, his thoughts went back. "I thought you said just now we did—recognising, as you ought, that you were keen about a chase of which I washed my hands."

"No—I wasn't keen. You've just mentioned that you remember my giving up. I washed my hands too."

It seemed to leave him with the moral of this. "Then, if our hands are clean, what are we talking about?"

I turned, on it, a little more to him, and looked at him so long that he had at last to look at me; with which, after holding his eyes another moment, I made my point. "Our hands are not clean."

"Ah, speak for your own!"—and as he moved back I might really have thought him uneasy. There was a hint of the same note in the way he went on: "I assure you I decline all responsibility. I see the responsibility as quite beautifully yours."

"Well," I said, "I only want to be fair. You were the first to bring it out that she was changed."

"Well, she isn't changed!" said my friend with an almost startling effect, for me, of suddenness. "Or rather," he immediately and incongruously added, "she *is*. She's changed back."

"'Back'?" It made me stare.

"Back," he repeated with a certain sharpness and as if to have done at last, for himself, with the muddle of it.

But there was that in me that could let him see he had far from done; and something, above all, told me now that he absolutely mustn't have before I had. I quickly moreover saw that I must, with an art, make him want not to. "Back to what she was when you painted her?"

He had to think an instant for this. "No—not quite to that."

"To what then?"

He tried in a manner to oblige me. "To something else."

It seemed so, for my thought, the gleam of something that fitted, that I was almost afraid of quenching the gleam by pressure. I must then get everything I could from him without asking too much. "You don't quite know to *what* else?"

"No—I don't quite know." But there was a sound in it, this time, that I took as the hint of a wish to know—almost a recognition that I might help him.

I helped him accordingly as I could and, I may add, as far as the positive flutter he had stirred in me suffered. It fitted—it fitted! "If her change is to something other, I suppose then a change back is not quite the exact name for it."

"Perhaps not." I fairly thrilled at his taking the suggestion as if it were an assistance. "She isn't at any rate what I thought her yesterday."

It was amazing into what depths this dropped for me and with what possibilities it mingled. "I remember what you said of her yesterday."

I drew him on so that I brought back for him the very words he had used. "She was so beastly unhappy." And he used them now visibly not as a remembrance of what he had said, but for the contrast of the fact with what he at present perceived; so that the value this gave for me to what he at present perceived was immense.

"And do you mean that that's gone?"

He hung fire, however, a little as to saying so much what he meant, and while he waited he again looked at me. "What do *you* mean? Don't you think so yourself?"

I laid my hand on his arm and held him a moment with a grip that betrayed, I daresay, the effort in me to keep my thoughts together and lose not a thread. It betrayed at once, doubtless, the danger of that failure and the sharp foretaste of success. I remember that with it, absolutely, I struck myself as knowing again the joy of the intellectual mastery of things unamenable, that joy of determining, almost of creating results, which I have already mentioned as an exhilaration attached to some of my plunges of insight. "It would take long to tell you what I mean."

The tone of it made him fairly watch me as I had been watching him. "Well, haven't we got the whole night?"

"Oh, it would take more than the whole night—even if we had it!"

"By which you suggest that we haven't it?"

"No—we haven't it. I want to get away."

"To go to bed? I thought you were so keen."

"I *am* keen. Keen is no word for it. I don't want to go to bed. I want to get away."

"To leave the house—in the middle of the night?"

"Yes—absurd as it may seem. You excite me too much. You don't know what you do to me."

He continued to look at me; then he gave a laugh which was not the contradiction, but quite the attestation, of the effect produced on him by my grip. If I had wanted to hold him I held him. It only came to me even that I held him too much. I felt this in fact with the next thing he said. "If you're too excited, then, to be coherent now, will you tell me to-morrow?"

I took time myself now to relight. Ridiculous as it may sound, I had my nerves to steady; which is a proof, surely, that for real excitement there are no such adventures as intellectual ones. "Oh, to-morrow I shall be off in space!"

"Certainly we shall neither of us be here. But can't we arrange, say, to meet in town, or even to go up together in such conditions as will enable us to talk?"

I patted his arm again. "Thank you for your patience. It's really good of you. Who knows if I shall be alive to-morrow? We *are* meeting. We *do* talk."

But with all I had to think of I must have fallen, on this, into the deepest of silences, for the next thing I remember is his returning: "We don't!" I repeated my gesture of reassurance, I conveyed that I should be with him again in a minute, and presently, while he gave me time, he came back to something of his own. "My wink, at all events, would have been nothing for any question between us, as I've just said, without yours. That's what I call your responsibility. It was, as we put the matter, the torch of your analogy——"

"Oh, the torch of my analogy!"

I had so groaned it—as if for very ecstasy—that it pulled him up, and I could see his curiosity as indeed reaffected. But he went on with a coherency that somewhat admonished me: "It was your making me, as I told you this morning, think over what you had said about Brissenden and his wife: it was *that*——"

331

"That made you think over"—I took him straight up—"what you yourself had said about our troubled lady? Yes, precisely. That *was* the torch of my analogy. What I showed you in the one case seemed to tell you what to look for in the other. You thought it over. I accuse you of nothing worse than of *having* thought it over. But you see what thinking it over does for it."

The way I said this appeared to amuse him. "I see what it does for *you*!"

"No, you don't! Not at all yet. That's just the embarrassment."

"Just whose?" If I had thanked him for his patience he showed that he deserved it. "Just yours?"

"Well, say mine. But when you do——!" And I paused as for the rich promise of it.

"When I do see where you are, you mean?"

"The only difficulty is whether you *can* see. But we must try. You've set me whirling round, but we must go step by step. Oh, but it's all in your germ!"—I kept that up. "If she isn't now beastly unhappy——"

"She's beastly happy?" he broke in, getting firmer hold, if not of the real impression he had just been gathering under my eyes, then at least of something he had begun to make out that my argument required. "Well, that *is* the way I see her difference. Her difference, I mean," he added, in his evident wish to work with me, "her difference from her other difference! There!" He laughed as if, also, he had found himself fairly fantastic. "Isn't *that* clear for you?"

"Crystalline—for *me*. But that's because I know why."

I can see again now the long look that, on this, he gave me. I made out already much of what was in it. "So then do I!"

"But how in the world——? I know, for myself, *how* I know."

"So then do I," he after a moment repeated.

"And can you tell me?"

"Certainly. But what I've already named to you—the torch of your analogy."

I turned this over. "You've made evidently an admirable use of it. But the wonderful thing is that you seem to have done so without having all the elements."

He on his side considered. "What do you call all the elements?"

"Oh, it would take me long to tell you!" I couldn't help laughing at the comparative simplicity with which he asked it. "That's the sort of thing we just now spoke of taking a day for. At any rate, such as they are, these elements," I went on, "I believe myself practically in possession of them. But what I don't quite see is how *you* can be."

Well, he was able to tell me. "Why in the world shouldn't your analogy have put me?" He spoke with gaiety, but with lucidity. "I'm not an idiot either."

"I see." But there was so much!

"Did you think I *was*?" he amiably asked.

"No. I see," I repeated. Yet I didn't, really, fully; which he presently perceived.

"You made me think of your view of the Brissenden pair till I could think of nothing else."

"Yes—yes," I said. "Go on."

"Well, as you had planted the theory in me, it began to bear fruit. I began to watch them. I continued to watch them. I did nothing but watch them."

The sudden lowering of his voice in this confession—as if it had represented a sort of darkening of his consciousness—again amused me. "You too? How then we've been occupied! For I, you see, have watched—or had, until I found you just now with Mrs. Server—everyone, everything *but* you."

"Oh, I've watched *you*," said Ford Obert as if he had then perhaps after all the advantage of me. "I admit that I made you out for myself to be back on the scent; for I thought I made you out baffled."

To learn whether I really had been was, I saw, what he would most have liked; but I also saw that he had, as to this, a scruple about asking me. What I most saw, however, was that to tell him I should have to understand. "What scent do you allude to?"

He smiled as if I might have fancied I could fence. "Why, the pursuit of the identification that's none of our business—the identification of her lover."

"Ah, it's as to that," I instantly replied, "you've judged me baffled? I'm afraid," I almost as quickly added, "that I must admit I *have* been. Luckily, at all events, it *is* none of our business."

"Yes," said my friend, amused on his side, "nothing's our business that we can't find out. I saw you hadn't found him. And what," Obert continued, "does he matter now?"

It took but a moment to place me for seeing that my companion's conviction on this point was a conviction decidedly to respect; and even that amount of hesitation was but the result of my wondering how he had reached it. "What, indeed?" I promptly replied. "But how did you see I had failed?"

"By seeing that I myself had. For I've been looking too. He isn't here," said Ford Obert.

Delighted as I was that he should believe it, I was yet struck by the complacency of his confidence, which connected itself again with my observation of their so recent colloquy. "Oh, for you to be so sure, has Mrs. Server squared you?"

"*Is* he here?" he for all answer to this insistently asked.

I faltered but an instant. "No; he isn't here. It's no thanks to one's scruples, but perhaps it's lucky for one's manners. I speak at least for mine. If you've watched," I pursued, "you've doubtless sufficiently seen what has already become of mine. He isn't here, at all events," I repeated, "and we must do without his identity. What, in fact, are we showing each other," I asked, "but that we *have* done without it?"

"*I* have!" my friend declared with supreme frankness and with something of the note, as I was obliged to recognise, of my own constructive joy. "I've done perfectly without it."

I saw in fact that he had, and it struck me really as wonderful. But I controlled the expression of my wonder. "So that if you spoke therefore just now of watching them——"

"I meant of course"—he took it straight up—"watching the Brissendens. And naturally, above all," he as quickly subjoined, "the wife."

I was now full of concurrence. "Ah, naturally, above all, the wife."

So far as was required it encouraged him. "A woman's lover doesn't matter—doesn't matter at least to anyone but himself, doesn't matter to you or to me or to her—when once she has given him up."

It made me, this testimony of his observation, show, in spite of my having by this time so counted on it, something of the vivacity of my emotion. "She *has* given him up?"

But the surprise with which he looked round put me back on my guard. "Of what else then are we talking?"

"Of nothing else, of course," I stammered. "But the way you see——!" I found my refuge in the gasp of my admiration.

"I do see. But"—he *would* come back to that—"only through your having seen first. You gave me the pieces. I've but put them together. You gave me the Brissendens—bound hand and foot; and I've but made them, in that sorry state, pull me through. I've blown on my torch, in other words, till, flaring and smoking, it has guided me, through a magnificent chiaroscuro of colour and shadow, out into the light of day."

I was really dazzled by his image, for it represented his personal work. "You've done more than I, it strikes me—and with less to do it with. If I gave you the Brissendens I gave you all I had."

"But all you had was immense, my dear man. The Brissendens are immense."

"Of course the Brissendens are immense! If they hadn't been immense they wouldn't have been—*nothing* would have been—anything." Then after a pause, "Your image is splendid," I went on—"your being out of the cave. But what is it exactly," I insidiously threw out, "that you *call* the 'light of day'?"

I remained a moment, however, not sure whether I had been too subtle or too simple. He had another of his cautions. "What do *you*——?"

But I was determined to make him give it me all himself, for it was from my not prompting him that its value would come. "You tell me," I accordingly rather crudely pleaded, "first."

It gave us a moment during which he so looked as if I asked too much, that I had a fear of losing all. He even spoke with some impatience. "If you really haven't found it for yourself, you know. I scarce see what you *can* have found."

Then I had my inspiration. I risked an approach to roughness, and all the more easily that my words were strict truth. "Oh, don't be afraid—greater things than yours!"

It succeeded, for it played upon his curiosity, and he visibly imagined that, with impatience controlled, he should learn what these things were. He relaxed, he responded, and the next moment I was in all but full enjoyment of the piece wanted to make all my other pieces right—right because of that special beauty in my scheme through which the whole depended so on each part and each part so guaranteed the whole. "What I call the light of day is the sense I've arrived at of her vision."

"Her vision?"—I just balanced in the air.

"Of what they have in common. *His*—poor chap's—extraordinary situation too."

"Bravo! And you see in that——?"

"What, all these hours, has touched, fascinated, drawn her. It has been an instinct with her."

"Bravissimo!"

It saw him, my approval, safely into port. "The instinct of sympathy, pity—the response to fellowship in misery; the sight of another fate as strange, as monstrous as her own."

I couldn't help jumping straight up—I stood before him. "So that whoever may have *been* the man, the man *now*, the actual man——"

"Oh," said Obert, looking, luminous and straight, up at me from his seat, "the man now, the actual man——!" But he stopped short, with his eyes suddenly quitting me and his words becoming a formless ejaculation. The door of the room, to which my back was turned, had opened, and I quickly looked round. It was Brissenden himself who, to my supreme surprise, stood there, with rapid inquiry in his attitude and face. I saw, as soon as he caught mine, that I was what he wanted, and, immediately excusing myself for an instant to Obert, I anticipated, by moving across the room, the need, on poor Briss's part, of my further demonstration. My whole sense of the situation blazed up at the touch of his presence, and even before I reached him it had rolled over me in a prodigious wave that I had lost nothing whatever. I can't begin to say how the fact of his appearance crowned the communication my interlocutor had just made me, nor in what a bright confusion of many things I found myself facing poor Briss. One of these things was precisely that he had never been so much poor Briss as at this moment. That ministered to the confusion as well as to the brightness, for if his being there at all renewed my sources and replenished my current—spoke all, in short, for my gain—so, on the other hand, in the light of what I had just had from Obert, his particular aspect was something of a shock. I can't present this especial impression better than by the mention of my instant certitude that what he had come for was to bring me a message and that somehow—yes, indubitably—this circumstance seemed to have placed him again at the very bottom of his hole. It was down in that depth that he let me see him—it was out of it that he delivered himself. Poor Briss! poor Briss!—I had asked myself before he spoke with what kindness enough I could meet him. Poor Briss! poor Briss!—I am not even now sure that I didn't first meet him by *that* irrepressible murmur. It was in it all for me that, thus, at midnight, he had traversed on his errand the length of the great dark house. I trod with him, over the velvet and the marble, through the twists and turns, among the glooms and glimmers and echoes, every inch of the way, and I don't know what humiliation, for him, was constituted there, between us, by his long pilgrimage. It was the final expression of his sacrifice.

"My wife has something to say to you."

"Mrs. Briss? Good!"—and I could only hope the candour of my surprise was all I tried to make it. "Is she with you there?"

"No, but she has asked me to say to you that if you'll presently be in the drawing-room she'll come."

Who could doubt, as I laid my hand on his shoulder, fairly patting it, in spite of myself, for applause—who could doubt where I would presently be? "It's most uncommonly good of both of you."

There was something in his inscrutable service that, making him almost august, gave my dissimulated eagerness the sound of a heartless compliment. *I* stood for the hollow chatter of the vulgar world, and he—oh, he was as serious as he was conscious; which was enough. "She says you'll know what she wishes—and she was sure I'd find you here. So I may tell her you'll come?"

His courtesy half broke my heart. "Why, my dear man, with all the pleasure——! So many thousand thanks. I'll be with her."

"Thanks to *you*. She'll be down. Good-night." He looked round the room—at the two or three clusters of men, smoking, engaged, contented, on their easy seats and among their popped corks; he looked over an instant at Ford Obert, whose eyes, I thought, he momentarily held. It was absolutely as if, for me, he were seeking such things—out of what was closing over him—for the last time. Then he turned again to the door, which, just not to fail humanly to accompany him a step, I had opened. On the other side of it

I took leave of him. The passage, though there was a light in the distance, was darker than the smoking-room, and I had drawn the door to.

"Good-night, Brissenden. I shall be gone to-morrow before you show."

I shall never forget the way that, struck by my word, he let his white face fix me in the dusk. "'Show'? *What* do I show?"

I had taken his hand for farewell, and, inevitably laughing, but as the falsest of notes, I gave it a shake. "You show nothing! You're magnificent."

He let me keep his hand while things unspoken and untouched, unspeakable and untouchable, everything that had been between us in the wood a few hours before, were between us again. But so we could only leave them, and, with a short, sharp "Good-bye!" he completely released himself. With my hand on the latch of the closed door I watched a minute his retreat along the passage, and I remember the reflection that, before rejoining Obert, I made on it. I seemed perpetually, at Newmarch, to be taking his measure from behind.

Ford Obert has since told me that when I came back to him there were tears in my eyes, and I didn't know at the moment how much the words with which he met me took for granted my consciousness of them. "He looks a hundred years old!"

"Oh, but you should see his shoulders, always, as he goes off! *Two* centuries—ten! Isn't it amazing?"

It was so amazing that, for a little, it made us reciprocally stare. "I should have thought," he said, "that he would have been on the contrary——"

"Visibly rejuvenated? So should I. I must make it out," I added. "I *shall*."

But Obert, with less to go upon, couldn't wait. It was wonderful, for that matter—and for all I had to go upon—how I myself could. I did so, at this moment, in my refreshed intensity, by the help of confusedly lighting another cigarette, which I should have no time to smoke. "I should have thought," my friend continued, "that he too might have changed back."

I took in, for myself, so much more of it than I could say! "Certainly. You wouldn't have thought he would have changed forward." Then with an impulse that bridged over an abyss of connections I jumped to another place. "Was what you most saw while you were there with *her*—was this that her misery, the misery you first phrased to me, has dropped?"

"Dropped, yes." He was clear about it. "I called her beastly unhappy to you though I even then knew that beastly unhappiness wasn't quite all of it. It was part of it, it was enough of it; for she was—well, no doubt you could tell *me*. Just now, at all events"—and recalling, reflecting, deciding, he used, with the strongest effect, as he so often did in painting, the simplest term—"just now she's all right."

"All right?"

He couldn't know how much more than was possible my question gave him to answer. But he answered it on what he had; he repeated: "All right."

I wondered, in spite of the comfort I took, as I had more than once in life had occasion to take it before, at the sight of the painter-sense deeply applied. My wonder came from the fact that Lady John had also found Mrs. Server all right, and Lady John had a vision as closed as Obert's was open. It didn't suit my book for both these observers to have been affected in the same way. "You mean you saw nothing whatever in her that was the least bit strange?"

"Oh, I won't say as much as that. But nothing that was more strange than that she *should* be—well, after all, all right."

"All there, eh?" I after an instant risked.

I couldn't put it to him more definitely than that, though there was a temptation to try to do so. For Obert to have found her all there an hour or two after I had found her all absent, made me again, in my nervousness, feel even now a trifle menaced. Things *had*, from step to step, to hang together, and just here they seemed—with all allowances—to hang a little apart. My whole superstructure, I could only remember, reared itself on my view of Mrs. Server's condition; but it was part of my predicament—really equal in its way to her own—that I couldn't without dishonouring myself give my interlocutor a practical lead. The question of her happiness was essentially subordinate; what I stood or fell by was that of her faculty. But I couldn't, on the other hand—and remain "straight"—insist to my friend on the whereabouts of this stolen property. If he hadn't missed it in her for himself I mightn't put him on the track of it; since, with the demonstration he had before my eyes received of the rate at which Long was, as one had to call it, intellectually living, nothing would be more natural than that he should make the cases fit. Now my personal problem, unaltered in the least particular by anything, was for me to have worked to the end without breathing in another ear that Long had been her lover. That was the only thing in the whole business that was simple. It made me cling an instant the more, both for bliss and bale, to the bearing of this fact of Obert's insistence. Even as a sequel to his vision of her change, almost everything was wrong for her being all right except the one fact of my recent view, from the window, of the man unnamed. I saw him again sharply in these seconds, and to notice how he still kept clear of our company was almost to add certitude to the presumption of his rare reasons. Mrs. Server's being now, by a wonderful turn, all right would at least decidedly offer to these reasons a basis. It would be something Long's absence would fit. It would supply ground, in short, for the possibility that, by a process not less wonderful, he himself was all wrong. If he *was* all wrong my last impression of him would be amply accounted for. If he was all wrong—if he, in any case, felt himself going so—what more consequent than that he should have wished to hide it, and that the most immediate way for this should have seemed to him, markedly gregarious as he usually was, to keep away from the smokers? It came to me unspeakably that he *was* still hiding it and *was* keeping away. How, accordingly, must he not—and must not Mrs. Briss—have been in the spirit of this from the moment that, while I talked with Lady John, the sight of these two seated together had given me its message! But Obert's answer to my guarded challenge had meanwhile come. "Oh, when a woman's so clever——!"

That was all, with its touch of experience and its hint of philosophy; but it was stupefying. She was already then positively again "so clever?" This was really more than I could as yet provide an explanation for, but I was pressed;

Brissenden would have reached his wife's room again, and I temporised. "It was her cleverness that held you so that when I passed you couldn't look at me?"

He looked at me at present well enough. "I knew you were passing, but I wanted precisely to mark for you the difference. If you really want to know," the poor man confessed, "I was a little ashamed of myself. I had given her away to you, you know, rather, before."

"And you were bound you wouldn't do it again?"

He smiled in his now complete candour. "Ah, there was no reason." Then he used, happily, to right himself, my own expression. "She was all there."

"I see—I see." Yet I really didn't see enough not to have for an instant to turn away.

"Where are you going?" he asked.

"To do what Brissenden came to me for."

"But I don't *know*, you see, what Brissenden came to you for."

"Well, with a message. She was to have seen me this evening, but, as she gave me no chance, I was afraid I had lost it and that, so rather awkwardly late, she didn't venture. But what he arrived for just now, at her request, was to say she does venture."

My companion stared. "At this extraordinary hour?"

"Ah, the hour," I laughed, "is no more extraordinary than any other part of the business: no more so, for instance, than this present talk of yours and mine. What part of the business isn't extraordinary? If it *is*, at all events, remarkably late, that's *her* fault."

Yet he not unnaturally, in spite of my explanation, continued to wonder. "And—a—where is it then you meet?"

"Oh, in the drawing-room or the hall. So good-night."

He got up to it, moving with me to the door; but his mystification, little as I could, on the whole, soothe it, still kept me. "The household sits up for you?"

I wondered myself, but found an assurance. "She must have squared the household! And it won't probably take us very long."

His mystification frankly confessed itself, at this, plain curiosity. The ground of such a conference, for all the point I had given his ingenuity, simply baffled him. "Do you mean you propose to discuss with her——?"

"My dear fellow," I smiled with my hand on the door, "it's *she*—don't you see?—who proposes."

"But what in the world——?"

"Oh, *that* I shall have to wait to tell you."

"With all the other things?" His face, while he sounded mine, seemed to say that I must then take his expectation as serious. But it seemed to say also that he was—definitely, yes—more at a loss than consorted with being quite sure of me. "Well, it will make a lot, really——!" But he broke off. "You do," he sighed with an effort at resignation, "know more than I!"

"And haven't I admitted that?"

"I'll be hanged if you *don't* know who he is!" the poor fellow, for all answer, now produced.

He said it as if I had, after all, not been playing fair, and it made me for an instant hesitate. "No, I really don't know. But it's exactly what I shall perhaps now learn."

"You mean that what she has proposed is to *tell* you?"

His darkness had so deepened that I saw only now what I should have seen sooner—the misconception that, in my excessive estimate of the distance he had come with me, I had not at first caught. But it was a misconception that only enriched his testimony; it involved such a conviction of the new link between our two sacrificed friends that it immediately constituted for me the strongest light he would, in our whole talk, have thrown. Yes, he had not yet thrown so much as in this erroneous supposition of the source of my summons. It took me of course, at the same time, but a few seconds to remind myself again of the innumerable steps he had necessarily missed. His question meanwhile, rightly applied by my own thought, brought back to that thought, by way of answer, an immense suggestion, which moreover, for him too, was temporarily answer enough. "She'll tell me who he *won't* have been!"

He looked vague. "Ah, but *that*——"

"That," I declared, "will be luminous."

He made it out. "As a sign, you think, that he must be the very one she denies?"

"The very one!" I laughed; and I left him under this simple and secure impression that my appointment was with Mrs. Server.

I went from one room to the other, but to find only, at first, as on my previous circuit, a desert on which the sun had still not set. Mrs. Brissenden was nowhere, but the whole place waited as we had left it, with seats displaced and flowers dispetalled, a fan forgotten on a table, a book laid down upon a chair. It came over me as I looked about that if she *had* "squared" the household, so large an order, as they said, was a sign sufficient of what I was to have from her. I had quite rather it were her doing—not mine; but it showed with eloquence that she had after all judged some effort or other to be worth her while. Her renewed delay moreover added to my impatience of mind in respect to the nature of this effort by striking me as already part of it. What, I asked myself, could be so much worth her while as to have to be paid for by so much apparent reluctance? But at last I saw her through a vista of open doors, and as I forthwith went to her—she took no step to meet me—I was doubtless impressed afresh with the "pull" that in social intercourse a woman always has. She was able to assume on the spot by mere attitude and air the appearance of having been ready and therefore inconvenienced. Oh, I saw soon enough that she was ready and that one of the forms of her readiness would be precisely to offer herself as having acted entirely to oblige me—to give me, as a sequel to what had already passed between us, the opportunity for which she had assured me I should thank her before I had done with her. Yet, as I felt sure, at the same time, that she had taken a line, I was curious as to how, in her interest, our situation could be worked. What it had originally left us with was her knowing I was wrong. I had promised her, on my honour, to be candid, but even if I were disposed to cease to contest her identification of Mrs. Server I was scarce to be looked to for such an exhibition of gratitude as might be held to repay her for staying so long out of bed. There were in short elements in the business that I couldn't quite clearly see handled as favours to me. Her dress gave, with felicity, no sign whatever of preparation for the night, and if, since our last words, she had stood with any anxiety whatever before her glass, it had not been to remove a jewel or to alter the place of a flower. She was as much under arms as she had been on descending to dinner—as fresh in her array as if that banquet were still to come. She met me in fact as admirably—that was the truth that covered every other—as if she had been able to guess the most particular curiosity with which, from my end of the series of rooms, I advanced upon her.

A part of the mixture of my thoughts during these seconds had been the possibility—absurd, preposterous though it looks when phrased here—of some change in her person that would correspond, for me to the other changes I had had such keen moments of flattering myself I had made out. I had just had them over in the smoking-room, some of these differences, and then had had time to ask myself if I were not now to be treated to the vision of the greatest, the most wonderful, of all. I had already, on facing her, after my last moments with Lady John, seen difference peep out at me, and I had seen the impression of it confirmed by what had afterwards happened. It had been in her way of turning from me after that brief passage; it had been in her going up to bed without seeing me again; it had been once more in her thinking, for reasons of her own, better of that; and it had been most of all in her sending her husband down to me. Well, wouldn't it finally be, still more than most of all——? But I scarce had known, at this point, what grossness or what fineness of material correspondence to forecast. I only had waited there with these general symptoms so present that almost any further development of them occurred to me as conceivable. So much as this was true, but I was after a moment to become aware of something by which I was as strongly affected as if I had been quite unprepared. Yes, literally, that final note, in the smoking-room, the note struck in Obert's ejaculation on poor Briss's hundred years, had failed to achieve for me a worthy implication. I was forced, after looking at Grace Brissenden a minute, to recognise that my imagination had not risen to its opportunity. The full impression took a minute—a minute during which she said nothing; then it left me deeply and above all, as I felt, discernibly conscious of the prodigious thing, *the* thing, I had not thought of. This it was that gave her such a beautiful chance not to speak: she was so quite sufficiently occupied with seeing what I hadn't thought of, and with seeing me, to make up for lost time, breathlessly think of it while she watched me.

All I had at first taken in was, as I say, her untouched splendour; I don't know why that should have impressed me—as if it had been probable she would have appeared in her dressing-gown; it was the only thing to have expected. And it in fact plumed and enhanced her assurance, sustained her propriety, lent our belated interview the natural and casual note. But there was another service it still more rendered her: it so covered, at the first blush, the real message of her aspect, that she enjoyed the luxury—and I felt her enjoy it—of seeing my perception in arrest. Amazing, when I think of it, the number of things that occurred in these stayed seconds of our silence; but they are perhaps best represented by the two most marked intensities of my own sensation: the first the certitude that she had at no moment since her marriage so triumphantly asserted her defeat of time, and the second the conviction that I, losing with her while, as it were, we closed, a certain advantage I should never recover, had at no moment since the day before made so poor a figure on my own ground. Ah, it may have been only for six seconds that she caught me gaping at her renewed beauty; but six seconds, it was inevitable to feel, were quite enough for every purpose with which she had come down to me. She might have been a large, fair, rich, prosperous person of twenty-five; she was at any rate near enough to it to put me for ever in my place. It was a success, on her part, that, though I couldn't as yet fully measure it, there could be no doubt of whatever, any more than of my somehow paying for it. Her being there at all, at such an hour, in such conditions, became, each moment, on the whole business, more and more a part of her advantage; the case for her was really in almost any aspect she could now make it wear to my imagination. My wealth of that faculty, never so stimulated, was thus, in a manner, her strength; by which I mean the impossibility of my indifference to the mere immense suggestiveness of our circumstances. How can I tell now to what tune the sense of all these played into my mind?—the huge oddity of the nameless idea on which we foregathered, the absence and hush of everything except that idea, so magnified in consequence and yet still, after all, altogether fantastic. There remained for her, there spoke for her too, her vividly "unconventional" step, the bravery of her rustling, on an understanding so difficult to give an account of, through places and times only made safe by the sleep of the unsuspecting. My imagination, in short, since I have spoken of it, couldn't do other than work for her from the moment she had, so simply yet so wonderfully, not failed me. Therefore it was all with me again, the vision of her reasons. They were in fact sufficiently in the sound of what she presently said. "Perhaps you don't know—but I mentioned in the proper quarter that I should sit up a little. They're of a kindness here, luckily——! So it's all right." It was all right, obviously—she made it so; but she made it so as well that, in spite of the splendour she showed me, she should be a little nervous. "We shall only take moreover," she added, "a minute."

I should perhaps have wondered more what she proposed to do in a minute had I not felt it as already more or less done. Yes, she might have been twenty-five, and it was a short time for *that* to have taken. However, what I clutched at, what I clung to, was that it was a nervous twenty-five. I might pay for her assurance, but wasn't there something of mine for which *she* might pay? I was nervous also, but, as I took in again, with a glance through our great chain of chambers, the wonderful conditions that protected us, I did my best to feel sure that it was only because I was so amused. That—in so high a form—was what it came to in the end. "I supposed," I replied, "that you'd have arranged; for, in spite of the way things were going, I hadn't given you up. I haven't understood, I confess," I went on, "why you've preferred a conference so intensely nocturnal—of which I quite feel, however, that, if it has happened to suit you, it isn't for me to complain. But I felt sure of you—that was the great thing—from the moment, half an hour ago, you so kindly spoke to me. I gave you, you see," I laughed, "what's called 'rope.'"

"I don't suppose you mean," she exclaimed, "for me to hang myself!—for that, I assure you, is not at all what I'm prepared for." Then she seemed again to give me the magnificence of her youth. It wasn't, throughout, I was to feel, that she at all had abysses of irony, for she in fact happily needed none. Her triumph was in itself ironic enough, and all her point in her sense of her freshness. "Were you really so impatient?" But as I inevitably hung fire a little she continued before I could answer; which somewhat helped me indeed by showing the one flaw in her confidence. More extraordinary perhaps than anything else, moreover, was just my perception of this; which gives the value of all that each of us so visibly felt the other to have put together, to have been making out and gathering in, since we parted, on the terrace, after seeing Mrs. Server and Briss come up from under their tree. We *had*, of a truth, arrived at our results—though mine were naturally the ones for me to believe in; and it was prodigious that we openly met not at all where we had last left each other, but exactly on what our subsequent suppressed processes had achieved. We hadn't named them—hadn't alluded to them, and we couldn't, no doubt, have done either; but they were none the less intensely there between us, with the whole bright, empty scene given up to them. Only she had her shrewd sense that mine, for reasons, might have been still more occult than her own. Hadn't I possibly burrowed the deeper—to come out in some uncalculated place behind her back? That was the flaw in her confidence. She had in spite of it her firm ground, and I could feel, to do her justice, how different a complacency it was from such smug ignorance as Lady John's. If I didn't fear to seem to drivel about my own knowledge I should say that she had, in addition to all the rest of her "pull," the benefit of striking me as worthy of me. She was *in* the mystic circle—not one of us more; she knew the size of it; and it was our now being in it alone together, with everyone else out and with the size greater than it had yet been at all—it was this that gave the hour, in fine, so sharp a stamp.

But she had meanwhile taken up my allusion to her having preferred so to wait. "I wanted to see you quietly; which was what I tried—not altogether successfully, it rather struck me at the moment—to make you understand when I let you know about it. You stared so that I didn't quite know what was the matter. Nothing could be quiet, I saw, till the going to bed was over, and I felt it coming off then from one minute to the other. I didn't wish publicly to be called away for it from this putting of our heads together, and, though you may think me absurd, I had a dislike to having our question of May up so long as she was hanging about. I knew of course that she would hang about till the very last moment, and that was what I perhaps a little clumsily—if it was my own fault!—made the effort to convey to you. She may be hanging about still," Mrs. Briss continued, with her larger look round—her looks round were now immense; "but at any rate I shall have done what I could. I had a feeling—perfectly preposterous, I admit!—against her seeing us together; but if she comes down again, as I've so boldly done, and finds us, she'll have no one but herself to thank. It's a funny house, for that matter," my friend rambled on, "and I'm not sure that anyone *has* gone to bed. One does what one likes; I'm an old woman, at any rate, and *I* do!" She explained now, she explained too much, she abounded, talking herself stoutly into any assurance that failed her. I had meanwhile with every word she uttered a sharper sense of the pressure, behind them all, of a new consciousness. It was full of everything she didn't say, and what she said was no representation whatever of what was most in her mind. We had indeed taken a jump since noon—we had indeed come out further on. Just this fine dishonesty of her eyes, moreover—the light of a part to play, the excitement (heaven knows what it struck me as being!) of a happy duplicity—may well have been what contributed most to her present grand air.

It was in any case what evoked for me most the contrasted image, so fresh with me, of the other, the tragic lady—the image that had so embodied the unutterable opposite of everything actually before me. What was actually before me was the positive pride of life and expansion, the amplitude of conscious action and design; not the arid channel forsaken by the stream, but the full-fed river sweeping to the sea, the volume of water, the stately current, the flooded banks into which the source had swelled. There was nothing Mrs. Server had been able to risk, but there was a rich indifference to risk in the mere carriage of Grace Brissenden's head. Her reference, for that matter, to our discussed subject had the effect of relegating to the realm of dim shades the lady representing it, and there was small soundness in her glance at the possibility on the part of this person of an anxious prowl back. There was indeed—there could be—small sincerity in any immediate demonstration from a woman so markedly gaining time and getting her advantages in hand. The connections between the two, certainly, were indirect and intricate, but it was positive to me that, for the spiritual ear, my companion's words had the sound of a hard bump, a contact from the force of which the weaker vessel might have been felt to crack. At last, merciful powers, it was in pieces! The shock of the brass had told upon the porcelain, and I fancied myself for an instant facing Mrs. Briss over the damage—a damage from which I was never, as I knew, to see the poor banished ghost recover. As strange as anything was this effect almost of surprise for me in the freedom of her mention of "May."

For what had she come to me, if for anything, but to insist on her view of May, and what accordingly was more to the point than to mention her? Yet it was almost already as if to mention her had been to get rid of her. She was mentioned, however, inevitably and none the less promptly, anew—even as if simply to receive a final shake before being quite dropped. My friend kept it up. "If you were so bent on not losing what I might have to give you that you fortunately stuck to the ship, for poor Briss to pick you up, wasn't this also"— she roundly put it to me—"a good deal because you've been nursing all day the grievance with which I this morning so comfortably furnished you?"

I just waited, but fairly for admiration. "Oh, I certainly had my reasons—as I've no less certainly had my luck—for not indeed deserting our dear little battered, but still just sufficiently buoyant vessel, from which everyone else appears, I recognise, to *s'être sauvé*. She'll float a few minutes more! But (before she sinks!) do you mean by my grievance——"

"Oh, you know what I mean by your grievance!" *She* had no intention, Mrs. Briss, of sinking. "I was to give you time to make up your mind that Mrs. Server was our lady. You so resented, for some reason, my suggesting it that I scarcely believed you'd consider it at all; only I hadn't forgotten, when I spoke to you a while since, that you had nevertheless handsomely promised me that you would do your best."

"Yes, and, still more handsomely, that if I changed my mind, I would eat, in your presence, for my error, the largest possible slice of humble pie. If you didn't see this morning," I continued, "quite why I should have cared so much, so I don't quite see why, in your different way, *you* should; at the same time that I do full justice to the good faith with which you've given me my chance. Please believe that if I *could* candidly embrace that chance I should feel all the joy in the world in repaying you. It's only, alas! because I cling to my candour that I venture to disappoint you. If I cared this morning it was really simple enough. You didn't convince me, but I should have cared just as much if you had. I only didn't see what *you* saw. I needed more than you could then give me. I knew, you see, what I needed—I mean before I struck! It was the element of collateral support that we both lacked. I couldn't do without it as you could. This was what I, clumsily enough, tried to show you I felt.

You, on your side," I pursued, "grasped admirably the evident truth that that element *could* be present only in such doses as practically to escape detection." I kept it up as she had done, and I remember striking myself as scarce less excitedly voluble. I was conscious of being at a point at which I should have to go straight, to go fast, to go it, as the phrase is, blind, in order to go at all. I was also conscious—and it came from the look with which she listened to me and that told me more than she wished—I felt sharply, though but instinctively, in fine, that I should still, whatever I practically had lost, make my personal experience most rich and most complete by putting it definitely to her that, sorry as I might be not to oblige her, I had, even at this hour, no submission to make. I doubted in fact whether my making one *would* have obliged her; but I felt that, for all so much had come and gone, I was not there to take, for her possible profit, any new tone with her. She would sufficiently profit, at the worst, by the old. My old motive—old with the prodigious antiquity the few hours had given it—had quite left me; I seemed to myself to know little now of my desire to "protect" Mrs. Server. She was certainly, with Mrs. Briss at least, past all protection; and the conviction had grown with me, in these few minutes, that there was now no rag of the queer truth that Mrs. Briss hadn't secretly—by which I meant morally—handled. But I none the less, on a perfectly simple reasoning, stood to my guns, and with no sense whatever, I must add, of now breaking my vow of the morning. I had made another vow since then—made it to the poor lady herself as we sat together in the wood; passed my word to *her* that there was no approximation I pretended even to myself to have made. How then was I to pretend to Mrs. Briss, and what facts *had* I collected on which I could respectably ground an acknowledgment to her that I had come round to her belief? If I had "caught" our incriminated pair together—really together—even for three minutes, I would, I sincerely considered, have come round. But I was to have performed this revolution on nothing less, as I now went on to explain to her. "Of course if you've got new evidence I shall be delighted to hear it; and of course I can't help wondering whether the possession of it and the desire to overwhelm me with it aren't, together, the one thing you've been nursing till now."

Oh, how intensely she didn't like such a tone! If she hadn't looked so handsome I would say she made a wry face over it, though I didn't even yet see where her dislike would make her come out. Before she came out, in fact, she waited as if it were a question of dashing her head at a wall. Then, at last, she charged. "It's nonsense. I've nothing to tell you. I feel there's nothing in it and I've given it up."

I almost gaped—by which I mean that I looked as if I did—for surprise. "You agree that it's not she——?" Then, as she again waited, "It's *you* who've come round?" I insisted.

"To your doubt of its being May? Yes—I've come round."

"Ah, pardon me," I returned; "what I expressed this morning was, if I remember rightly, not at all a 'doubt,' but a positive, intimate conviction that was inconsistent with *any* doubt. I was emphatic—purely and simply—that I didn't see it."

She looked, however, as if she caught me in a weakness here. "Then why did you say to me that if you should reconsider——"

"You should handsomely have it from me, and my grounds? Why, as I've just reminded you, as a form of courtesy to you—magnanimously to help you, as it were, to feel as comfortable as I conceived you naturally would desire to feel in your own conviction. Only for that. And now," I smiled, "I'm to understand from you that, in spite of that immense allowance, you *haven't*, all this while, felt comfortable?"

She gave, on this, in a wonderful, beautiful way, a slow, simplifying headshake. "Mrs. Server isn't in it!"

The only way then to take it from her was that her concession was a prelude to something still better; and when I had given her time to see this dawn upon me I had my eagerness and I jumped into the breathless. "You've made out then who *is*?"

"Oh, I don't make out, you know," she laughed, "so much as you! *She* isn't," she simply repeated.

I looked at it, on my inspiration, quite ruefully—almost as if I now wished, after all, she were. "Ah, but, do you know? it really strikes me you make out marvels. You made out this morning quite what I couldn't. I hadn't put together anything so extraordinary as that—in the total absence of everything—it *should* have been our friend."

Mrs. Briss appeared, on her side, to take in the intention of this. "What do you mean by the total absence? When I made my mistake," she declared as if in the interest of her dignity, "I didn't think everything absent."

"I see," I admitted. "I see," I thoughtfully repeated. "And do you, then, think everything now?"

"I had my honest impression of the moment," she pursued as if she had not heard me. "There were appearances that, as it at the time struck me, fitted."

"Precisely"—and I recalled for her the one she had made most of. "There was in especial the appearance that she was at a particular moment using Brissenden to show whom she was not using. You felt *then*," I ventured to observe, "the force of that."

I ventured less than, already, I should have liked to venture; yet I none the less seemed to see her try on me the effect of the intimation that I was going far. "Is it your wish," she inquired with much nobleness, "to confront me, to my confusion, with my inconsistency?" Her nobleness offered itself somehow as such a rebuke to my mere logic that, in my momentary irritation, I might have been on the point of assenting to her question. This imminence of my assent, justified by my horror of her huge egotism, but justified by nothing else and precipitating everything, seemed as marked for these few seconds as if we each had our eyes on it. But I sat so tight that the danger passed, leaving my silence to do what it could for my manners. She proceeded meanwhile to add a very handsome account of her own. "You should do me the justice to recognise how little I need have spoken another word to you, and how little, also, this amiable explanation to you is in the interest of one's natural pride. It seems to me I've come to you here altogether in the interest of *yours*. You talk about humble pie, but I think that, upon my word—with all I've said to you—it's I who have had to eat it. The magnanimity you speak of," she continued with all her grandeur—"I really don't see, either, whose it

354

is but mine. I don't see what account of anything I'm in any way obliged to give."

I granted it quickly and without reserve. "You're not obliged to give any—you're quite right: you do it only because you're such a large, splendid creature. I quite feel that, beside you"—I did, at least, treat myself to the amusement of saying—"I move in a tiny circle. Still, I won't have it"—I could also, again, keep it up—"that our occasion has nothing for you but the taste of abasement. You gulp your mouthful down, but hasn't it been served on gold plate? You've had a magnificent day—a brimming cup of triumph, and you're more beautiful and fresh, after it all, and at an hour when fatigue would be almost positively graceful, than you were even this morning, when you met me as a daughter of the dawn. That's the sort of sense," I laughed, "that must sustain a woman!" And I wound up on a complete recovery of my good-humour. "No, no. I thank you—thank you immensely. But I don't pity you. You can afford to lose." I wanted her perplexity—the proper sharp dose of it—to result both from her knowing and her not knowing sufficiently what I meant; and when I in fact saw how perplexed she could be and how little, again, she could enjoy it, I felt anew my private wonder at her having cared and dared to meet me. Where *was* enjoyment, for her, where the insolence of success, if the breath of irony could chill them? Why, since she was bold, should she be susceptible, and how, since she was susceptible, could she be bold? I scarce know what, at this moment, determined the divination; but everything, the distinct and the dim alike, had cleared up the next instant at the touch of the real truth. The certitude of the source of my present opportunity had rolled over me before we exchanged another word. The source was simply Gilbert Long, and she was there because he had directed it. This connection hooked itself, like a sudden picture and with a click that fairly resounded through our empty rooms, into the array of the other connections, to the immense enrichment, as it was easy to feel, of the occasion, and to the immense confirmation of the very idea that, in the course of the evening, I had come near dismissing from my mind as too fantastic even for the rest of the company it should enjoy there. What I now was sure of flashed back, at any rate, every syllable of sense I could have desired into the suggestion I had, after the music, caught from the juxtaposition of these two. Thus solidified, this conviction, it spread and spread to a distance greater than I could just then traverse under Mrs. Briss's eyes, but which, exactly for that reason perhaps, quickened my pride in the kingdom of thought I had won. I was really not to have felt more, in the whole business, than I felt at this moment that by my own right hand I had gained the kingdom. Long and she were together, and I was alone thus in face of them, but there was none the less not a single flower of the garden that my woven wreath should lack.

I must have looked queer to my friend as I grinned to myself over this vow; but my relish of the way I was keeping things together made me perhaps for the instant unduly rash. I cautioned myself, however, fortunately, before it could leave her—scared a little, all the same, even with Long behind her—an advantage to take, and, in infinitely less time than I have needed to tell it, I had achieved my flight into luminous ether and, alighting gracefully on my feet, reported myself at my post. I had in other words taken in both the full prodigy of the *entente* between Mrs. Server's lover and poor Briss's wife, and the finer strength it gave the last-named as the representative of their interest. I may add too that I had even taken time fairly not to decide which of these two branches of my vision—that of the terms of their intercourse, or that of their need of it—was likely to prove, in delectable retrospect, the more exquisite. All this, I admit, was a good deal to have come and gone while my privilege trembled, in its very essence, in the scale. Mrs. Briss had but a back to turn, and everything was over. She had, in strictness, already uttered what saved her honour, and her revenge on impertinence might easily be her withdrawing with one of her sweeps. I couldn't certainly in that case hurry after her without spilling my cards. As my accumulations of lucidity, however, were now such as to defy all leakage, I promptly recognised the facilities involved in a superficial sacrifice; and with one more glance at the beautiful fact that she knew the strength of Long's hand, I again went steadily and straight. She was acting not only for herself, and since she had another also to serve and, as I was sure, report to, I should sufficiently hold her. I knew moreover that I held her as soon as I had begun afresh. "I don't mean that anything alters the fact that you lose gracefully. It *is* awfully charming, your thus giving yourself up, and yet, justified as I am by it, I can't help regretting a little the excitement I found it this morning to pull a different way from you. Shall I tell you," it suddenly came to me to put to her, "what, for some reason, a man feels aware of?" And then as, guarded, still uneasy, she would commit herself to no permission: "That pulling against you also had its thrill. You defended your cause. Oh," I quickly added, "I know—who should know better?—that it was bad. Only—what shall I say?—*you* weren't bad, and one had to fight. And then there was what one was fighting for! Well, you're not bad now, either; so that you may ask me, of course, what more I want." I tried to think a moment. "It isn't that, thrown back on the comparative dullness of security, I find—as people have been known to—my own cause less good: no, it isn't that." After which I had my illumination. "I'll tell you what it is: it's the come-down of ceasing to work with you!"

She looked as if she were quite excusable for not following me. "To 'work'?"

I immediately explained. "Even fighting was working, for we struck, you'll remember, sparks, and sparks were what we wanted. There we are then," I cheerfully went on. "Sparks are what we still want, and you've not come to me, I trust, with a mere spent match. I depend upon it that you've another to strike." I showed her without fear all I took for granted. "Who, then, *has*?"

She was superb in her coldness, but her stare was partly blank. "Who then has what?"

"Why, done it." And as even at this she didn't light I gave her something of a jog. "You haven't, with the force of your revulsion, I hope, literally lost our thread." But as, in spite of my thus waiting for her to pick it up she did nothing, I offered myself as fairly stooping to the carpet for it and putting it back in her hand. "Done what we spent the morning wondering at. Who then, if it isn't, certainly, Mrs. Server, *is* the woman who has made Gilbert Long—well, what you know?"

I had needed the moment to take in the special shade of innocence she was by this time prepared to show me. It was an innocence, in particular, in respect to the relation of anyone, in all the vast impropriety of things, to anyone. "I'm afraid I know nothing."

I really wondered an instant how she could expect help from such extravagance. "But I thought you just recognised that you do enjoy the sense of your pardonable mistake. You knew something when you knew enough to see you had made it."

She faced me as with the frank perception that, of whatever else one might be aware, I abounded in traps, and that this would probably be one of my worst. "Oh, I think one generally knows when one has made a mistake."

"That's all then I invite you—*a* mistake, as you properly call it—to allow me to impute to you. I'm not accusing you of having made fifty. You made none whatever, I hold, when you agreed with me with such eagerness about the striking change in him."

She affected me as asking herself a little, on this, whether vagueness, the failure of memory, the rejection of nonsense, mightn't still serve her. But she saw the next moment a better way. It all came back to her, but from so very far off. "The change, do you mean, in poor Mr. Long?"

"Of what other change—except, as you may say, your own—have you met me here to speak of? Your own, I needn't remind you, is part and parcel of Long's."

"Oh, my own," she presently returned, "is a much simpler matter even than that. My own is the recognition that I just expressed to you and that I can't consent, if you please, to your twisting into the recognition of anything else. It's the recognition that I know nothing of any other change. I stick, if you'll allow me, to my ignorance."

"I'll allow you with joy," I laughed, "if you'll let me stick to it *with* you. Your own change is quite sufficient—it gives us all we need. It will give us, if we retrace the steps of it, everything, everything!"

Mrs. Briss considered. "I don't quite see, do I? why, at this hour of the night, we should begin to retrace steps."

"Simply because it's the hour of the night you've happened, in your generosity and your discretion, to choose. I'm struck, I confess," I declared with a still sharper conviction, "with the wonderful charm of it for our purpose."

"And, pray, what do you call with such solemnity," she inquired, "our purpose?"

I had fairly recovered at last—so far from being solemn—an appropriate gaiety. "I can only, with positiveness, answer for mine! That has remained all day the same—to get at the truth: not, that is, to relax my grasp of that tip of the tail of it which you so helped me this morning to fasten to. If you've ceased to *care* to help me," I pursued, "that's a difference indeed. But why," I candidly, pleadingly asked, "*should* you cease to care?" It was more and more of a comfort to feel her imprisoned in her inability really to explain her being there. To show herself as she was explained it only so far as she could express that; which was just the freedom she could least take. "What on earth is between us, anyhow," I insisted, "but our confounded interest? That's only quickened, for me, don't you see? by the charming way you've come round; and I don't see how it can logically be anything less than quickened for yourself. We're like the messengers and heralds in the tale of Cinderella, and I protest, I assure you, against any sacrifice of our dénoûment. We've still the glass shoe to fit."

I took pleasure at the moment in my metaphor; but this was not the case, I soon enough perceived, with my companion. "How can I tell, please," she demanded, "what you consider you're talking about?"

I smiled; it was so quite the question Ford Obert, in the smoking-room, had begun by putting me. I hadn't to take time to remind myself how I had dealt with *him*. "And you knew," I sighed, "so beautifully, you glowed over it so, this morning!" She continued to give me, in every way, her disconnection from this morning, so that I had only to proceed: "You've not availed yourself of this occasion to pretend to me that poor Mr. Long, as you call him, is, after all, the same limited person——"

"That he always was, and that you, yesterday, so suddenly discovered him to have ceased to be?"—for with this she had waked up. But she was still thinking how she could turn it. "You see too much."

"Oh, I know I do—ever so much too much. And much as I see, I express only half of it—so you may judge!" I laughed. "But what will you have? I see what I see, and this morning, for a good bit, you did me the honour to do the same. I returned, also, the compliment, didn't I? by seeing something of what *you* saw. We put it, the whole thing, together, and we shook the bottle hard. I'm to take from you, after this," I wound up, "that what it contains is a perfectly colourless fluid?"

I paused for a reply, but it was not to come so happily as from Obert. "You talk too much!" said Mrs. Briss.

I met it with amazement. "Why, whom have I told?"

I looked at her so hard with it that her colour began to rise, which made me promptly feel that she wouldn't press that point. "I mean you're carried away—you're abused by a fine fancy: so that, with your art of putting things, one doesn't know where one is—nor, if you'll allow me to say so, do I quite think *you* always do. Of course I don't deny you're awfully clever. But you build up," she brought out with a regret so indulgent and a reluctance so marked that she for some seconds fairly held the blow—"you build up houses of cards."

I had been impatient to learn what, and, frankly, I was disappointed. This broke from me, after an instant, doubtless, with a bitterness not to be mistaken. "Long *isn't* what he seems?"

"Seems to whom?" she asked sturdily.

"Well, call it—for simplicity—to *me*. For you see"—and I spoke as to show *what* it was to see—"it all stands or falls by that."

The explanation presently appeared a little to have softened her. If it all stood or fell only by *that*, it stood or fell by something that, for her comfort, might be not so unsuccessfully disposed of. She exhaled, with the swell of her fine person, a comparative blandness—seemed to play with the idea of a smile. She had, in short, her own explanation. "The trouble with you is that you over-estimate the penetration of others. How can it approach your own?"

"Well, yours had for a while, I should say, distinct moments of keeping up with it. Nothing is more possible," I went on, "than that I do talk too much; but I've done so—about the question in dispute between us—only to *you*. I haven't, as I conceived we were absolutely not to do, mentioned it to anyone else, nor given anyone a glimpse of our difference. If you've not understood yourself as pledged to the same reserve, and have consequently," I went on, "appealed to the light of other wisdom, it shows at least that, in spite of my intellectual pace, you must more or less have followed me. What am I *not*, in fine, to think of your intelligence," I asked, "if, deciding for a resort to headquarters, you've put the question to Long himself?"

"The question?" She was straight out to sea again.

"Of the identity of the lady."

She slowly, at this, headed about. "To Long himself?"

I had felt I could risk such directness only by making it extravagant—by suggesting it as barely imaginable that she could so have played our game; and during the instant for which I had now pulled her up I could judge I had been right. It was an instant that settled everything, for I saw her, with intensity, with gallantry too, surprised but not really embarrassed, recognise that of course she must simply lie. I had been justified by making it so possible for her to lie. "It would have been a short cut," I said, "and even more strikingly perhaps—to do it justice—a bold deed. But it would have been, in strictness, a departure—wouldn't it?—from our so distinguished little compact. Yet while I look at you," I went on, "I wonder. Bold deeds are, after all, quite in your line; and I'm not sure I don't rather want not to have missed so much possible comedy. 'I have it for you from Mr. Long himself that, every appearance to the contrary notwithstanding, his stupidity is unimpaired'—isn't that, for the beauty of it, after all, what you've veraciously to give me?" We stood face to face a moment, and I laughed out. "The beauty of it would be great!"

I had given her time; I had seen her safely to shore. It was quite what I had meant to do, but she now took still better advantage than I had expected of her opportunity. She not only scrambled up the bank, she recovered breath and turned round. "Do you imagine he would have told me?"

It was magnificent, but I felt she was still to better it should I give her a new chance. "Who the lady really is? Well, hardly; and that's why, as you so acutely see, the question of your having risked such a step has occurred to me only as a jest. Fancy indeed"—I piled it up—"your saying to him: 'We're all noticing that you're so much less of an idiot than you used to be, and we've different views of the miracle'!"

I had been going on, but I was checked without a word from her. Her look alone did it, for, though it was a look that partly spoiled her lie, it—by that very fact—sufficed to my confidence. "I've not spoken to a creature."

It was beautifully said, but I felt again the abysses that the mere saying of it covered, and the sense of these wonderful things was not a little, no doubt, in my immediate cheer. "Ah, then, we're all right!" I could have rubbed my hands over it. "I mean, however," I quickly added, "only as far as that. I don't at all feel comfortable about your new theory itself, which puts me so wretchedly in the wrong."

"Rather!" said Mrs. Briss almost gaily. "Wretchedly indeed in the wrong!"

"Yet only—equally of course," I returned after a brief brooding, "if I come within a conceivability of accepting it. Are you conscious that, in default of Long's own word—equivocal as that word would be—you press it upon me without the least other guarantee?"

"And pray," she asked, "what guarantee had *you?*"

"For the theory with which we started? Why, our recognised fact. The change in the man. You may say," I pursued, "that I was the first to speak for him; but being the first didn't, in your view, constitute a weakness when it came to your speaking yourself for Mrs. Server. By which I mean," I added, "speaking against her."

She remembered, but not for my benefit. "Well, you then asked me *my* warrant. And as regards Mr. Long and your speaking against *him*——"

"Do you describe what I say as 'against' him?" I immediately broke in.

It took her but an instant. "Surely—to have made him out horrid."

I could only want to fix it. "'Horrid'——?"

"Why, having such secrets." She was roundly ready now. "Sacrificing poor May."

"But *you*, dear lady, sacrificed poor May! It didn't strike you as horrid *then*."

"Well, that was only," she maintained, "because you talked me over."

I let her see the full process of my taking—or not taking—this in. "And who is it then that—if, as you say, you've spoken to no one—has, as I may call it, talked you under?"

She completed, on the spot, her statement of a moment before. "Not a creature has spoken to me."

I felt somehow the wish to make her say it in as many ways as possible—I seemed so to enjoy her saying it. This helped me to make my tone approve and encourage. "You've communicated so little with anyone!" I didn't even make it a question.

It was scarce yet, however, quite good enough. "So little? I've not communicated the least mite."

"Precisely. But don't think me impertinent for having for a moment wondered. What I should say to you if you had, you know, would be that you just accused me."

"Accused you?"

"Of talking too much."

It came back to her dim. "Are we accusing each other?"

Her tone seemed suddenly to put us nearer together than we had ever been at all. "Dear no," I laughed—"not each other; only with each other's help, a few of our good friends."

"A few?" She handsomely demurred. "But one or two at the best."

"Or at the worst!"—I continued to laugh. "And not even those, it after all appears, very much!"

She didn't like my laughter, but she was now grandly indulgent. "Well, I accuse no one."

I was silent a little; then I concurred. "It's doubtless your best line; and I really quite feel, at all events, that when you mentioned a while since that I talk too much you only meant too much to *you*."

"Yes—I wasn't imputing to you the same direct appeal. I didn't suppose," she explained, "that—to match your own supposition of *me*—you had resorted to May herself."

"You didn't suppose I had asked her?" The point was positively that she didn't; yet it made us look at each other almost as hard as if she did. "No, of course you couldn't have supposed anything so cruel—all the more that, as you knew, I had not admitted the possibility."

She accepted my assent; but, oddly enough, with a sudden qualification that showed her as still sharply disposed to make use of any loose scrap of her embarrassed acuteness. "Of course, at the same time, you yourself saw that your not admitting the possibility would have taken the edge from your cruelty. It's not the innocent," she suggestively remarked, "that we fear to frighten."

"Oh," I returned, "I fear, mostly, I think, to frighten *any* one. I'm not particularly brave. I haven't, at all events, in spite of my certitude, interrogated Mrs. Server, and I give you my word of honour that I've not had any denial from her to prop up my doubt. It still stands on its own feet, and it was its own battle that, when I came here at your summons, it was prepared to fight. Let me accordingly remind you," I pursued, "in connection with that, of the one sense in which you were, as you a moment ago said, talked over by me. I persuaded you apparently that Long's metamorphosis was not the work of Lady John. I persuaded you of nothing else."

She looked down a little, as if again at a trap. "You persuaded me that it was the work of somebody." Then she held up her head. "It came to the same thing."

If I had credit then for my trap it at least might serve. "The same thing as what?"

"Why, as claiming that it *was* she."

"Poor May—'claiming'? When I insisted it wasn't!"

Mrs. Brissenden flushed. "You didn't insist it wasn't anybody!"

"Why should I when I didn't believe so? I've left you in no doubt," I indulgently smiled, "of my beliefs. It was somebody—and it still is."

She looked about at the top of the room. "The mistake's now yours."

I watched her an instant. "Can you tell me then what one does to recover from such mistakes?"

"One thinks a little."

"Ah, the more I've thought the deeper I've sunk! And that seemed to me the case with you this morning," I added, "the more *you* thought."

"Well, then," she frankly declared, "I must have stopped thinking!"

It was a phenomenon, I sufficiently showed, that thought only could meet. "Could you tell me then at what point?"

She had to think even to do that. "At what point?"

"What in particular determined, I mean, your arrest? You surely didn't—launched as you were—stop short all of yourself."

She fronted me, after all, still so bravely that I believed her for an instant not to be, on this article, without an answer she could produce. The unexpected therefore broke for me when she fairly produced none. "I confess I don't make out," she simply said, "while you seem so little pleased that I agree with you."

I threw back, in despair, both head and hands. "But, you poor, dear thing, you don't in the *least* agree with me! You flatly contradict me. You deny my miracle."

"I don't believe in miracles," she panted.

"So I exactly, at this late hour, learn. But I don't insist on the name. Nothing *is*, I admit, a miracle from the moment one's on the track of the cause, which was the scent we were following. Call the thing simply my fact."

She gave her high head a toss. "If it's yours it's nobody else's!"

"Ah, there's just the question—if we could know all! But my point is precisely, for the present, that you do deny it."

"Of course I deny it," said Mrs. Briss.

I took a moment, but my silence held her. "Your 'of course' would be what I would again contest, what I would denounce and brand as the word too much—the word that spoils, were it not that it seems best, that it in any case seems necessary, to let all question of your consistency go."

On that I had paused, and, as I felt myself still holding her, I was not surprised when my pause had an effect. "You do let it go?"

She had tried, I could see, to put the inquiry as all ironic. But it was not all ironic; it was, in fact, little enough so to suggest for me some intensification—not quite, I trust, wanton—of her suspense. I should be at a loss to say indeed how much it suggested or half of what it told. These things again almost violently moved me, and if I, after an instant, in my silence, turned away, it was not only to keep her waiting, but to make my elation more private. I turned away to that tune that I literally, for a few minutes, quitted her, availing myself thus, superficially, of the air of weighing a consequence. I wandered off twenty steps and, while I passed my hand over my troubled head, looked vaguely at objects on tables and sniffed absently at flowers in bowls. I don't know how long I so lost myself, nor quite why—as I must for some time have kept it up—my companion didn't now really embrace her possible alternative of rupture and retreat. Or rather, as to her action in this last matter, I am, and was on the spot, clear: I knew at that moment how much *she* knew she must not leave me without having got from me. It came back in waves, in wider glimpses, and produced in so doing the excitement I had to control. It could *not* but be exciting to talk, as we talked, on the basis of those suppressed processes and unavowed references which made the meaning of our meeting so different from its form. We knew ourselves—what moved me, that is, was that she knew me—to mean, at every point, immensely more than I said or than she answered; just as she saw me, at the same points, measure the space by which her answers fell short. This made my conversation with her a totally other and a far more interesting thing than any colloquy I had ever enjoyed;

it had even a sharpness that had not belonged, a few hours before, to my extraordinary interview with Mrs. Server. She couldn't afford to quarrel with me for catechising her; she couldn't afford not to have kept, in her way, faith with me; she couldn't afford, after inconceivable passages with Long, not to treat me as an observer to be squared. She had come down to square me; she was hanging on to square me; she was suffering and stammering and lying; she was both carrying it grandly off and letting it desperately go: all, all to square me. And I caught moreover perfectly her vision of her way, and I followed her way even while I judged it, feeling that the only personal privilege I could, after all, save from the whole business was that of understanding. I couldn't save Mrs. Server, and I couldn't save poor Briss; I *could*, however, guard, to the last grain of gold, my precious sense of their loss, their disintegration and their doom; and it was for this I was now bargaining.

It was of giving herself away just enough not to spoil for me my bargain over my treasure that Mrs. Briss's bribe would consist. She would let me see as far as I would if she could feel sure I would *do* nothing; and it was exactly in this question of how much I might have scared my couple into the sense I *could* "do" that the savour of my suspense most dwelt. I could have made them uneasy, of course, only by making them fear my intervention; and yet the idea of their being uneasy was less wonderful than the idea of my having, with all my precautions, communicated to them a consciousness. This was so the last thing I had wanted to do that I felt, during my swift excursion, how much time I should need in the future for recovery of the process— all of the finest wind-blown intimations, woven of silence and secrecy and air—by which their suspicion would have throbbed into life. I could only, provisionally and sketchily, figure it out, this suspicion, as having, little by little—not with a sudden start—felt itself in the presence of my own, just as my own now returned the compliment. What came back to me, as I have said, in waves and wider glimpses, was the marvel of their exchange of signals, the phenomenon, scarce to be represented, of their breaking ground with each other. They both had their treasure to guard, and they had looked to each other with the instinct of help. They had felt, on either side, the victim possibly slip, and they had connected the possibility with an interest discernibly inspired in me by this personage, and with a relation discoverably established by that interest. It wouldn't have been a danger, perhaps, if the two victims hadn't slipped together; and more amazing, doubtless, than anything else was the recognition by my sacrificing couple of the opportunity drawn by my sacrificed from being conjoined in my charity. How could they know, Gilbert Long and Mrs. Briss, that actively to communicate a consciousness to my other friends had no part in my plan? The most I had dreamed of, I could honourably feel, was to assure myself of their independent possession of one. These things were with me while, as I have noted, I made Grace Brissenden wait, and it was also with me that, though I condoned her deviation, she must take it from me as a charity. I had presently achieved another of my full revolutions, and I faced her again with a view of her overture and my answer to her last question. The terms were not altogether what my pity could have wished, but I sufficiently kept everything together to have to see that there were limits to my choice. "Yes, I let it go, your change of front, though it vexes me a little—and I'll in a moment tell you why—to have to. But let us put it that it's on a condition."

"Change of front?" she murmured while she looked at me. "Your expressions are not of the happiest."

But I saw it was only again to cover a doubt. My condition, for her, was questionable, and I felt it would be still more so on her hearing what it was. Meanwhile, however, in spite of her qualification of it, I had fallen back, once and for all, on pure benignity. "It scarce matters if I'm clumsy when you're practically so bland. I wonder if you'll understand," I continued, "if I make you an explanation."

"Most probably," she answered, as handsome as ever, "not."

"Let me at all events try you. It's moreover the one I just promised; which was no more indeed than the development of a feeling I've already permitted myself to show you. I lose"—I brought it out—"by your agreeing with me!"

"'Lose'?"

369

"Yes; because while we disagreed you were, in spite of that, on the right side."

"And what do you call the right side?"

"Well"—I brought it out again—"on the same side as my imagination."

But it gave her at least a chance. "Oh, your imagination!"

"Yes—I know what you think of it; you've sufficiently hinted how little that is. But it's precisely because you regard it as rubbish that I now appeal to you."

She continued to guard herself by her surprises. "Appeal? I thought you were on the ground, rather," she beautifully smiled, "of dictation."

"Well, I'm that too. I dictate my terms. But my terms are in themselves the appeal." I was ingenious but patient. "See?"

"How in the world can I see?"

"*Voyons*, then. Light or darkness, my imagination rides me. But of course if it's all wrong I want to get rid of it. You can't, naturally, help me to destroy the faculty itself, but you can aid in the defeat of its application to a particular case. It was because you so smiled, before, on that application, that I valued even my minor difference with you; and what I refer to as my loss is the fact that your frown leaves me struggling alone. The best thing for me, accordingly, as I feel, is to get rid altogether of the obsession. The way to do that, clearly, since *you've* done it, is just to quench the fire. By the fire I mean the flame of the fancy that blazed so for us this morning. What the deuce have you, for yourself, poured on it? Tell me," I pleaded, "and teach me."

Equally with her voice her face echoed me again. "Teach you?"

"To abandon my false gods. Lead me back to peace by the steps *you've* trod. By so much as they must have remained traceable to you, shall I find them of interest and profit. They must in fact be most remarkable: won't they even— for what *I* may find in them—be more remarkable than those we should now be taking together if we hadn't separated, if we hadn't pulled up?" That was a proposition I could present to her with candour, but before her absence of precipitation had permitted her much to consider it I had already followed it on. "You'll just tell me, however, that since I do pull up and turn back with you we shall just have *not* separated. Well, then, so much the better—I see you're right. But I want," I earnestly declared, "not to lose an inch of the journey."

She watched me now as a Roman lady at the circus may have watched an exemplary Christian. "The journey has been a very simple one," she said at last. "With my mind made up on a single point, it was taken at a stride."

I was all interest. "On a single point?" Then, as, almost excessively deliberate, she still kept me: "You mean the still commonplace character of Long's—a—consciousness?"

She had taken at last again the time she required. "Do you know what I think?"

"It's exactly what I'm pressing you to make intelligible."

"Well," said Mrs. Briss, "I think you're crazy."

It naturally struck me. "Crazy?"

"Crazy."

I turned it over. "But do you call that intelligible?"

She did it justice. "No: I don't suppose it *can* be so for you if you *are* insane."

I risked the long laugh which might have seemed that of madness. "'If I am' is lovely!" And whether or not it was the special sound, in my ear, of my hilarity, I remember just wondering if perhaps I mightn't be. "Dear woman, it's the point at issue!"

But it was as if she too had been affected. "It's not at issue for me now."

I gave her then the benefit of my stirred speculation. "It always happens, of course, that one is one's self the last to know. You're perfectly convinced?"

She not ungracefully, for an instant, faltered; but since I really would have it——! "Oh, so far as what we've talked of is concerned, perfectly!"

"And it's actually what you've come down then to tell me?"

"Just exactly what. And if it's a surprise to you," she added, "that I *should* have come down—why, I can only say I was prepared for anything."

"Anything?" I smiled.

"In the way of a surprise."

I thought; but her preparation was natural, though in a moment I could match it. "Do you know that's what I was too?"

"Prepared——?"

"For anything in the way of a surprise. But only *from* you," I explained. "And of course—yes," I mused, "I've got it. If I *am* crazy," I went on—"it's indeed simple."

She appeared, however, to feel, from the influence of my present tone, the impulse, in courtesy, to attenuate. "Oh, I don't pretend it's simple!"

"No? I thought that was just what you did pretend."

"I didn't suppose," said Mrs. Briss, "that you'd like it. I didn't suppose that you'd accept it or even listen to it. But I owed it to you——" She hesitated.

"You owed it to me to let me know what you thought of me even should it prove very disagreeable?"

That perhaps was more than she could adopt. "I owed it to myself," she replied with a touch of austerity.

"To let me know I'm demented?"

"To let you know I'm *not*." We each looked, I think, when she had said it, as if she had done what she said. "That's all."

"All?" I wailed. "Ah, don't speak as if it were so little. It's much. It's everything."

"It's anything you will!" said Mrs. Briss impatiently. "Good-night."

"Good-night?" I was aghast. "You leave me on it?"

She appeared to profess for an instant all the freshness of her own that she was pledged to guard. "I must leave you on something. I couldn't come to spend a whole hour."

"But do you think it's so quickly done—to persuade a man he's crazy?"

"I haven't expected to persuade you."

"Only to throw out the hint?"

"Well," she admitted, "it would be good if it could work in you. But I've told you," she added as if to wind up and have done, "what determined me."

"I beg your pardon"—oh, I protested! "That's just what you've not told me. The reason of your change——"

"I'm not speaking," she broke in, "of my change."

"Ah, but *I* am!" I declared with a sharpness that threw her back for a minute on her reserves. "It's your change," I again insisted, "that's the interesting thing. If I'm crazy, I must once more remind you, you were simply crazy *with* me; and how can I therefore be indifferent to your recovery of your wit or let you go without having won from you the secret of your remedy?" I shook my head with kindness, but with decision. "You mustn't leave me till you've placed it in my hand."

The reserves I had spoken of were not, however, to fail her. "I thought you just said that you let my inconsistency go."

"Your moral responsibility for it—perfectly. But how can I show a greater indulgence than by positively desiring to enter into its history? It's in that sense that, as I say," I developed, "I do speak of your change. There must have been a given moment when the need of it—or when, in other words, the truth of my personal state—dawned upon you. That moment is the key to your whole position—the moment for us to fix."

"Fix it," said poor Mrs. Briss, "when you like!"

"I had much rather," I protested, "fix it when *you* like. I want—you surely must understand if I want anything of it at all—to get it absolutely right." Then as this plea seemed still not to move her, I once more compressed my palms. "You *won't* help me?"

She bridled at last with a higher toss. "It wasn't with such views I came. I don't believe," she went on a shade more patiently, "I don't believe—if you want to know the reason—that you're really sincere."

Here indeed was an affair. "Not sincere—*I?*"

"Not properly honest. I mean in giving up."

"Giving up what?"

"Why, everything."

"Everything? Is it a question"—I stared—"of *that?*"

"You would if you *were* honest."

"Everything?" I repeated.

Again she stood to it. "Everything."

"But is that quite the readiness I've professed?"

"If it isn't then, what is?"

I thought a little. "Why, isn't it simply a matter rather of the renunciation of a confidence?"

"In your sense and your truth?" This, she indicated, was all she asked. "Well, what is that but everything?"

"Perhaps," I reflected, "perhaps." In fact, it no doubt was. "We'll take it then for everything, and it's as so taking it that I renounce. I keep nothing at all. Now do you believe I'm honest?"

She hesitated. "Well—yes, if you say so."

"Ah," I sighed, "I see you don't! What can I do," I asked, "to prove it?"

"You can easily prove it. You can let me go."

"Does it strike you," I considered, "that I should take your going as a sign of your belief?"

"Of what else, then?"

"Why, surely," I promptly replied, "my assent to your leaving our discussion where it stands would constitute a very different symptom. Wouldn't it much rather represent," I inquired, "a failure of belief on my own part in *your* honesty? If you can judge me, in short, as only pretending——"

"Why shouldn't you," she put in for me, "also judge *me*? What have I to gain by pretending?"

"I'll tell you," I returned, laughing, "if you'll tell me what *I* have."

She appeared to ask herself if she could, and then to decide in the negative. "If I don't understand you in any way, of course I don't in that. Put it, at any rate," she now rather wearily quavered, "that one of us has as little to gain as the other. I believe you," she repeated. "There!"

"Thanks," I smiled, "for the way you say it. If you don't, as you say, understand me," I insisted, "it's because you think me crazy. And if you think me crazy I don't see how you *can* leave me."

She presently met this. "If I believe you're sincere in saying you give up I believe you've recovered. And if I believe you've recovered I don't think you crazy. It's simple enough."

"Then why isn't it simple to understand me?"

She turned about, and there were moments in her embarrassment, now, from which she fairly drew beauty. Her awkwardness was somehow noble; her sense of her predicament was in itself young. "Is it *ever*?" she charmingly threw out.

I felt she must see at this juncture how wonderful I found her, and even that that impression—one's whole consciousness of her personal victory—was a force that, in the last resort, was all on her side. "It was quite worth your while, this sitting up to this hour, to show a fellow how you bloom when other women are fagged. If that was really, with the truth that we're so pulling about laid bare, what you did most want to show, why, then, you've splendidly triumphed, and I congratulate and thank you. No," I quickly went on, "I daresay, to do you justice, the interpretation of my tropes and figures *isn't* 'ever' perfectly simple. You doubtless *have* driven me into a corner with my dangerous explosive, and my only fair course must be therefore to sit on it till you get out of the room. I'm sitting on it now; and I think you'll find you can get out as soon as you've told me *this*. Was the moment your change of view dawned upon you the moment of our exchanging a while ago, in the drawing-room, our few words?"

The light that, under my last assurances, had so considerably revived faded in her a little as she saw me again tackle the theme of her inconstancy; but the prospect of getting rid of me on these terms made my inquiry, none the less, worth trying to face. "That moment?" She showed the effort to think back.

I gave her every assistance. "It was when, after the music, I had been talking to Lady John. You were on a sofa, not far from us, with Gilbert Long; and when, on Lady John's dropping me, I made a slight movement toward you, you most graciously met it by rising and giving me a chance while Mr. Long walked away."

It was as if I had hung the picture before her, so that she had fairly to look at it. But the point that she first, in her effort, took up was not, superficially, the most salient. "Mr. Long walked away?"

"Oh, I don't mean to say that that had anything to do with it."

She continued to think. "To do with what?"

"With the way the situation comes back to me now as possibly marking your crisis."

She wondered. "Was it a 'situation'?"

"That's just what I'm asking you. *Was* it? Was it *the* situation?"

But she had quite fallen away again. "I remember the moment you mean—it was when I said I would come to you here. But why should it have struck you as a crisis?"

"It didn't in the least at the time, for I didn't then know you were no longer 'with' me. But in the light of what I've since learned from you I seem to recover an impression which, on the spot, was only vague. The impression," I explained, "of your taking a decision that presented some difficulty, but that was determined by something that had then—and even perhaps a little suddenly—come up for you. That's the point"—I continued to unfold my case—"on which my question bears. *Was* this 'something' your conclusion, then and there, that there's nothing in anything?"

She kept her distance. "'In anything'?"

"And that I could only be, accordingly, out of my mind? Come," I patiently pursued; "such a perception as that had, at some instant or other, to *begin*; and I'm only trying to aid you to recollect when the devil it did!"

"Does it particularly matter?" Mrs. Briss inquired.

I felt my chin. "That depends a little—doesn't it?—on what you mean by 'matter'! It matters for your meeting my curiosity, and that matters, in its turn, as we just arranged, for my releasing you. You may ask of course if my curiosity itself matters; but to that, fortunately, my reply can only be of the clearest. The satisfaction of my curiosity is the pacification of my mind. We've granted, we've accepted, I again press upon you, in respect to that precarious quantity, its topsy-turvy state. Only give me a lead; I don't ask you for more. Let me for an instant see play before me any feeble reflection whatever of the flash of new truth that unsettled you."

I thought for a moment that, in her despair, she would find something that would do. But she only found: "It didn't come in a flash."

I remained all patience. "It came little by little? It began then perhaps earlier in the day than the moment to which I allude? And yet," I continued, "we were pretty well on in the day, I must keep in mind, when I had your last news of your credulity."

"My credulity?"

"Call it then, if you don't like the word, your sympathy."

I had given her time, however, to produce at last something that, it visibly occurred to her, might pass. "As soon as I was not with you—I mean with you personally—you *never* had my sympathy."

"Is my person then so irresistible?"

Well, she was brave. "It *was*. But it's not, thank God, now!"

"Then there we are again at our mystery! I don't think, you know," I made out for her, "it was my person, really, that gave its charm to my theory; I think it was much more my theory that gave its charm to my person. My person, I flatter myself, has remained through these few hours—hours of tension, but of a tension, you see, purely intellectual—as good as ever; so that if we're not, even in our anomalous situation, in danger from any such source, it's simply that my theory is dead and that the blight of the rest is involved."

My words were indeed many, but she plumped straight through them. "As soon as I was away from you I hated you."

"Hated *me*?"

"Well, hated what you call 'the rest'—hated your theory."

"I see. Yet," I reflected, "you're not at present—though you wish to goodness, no doubt, you *were*—away from me."

"Oh, I don't care now," she said with courage; "since—for you see I believe you—we're away from your delusions."

"You wouldn't, in spite of your belief,"—I smiled at her—"like to be a little further off yet?" But before she could answer, and because also, doubtless, the question had too much the sound of a taunt, I came up, as if for her real convenience, quite in another place. "Perhaps my idea—my timing, that is, of your crisis—is the result, in my mind, of my own association with that particular instant. It comes back to me that what I was most full of while your face signed to me and your voice then so graciously confirmed it, and while too, as I've said, Long walked away—what I was most full of, as a consequence of another go, just ended, at Lady John, was, once more, this same Lady John's want of adjustability to the character you and I, in our associated speculation of the morning, had so candidly tried to fit her with. I was still even then, you see, speculating—all on my own hook, alas!—and it had just rolled over me with renewed force that she was nothing whatever, not the least little bit, to our purpose. The moment, in other words, if you understand, happened to be one of *my* moments; so that, by the same token, I simply wondered if it mightn't likewise have happened to be one of yours."

"It *was* one of mine," Mrs. Briss replied as promptly as I could reasonably have expected; "in the sense that—as you've only to consider—it was to lead more or less directly to these present words of ours."

If I had only to consider, nothing was more easy; but each time I considered, I was ready to show, the less there seemed left by the act. "Ah, but you had then *already* backed out. *Won't* you understand—for you're a little discouraging—that I want to catch you at the earlier stage?"

"To 'catch' me?" I had indeed expressions!

"Absolutely catch! Focus you under the first shock of the observation that was to make everything fall to pieces for you."

"But I've told you," she stoutly resisted, "that there was no 'first' shock."

"Well, then, the second or the third."

"There was no shock," Mrs. Briss magnificently said, "at all."

It made me somehow break into laughter. "You found it so natural then—and you so rather liked it—to make up your mind of a sudden that you had been steeped in the last intellectual intimacy with a maniac?"

She thought once more, and then, as I myself had just previously done, came up in another place. "I had at the moment you speak of wholly given up any idea of Lady John."

But it was so feeble it made me smile. "Of course you had, you poor innocent! You couldn't otherwise, hours before, have strapped the saddle so tight on another woman."

"I had given up everything," she stubbornly continued.

"It's exactly what, in reference to that juncture, I perfectly embrace."

"Well, even in reference to that juncture," she resumed, "you may catch me as much as you like." With which, suddenly, during some seconds, I saw her hold herself for a leap. "You talk of 'focussing,' but what else, even in those minutes, were you in fact engaged in?"

"Ah, then, you do recognise them," I cried—"those minutes?"

She took her jump, though with something of a flop. "Yes—as, consenting thus to be catechised, I cudgel my brain for your amusement—I do recognise them. I remember what I thought. You focussed—I felt you focus. I saw you wonder whereabouts, in what you call our associated speculation, I would by that time be. I asked myself whether you'd understand if I should try to convey to you simply by my expression such a look as would tell you all. By 'all' I meant the fact that, sorry as I was for you—or perhaps for myself—it had struck me as only fair to let you know as straight as possible that I was nowhere. That was why I stared so, and I of course couldn't explain to you," she lucidly pursued, "to whom my stare had reference."

I hung on her lips. "But you can *now?*"

"Perfectly. To Mr. Long."

I remained suspended. "Ah, but this is lovely! It's what I want."

I saw I should have more of it, and more in fact came. "You were saying just now what you were full of, and I can do the same. I was full of *him.*"

380

I, on my side, was now full of eagerness. "Yes? He had left you full as he walked away?"

She winced a little at this renewed evocation of his retreat, but she took it as she had not done before, and I felt that with another push she would be fairly afloat. "He had reason to walk!"

I wondered. "What had you said to him?"

She pieced it out. "Nothing—or very little. But I had listened."

"And to *what?*"

"To what he says. To his platitudes."

"His platitudes?" I stared. "Long's?"

"Why, don't you know he's a prize fool?"

I mused, sceptical but reasonable. "He *was*."

"He *is!*"

Mrs. Briss was superb, but, as I quickly felt I might remind her, there was her possibly weak judgment. "Your confidence is splendid; only mustn't I remember that your sense of the finer kinds of cleverness isn't perhaps absolutely secure? Don't you know?—you also, till just now, thought *me* a prize fool."

If I had hoped, however, here to trip her up, I had reckoned without the impulse, and even perhaps the example, that she properly owed to me. "Oh, no—not anything of that sort, you, at all. Only an intelligent man gone wrong."

I followed, but before I caught up, "Whereas Long's only a stupid man gone right?" I threw out.

It checked her too briefly, and there was indeed something of my own it brought straight back. "I thought that just what you told me, this morning or yesterday, was that you had never known a case of the conversion of an idiot."

I laughed at her readiness. Well, I had wanted to make her fight! "It's true it would have been the only one."

"Ah, you'll have to do without it!" Oh, she was brisk now. "And if you know what I think of him, you know no more than *he* does."

"You mean you told him?"

She hung fire but an instant. "I told him, practically—and it was in fact all I did have to say to him. It was enough, however, and he disgustedly left me on it. Then it was that, as you gave me the chance, I tried to telegraph you—to say to you on the spot and under the sharp impression: 'What on earth do you mean by your nonsense? It doesn't hold water!' It's a pity I didn't succeed!" she continued—for she had become almost voluble. "It would have settled the question, and I should have gone to bed."

I weighed it with the grimace that, I feared, had become almost as fixed as Mrs. Server's. "It would have settled the question perhaps; but I should have lost this impression of you."

"Oh, this impression of me!"

"Ah, but don't undervalue it: it's what I want! What was it then Long had said?"

She had it more and more, but she had it as nothing at all. "Not a word to repeat—you wouldn't believe! He does say nothing at all. One can't remember. It's what I mean. I tried him on purpose, while I thought of you. But he's perfectly stupid. I don't see how we can have fancied——!" I had interrupted her by the movement with which again, uncontrollably tossed on one of my surges of certitude, I turned away. *How* deep they must have been in together for her to have so at last gathered herself up, and in how doubly interesting a light, above all, it seemed to present Long for the future! That was, while I warned myself, what I most read in—literally an implication of the enhancement of this latter side of the prodigy. If his cleverness, under the alarm that, first stirring their consciousness but dimly, had so swiftly developed as to make next of each a mirror for the other, and then to precipitate for them, in some silence deeper than darkness, the exchange of recognitions, admissions and, as they certainly would have phrased it, tips—if his excited acuteness was henceforth to protect itself by dissimulation, what wouldn't perhaps, for one's diversion, be the new spectacle and wonder? I could in a manner already measure this larger play by the amplitude freshly determined in Mrs. Briss, and I was for a moment actually held by the thought of the possible finish our friend would find it in him to give to a represented, a fictive ineptitude. The sharpest jostle to my thought, in this rush, might well have been, I confess, the reflection that as it was I who had arrested, who had spoiled their unconsciousness, so it was natural they should fight against me for a possible life in the state I had given them instead. I had spoiled their unconsciousness, I had destroyed it, and it was consciousness alone that could make them effectively cruel. Therefore, if they were cruel, it was I who had determined it, inasmuch as, consciously, they could only want, they could only intend, to live. Wouldn't that question have been, I managed even now to ask myself, the very basis on which they had inscrutably come together? "It's life, you know," each had said to the other, "and I, accordingly, can only cling to mine. But you, poor dear—shall *you* give up?" "Give up?" the other had replied; "for what do you take me? I shall fight by your side, please, and we can compare and exchange weapons and manœuvres, and you may in every way count upon me."

That was what, with greater vividness, was for the rest of the occasion before me, or behind me; and that I had done it all and had only myself to thank for it was what, from this minute, by the same token, was more and more for me the inner essence of Mrs. Briss's attitude. I know not what heavy admonition of my responsibility had thus suddenly descended on me; but nothing, under it, was indeed more sensible than that practically it paralysed me. And I could only say to myself that this was the price—the price of the secret success, the lonely liberty and the intellectual joy. There were things that for so private and splendid a revel—that of the exclusive king with his Wagner opera—I could only let go, and the special torment of my case was that the condition of light, of the satisfaction of curiosity and of the attestation of triumph, was in this direct way the sacrifice of feeling. There was no point at which my assurance could, by the scientific method, judge itself complete enough not to regard feeling as an interference and, in consequence, as a possible check. If it had to go I knew well who went with it, but I wasn't there to save *them*. I was there to save my priceless pearl of an inquiry and to harden, to that end, my heart. I should need indeed all my hardness, as well as my brightness, moreover, to meet Mrs. Briss on the high level to which I had at last induced her to mount, and, even while I prolonged the movement by which I had momentarily stayed her, the intermission of her speech became itself for me a hint of the peculiar pertinence of caution. It lasted long enough, this drop, to suggest that her attention was the sharper for my having turned away from it, and I should have feared a renewed challenge if she hadn't, by good luck, presently gone on: "There's really nothing in him at all!"

I had faced her again just in time to take it, and I immediately made up my mind how best to do so. "Then I go utterly to pieces!"

"You shouldn't have perched yourself," she laughed—she could by this time almost coarsely laugh—"in such a preposterous place!"

"Ah, that's my affair," I returned, "and if I accept the consequences I don't quite see what you've to say to it. That I do accept them—so far as I make them out as not too intolerable and you as not intending them to be— that I do accept them is what I've been trying to signify to you. Only my fall," I added, "is an inevitable shock. You remarked to me a few minutes since that you didn't recover yourself in a flash. I differ from you, you see, in that *I* do; I take my collapse all at once. Here then I am. I'm smashed. I don't see, as I look about me, a piece I can pick up. I don't attempt to account for my going wrong; I don't attempt to account for yours with me; I don't attempt to account for anything. If Long *is* just what he always was it settles the matter, and the special clincher for us can be but your honest final impression, made precisely more aware of itself by repentance for the levity with which you had originally yielded to my contagion."

She didn't insist on her repentance; she was too taken up with the facts themselves. "Oh, but add to my impression everyone else's impression! Has anyone noticed anything?"

"Ah, I don't know what anyone has noticed. I haven't," I brooded, "ventured—as you know—to ask anyone."

"Well, if you had you'd have seen—seen, I mean, all they don't see. If they had been conscious they'd have talked."

I thought. "To me?"

"Well, I'm not sure to you; people have such a notion of what you embroider on things that they're rather afraid to commit themselves or to lead you on: they're sometimes in, you know," she luminously reminded me, "for more than they bargain for, than they quite know what to do with, or than they care to have on their hands."

I tried to do justice to this account of myself. "You mean I see so much?"

It was a delicate matter, but she risked it. "Don't you sometimes see horrors?"

I wondered. "Well, names are a convenience. People catch me in the act?"

"They certainly think you critical."

"And is criticism the vision of horrors?"

She couldn't quite be sure where I was taking her. "It isn't, perhaps, so much that you see them——"

I started. "As that I perpetrate them?"

She was sure now, however, and wouldn't have it, for she was serious. "Dear no—you don't perpetrate anything. Perhaps it would be better if you did!" she tossed off with an odd laugh. "But—always by people's idea—you like them."

I followed. "Horrors?"

"Well, you don't——"

"Yes——?"

But she wouldn't be hurried now. "You take them too much for what they are. You don't seem to want——"

"To come down on them strong? Oh, but I often do!"

"So much the better then."

"Though I do like—whether for that or not," I hastened to confess, "to look them first well in the face."

Our eyes met, with this, for a minute, but she made nothing of that. "When they *have* no face, then, you can't do it! It isn't at all events now a question," she went on, "of people's keeping anything back, and you're perhaps in any case not the person to whom it would first have come."

I tried to think then who the person would be. "It would have come to Long himself?"

But she was impatient of this. "Oh, one doesn't know what comes—or what doesn't—to Long himself! I'm not sure he's too modest to misrepresent—if he had the intelligence to play a part."

"Which he hasn't!" I concluded.

"Which he hasn't. It's to *me* they might have spoken—or to each other."

"But I thought you exactly held they *had* chattered in accounting for his state by the influence of Lady John."

She got the matter instantly straight. "Not a bit. That chatter was mine only—and produced to meet yours. There had so, by your theory, to be a woman——"

"That, to oblige me, you invented *her*? Precisely. But I thought——"

"You needn't have thought!" Mrs. Briss broke in. "I didn't invent her."

"Then what are you talking about?"

"I didn't invent her," she repeated, looking at me hard. "She's true." I echoed it in vagueness, though instinctively again in protest; yet I held my breath, for this was really the point at which I felt my companion's forces most to have mustered. Her manner now moreover gave me a great idea of them, and her whole air was of taking immediate advantage of my impression. "Well, see here: since you've wanted it, I'm afraid that, however little you may like it, you'll have to take it. You've pressed me for explanations and driven me much harder than you must have seen I found convenient. If I've seemed to beat about the bush it's because I hadn't only myself to think of. One can be simple for one's self—one can't be, always, for others."

"Ah, to whom do you say it?" I encouragingly sighed; not even yet quite seeing for what issue she was heading.

She continued to make for the spot, whatever it was, with a certain majesty. "I should have preferred to tell you nothing more than what I *have* told you. I should have preferred to close our conversation on the simple announcement of my recovered sense of proportion. But you *have*, I see, got me in too deep."

"O-oh!" I courteously attenuated.

"You've made of me," she lucidly insisted, "too big a talker, too big a thinker, of nonsense."

"Thank you," I laughed, "for intimating that I trifle so agreeably."

"Oh, *you've* appeared not to mind! But let me then at last not fail of the luxury of admitting that *I* mind. Yes, I mind particularly. I may be bad, but I've a grain of gumption."

"'Bad'?" It seemed more closely to concern me.

"Bad I may be. In fact," she pursued at this high pitch and pressure, "there's no doubt whatever I *am*."

"I'm delighted to hear it," I cried, "for it was exactly something strong I wanted of you!"

"It *is* then strong"—and I could see indeed she was ready to satisfy me. "You've worried me for my motive and harassed me for my 'moment,' and I've had to protect others and, at the cost of a decent appearance, to pretend to be myself half an idiot. I've had even, for the same purpose—if you must have it—to depart from the truth; to give you, that is, a false account of the manner of my escape from your tangle. But now the truth shall be told, and others can take care of themselves!" She had so wound herself up with this, reached so the point of fairly heaving with courage and candour, that I for an instant almost miscalculated her direction and believed she was really throwing up her cards. It was as if she had decided, on some still finer lines, just to rub my nose into what I had been spelling out; which would have been an anticipation of my own journey's crown of the most disconcerting sort. I wanted my personal confidence, but I wanted nobody's confession, and without the journey's crown where *was* the personal confidence? Without the personal confidence, moreover, where was the personal honour? That would be really the single thing to which I could attach authority, for a confession might, after all, be itself a lie. Anybody, at all events, could fit the shoe to one. My friend's intention, however, remained but briefly equivocal; my danger passed, and I recognised in its place a still richer assurance. It was not the unnamed, in short, who were to be named. "Lady John *is* the woman."

Yet even this was prodigious. "But I thought your present position was just that she's *not!*"

"Lady John *is* the woman," Mrs. Briss again announced.

"But I thought your present position was just that nobody is!"

"Lady John *is* the woman," she a third time declared.

It naturally left me gaping. "Then there *is* one?" I cried between bewilderment and joy.

"A woman? There's *her!*" Mrs. Briss replied with more force than grammar. "I know," she briskly, almost breezily added, "that I said she wouldn't do (as I had originally said she would do better than any one), when you a while ago mentioned her. But that was to save her."

"And you don't care now," I smiled, "if she's lost!"

She hesitated. "She *is* lost. But she can take care of herself."

I could but helplessly think of her. "I'm afraid indeed that, with what you've done with her, *I* can't take care of her. But why is she now to the purpose," I articulately wondered, "any more than she was?"

"Why? On the very system you yourself laid down. When we took him for brilliant, she couldn't be. But now that we see him as he is———"

"We can only see her also as *she* is?" Well, I tried, as far as my amusement would permit, so to see her; but still there were difficulties. "Possibly!" I at most conceded. "Do you owe your discovery, however, wholly to my system? My system, where so much made for protection," I explained, "wasn't intended to have the effect of exposure."

"It appears to have been at all events intended," my companion returned, "to have the effect of driving me to the wall; and the consequence of *that* effect is nobody's fault but your own."

She was all logic now, and I could easily see, between my light and my darkness, how she would remain so. Yet I was scarce satisfied. "And it's only on 'that effect'——?"

"That I've made up my mind?" She was positively free at last to enjoy my discomfort. "Wouldn't it be surely, if your ideas were worth anything, enough? But it isn't," she added, "only on that. It's on something else."

I had after an instant extracted from this the single meaning it could appear to yield. "I'm to understand that you *know*?"

"That they're intimate enough for anything?" She faltered, but she brought it out. "I know."

It was the oddest thing in the world for a little, the way this affected me without my at all believing it. It was preposterous, hang though it would with her somersault, and she had quite succeeded in giving it the note of sincerity. It was the mere sound of it that, as I felt even at the time, made it a little of a blow—a blow of the smart of which I was conscious just long enough inwardly to murmur: "What if she *should* be right?" She had for these seconds the advantage of stirring within me the memory of her having indeed, the day previous, at Paddington, "known" as I hadn't. It had been really on what she *then* knew that we originally started, and an element of our start had been that I admired her freedom. The form of it, at least—so beautifully had she recovered herself—was all there now. Well, I at any rate reflected, it wasn't the form that need trouble me, and I quickly enough put her a question that related only to the matter. "Of course if she is—it *is* smash!"

"And haven't you yet got used to its being?"

I kept my eyes on her; I traced the buried figure in the ruins. "She's good enough for a fool; and so"—I made it out—"is he! If he *is* the same ass—yes—they *might* be."

"*And* he is," said Mrs. Briss, "the same ass!"

I continued to look at her. "He would have no need then of her having transformed and inspired him."

"Or of her having *de*formed and idiotised herself," my friend subjoined.

Oh, how it sharpened my look! "No, no—she wouldn't need that."

"The great point is that *he* wouldn't!" Mrs. Briss laughed.

I kept it up. "She would do perfectly."

Mrs. Briss was not behind. "My dear man, she has *got* to do!"

This was brisker still, but I held my way. "Almost anyone would do."

It seemed for a little, between humour and sadness, to strike her. "Almost anyone *would*. Still," she less pensively declared, "we want the right one."

"Surely; the right one"—I could only echo it. "But how," I then proceeded, "has it happily been confirmed to you?"

It pulled her up a trifle. "'Confirmed'——?"

"That he's her lover."

My eyes had been meeting hers without, as it were, hers quite meeting mine. But at this there had to be intercourse. "By my husband."

It pulled *me* up a trifle. "Brissenden knows?"

She hesitated; then, as if at my tone, gave a laugh. "Don't you suppose I've told him?"

I really couldn't but admire her. "Ah—so you *have* talked!"

It didn't confound her. "One's husband isn't talk. You're cruel moreover," she continued, "to my joke. It was Briss, poor dear, who talked—though, I mean, only to me. *He* knows."

I cast about. "Since when?"

But she had it ready. "Since this evening."

Once more I couldn't but smile. "Just in time then! And the *way* he knows——?"

"Oh, the way!"—she had at this a slight drop. But she came up again. "I take his word."

"You haven't then asked him?"

"The beauty of it was—half an hour ago, upstairs—that I *hadn't* to ask. He came out with it himself, and *that*—to give you the whole thing—was, if you like, my moment. He dropped it on me," she continued to explain, "without in the least, sweet innocent, knowing what he was doing; more, at least, that is, than give her away."

"Which," I concurred, "was comparatively nothing!"

But she had no ear for irony, and she made out still more of her story. "He's simple—but he sees."

"And when he sees"—I completed the picture—"he luckily tells."

She quite agreed with me that it was lucky, but without prejudice to his acuteness and to what had been in him moreover a natural revulsion. "He has seen, in short; there comes some chance when one does. His, as luckily as you please, came this evening. If you ask me what it showed him you ask more than *I've* either cared or had time to ask. Do you consider, for that matter"— she put it to me—"that one does ask?" As her high smoothness—such was the wonder of this reascendancy—almost deprived me of my means, she was wise and gentle with me. "Let us leave it alone."

I fairly, while my look at her turned rueful, scratched my head. "Don't you think it a little late for that?"

"Late for everything!" she impatiently said. "But there you are."

I fixed the floor. There indeed I was. But I tried to stay there—just there only—as short a time as possible. Something, moreover, after all, caught me up. "But if Brissenden already knew——?"

"If he knew——?" She still gave me, without prejudice to her ingenuity—and indeed it was a part of this—all the work she could.

"Why, that Long and Lady John were thick?"

"Ah, then," she cried, "you admit they *are*!"

"Am I not admitting everything you tell me? But the more I admit," I explained, "the more I must understand. It's *to* admit, you see, that I inquire. If Briss came down with Lady John yesterday to oblige Mr. Long——"

"He didn't come," she interrupted, "to oblige Mr. Long!"

"Well, then, to oblige Lady John herself——"

"He didn't come to oblige Lady John herself!"

"Well, then, to oblige his clever wife——"

"He didn't come to oblige his clever wife! He came," said Mrs. Briss, "just to amuse himself. He *has* his amusements, and it's odd," she remarkably laughed, "that you should grudge them to him!"

"It would be odd indeed if I did! But put his proceeding," I continued, "on any ground you like; you described to me the purpose of it as a screening of the pair."

"I described to you the purpose of it as nothing of the sort. I didn't describe to you the purpose of it," said Mrs. Briss, "at all. I described to you," she triumphantly set forth, "the *effect* of it—which is a very different thing."

I could only meet her with admiration. "You're of an astuteness——!"

"Of course I'm of an astuteness! I *see* effects. And I saw that one. How much Briss himself had seen it is, as I've told you, another matter; and what he had, at any rate, quite taken the affair for was the sort of flirtation in which, if one is a friend to either party, and one's own feelings are not at stake, one may now and then give people a lift. Haven't I asked you before," she demanded, "if you suppose he would have given one had he had an idea where these people *are?*"

"I scarce know what you have asked me before!" I sighed; "and 'where they are' is just what you haven't told me."

"It's where my husband was so annoyed unmistakably to discover them." And as if she had quite fixed the point she passed to another. "He's peculiar, dear old Briss, but in a way by which, if one uses him—by which, I mean, if one depends on him—at all, one gains, I think, more than one loses. Up to a certain point, in any case that's the least a case for subtlety, he sees nothing at all; but beyond it—when once he does wake up—he'll go through a house. Nothing then escapes him, and what he drags to light is sometimes appalling."

"Rather," I thoughtfully responded—"since witness this occasion!"

"But isn't the interest of this occasion, as I've already suggested," she propounded, "simply that it makes an end, bursts a bubble, rids us of an incubus and permits us to go to bed in peace? I thank God," she moralised, "for dear old Briss to-night."

"So do I," I after a moment returned; "but I shall do so with still greater fervour if you'll have for the space of another question a still greater patience." With which, as a final movement from her seemed to say how much this was to ask, I had on my own side a certain exasperation of soreness for all I had to acknowledge—even were it mere acknowledgment—that she had brought rattling down. "Remember," I pleaded, "that you're costing me a perfect palace of thought!"

I could see too that, held unexpectedly by something in my tone, she really took it in. Couldn't I even almost see that, for an odd instant, she regretted the blighted pleasure of the pursuit of truth with me? I needed, at all events, no better proof either of the sweet or of the bitter in her comprehension than the accent with which she replied: "Oh, those who live in glass houses——"

"Shouldn't—no, I know they shouldn't—throw stones; and that's precisely why I don't." I had taken her immediately up, and I held her by it and by something better still. "You, from your fortress of granite, can chuck them about as you will! All the more reason, however," I quickly added, "that, before my frail, but, as I maintain, quite sublime structure, you honour me, for a few seconds, with an intelligent look at it. I seem myself to see it again, perfect in every part," I pursued, "even while I thus speak to you, and to feel afresh that, weren't the wretched accident of its weak foundation, it wouldn't have the shadow of a flaw. I've spoken of it in my conceivable regret," I conceded, "as already a mere heap of disfigured fragments; but that was the extravagance of my vexation, my despair. It's in point of fact so beautifully fitted that it comes apart piece by piece—which, so far as that goes, you've seen it do in the last quarter of an hour at your own touch, quite handing me the pieces, one by one, yourself and watching me stack them along the ground. They're not even in this state—see!" I wound up—"a pile of ruins!" I wound up, as I say, but only for long enough to have, with the vibration, the exaltation, of my eloquence, my small triumph as against her great one. "I should almost like, piece by piece, to hand them back to you." And this time I completed my figure. "I believe that, for the very charm of it, you'd find yourself placing them by your own sense in their order and rearing once more the splendid pile. Will you take just *one* of them from me again," I insisted, "and let me see if only to have it in your hands doesn't positively start you off? That's what I meant just now by asking you for another answer." She had remained silent, as if really in the presence of the rising magnificence of my metaphor, and it was not too late for the one chance left me. "There was nothing, you know, I had so fitted as your account of poor Mrs. Server when, on our seeing them, from the terrace, together below, you struck off your explanation that old Briss was *her* screen for Long."

"Fitted?"—and there was sincerity in her surprise. "I thought my stupid idea the one for which you had exactly no use!"

"I had no use," I instantly concurred, "for your stupid idea, but I had great use for your stupidly, alas! having it. *That* fitted beautifully," I smiled, "till the piece came out. And even now," I added, "I don't feel it quite accounted for."

"Their being there together?"

"No. Your not liking it that they were."

She stared. "Not liking it?"

I could see how little indeed she minded now, but I also kept the thread of my own intellectual history. "Yes. Your not liking it is what I speak of as the piece. I hold it, you see, up before you. What, artistically, would you do with it?"

But one might take a horse to water——! I held it up before her, but I couldn't make her look at it. "How do you know what I mayn't, or may, have liked?"

It did bring me to. "Because you were conscious of not telling me? Well, even if you didn't——!"

"That made no difference," she inquired with a generous derision, "because you could always imagine? Of course you could always imagine—which is precisely what is the matter with you! But I'm surprised at your coming to me with it once more as evidence of anything."

I stood rebuked, and even more so than I showed her, for she need, obviously, only decline to take one of my counters to deprive it of all value as coin. When she pushed it across I had but to pocket it again. "It *is* the weakness of my case," I feebly and I daresay awkwardly mused at her, "that any particular thing you don't grant me becomes straightway the strength of yours. Of course, however"—and I gave myself a shake—"I'm absolutely rejoicing (am I not?) in the strength of yours. The weakness of my own is what, under your instruction, I'm now going into; but don't you see how much weaker it will show if I draw from you the full expression of your indifference? How *could* you in fact care when what you were at the very moment urging on me so hard was the extravagance of Mrs. Server's conduct? That extravagance then proved her, to your eyes, the woman who had a connection with Long to keep the world off the scent of—though you maintained that in spite of the dust she kicked up by it she was, at a pinch, now and then to be caught with him. That instead of being caught with him she was caught only with Brissenden annoyed you naturally for the moment; but what was that annoyance compared to your appreciation of her showing—by undertaking your husband, of all people!—just the more markedly *as* extravagant?"

She had been sufficiently interested this time to follow me. "What was it indeed?"

I greeted her acquiescence, but I insisted. "And yet if she *is* extravagant—what do you do with it?"

"I thought you wouldn't hear of it!" she exclaimed.

I sought to combine firmness with my mildness. "What do you do with it?"

But she could match me at this. "I thought you wouldn't hear of it!"

"It's not a question of *my* dispositions. It's a question of her having been, or not been, for you 'all over the place,' and of everyone's also being, for you, on the chatter about it. You go by that in respect to Long—by your holding, that is, that nothing has been noticed; therefore mustn't you go by it in respect to *her*—since I understand from you that everything has?"

"Everything always is," Mrs. Briss agreeably replied, "in a place and a party like this; but so little—anything in particular—that, with people moving 'every which' way, it comes to the same as if nothing was. Things are not, also, gouged out to *your* tune, and it depends, still further, on what you mean by 'extravagant.'"

"I mean whatever you yourself meant."

"Well, I myself mean no longer, you know, what I did mean."

"She isn't then——?"

But suddenly she was almost sharp with me. "Isn't what?"

"What the woman we so earnestly looked for would have to be."

"All gone?" She had hesitated, but she went on with decision. "No, she isn't all gone, since there was enough of her left to make up to poor Briss."

"Precisely—and it's just what we saw, and just what, with her other dashes of the same sort, led us to have to face the question of her being—well, what I say. Or rather," I added, "what *you* say. That is," I amended, to keep perfectly straight, "what you say you *don't* say."

I took indeed too many precautions for my friend not to have to look at them. "Extravagant?" The irritation of the word had grown for her, yet I risked repeating it, and with the effect of its giving her another pause. "I tell you she *isn't*, that!"

"Exactly; and it's only to ask you what in the world then she *is*."

"She's horrid!" said Mrs. Briss.

"'Horrid'?" I gloomily echoed.

"Horrid. It wasn't," she then developed with decision, "a 'dash,' as you say, 'of the same sort'—though goodness knows of what sort you mean; it wasn't, to be plain, a 'dash' at all." My companion *was* plain. "She settled. She stuck." And finally, as I could but echo her again: "She made love to him."

"But—a—really?"

"Really. That's how I knew."

I was at sea. "'Knew'? But you saw."

"I knew—that is I learnt—more than I saw. I knew she couldn't be gone."

It in fact brought light. "Knew it by *him*?"

"He told me," said Mrs. Briss.

It brought light, but it brought also, I fear, for me, another queer grimace. "Does he then regularly tell?"

"Regularly. But what he tells," she did herself the justice to declare, "is not always so much to the point as the two things I've repeated to you."

Their weight then suggested that I should have them over again. "His revelation, in the first place, of Long and Lady John?"

"And his revelation in the second"—she spoke of it as a broad joke—"of May Server and himself."

There was something in her joke that was a chill to my mind; but I nevertheless played up. "And what does he say that's further interesting about *that*?"

"Why, that she's awfully sharp."

I gasped—she turned it out so. "*She*—Mrs. Server?"

It made her, however, equally stare. "Why, isn't it the very thing you maintained?"

I felt her dreadful logic, but I couldn't—with my exquisite image all contrasted, as in a flash from flint, with this monstrosity—so much as entertain her question. I could only stupidly again sound it. "Awfully sharp?"

"You after all then now don't?" It was she herself whom the words at present described! "Then what on earth *do* you think?" The strange mixture in my face naturally made her ask it, but everything, within a minute, had somehow so given way under the touch of her supreme assurance, the presentation of her own now finished system, that I dare say I couldn't at the moment have in the least trusted myself to tell her. She left me, however, in fact, small time—she only took enough, with her negations arrayed and her insolence recaptured, to judge me afresh, which she did as she gathered herself up into the strength of twenty-five. I didn't after all—it appeared part of my smash—know the weight of her husband's years, but I knew the weight of my own. They might have been a thousand, and nothing but the sense of them would in a moment, I saw, be left me. "My poor dear, you *are* crazy, and I bid you good-night!"

Nothing but the sense of them—on my taking it from her without a sound and watching her, through the lighted rooms, retreat and disappear—*was* at first left me; but after a minute something else came, and I grew conscious that her verdict lingered. She had so had the last word that, to get out of its planted presence, I shook myself, as I had done before, from my thought. When once I had started to my room indeed—and to preparation for a livelier start as soon as the house should stir again—I almost breathlessly hurried. Such a last word—the word that put me altogether nowhere—was too unacceptable not to prescribe afresh that prompt test of escape to other air for which I had earlier in the evening seen so much reason. I *should* certainly never again, on the spot, quite hang together, even though it wasn't really that I hadn't three times her method. What I too fatally lacked was her tone.

THE END

THE SPOILS OF POYNTON

I

Mrs. Gereth had said she would go with the rest to church, but suddenly it seemed to her that she should not be able to wait even till church-time for relief: breakfast, at Waterbath, was a punctual meal, and she had still nearly an hour on her hands. Knowing the church to be near, she prepared in her room for the little rural walk, and on her way down again, passing through corridors and observing imbecilities of decoration, the æsthetic misery of the big commodious house, she felt a return of the tide of last night's irritation, a renewal of everything she could secretly suffer from ugliness and stupidity. Why did she consent to such contacts, why did she so rashly expose herself? She had had, heaven knew, her reasons, but the whole experience was to be sharper than she had feared. To get away from it and out into the air, into the presence of sky and trees, flowers and birds, was a necessity of every nerve. The flowers at Waterbath would probably go wrong in color and the nightingales sing out of tune; but she remembered to have heard the place described as possessing those advantages that are usually spoken of as natural. There were advantages enough it clearly didn't possess. It was hard for her to believe that a woman could look presentable who had been kept awake for hours by the wall-paper in her room; yet none the less, as in her fresh widow's weeds she rustled across the hall, she was sustained by the consciousness, which always added to the unction of her social Sundays, that she was, as usual, the only person in the house incapable of wearing in her preparation the horrible stamp of the same exceptional smartness that would be conspicuous in a grocer's wife. She would rather have perished than have looked *endimanchée*.

She was fortunately not challenged, the hall being empty of the other women, who were engaged precisely in arraying themselves to that dire end. Once in the grounds, she recognized that, with a site, a view that struck the note, set an example to its inmates, Waterbath ought to have been charming. How she herself, with such elements to handle, would have taken the fine hint of nature! Suddenly, at the turn of a walk, she came on a member of the party, a young lady seated on a bench in deep and lonely meditation.

She had observed the girl at dinner and afterwards: she was always looking at girls with an apprehensive or speculative reference to her son. Deep in her heart was a conviction that Owen would, in spite of all her spells, marry at last a frump; and this from no evidence that she could have represented as adequate, but simply from her deep uneasiness, her belief that such a special sensibility as her own could have been inflicted on a woman only as a source of anguish. It would be her fate, her discipline, her cross, to have a frump brought hideously home to her. This girl, one of the two Vetches, had no beauty, but Mrs. Gereth, scanning the dullness for a sign of life, had been straightway able to classify such a figure as the least, for the moment, of her afflictions. Fleda Vetch was dressed with an idea, though perhaps with not much else; and that made a bond when there was none other, especially as in this case the idea was real, not imitation. Mrs. Gereth had long ago generalized the truth that the temperament of the frump is amply consistent with a certain usual prettiness. There were five girls in the party, and the prettiness of this one, slim, pale, and black-haired, was less likely than that of the others ever to occasion an exchange of platitudes. The two less developed Brigstocks, daughters of the house, were in particular tiresomely "lovely." A second glance, this morning, at the young lady before her conveyed to Mrs. Gereth the soothing assurance that she also was guiltless of looking hot and fine. They had had no talk as yet, but this was a note that would effectually introduce them if the girl should show herself in the least conscious of their community. She got up from her seat with a smile that but partly dissipated the prostration Mrs. Gereth had recognized in her attitude. The elder woman drew her down again, and for a minute, as they sat together, their eyes met and sent out mutual soundings. "Are you safe? Can I utter it?" each of them said to the other, quickly recognizing, almost proclaiming, their common need to escape. The tremendous fancy, as it came to be called, that Mrs. Gereth was destined to take to Fleda Vetch virtually began with this discovery that the poor child had been moved to flight even more promptly than herself. That the poor child no less quickly perceived how far she could now go was proved by the immense friendliness with which she instantly broke out: "Isn't it too dreadful?"

"Horrible—horrible!" cried Mrs. Gereth, with a laugh, "and it's really a comfort to be able to say it." She had an idea, for it was her ambition, that she successfully made a secret of that awkward oddity, her proneness to be rendered unhappy by the presence of the dreadful. Her passion for the exquisite was the cause of this, but it was a passion she considered that she never advertised nor gloried in, contenting herself with letting it regulate her steps and show quietly in her life, remembering at all times that there are few things more soundless than a deep devotion. She was therefore struck with the acuteness of the little girl who had already put a finger on her hidden spring. What was dreadful now, what was horrible, was the intimate ugliness of Waterbath, and it was of that phenomenon these ladies talked while they sat in the shade and drew refreshment from the great tranquil sky, from which no blue saucers were suspended. It was an ugliness fundamental and systematic, the result of the abnormal nature of the Brigstocks, from whose composition the principle of taste had been extravagantly omitted. In the arrangement of their home some other principle, remarkably active, but uncanny and obscure, had operated instead, with consequences depressing to behold, consequences that took the form of a universal futility. The house was bad in all conscience, but it might have passed if they had only let it alone. This saving mercy was beyond them; they had smothered it with trumpery ornament and scrapbook art, with strange excrescences and bunchy draperies, with gimcracks that might have been keepsakes for maid-servants and nondescript conveniences that might have been prizes for the blind. They had gone wildly astray over carpets and curtains; they had an infallible instinct for disaster, and were so cruelly doom-ridden that it rendered them almost tragic. Their drawing-room, Mrs. Gereth lowered her voice to mention, caused her face to burn, and each of the new friends confided to the other that in her own apartment she had given way to tears. There was in the elder lady's a set of comic water-colors, a family joke by a family genius, and in the younger's a souvenir from some centennial or other Exhibition, that they shudderingly alluded to. The house was perversely full of souvenirs of places even more ugly than itself and of things it would have been a pious duty to forget. The worst horror was the acres of varnish, something advertised and smelly, with which everything was smeared; it was Fleda Vetch's conviction that the application of it, by their own hands and hilariously shoving each other, was the amusement of the Brigstocks on rainy days.

When, as criticism deepened, Fleda dropped the suggestion that some people would perhaps see something in Mona, Mrs. Gereth caught her up with a groan of protest, a smothered familiar cry of "Oh, my dear!" Mona was the eldest of the three, the one Mrs. Gereth most suspected. She confided to her young friend that it was her suspicion that had brought her to Waterbath; and this was going very far, for on the spot, as a refuge, a remedy, she had clutched at the idea that something might be done with the girl before her. It was her fancied exposure at any rate that had sharpened the shock; made her ask herself with a terrible chill if fate could really be plotting to saddle her with a daughter-in-law brought up in such a place. She had seen Mona in her appropriate setting and she had seen Owen, handsome and heavy, dangle beside her; but the effect of these first hours had happily not been to darken the prospect. It was clearer to her that she could never accept Mona, but it was after all by no means certain that Owen would ask her to. He had sat by somebody else at dinner, and afterwards he had talked to Mrs. Firmin, who was as dreadful as all the rest, but redeemingly married. His heaviness, which in her need of expansion she freely named, had two aspects: one of them his monstrous lack of taste, the other his exaggerated prudence. If it should come to a question of carrying Mona with a high hand there would be no need to worry, for that was rarely his manner of proceeding.

Invited by her companion, who had asked if it weren't wonderful, Mrs. Gereth had begun to say a word about Poynton; but she heard a sound of voices that made her stop short. The next moment she rose to her feet, and Fleda could see that her alarm was by no means quenched. Behind the place where they had been sitting the ground dropped with a certain steepness, forming a long grassy bank, up which Owen Gereth and Mona Brigstock, dressed for church but making a familiar joke of it, were in the act of scrambling and helping each other. When they had reached the even ground Fleda was able to read the meaning of the exclamation in which Mrs. Gereth had expressed her reserves on the subject of Miss Brigstock's personality. Miss Brigstock had been laughing and even romping, but the circumstance hadn't contributed the ghost of an expression to her countenance. Tall, straight and fair, long-limbed and strangely festooned, she stood there without a look in her eye or any perceptible intention of any sort in any other feature. She belonged to the type in which speech is an unaided emission of sound and the secret of being is impenetrably and incorruptibly kept. Her expression would probably have been beautiful if she had had one, but whatever she communicated she communicated, in a manner best known to herself, without signs. This was not the case with Owen Gereth, who had plenty of them, and all very simple and immediate. Robust and artless, eminently natural, yet perfectly correct, he looked pointlessly active and pleasantly dull. Like his mother and like Fleda Vetch, but not for the same reason, this young pair had come out to take a turn before church.

The meeting of the two couples was sensibly awkward, and Fleda, who was sagacious, took the measure of the shock inflicted on Mrs. Gereth. There had been intimacy—oh yes, intimacy as well as puerility—in the horse-play of which they had just had a glimpse. The party began to stroll together to the house, and Fleda had again a sense of Mrs. Gereth's quick management in the way the lovers, or whatever they were, found themselves separated. She strolled behind with Mona, the mother possessing herself of her son, her exchange of remarks with whom, however, remained, as they went, suggestively inaudible. That member of the party in whose intenser consciousness we shall most profitably seek a reflection of the little drama with which we are concerned received an even livelier impression of Mrs. Gereth's intervention from the fact that ten minutes later, on the way to church, still another pairing had been effected. Owen walked with Fleda, and it was an amusement to the girl to feel sure that this was by his mother's direction. Fleda had other amusements as well: such as noting that Mrs. Gereth was now with Mona Brigstock; such as observing that she was all affability to that young woman; such as reflecting that, masterful and clever, with a great bright spirit, she was one of those who impose themselves as an influence; such as feeling finally that Owen Gereth was absolutely beautiful and delightfully dense. This young person had even from herself wonderful secrets of delicacy and pride; but she came as near distinctness as in the consideration of such matters she had ever come at all in now surrendering herself to the idea that it was of a pleasant effect and rather remarkable to be stupid without offense—of a pleasanter effect and more remarkable indeed than to be clever and horrid. Owen Gereth at any rate, with his inches, his features, and his lapses, was neither of these latter things. She herself was prepared, if she should ever marry, to contribute all the cleverness, and she liked to think that her husband would be a force grateful for direction. She was in her small way a spirit of the same family as Mrs. Gereth. On that flushed and huddled Sunday a great matter occurred; her little life became aware of a singular quickening. Her meagre past fell away from her like a garment of the wrong fashion, and as she came up to town on the Monday what she stared at in the suburban fields from the train was a future full of the things she particularly loved.

II

These were neither more nor less than the things with which she had had time to learn from Mrs. Gereth that Poynton overflowed. Poynton, in the south of England, was this lady's established, or rather her disestablished home, having recently passed into the possession of her son. The father of the boy, an only child, had died two years before, and in London, with his mother, Owen was occupying for May and June a house good-naturedly lent them by Colonel Gereth, their uncle and brother-in-law. His mother had laid her hand so engagingly on Fleda Vetch that in a very few days the girl knew it was possible they should suffer together in Cadogan Place almost as much as they had suffered together at Waterbath. The kind colonel's house was also an ordeal, but the two women, for the ensuing month, had at least the relief of their confessions. The great drawback of Mrs. Gereth's situation was that, thanks to the rare perfection of Poynton, she was condemned to wince wherever she turned. She had lived for a quarter of a century in such warm closeness with the beautiful that, as she frankly admitted, life had become for her a kind of fool's paradise. She couldn't leave her own house without peril of exposure. She didn't say it in so many words, but Fleda could see she held that there was nothing in England really to compare to Poynton. There were places much grander and richer, but there was no such complete work of art, nothing that would appeal so to those who were really informed. In putting such elements into her hand fortune had given her an inestimable chance; she knew how rarely well things had gone with her and that she had tasted a happiness altogether rare.

There had been in the first place the exquisite old house itself, early Jacobean, supreme in every part: it was a provocation, an inspiration, a matchless canvas for the picture. Then there had been her husband's sympathy and generosity, his knowledge and love, their perfect accord and beautiful life together, twenty-six years of planning and seeking, a long, sunny harvest of taste and curiosity. Lastly, she never denied, there had been her personal gift, the genius, the passion, the patience of the collector—a patience, an almost infernal cunning, that had enabled her to do it all with a limited command of money. There wouldn't have been money enough for any one else, she said with pride, but there had been money enough for her. They had saved on lots of things in life, and there were lots of things they hadn't had, but they had had in every corner of Europe their swing among the Jews. It was fascinating to poor Fleda, who hadn't a penny in the world nor anything nice at home, and whose only treasure was her subtle mind, to hear this genuine English lady, fresh and fair, young in the fifties, declare with gayety and conviction that she was herself the greatest Jew who had ever tracked a victim. Fleda, with her mother dead, hadn't so much even as a home, and her nearest chance of one was that there was some appearance her sister would become engaged to a curate whose eldest brother was supposed to have property and would perhaps allow him something. Her father paid some of her bills, but he didn't like her to live with him; and she had lately, in Paris, with several hundred other young women, spent a year in a studio, arming herself for the battle of life by a course with an impressionist painter. She was determined to work, but her impressions, or somebody's else, were as yet her only material. Mrs. Gereth had told her she liked her because she had an extraordinary *flair*; but under the circumstances a *flair* was a questionable boon: in the dry places in which she had mainly moved she could have borne a chronic catarrh. She was constantly summoned to Cadogan Place, and before the month was out was kept to stay, to pay a visit of which the end, it was agreed, should have nothing to do with the beginning. She had a sense, partly exultant and partly alarmed, of having quickly become necessary to her imperious friend, who indeed gave a reason quite sufficient for it in telling her there was nobody else who understood. From Mrs. Gereth there was in these days an immense deal to understand, though it might be freely summed up in the circumstance that she was wretched. She told Fleda that she couldn't completely know why till she should have seen the things at Poynton. Fleda could perfectly grasp this connection, which was exactly one of the matters that, in their inner mystery, were a blank to everybody else.

The girl had a promise that the wonderful house should be shown her early in July, when Mrs. Gereth would return to it as to her home; but even before this initiation she put her finger on the spot that in the poor lady's troubled soul ached hardest. This was the misery that haunted her, the dread of the inevitable surrender. What Fleda had to sit up to was the confirmed appearance that Owen Gereth would marry Mona Brigstock, marry her in his mother's teeth, and that such an act would have incalculable bearings. They were present to Mrs. Gereth, her companion could see, with a vividness that at moments almost ceased to be that of sanity. She would have to give up Poynton, and give it up to a product of Waterbath—that was the wrong that rankled, the humiliation at which Fleda would be able adequately to shudder only when she should know the place. She did know Waterbath, and she despised it—she had that qualification for sympathy. Her sympathy was intelligent, for she read deep into the matter; she stared, aghast, as it came home to her for the first time, at the cruel English custom of the expropriation of the lonely mother. Mr. Gereth had apparently been a very amiable man, but Mr. Gereth had left things in a way that made the girl marvel. The house and its contents had been treated as a single splendid object; everything was to go straight to his son, and his widow was to have a maintenance and a cottage in another county. No account whatever had been taken of her relation to her treasures, of the passion with which she had waited for them, worked for them, picked them over, made them worthy of each other and the house, watched them, loved them, lived with them. He appeared to have assumed that she would settle questions with her son, that he could depend upon Owen's affection. And in truth, as poor Mrs. Gereth inquired, how could he possibly have had a prevision—he who turned his eyes instinctively from everything repulsive—of anything so abnormal as a Waterbath Brigstock? He had been in ugly houses enough, but had escaped that particular nightmare. Nothing so perverse could have been expected to happen as that the heir to the loveliest thing in England should be inspired to hand it over to a girl so exceptionally tainted. Mrs. Gereth spoke of poor Mona's taint as if to mention it were almost a violation of decency, and a person who had listened without enlightenment would have wondered of what fault the girl had been or had indeed not been guilty. But Owen had from a boy never cared, had never had the least pride or pleasure in his home.

"Well, then, if he doesn't care!"—Fleda exclaimed, with some impetuosity; stopping short, however, before she completed her sentence.

Mrs. Gereth looked at her rather hard. "If he doesn't care?"

Fleda hesitated; she had not quite had a definite idea. "Well—he'll give them up."

"Give what up?"

"Why, those beautiful things."

"Give them up to whom?" Mrs. Gereth more boldly stared.

"To you, of course—to enjoy, to keep for yourself."

"And leave his house as bare as your hand? There's nothing in it that isn't precious."

Fleda considered; her friend had taken her up with a smothered ferocity by which she was slightly disconcerted. "I don't mean of course that he should surrender everything; but he might let you pick out the things to which you're most attached."

"I think he would if he were free," said Mrs. Gereth.

"And do you mean, as it is, that *she*'ll prevent him?" Mona Brigstock, between these ladies, was now nothing but "she."

"By every means in her power."

"But surely not because she understands and appreciates them?"

"No," Mrs. Gereth replied, "but because they belong to the house and the house belongs to Owen. If I should wish to take anything, she would simply say, with that motionless mask: 'It goes with the house.' And day after day, in the face of every argument, of every consideration of generosity, she would repeat, without winking, in that voice like the squeeze of a doll's stomach: 'It goes with the house—it goes with the house.' In that attitude they'll shut themselves up."

Fleda was struck, was even a little startled with the way Mrs. Gereth had turned this over—had faced, if indeed only to recognize its futility, the notion of a battle with her only son. These words led her to make an inquiry which she had not thought it discreet to make before; she brought out the idea of the possibility, after all, of her friend's continuing to live at Poynton. Would they really wish to proceed to extremities? Was no good-humored, graceful compromise to be imagined or brought about? Couldn't the same roof cover them? Was it so very inconceivable that a married son should, for the rest of her days, share with so charming a mother the home she had devoted more than a score of years to making beautiful for him? Mrs. Gereth hailed this question with a wan, compassionate smile; she replied that a common household, in such a case, was exactly so inconceivable that Fleda had only to glance over the fair face of the English land to see how few people had ever conceived it. It was always thought a wonder, a "mistake," a piece of overstrained sentiment; and she confessed that she was as little capable of a flight of that sort as Owen himself. Even if they both had been capable, they would still have Mona's hatred to reckon with. Fleda's breath was sometimes taken away by the great bounds and elisions which, on Mrs. Gereth's lips, the course of discussion could take. This was the first she had heard of Mona's hatred, though she certainly had not needed Mrs. Gereth to tell her that in close quarters that young lady would prove secretly mulish. Later Fleda perceived indeed that perhaps almost any girl would hate a person who should be so markedly averse to having anything to do with her. Before this, however, in conversation with her young friend, Mrs. Gereth furnished a more vivid motive for her despair by asking how she could possibly be expected to sit there with the new proprietors and accept—or call it, for a day, endure—the horrors they would perpetrate in the house. Fleda reasoned that they wouldn't after all smash things nor burn them up; and Mrs. Gereth admitted when pushed that she didn't quite suppose they would. What she meant was that they would neglect them, ignore them, leave them to clumsy servants (there wasn't an object of them all but should be handled with perfect love), and in many cases probably wish to replace them by pieces answerable to some vulgar modern notion of the convenient. Above all, she saw in advance, with dilated eyes, the abominations they would inevitably mix up with them—the maddening relics of Waterbath, the little brackets and pink vases, the sweepings of bazaars, the family photographs and illuminated texts, the "household art" and household piety of Mona's hideous home. Wasn't it

415

enough simply to contend that Mona would approach Poynton in the spirit of a Brigstock, and that in the spirit of a Brigstock she would deal with her acquisition? Did Fleda really see *her*, Mrs. Gereth demanded, spending the remainder of her days with such a creature's elbow in her eye?

Fleda had to declare that she certainly didn't, and that Waterbath had been a warning it would be frivolous to overlook. At the same time she privately reflected that they were taking a great deal for granted, and that, inasmuch as to her knowledge Owen Gereth had positively denied his betrothal, the ground of their speculations was by no means firm. It seemed to our young lady that in a difficult position Owen conducted himself with some natural art; treating this domesticated confidant of his mother's wrongs with a simple civility that almost troubled her conscience, so deeply she felt that she might have had for him the air of siding with that lady against him. She wondered if he would ever know how little really she did this, and that she was there, since Mrs. Gereth had insisted, not to betray, but essentially to confirm and protect. The fact that his mother disliked Mona Brigstock might have made him dislike the object of her preference, and it was detestable to Fleda to remember that she might have appeared to him to offer herself as an exemplary contrast. It was clear enough, however, that the happy youth had no more sense for a motive than a deaf man for a tune, a limitation by which, after all, she could gain as well as lose. He came and went very freely on the business with which London abundantly furnished him, but he found time more than once to say to her, "It's awfully nice of you to look after poor Mummy." As well as his quick speech, which shyness made obscure—it was usually as desperate as a "rush" at some violent game—his child's eyes in his man's face put it to her that, you know, this really meant a good deal for him and that he hoped she would stay on. With a person in the house who, like herself, was clever, poor Mummy was conveniently occupied; and Fleda found a beauty in the candor and even in the modesty which apparently kept him from suspecting that two such wiseheads could possibly be occupied with Owen Gereth.

III

They went at last, the wiseheads, down to Poynton, where the palpitating girl had the full revelation. "*Now* do you know how I feel?" Mrs. Gereth asked when in the wonderful hall, three minutes after their arrival, her pretty associate dropped on a seat with a soft gasp and a roll of dilated eyes. The answer came clearly enough, and in the rapture of that first walk through the house Fleda took a prodigious span. She perfectly understood how Mrs. Gereth felt—she had understood but meagrely before; and the two women embraced with tears over the tightening of their bond—tears which on the younger one's part were the natural and usual sign of her submission to perfect beauty. It was not the first time she had cried for the joy of admiration, but it was the first time the mistress of Poynton, often as she had shown her house, had been present at such an exhibition. She exulted in it; it quickened her own tears; she assured her companion that such an occasion made the poor old place fresh to her again and more precious than ever. Yes, nobody had ever, that way, felt what she had achieved: people were so grossly ignorant, and everybody, even the knowing ones, as they thought themselves, more or less dense. What Mrs. Gereth had achieved was indeed an exquisite work; and in such an art of the treasure-hunter, in selection and comparison refined to that point, there was an element of creation, of personality. She had commended Fleda's *flair*, and Fleda now gave herself up to satiety. Preoccupations and scruples fell away from her; she had never known a greater happiness than the week she passed in this initiation.

Wandering through clear chambers where the general effect made preferences almost as impossible as if they had been shocks, pausing at open doors where vistas were long and bland, she would, even if she had not already known, have discovered for herself that Poynton was the record of a life. It was written in great syllables of color and form, the tongues of other countries and the hands of rare artists. It was all France and Italy, with their ages composed to rest. For England you looked out of old windows—it was England that was the wide embrace. While outside, on the low terraces, she contradicted gardeners and refined on nature, Mrs. Gereth left her guest to finger fondly the brasses that Louis Quinze might have thumbed, to sit with Venetian velvets just held in a loving palm, to hang over cases of enamels and pass and repass before cabinets. There were not many pictures—the panels and the stuffs were themselves the picture; and in all the great wainscoted house there was not an inch of pasted paper. What struck Fleda most in it was the high pride of her friend's taste, a fine arrogance, a sense of style which, however amused and amusing, never compromised nor stooped. She felt indeed, as this lady had intimated to her that she would, both a respect and a compassion that she had not known before; the vision of the coming surrender filled her with an equal pain. To give it all up, to die to it—that thought ached in her breast. She herself could imagine clinging there with a closeness separate from dignity. To have created such a place was to have had dignity enough; when there was a question of defending it the fiercest attitude was the right one. After so intense a taking of possession she too was to give it up; for she reflected that if Mrs. Gereth's remaining there would have offered her a sort of future—stretching away in safe years on the other side of a gulf—the advent of the others could only be, by the same law, a great vague menace, the ruffling of a still water. Such were the emotions of a hungry girl whose sensibility was almost as great as her opportunities for comparison had been small. The museums had done something for her, but nature had done more.

If Owen had not come down with them nor joined them later, it was because he still found London jolly; yet the question remained of whether the jollity of London was not merely the only name his small vocabulary yielded for the jollity of Mona Brigstock. There was indeed in his conduct another ambiguity—something that required explaining so long as his motive didn't come to the surface. If he was in love, what was the matter? And what was the matter still more if he wasn't? The mystery was at last cleared up: this Fleda gathered from the tone in which, one morning at breakfast, a letter just opened made Mrs. Gereth cry out. Her dismay was almost a shriek: "Why, he's bringing her down—he wants her to see the house!" They flew, the two women, into each other's arms and, with their heads together, soon made out that the reason, the baffling reason why nothing had yet happened, was that

Mona didn't know, or Owen didn't, whether Poynton would really please her. She was coming down to judge; and could anything in the world be more like poor Owen than the ponderous probity which had kept him from pressing her for a reply till she should have learned whether she approved what he had to offer her? That was a scruple it had naturally been impossible to impute. If only they might fondly hope, Mrs. Gereth wailed, that the girl's expectations would be dashed! There was a fine consistency, a sincerity quite affecting, in her arguing that the better the place should happen to look and to express the conceptions to which it owed its origin, the less it would speak to an intelligence so primitive. How could a Brigstock possibly understand what it was all about? How, really, could a Brigstock logically do anything but hate it? Mrs. Gereth, even as she whisked away linen shrouds, persuaded herself of the possibility on Mona's part of some bewildered blankness, some collapse of admiration that would prove disconcerting to her swain—a hope of which Fleda at least could see the absurdity and which gave the measure of the poor lady's strange, almost maniacal disposition to thrust in everywhere the question of "things," to read all behavior in the light of some fancied relation to them. "Things" were of course the sum of the world; only, for Mrs. Gereth, the sum of the world was rare French furniture and Oriental china. She could at a stretch imagine people's not having, but she couldn't imagine their not wanting and not missing.

The young couple were to be accompanied by Mrs. Brigstock, and with a prevision of how fiercely they would be watched Fleda became conscious, before the party arrived, of an amused, diplomatic pity for them. Almost as much as Mrs. Gereth's her taste was her life, but her life was somehow the larger for it. Besides, she had another care now: there was some one she wouldn't have liked to see humiliated even in the form of a young lady who would contribute to his never suspecting so much delicacy. When this young lady appeared Fleda tried, so far as the wish to efface herself allowed, to be mainly the person to take her about, show her the house, and cover up her ignorance. Owen's announcement had been that, as trains made it convenient, they would present themselves for luncheon and depart before dinner; but Mrs. Gereth, true to her system of glaring civility, proposed and obtained an extension, a dining and spending of the night. She made her young friend wonder against what rebellion of fact she was sacrificing in advance so profusely to form. Fleda was appalled, after the first hour, by the rash innocence with which Mona had accepted the responsibility of observation, and indeed by the large levity with which, sitting there like a bored tourist in fine scenery, she exercised it. She felt in her nerves the effect of such a manner on her companion's, and it was this that made her want to entice the girl away, give her some merciful warning or some jocular cue. Mona met intense looks, however, with eyes that might have been blue beads, the only ones she had—eyes into which Fleda thought it strange Owen Gereth should have to plunge for his fate and his mother for a confession of whether Poynton was a success. She made no remark that helped to supply this light; her impression at any rate had nothing in common with the feeling that, as the beauty of the place throbbed out like music, had caused Fleda Vetch to burst into tears. She was as content to say nothing as if, Mrs. Gereth afterwards exclaimed, she had been keeping her mouth shut in a railway-tunnel. Mrs. Gereth contrived at the end of an hour to convey to Fleda that it was plain she was brutally ignorant; but Fleda more subtly discovered that her ignorance was obscurely active.

She was not so stupid as not to see that something, though she scarcely knew what, was expected of her that she couldn't give; and the only mode her intelligence suggested of meeting the expectation was to plant her big feet and pull another way. Mrs. Gereth wanted her to rise, somehow or somewhere, and was prepared to hate her if she didn't: very well, she couldn't, she wouldn't rise; she already moved at the altitude that suited her, and was able to see that, since she was exposed to the hatred, she might at least enjoy the calm. The smallest trouble, for a girl with no nonsense about her, was to earn what she incurred; so that, a dim instinct teaching her she would earn it best by not being effusive, and combining with the conviction that she now held Owen, and therefore the place, she had the pleasure of her honesty as well as of her security. Didn't her very honesty lead her to be belligerently blank about Poynton, inasmuch as it was just Poynton that was forced upon her as a subject for effusiveness? Such subjects, to Mona Brigstock, had an air almost of indecency, and the house became uncanny to her through such an appeal—an appeal that, somewhere in the twilight of her being, as Fleda was sure, she thanked heaven she *was* the girl stiffly to draw back from. She was a person whom pressure at a given point infallibly caused to expand in the wrong place instead of, as it is usually administered in the hope of doing, the right one. Her mother, to make up for this, broke out universally, pronounced everything "most striking," and was visibly happy that Owen's captor should be so far on the way to strike: but she jarred upon Mrs. Gereth by her formula of admiration, which was that anything she looked at was "in the style" of something else. This was to show how much she had seen, but it only showed she had seen nothing; everything at Poynton was in the style of Poynton, and poor Mrs. Brigstock, who at least was determined to rise, and had brought with her a trophy of her journey, a "lady's magazine" purchased at the station, a horrible thing with patterns for antimacassars, which, as it was quite new, the first number, and seemed so clever, she kindly offered to leave for the house, was in the style of a vulgar old woman who wore silver jewelry and tried to pass off a gross avidity as a sense of the beautiful.

By the day's end it was clear to Fleda Vetch that, however Mona judged, the day had been determinant; whether or no she felt the charm, she felt the challenge: at an early moment Owen Gereth would be able to tell his mother the worst. Nevertheless, when the elder lady, at bedtime, coming in a dressing-gown and a high fever to the younger one's room, cried out, "She hates it; but what will she do?" Fleda pretended vagueness, played at obscurity and assented disingenuously to the proposition that they at least had a respite. The future was dark to her, but there was a silken thread she could clutch in the gloom—she would never give Owen away. He might give himself— he even certainly would; but that was his own affair, and his blunders, his innocence, only added to the appeal he made to her. She would cover him, she would protect him, and beyond thinking her a cheerful inmate he would never guess her intention, any more than, beyond thinking her clever enough for anything, his acute mother would discover it. From this hour, with Mrs. Gereth, there was a flaw in her frankness: her admirable friend continued to know everything she did; what was to remain unknown was the general motive.

421

From the window of her room, the next morning before breakfast, the girl saw Owen in the garden with Mona, who strolled beside him with a listening parasol, but without a visible look for the great florid picture that had been hung there by Mrs. Gereth's hand. Mona kept dropping her eyes, as she walked, to catch the sheen of her patent-leather shoes, which resembled a man's and which she kicked forward a little—it gave her an odd movement—to help her see what she thought of them. When Fleda came down Mrs. Gereth was in the breakfast-room; and at that moment Owen, through a long window, passed in alone from the terrace and very endearingly kissed his mother. It immediately struck the girl that she was in their way, for hadn't he been borne on a wave of joy exactly to announce, before the Brigstocks departed, that Mona had at last faltered out the sweet word he had been waiting for? He shook hands with his friendly violence, but Fleda contrived not to look into his face: what she liked most to see in it was not the reflection of Mona's big boot-toes. She could bear well enough that young lady herself, but she couldn't bear Owen's opinion of her. She was on the point of slipping into the garden when the movement was checked by Mrs. Gereth's suddenly drawing her close, as if for the morning embrace, and then, while she kept her there with the bravery of the night's repose, breaking out: "Well, my dear boy, what *does* your young friend there make of our odds and ends?"

"Oh, she thinks they're all right!"

Fleda immediately guessed from his tone that he had not come in to say what she supposed; there was even something in it to confirm Mrs. Gereth's belief that their danger had dropped. She was sure, moreover, that his tribute to Mona's taste was a repetition of the eloquent words in which the girl had herself recorded it; she could indeed hear, with all vividness, the pretty passage between the pair. "Don't you think it's rather jolly, the old shop?" "Oh, it's all right!" Mona had graciously remarked; and then they had probably, with a slap on a back, run another race up or down a green bank. Fleda knew Mrs. Gereth had not yet uttered a word to her son that would have shown him how much she feared; but it was impossible to feel her friend's arm round her and not become aware that this friend was now throbbing with a strange intention. Owen's reply had scarcely been of a nature to usher in a discussion of Mona's ensibilities; but Mrs. Gereth went on, in a moment, with an innocence of which Fleda could measure the cold hypocrisy: "Has she any sort of feeling for nice old things?" The question was as fresh as the morning light.

"Oh, of course she likes everything that's nice." And Owen, who constitutionally disliked questions—an answer was almost as hateful to him as a "trick" to a big dog—smiled kindly at Fleda and conveyed that she would understand what he meant even if his mother didn't. Fleda, however, mainly understood that Mrs. Gereth, with an odd, wild laugh, held her so hard that she hurt her.

"I could give up everything without a pang, I think, to a person I could trust, I could respect." The girl heard her voice tremble under the effort to show nothing but what she wanted to show, and felt the sincerity of her implication that the piety most real to her was to be on one's knees before one's high standard. "The best things here, as you know, are the things your father and I collected, things all that we worked for and waited for and suffered for. Yes," cried Mrs. Gereth, with a fine freedom of fancy, "there are things in the house that we almost starved for! They were our religion, they were our life, they were *us*! And now they're only *me*—except that they're also *you*, thank God, a little, you dear!" she continued, suddenly inflicting on Fleda a kiss apparently intended to knock her into position. "There isn't one of them I don't know and love—yes, as one remembers and cherishes the happiest moments of one's life. Blindfold, in the dark, with the brush of a finger, I could tell one from another. They're living things to me; they know me, they return the touch of my hand. But I could let them all go, since I have to, so strangely, to another affection, another conscience. There's a care they want, there's a sympathy that draws out their beauty. Rather than make them over to a woman ignorant and vulgar, I think I'd deface them with my own hands. Can't you see me, Fleda, and wouldn't you do it yourself?"—she appealed to her companion with glittering eyes. "I couldn't bear the thought of such a woman here—I *couldn't*. I don't know what she'd do; she'd be sure to invent some deviltry, if it should be only to bring in her own little belongings and horrors. The world is full of cheap gimcracks, in this awful age, and they're thrust in at one at every turn. They'd be thrust in here, on top of my treasures, my own. Who would save *them* for me—I ask you who *would?*" and she turned again to Fleda with a dry, strained smile. Her handsome, high-nosed, excited face might have been that of Don Quixote tilting at a windmill. Drawn into the eddy of this outpouring, the girl, scared and embarrassed, laughed off her exposure; but only to feel herself more passionately caught up and, as it seemed to her, thrust down the fine open mouth (it showed such perfect teeth) with which poor Owen's slow cerebration gaped. "*You* would, of course—only you, in all the world, because you know, you feel, as I do myself, what's good and true and pure." No severity of the moral law could have taken a higher tone in this implication of the young lady who had not the only virtue Mrs. Gereth actively esteemed. "*You* would replace me, *you* would watch over them, *you* would keep the place right," she austerely pursued, "and with you here—yes, with you, I believe I might rest, at last, in my grave!" She threw herself on Fleda's neck, and before Fleda, horribly shamed, could shake her off, had burst into tears which couldn't have been explained, but which might perhaps have been understood.

IV

A week later Owen Gereth came down to inform his mother that he had settled with Mona Brigstock; but it was not at all a joy to Fleda, conscious how much to himself it would be a surprise, that he should find her still in the house. That dreadful scene before breakfast had made her position false and odious; it had been followed, after they were left alone, by a scene of her own making with her extravagant friend. She notified Mrs. Gereth of her instant departure: she couldn't possibly remain after being offered to Owen, that way, before her very face, as his mother's candidate for the honor of his hand. That was all he could have seen in such an outbreak and in the indecency of her standing there to enjoy it. Fleda had on the prior occasion dashed out of the room by the shortest course and in her confusion had fallen upon Mona in the garden. She had taken an aimless turn with her, and they had had some talk, rendered at first difficult and almost disagreeable by Mona's apparent suspicion that she had been sent out to spy, as Mrs. Gereth had tried to spy, into her opinions. Fleda was sagacious enough to treat these opinions as a mystery almost awful; which had an effect so much more than reassuring that at the end of five minutes the young lady from Waterbath suddenly and perversely said: "Why has she never had a winter garden thrown out? If ever I have a place of my own I mean to have one." Fleda, dismayed, could see the thing—something glazed and piped, on iron pillars, with untidy plants and cane sofas; a shiny excrescence on the noble face of Poynton. She remembered at Waterbath a conservatory where she had caught a bad cold in the company of a stuffed cockatoo fastened to a tropical bough and a waterless fountain composed of shells stuck into some hardened paste. She asked Mona if her idea would be to make something like this conservatory; to which Mona replied: "Oh no, much finer; we haven't got a winter garden at Waterbath." Fleda wondered if she meant to convey that it was the only grandeur they lacked, and in a moment Mona went on: "But we have got a billiard-room— that I will say for us!" There was no billiard-room at Poynton, but there would evidently be one, and it would have, hung on its walls, framed at the "Stores," caricature-portraits of celebrities, taken from a "society-paper."

When the two girls had gone in to breakfast it was for Fleda to see at a glance that there had been a further passage, of some high color, between Owen and his mother; and she had turned pale in guessing to what extremity, at her expense, Mrs. Gereth had found occasion to proceed. Hadn't she, after her clumsy flight, been pressed upon Owen in still clearer terms? Mrs. Gereth would practically have said to him: "If you'll take *her*, I'll move away without a sound. But if you take any one else, any one I'm not sure of, as I am of her—heaven help me, I'll fight to the death!" Breakfast, this morning, at Poynton, had been a meal singularly silent, in spite of the vague little cries with which Mrs. Brigstock turned up the underside of plates and the knowing but alarming raps administered by her big knuckles to porcelain cups. Some one had to respond to her, and the duty assigned itself to Fleda, who, while pretending to meet her on the ground of explanation, wondered what Owen thought of a girl still indelicately anxious, after she had been grossly hurled at him, to prove by exhibitions of her fine taste that she was really what his mother pretended. This time, at any rate, their fate was sealed: Owen, as soon as he should get out of the house, would describe to Mona that lady's extraordinary conduct, and if anything more had been wanted to "fetch" Mona, as he would call it, the deficiency was now made up. Mrs. Gereth in fact took care of that—took care of it by the way, at the last, on the threshold, she said to the younger of her departing guests, with an irony of which the sting was wholly in the sense, not at all in the sound: "We haven't had the talk we might have had, have we? You'll feel that I've neglected you, and you'll treasure it up against me. *Don't*, because really, you know, it has been quite an accident, and I've all sorts of information at your disposal. If you should come down again (only you won't, ever,—I feel that!) I should give you plenty of time to worry it out of me. Indeed there are some things I should quite insist on your learning; not permit you at all, in any settled way, *not* to learn. Yes indeed, you'd put me through, and I should put you, my dear! We should have each other to reckon with, and you would see me as I really am. I'm not a bit the vague, mooning, easy creature I dare say you think. However, if you won't come, you won't; *n'en parlons plus*. It *is* stupid here after what you're accustomed to. We can only, all round, do what we can, eh? For heaven's sake, don't let your mother forget her precious publication, the female magazine, with the what-do-you-call-'em?—the grease-catchers. There!"

Mrs. Gereth, delivering herself from the doorstep, had tossed the periodical higher in air than was absolutely needful—tossed it toward the carriage the retreating party was about to enter. Mona, from the force of habit, the reflex action of the custom of sport, had popped out, with a little spring, a long arm and intercepted the missile as easily as she would have caused a tennis-ball to rebound from a racket. "Good catch!" Owen had cried, so genuinely pleased that practically no notice was taken of his mother's impressive remarks. It was to the accompaniment of romping laughter, as Mrs. Gereth afterwards said, that the carriage had rolled away; but it was while that laughter was still in the air that Fleda Vetch, white and terrible, had turned upon her hostess with her scorching "How *could* you? Great God, how *could* you?" This lady's perfect blankness was from the first a sign of her serene conscience, and the fact that till indoctrinated she didn't even know what Fleda meant by resenting her late offense to every susceptibility gave our young woman a sore, scared perception that her own value in the house was just the value, as one might say, of a good agent. Mrs. Gereth was generously sorry, but she was still more surprised—surprised at Fleda's not having liked to be shown off to Owen as the right sort of wife for him. Why not, in the name of wonder, if she absolutely *was* the right sort? She had admitted on explanation that she could see what her young friend meant by having been laid, as Fleda called it, at his feet; but it struck the girl that the admission was only made to please her, and that Mrs. Gereth was secretly surprised at her not being as happy to be sacrificed to the supremacy of a high standard as she was happy to sacrifice her. She had taken a tremendous fancy to her, but that was on account of the fancy—to Poynton of course—Fleda herself had taken. Wasn't this latter fancy then so great after all? Fleda felt that she could declare it to be great indeed when really for the sake of it she could forgive what she had suffered and, after reproaches and tears, asseverations and kisses, after learning that she was cared for only as a priestess of the altar and a view of her bruised dignity which left no alternative to flight, could accept the shame with the balm, consent not to depart, take refuge in the thin comfort of at least knowing the truth. The truth was simply that all Mrs. Gereth's scruples were on one side and that her ruling passion had in a manner despoiled her of her humanity. On the second day, after the tide of emotion had somewhat ebbed, she said soothingly to her companion: "But you *would*, after all, marry him, you know, darling, wouldn't you, if that girl were not there? I mean of course if he were to ask you," Mrs. Gereth had thoughtfully added.

"Marry him if he were to ask me? Most distinctly not!"

The question had not come up with this definiteness before, and Mrs. Gereth was clearly more surprised than ever. She marveled a moment. "Not even to have Poynton?"

"Not even to have Poynton."

"But why on earth?" Mrs. Gereth's sad eyes were fixed on her.

Fleda colored; she hesitated. "Because he's too stupid!" Save on one other occasion, at which we shall in time arrive, little as the reader may believe it, she never came nearer to betraying to Mrs. Gereth that she was in love with Owen. She found a dim amusement in reflecting that if Mona had not been there and he had not been too stupid and he verily had asked her, she might, should she have wished to keep her secret, have found it possible to pass off the motive of her action as a mere passion for Poynton.

Mrs. Gereth evidently thought in these days of little but things hymeneal; for she broke out with sudden rapture, in the middle of the week: "I know what they'll do: they *will* marry, but they'll go and live at Waterbath!" There was positive joy in that form of the idea, which she embroidered and developed: it seemed so much the safest thing that could happen. "Yes, I'll have you, but I won't go *there*!" Mona would have said with a vicious nod at the southern horizon: "we'll leave your horrid mother alone there for life." It would be an ideal solution, this ingress the lively pair, with their spiritual need of a warmer medium, would playfully punch in the ribs of her ancestral home; for it would not only prevent recurring panic at Poynton—it would offer them, as in one of their gimcrack baskets or other vessels of ugliness, a definite daily felicity that Poynton could never give. Owen might manage his estate just as he managed it now, and Mrs. Gereth would manage everything else. When, in the hall, on the unforgettable day of his return, she had heard his voice ring out like a call to a terrier, she had still, as Fleda afterwards

428

learned, clutched frantically at the conceit that he had come, at the worst, to announce some compromise; to tell her she would have to put up with the girl, yes, but that some way would be arrived at of leaving her in personal possession. Fleda Vetch, whom from the first hour no illusion had brushed with its wing, now held her breath, went on tiptoe, wandered in outlying parts of the house and through delicate, muffled rooms, while the mother and son faced each other below. From time to time she stopped to listen; but all was so quiet she was almost frightened: she had vaguely expected a sound of contention. It lasted longer than she would have supposed, whatever it was they were doing; and when finally, from a window, she saw Owen stroll out of the house, stop and light a cigarette and then pensively lose himself in the plantations, she found other matter for trepidation in the fact that Mrs. Gereth didn't immediately come rushing up into her arms. She wondered whether she oughtn't to go down to her, and measured the gravity of what had occurred by the circumstance, which she presently ascertained, that the poor lady had retired to her room and wished not to be disturbed. This admonition had been for her maid, with whom Fleda conferred as at the door of a death-chamber; but the girl, without either fatuity or resentment, judged that, since it could render Mrs. Gereth indifferent even to the ministrations of disinterested attachment, the scene had been tremendous.

She was absent from luncheon, where indeed Fleda had enough to do to look Owen in the face; there would be so much to make that hateful in their common memory of the passage in which his last visit had terminated. This had been her apprehension at least; but as soon as he stood there she was constrained to wonder at the practical simplicity of the ordeal—a simplicity which was really just his own simplicity, the particular thing that, for Fleda Vetch, some other things of course aiding, made almost any direct relation with him pleasant. He had neither wit, nor tact, nor inspiration: all she could say was that when they were together the alienation these charms were usually depended on to allay didn't occur. On this occasion, for instance, he did so much better than "carry off" an awkward remembrance: he simply didn't have it. He had clean forgotten that she was the girl his mother would have fobbed off on him; he was conscious only that she was there in a manner for service—conscious of the dumb instinct that from the first had made him regard her not as complicating his intercourse with that personage, but as simplifying it. Fleda found beautiful that this theory should have survived the incident of the other day; found exquisite that whereas she was conscious, through faint reverberations, that for her kind little circle at large, whom it didn't concern, her tendency had begun to define itself as parasitical, this strong young man, who had a right to judge and even a reason to loathe her, didn't judge and didn't loathe, let her down gently, treated her as if she pleased him, and in fact evidently liked her to be just where she was. She asked herself what he did when Mona denounced her, and the only answer to the question was that perhaps Mona didn't denounce her. If Mona was inarticulate he wasn't such a fool, then, to marry her. That he was glad Fleda was there was at any rate sufficiently shown by the domestic familiarity with which he said to her: "I must tell you I've been having an awful row with my mother. I'm engaged to be married to Miss Brigstock."

"Ah, really?" cried Fleda, achieving a radiance of which she was secretly proud. "How very exciting!"

"Too exciting for poor Mummy. She won't hear of it. She has been slating her fearfully. She says she's a 'barbarian.'"

"Why, she's lovely!" Fleda exclaimed.

"Oh, she's all right. Mother must come round."

"Only give her time," said Fleda. She had advanced to the threshold of the door thus thrown open to her and, without exactly crossing it, she threw in an appreciative glance. She asked Owen when his marriage would take place, and in the light of his reply read that Mrs. Gereth's wretched attitude would have no influence at all on the event, absolutely fixed when he came down, and distant by only three months. He liked Fleda's seeming to be on his side, though that was a secondary matter, for what really most concerned him now was the line his mother took about Poynton, her declared unwillingness to give it up.

"Naturally I want my own house, you know," he said, "and my father made every arrangement for me to have it. But she may make it devilish awkward. What in the world's a fellow to do?" This it was that Owen wanted to know, and there could be no better proof of his friendliness than his air of depending on Fleda Vetch to tell him. She questioned him, they spent an hour together, and, as he gave her the scale of the concussion from which he had rebounded, she found herself saddened and frightened by the material he seemed to offer her to deal with. It *was* devilish awkward, and it was so in part because Owen had no imagination. It had lodged itself in that empty chamber that his mother hated the surrender because she hated Mona. He didn't of course understand why she hated Mona, but this belonged to an order of mysteries that never troubled him: there were lots of things, especially in people's minds, that a fellow didn't understand. Poor Owen went through life with a frank dread of people's minds: there were explanations he would have been almost as shy of receiving as of giving. There was therefore nothing that accounted for anything, though in its way it was vivid enough, in his picture to Fleda of his mother's virtual refusal to move. That was simply what it was; for didn't she refuse to move when she as good as declared that she would move only with the furniture? It was the furniture she wouldn't give up; and what was the good of Poynton without the furniture? Besides, the furniture happened to be his, just as everything else happened to be. The furniture—the word, on his lips, had somehow, for Fleda, the sound of washing-stands and copious bedding, and she could well imagine the note it might have struck for Mrs. Gereth. The girl, in this interview with him, spoke of the contents of the house only as "the works of art." It didn't, however, in the least matter to Owen what they were called; what did matter, she easily guessed, was that it had been laid upon him by Mona, been made in effect a condition of her consent, that he should hold his mother to the strictest accountability for them. Mona had already entered upon the enjoyment of her rights. She had made him feel that Mrs. Gereth had been liberally provided for, and had asked him cogently what room there would be at Ricks for the innumerable treasures of the big house. Ricks, the sweet little place offered to the mistress of Poynton as the refuge of her declining years, had been left to the late Mr. Gereth, a considerable time before his death, by an old maternal aunt, a good lady who had spent most of her life there. The house had in recent times been let, but it was amply furnished, it contained all the defunct aunt's possessions.

Owen had lately inspected it, and he communicated to Fleda that he had quietly taken Mona to see it. It wasn't a place like Poynton—what dower-house ever was?—but it was an awfully jolly little place, and Mona had taken a tremendous fancy to it. If there were a few things at Poynton that were Mrs. Gereth's peculiar property, of course she must take them away with her; but one of the matters that became clear to Fleda was that this transfer would be immediately subject to Miss Brigstock's approval. The special business that she herself now became aware of being charged with was that of seeing Mrs. Gereth safely and singly off the premises.

Her heart failed her, after Owen had returned to London, with the ugliness of this duty—with the ugliness, indeed, of the whole close conflict. She saw nothing of Mrs. Gereth that day; she spent it in roaming with sick sighs, in feeling, as she passed from room to room, that what was expected of her companion was really dreadful. It would have been better never to have had such a place than to have had it and lose it. It was odious to *her* to have to look for solutions: what a strange relation between mother and son when there was no fundamental tenderness out of which a solution would irrepressibly spring! Was it Owen who was mainly responsible for that poverty? Fleda couldn't think so when she remembered that, so far as he was concerned, Mrs. Gereth would still have been welcome to have her seat by the Poynton fire. The fact that from the moment one accepted his marrying one saw no very different course for Owen to take made her all the rest of that aching day find her best relief in the mercy of not having yet to face her hostess. She dodged and dreamed and romanced away the time; instead of inventing a remedy or a compromise, instead of preparing a plan by which a scandal might be averted, she gave herself, in her sentient solitude, up to a mere fairy tale, up to the very taste of the beautiful peace with which she would have filled the air if only something might have been that could never have been.

V

"I'll give up the house if they'll let me take what I require!" That, on the morrow, was what Mrs. Gereth's stifled night had qualified her to say, with a tragic face, at breakfast. Fleda reflected that what she "required" was simply every object that surrounded them. The poor woman would have admitted this truth and accepted the conclusion to be drawn from it, the reduction to the absurd of her attitude, the exaltation of her revolt. The girl's dread of a scandal, of spectators and critics, diminished the more she saw how little vulgar avidity had to do with this rigor. It was not the crude love of possession; it was the need to be faithful to a trust and loyal to an idea. The idea was surely noble: it was that of the beauty Mrs. Gereth had so patiently and consummately wrought. Pale but radiant, with her back to the wall, she rose there like a heroine guarding a treasure. To give up the ship was to flinch from her duty; there was something in her eyes that declared she would die at her post. If their difference should become public the shame would be all for the others. If Waterbath thought it could afford to expose itself, then Waterbath was welcome to the folly. Her fanaticism gave her a new distinction, and Fleda perceived almost with awe that she had never carried herself so well. She trod the place like a reigning queen or a proud usurper; full as it was of splendid pieces, it could show in these days no ornament so effective as its menaced mistress.

Our young lady's spirit was strangely divided; she had a tenderness for Owen which she deeply concealed, yet it left her occasion to marvel at the way a man was made who could care in any relation for a creature like Mona Brigstock when he had known in any relation a creature like Adela Gereth. With such a mother to give him the pitch, how could he take it so low? She wondered that she didn't despise him for this, but there was something that kept her from it. If there had been nothing else it would have sufficed that she really found herself from this moment the medium of communication with him.

"He'll come back to assert himself," Mrs. Gereth had said; and the following week Owen in fact reappeared. He might merely have written, Fleda could see, but he had come in person because it was at once "nicer" for his mother and stronger for his cause. He didn't like the row, though Mona probably did; if he hadn't a sense of beauty he had after all a sense of justice; but it was inevitable he should clearly announce at Poynton the date at which he must look to find the house vacant. "You don't think I'm rough or hard, do you?" he asked of Fleda, his impatience shining in his idle eyes as the dining-hour shines in club-windows. "The place at Ricks stands there with open arms. And then I give her lots of time. Tell her she can remove everything that belongs to her." Fleda recognized the elements of what the newspapers call a deadlock in the circumstance that nothing at Poynton belonged to Mrs. Gereth either more or less than anything else. She must either take everything or nothing, and the girl's suggestion was that it might perhaps be an inspiration to do the latter and begin again on a clean page. What, however, was the poor woman, in that case, to begin with? What was she to do at all, on her meagre income, but make the best of the *objets d'art* of Ricks, the treasures collected by Mr. Gereth's maiden aunt? She had never been near the place: for long years it had been let to strangers, and after that the foreboding that it would be her doom had kept her from the abasement of it. She had felt that she should see it soon enough, but Fleda (who was careful not to betray to her that Mona had seen it and had been gratified) knew her reasons for believing that the maiden aunt's principles had had much in common with the principles of Waterbath. The only thing, in short, that she would ever have to do with the objets d'art of Ricks would be to turn them out into the road. What belonged to her at Poynton, as Owen said, would conveniently mitigate the void resulting from that demonstration.

The exchange of observations between the friends had grown very direct by the time Fleda asked Mrs. Gereth whether she literally meant to shut herself up and stand a siege, or whether it was her idea to expose herself, more informally, to be dragged out of the house by constables. "Oh, I prefer the constables and the dragging!" the heroine of Poynton had answered. "I want to make Owen and Mona do everything that will be most publicly odious." She gave it out that it was her one thought now to force them to a line that would dishonor them and dishonor the tradition they embodied, though Fleda was privately sure that she had visions of an alternative policy. The strange thing was that, proud and fastidious all her life, she now showed so little distaste for the world's hearing of the squabble. What had taken place in her above all was that a long resentment had ripened. She hated the effacement to which English usage reduced the widowed mother: she had discoursed of it passionately to Fleda; contrasted it with the beautiful homage paid in other countries to women in that position, women no better than herself, whom she had seen acclaimed and enthroned, whom she had known and envied; made in short as little as possible a secret of the injury, the bitterness she found in it. The great wrong Owen had done her was not his "taking up" with Mona—that was disgusting, but it was a detail, an accidental form: it was his failure from the first to understand what it was to have a mother at all, to appreciate the beauty and sanctity of the character. She was just his mother as his nose was just his nose, and he had never had the least imagination or tenderness or gallantry about her. One's mother, gracious heaven, if one were the kind of fine young man one ought to be, the only kind Mrs. Gereth cared for, was a subject for poetry, for idolatry. Hadn't she often told Fleda of her friend Madame de Jaume, the wittiest of women, but a small, black, crooked person, each of whose three boys, when absent, wrote to her every day of their lives? She had the house in Paris, she had the house in Poitou, she had more than in the lifetime of her husband (to whom, in spite of her appearance, she had afforded repeated cause for jealousy), because she had to the end of her days the supreme word about everything. It was easy to see that Mrs. Gereth would have given again and again her complexion, her figure, and even perhaps the spotless virtue she had still more successfully retained, to have been the consecrated Madame de Jaume. She wasn't, alas, and this was what she had at present a magnificent occasion to protest against. She was of course fully aware of Owen's concession, his willingness to let her take away with her the few things she liked best; but as yet she only declared that to meet him on this ground would be to give him a triumph, to put him impossibly in the right. "Liked best"? There wasn't a thing in the house that she didn't like best, and what she liked better still was to be left where she was. How could Owen use such an expression without being conscious of his hypocrisy? Mrs. Gereth, whose criticism was often gay, dilated with sardonic humor on the happy look a dozen objects from Poynton would wear and the charming effect they would conduce to when interspersed with the peculiar features of Ricks. What had her whole life been but an effort toward completeness and perfection? Better Waterbath at once, in its cynical unity, than the ignominy of such a mixture!

All this was of no great help to Fleda, in so far as Fleda tried to rise to her mission of finding a way out. When at the end of a fortnight Owen came down once more, it was ostensibly to tackle a farmer whose proceedings had been irregular; the girl was sure, however, that he had really come, on the instance of Mona, to see what his mother was doing. He wished to satisfy himself that she was preparing her departure, and he wished to perform a duty, distinct but not less imperative, in regard to the question of the perquisites with which she would retreat. The tension between them was now such that he had to perpetrate these offenses without meeting his adversary. Mrs. Gereth was as willing as himself that he should address to Fleda Vetch whatever cruel remarks he might have to make: she only pitied her poor young friend for repeated encounters with a person as to whom she perfectly understood the girl's repulsion. Fleda thought it nice of Owen not to have expected her to write to him; he wouldn't have wished any more than herself that she should have the air of spying on his mother in his interest. What made it comfortable to deal with him in this more familiar way was the sense that she understood so perfectly how poor Mrs. Gereth suffered, and that she measured so adequately the sacrifice the other side did take rather monstrously for granted. She understood equally how Owen himself suffered, now that Mona had already begun to make him do things he didn't like. Vividly Fleda apprehended how *she* would have first made him like anything she would have made him do; anything even as disagreeable as this appearing there to state, virtually on Mona's behalf, that of course there must be a definite limit to the number of articles appropriated. She took a longish stroll with him in order to talk the matter over; to say if she didn't think a dozen pieces, chosen absolutely at will, would be a handsome allowance; and above all to consider the very delicate question of whether the advantage enjoyed by Mrs. Gereth mightn't be left to her honor. To leave it so was what Owen wished; but there was plainly a young lady at Waterbath to whom, on his side, he already had to render an account. He was as touching in his offhand annoyance as his mother was tragic in her intensity; for if he couldn't help having a sense of propriety about the whole matter, so he could as little help hating it. It was for his hating it, Fleda reasoned, that she liked him so, and her insistence to his mother on the hatred perilously resembled, on one or two occasions, a revelation of the liking. There were moments when, in conscience, that revelation pressed her; inasmuch as it was just on the ground of her not liking him that Mrs. Gereth trusted her so much. Mrs. Gereth herself didn't in these days like him at all, and she was of course and always on Mrs. Gereth's side. He ended really, while the preparations for his marriage went on, by quite a little custom of coming and going; but on no one of these occasions would his mother receive him. He talked only with Fleda and strolled with Fleda; and when he asked her, in regard to the great matter, if Mrs. Gereth were really doing nothing, the girl usually replied: "She pretends not to be, if I may say so; but I think she's really thinking over what she'll take." When her friend asked her what Owen was doing, she could have but one answer: "He's waiting, dear lady, to see what *you* do!"

Mrs. Gereth, a month after she had received her great shock, did something abrupt and extraordinary: she caught up her companion and went to have a look at Ricks. They had come to London first and taken a train from Liverpool Street, and the least of the sufferings they were armed against was that of passing the night. Fleda's admirable dressing-bag had been given her by her friend. "Why, it's charming!" she exclaimed a few hours later, turning back again into the small prim parlor from a friendly advance to the single plate of the window. Mrs. Gereth hated such windows, the one flat glass, sliding up and down, especially when they enjoyed a view of four iron pots on pedestals, painted white and containing ugly geraniums, ranged on the edge of a gravel-path and doing their best to give it the air of a terrace. Fleda had instantly averted her eyes from these ornaments, but Mrs. Gereth grimly gazed, wondering of course how a place in the deepest depths of Essex and three miles from a small station could contrive to look so suburban. The room was practically a shallow box, with the junction of the walls and ceiling guiltless of curve or cornice and marked merely by the little band of crimson paper glued round the top of the other paper, a turbid gray sprigged with silver flowers. This decoration was rather new and quite fresh; and there was in the

437

centre of the ceiling a big square beam papered over in white, as to which Fleda hesitated about venturing to remark that it was rather picturesque. She recognized in time that this remark would be weak and that, throughout, she should be able to say nothing either for the mantelpieces or for the doors, of which she saw her companion become sensible with a soundless moan. On the subject of doors especially Mrs. Gereth had the finest views: the thing in the world she most despised was the meanness of the single flap. From end to end, at Poynton, there were high double leaves. At Ricks the entrances to the rooms were like the holes of rabbit-hutches.

It was all, none the less, not so bad as Fleda had feared; it was faded and melancholy, whereas there had been a danger that it would be contradictious and positive, cheerful and loud. The house was crowded with objects of which the aggregation somehow made a thinness and the futility a grace; things that told her they had been gathered as slowly and as lovingly as the golden flowers of Poynton. She too, for a home, could have lived with them: they made her fond of the old maiden-aunt; they made her even wonder if it didn't work more for happiness not to have tasted, as she herself had done, of knowledge. Without resources, without a stick, as she said, of her own, Fleda was moved, after all, to some secret surprise at the pretensions of a shipwrecked woman who could hold such an asylum cheap. The more she looked about the surer she felt of the character of the maiden-aunt, the sense of whose dim presence urged her to pacification: the maiden-aunt had been a dear; she would have adored the maiden-aunt. The poor lady had had some tender little story; she had been sensitive and ignorant and exquisite: that too was a sort of origin, a sort of atmosphere for relics and rarities, though different from the sorts most prized at Poynton. Mrs. Gereth had of course more than once said that one of the deepest mysteries of life was the way that, by certain natures, hideous objects could be loved; but it wasn't a question of love, now, for these: it was only a question of a certain practical patience. Perhaps some thought of that kind had stolen over Mrs. Gereth when, at the end of a brooding hour, she exclaimed, taking in the house with a strenuous sigh: "Well, something can be done with it!" Fleda had repeated to her more than once the indulgent fancy about the maiden-aunt—she was so sure she had deeply suffered. "I'm sure I hope she did!" was, however, all that Mrs. Gereth had replied.

<u>VI</u>

It was a great relief to the girl at last to perceive that the dreadful move would really be made. What might happen if it shouldn't had been from the first indefinite. It was absurd to pretend that any violence was probable—a tussel, dishevelment, shrieks; yet Fleda had an imagination of a drama, a "great scene," a thing, somehow, of indignity and misery, of wounds inflicted and received, in which indeed, though Mrs. Gereth's presence, with movements and sounds, loomed large to her, Owen remained indistinct and on the whole unaggressive. He wouldn't be there with a cigarette in his teeth, very handsome and insolently quiet: that was only the way he would be in a novel, across whose interesting page some such figure, as she half closed her eyes, seemed to her to walk. Fleda had rather, and indeed with shame, a confused, pitying vision of Mrs. Gereth with her great scene left in a manner on her hands, Mrs. Gereth missing her effect and having to appear merely hot and injured and in the wrong. The symptoms that she would be spared even that spectacle resided not so much, through the chambers of Poynton, in an air of concentration as in the hum of buzzing alternatives. There was no common preparation, but one day, at the turn of a corridor, she found her hostess standing very still, with the hanging hands of an invalid and the active eyes of an adventurer. These eyes appeared to Fleda to meet her own with a strange, dim bravado, and there was a silence, almost awkward, before either of the friends spoke. The girl afterwards thought of the moment as one in which her hostess mutely accused her of an accusation, meeting it, however, at the same time, by a kind of defiant acceptance. Yet it was with mere melancholy candor that Mrs. Gereth at last sighingly exclaimed: "I'm thinking over what I had better take!" Fleda could have embraced her for this virtual promise of a concession, the announcement that she had finally accepted the problem of knocking together a shelter with the small salvage of the wreck.

Fleda had a depressed sense of not, after all, helping her much: this was lightened indeed by the fact that Mrs. Gereth, letting her off easily, didn't now seem to expect it. Her sympathy, her interest, her feeling for everything for which Mrs. Gereth felt, were a force that really worked to prolong the deadlock. "I only wish I bored you and my possessions bored you," that lady, with some humor, declared; "then you'd make short work with me, bundle me off, tell me just to pile certain things into a cart and have done." Fleda's sharpest difficulty was in having to act up to the character of thinking Owen a brute, or at least to carry off the inconsistency of seeing him when he came down. By good fortune it was her duty, her function, as well as a protection to Mrs. Gereth. She thought of him perpetually, and her eyes had come to rejoice in his manly magnificence more even than they rejoiced in the royal cabinets of the red saloon. She wondered, very faintly at first, why he came so often; but of course she knew nothing about the business he had in hand, over which, with men red-faced and leather-legged, he was sometimes closeted for an hour in a room of his own that was the one monstrosity of Poynton: all tobacco-pots and bootjacks, his mother had said—such an array of arms of aggression and castigation that he himself had confessed to eighteen rifles and forty whips. He was arranging for settlements on his wife, he was doing things that would meet the views of the Brigstocks. Considering the house was his own, Fleda thought it nice of him to keep himself in the background while his mother remained; making his visits, at some cost of ingenuity about trains from town, only between meals, doing everything to let it press lightly upon her that he was there. This was rather a stoppage to her meeting Mrs. Gereth on the ground of his being a brute; the most she really at last could do was not to contradict her when she repeated that he was watching—just insultingly watching. He *was* watching, no doubt; but he watched somehow with his head turned away. He knew that Fleda knew at present what he wanted of her, so that it would be gross of him to say it over and over. It existed as a confidence between them, and made him sometimes, with his wandering stare, meet her eyes as if a silence so pleasant could only unite them the more. He had no great flow of speech, certainly, and at first the girl took for granted that this was all there was to be said about the matter. Little by little she speculated as to whether, with a person who, like herself, could put him, after all, at a sort of domestic ease, it was not supposable that he would have more conversation if he were not keeping some of it back for Mona.

From the moment she suspected he might be thinking what Mona would say to his chattering so to an underhand "companion," who was all but paid, his young lady's repressed emotion began to require still more repression. She grew impatient of her situation at Poynton; she privately pronounced it false and horrid. She said to herself that she had let Owen know that she had, to the best of her power, directed his mother in the general sense he desired; that he quite understood it and that he also understood how unworthy it was of either of them to stand over the good lady with a notebook and a lash. Wasn't this practical unanimity just practical success? Fleda became aware of a sudden desire, as well as of pressing reasons, to bring her stay at Poynton to a close. She had not, on the one hand, like a minion of the law, undertaken to see Mrs. Gereth down to the train and locked, in sign of her abdication, into a compartment; neither had she on the other committed herself to hold Owen indefinitely in dalliance while his mother gained time or dug a counter-mine. Besides, people *were* saying that she fastened like a leech on other people— people who had houses where something was to be picked up: this revelation was frankly made her by her sister, now distinctly doomed to the curate and in view of whose nuptials she had almost finished, as a present, a wonderful piece of embroidery, suggested, at Poynton, by an old Spanish altar-cloth. She would have to exert herself still further for the intended recipient of this offering, turn her out for her marriage with more than that drapery. She would go up to town, in short, to dress Maggie; and their father, in lodgings at West Kensington, would stretch a point and take them in. He, to do him justice, never reproached her with profitable devotions; so far as they existed he consciously profited by them. Mrs. Gereth gave her up as heroically as if she had been a great bargain, and Fleda knew that she wouldn't at present miss any visit of Owen's, for Owen was shooting at Waterbath. Owen shooting was Owen lost, and there was scant sport at Poynton.

The first news she had from Mrs. Gereth was news of that lady's having accomplished, in form at least, her migration. The letter was dated from

Ricks, to which place she had been transported by an impulse apparently as sudden as the inspiration she had obeyed before. "Yes, I've literally come," she wrote, "with a bandbox and a kitchen-maid; I've crossed the Rubicon, I've taken possession. It has been like plumping into cold water: I saw the only thing was to do it, not to stand shivering. I shall have warmed the place a little by simply being here for a week; when I come back the ice will have been broken. I didn't write to you to meet me on my way through town, because I know how busy you are and because, besides, I'm too savage and odious to be fit company even for you. You'd say I really go too far, and there's no doubt whatever I do. I'm here, at any rate, just to look round once more, to see that certain things are done before I enter in force. I shall probably be at Poynton all next week. There's more room than I quite measured the other day, and a rather good set of old Worcester. But what are space and time, what's even old Worcester, to your wretched and affectionate A. G.?"

The day after Fleda received this letter she had occasion to go into a big shop in Oxford Street—a journey that she achieved circuitously, first on foot and then by the aid of two omnibuses. The second of these vehicles put her down on the side of the street opposite her shop, and while, on the curbstone, she humbly waited, with a parcel, an umbrella, and a tucked-up frock, to cross in security, she became aware that, close beside her, a hansom had pulled up short, in obedience to the brandished stick of a demonstrative occupant. This occupant was Owen Gereth, who had caught sight of her as he rattled along and who, with an exhibition of white teeth that, from under the hood of the cab, had almost flashed through the fog, now alighted to ask her if he couldn't give her a lift. On finding that her destination was only over the way he dismissed his vehicle and joined her, not only piloting her to the shop, but taking her in; with the assurance that his errands didn't matter, that it amused him to be concerned with hers. She told him she had come to buy a trimming for her sister's frock, and he expressed an hilarious interest in the purchase. His hilarity was almost always out of proportion to the case, but it struck her at present as more so than ever; especially when she had suggested that he might find it a good time to buy a garnishment of some sort for Mona. After wondering an instant whether he gave the full satiric meaning, such as it was, to this remark, Fleda dismissed the possibility as inconceivable. He stammered out that it was for *her* he would like to buy something, something "ripping," and that she must give him the pleasure of telling him what would best please her: he couldn't have a better opportunity for making her a present—the present, in recognition of all she had done for Mummy, that he had had in his head for weeks.

Fleda had more than one small errand in the big bazaar, and he went up and down with her, pointedly patient, pretending to be interested in questions of tape and of change. She had now not the least hesitation in wondering what Mona would think of such proceedings. But they were not her doing—they were Owen's; and Owen, inconsequent and even extravagant, was unlike anything she had ever seen him before. He broke off, he came back, he repeated questions without heeding answers, he made vague, abrupt remarks about the resemblances of shopgirls and the uses of chiffon. He unduly prolonged their business together, giving Fleda a sense that he was putting off something particular that he had to face. If she had ever dreamed of Owen Gereth as nervous she would have seen him with some such manner as this. But why should he be nervous? Even at the height of the crisis his mother hadn't made him so, and at present he was satisfied about his mother. The one idea he stuck to was that Fleda should mention something she would let him give her: there was everything in the world in the wonderful place, and he made her incongruous offers—a traveling-rug, a massive clock, a table for breakfast in bed, and above all, in a resplendent binding, a set of somebody's "works." His notion was a testimonial, a tribute, and the "works" would be a graceful intimation that it was her cleverness he wished above all to commemorate. He was immensely in earnest, but the articles he pressed upon her betrayed a delicacy that went to her heart: what he would really have liked, as he saw them tumbled about, was one of the splendid stuffs for a gown—a choice proscribed by his fear of seeming to patronize her, to refer to her small means and her deficiencies. Fleda found it easy to chaff him about his exaggeration of her deserts; she gave the just measure of them in consenting to accept a small pin-cushion, costing sixpence, in which the letter F was marked out with pins. A sense of loyalty to Mona was not needed to enforce this discretion, and after that first allusion to her she never sounded her name. She noticed on this occasion more things in Owen Gereth than she had ever noticed before, but what she noticed most was that he said no word of his intended. She asked herself what he had done, in so long a parenthesis, with his loyalty or at least his "form;" and then reflected that even if he had done something very good with them the situation in which such a question could come up was already a little strange. Of course he wasn't doing anything so vulgar as making love to her; but there was a kind of punctilio for a man who was engaged.

That punctilio didn't prevent Owen from remaining with her after they had left the shop, from hoping she had a lot more to do, and from pressing her to look with him, for a possible glimpse of something she might really let him give her, into the windows of other establishments. There was a moment when, under this pressure, she made up her mind that his tribute would be, if analyzed, a tribute to her insignificance. But all the same he wanted her to come somewhere and have luncheon with him: what was that a tribute to? She must have counted very little if she didn't count too much for a romp in a restaurant. She had to get home with her trimming, and the most, in his company, she was amenable to was a retracing of her steps to the Marble Arch and then, after a discussion when they had reached it, a walk with him across the Park. She knew Mona would have considered that she ought to take the omnibus again; but she had now to think for Owen as well as for herself—she couldn't think for Mona. Even in the Park the autumn air was thick, and as they moved westward over the grass, which was what Owen preferred, the cool grayness made their words soft, made them at last rare and everything else dim. He wanted to stay with her—he wanted not to leave her: he had dropped into complete silence, but that was what his silence said. What was it he had postponed? What was it he wanted still to postpone? She grew a little scared as they strolled together and she thought. It was too confused to be believed, but it was as if somehow he felt differently. Fleda Vetch didn't suspect him at first of feeling differently to *her*, but only of feeling differently to Mona; yet she was not unconscious that this latter difference would have had something to do with his being on the grass beside her. She had read in novels about gentlemen who on the eve of marriage, winding up the past, had surrendered themselves for the occasion to the influence of a former tie; and there was something in Owen's behavior now, something in his very face, that suggested a resemblance to one of those gentlemen. But whom and what, in that case, would Fleda herself resemble? She wasn't a former tie, she wasn't any tie at all; she was only a deep little person for whom happiness was a kind of pearl-diving plunge. It was down at the very bottom of all that had lately happened; for all that had lately happened was that Owen Gereth had come and gone at Poynton. That was the small sum of her experience, and what it had made for her was her own affair, quite consistent with her not having dreamed it had made a tie—at least what *she* called one—for Owen. The old one, at any rate, was Mona—Mona whom he had known so very much longer.

They walked far, to the southwest corner of the great Gardens, where, by the old round pond and the old red palace, when she had put out her hand to him in farewell, declaring that from the gate she must positively take a conveyance, it seemed suddenly to rise between them that this was a real separation. She was on his mother's side, she belonged to his mother's life, and his mother, in the future, would never come to Poynton. After what had passed she wouldn't even be at his wedding, and it was not possible now that Mrs. Gereth should mention that ceremony to the girl, much less express a wish that the girl should be present at it. Mona, from decorum and with reference less to the bridegroom than to the bridegroom's mother, would of course not invite any such girl as Fleda. Everything therefore was ended; they would go their different ways; this was the last time they would stand face to face. They looked at each other with the fuller sense of it and, on Owen's part, with an expression of dumb trouble, the intensification of his usual appeal to any interlocutor to add the right thing to what he said. To Fleda, at this moment, it appeared that the right thing might easily be the wrong. He only said, at any rate: "I want you to understand, you know—I want you to understand."

What did he want her to understand? He seemed unable to bring it out, and this understanding was moreover exactly what she wished not to arrive at. Bewildered as she was, she had already taken in as much as she should know what to do with; the blood also was rushing into her face. He liked her—it was stupefying—more than he really ought: that was what was the matter with him and what he desired her to assimilate; so that she was suddenly as frightened as some thoughtless girl who finds herself the object of an overture from a married man.

"Good-bye, Mr. Gereth—I *must* get on!" she declared with a cheerfulness that she felt to be an unnatural grimace. She broke away from him sharply, smiling, backing across the grass and then turning altogether and moving as fast as she could. "Good-bye, good-bye!" she threw off again as she went, wondering if he would overtake her before she reached the gate; conscious with a red disgust that her movement was almost a run; conscious too of just the confused, handsome face with which he would look after her. She felt as if she had answered a kindness with a great flouncing snub, but at any rate she had got away, though the distance to the gate, her ugly gallop down the Broad Walk, every graceless jerk of which hurt her, seemed endless. She signed from afar to a cab on the stand in the Kensington Road and scrambled into it, glad of the encompassment of the four-wheeler that had officiously obeyed her summons and that, at the end of twenty yards, when she had violently pulled up a glass, permitted her to recognize the fact that she was on the point of bursting into tears.

VII

As soon as her sister was married she went down to Mrs. Gereth at Ricks—a promise to this effect having been promptly exacted and given; and her inner vision was much more fixed on the alterations there, complete now, as she understood, than on the success of her plotting and pinching for Maggie's happiness. Her imagination, in the interval, had indeed had plenty to do and numerous scenes to visit; for when on the summons just mentioned it had taken a flight from West Kensington to Ricks, it had hung but an hour over the terrace of painted pots and then yielded to a current of the upper air that swept it straight off to Poynton and to Waterbath. Not a sound had reached her of any supreme clash, and Mrs. Gereth had communicated next to nothing; giving out that, as was easily conceivable, she was too busy, too bitter, and too tired for vain civilities. All she had written was that she had got the new place well in hand and that Fleda would be surprised at the way it was turning out. Everything was even yet upside down; nevertheless, in the sense of having passed the threshold of Poynton for the last time, the imputation, as she called it, had been performed. Her leg had come off—she had now begun to stump along with the lovely wooden substitute; she would stump for life, and what her young friend was to come and admire was the beauty of her movement and the noise she made about the house. The reserve of Poynton and Waterbath had been matched by the austerity of Fleda's own secret, under the discipline of which she had repeated to herself a hundred times a day that she rejoiced at having cares that excluded all thought of it. She had lavished herself, in act, on Maggie and the curate, and had opposed to her father's selfishness a sweetness quite ecstatic. The young couple wondered why they had waited so long, since everything was after all so easy. She had thought of everything, even to how the "quietness" of the wedding should be relieved by champagne and her father kept brilliant on a single bottle. Fleda knew, in short, and liked the knowledge, that for several weeks she had appeared exemplary in every relation of life.

She had been perfectly prepared to be surprised at Ricks, for Mrs. Gereth was a wonder-working wizard, with a command, when all was said, of good material; but the impression in wait for her on the threshold made her catch her breath and falter. Dusk had fallen when she arrived, and in the plain square hall, one of the few good features, the glow of a Venetian lamp just showed, on either wall, the richness of an admirable tapestry. This instant perception that the place had been dressed at the expense of Poynton was a shock: it was as if she had abruptly seen herself in the light of an accomplice. The next moment, folded in Mrs. Gereth's arms, her eyes were diverted; but she had already had, in a flash, the vision of the great gaps in the other house. The two tapestries, not the largest, but those most splendidly toned by time, had been on the whole its most uplifted pride. When she could really see again she was on a sofa in the drawing-room, staring with intensity at an object soon distinct as the great Italian cabinet that, at Poynton, had been in the red saloon. Without looking, she was sure the room was occupied with other objects like it, stuffed with as many as it could hold of the trophies of her friend's struggle. By this time the very fingers of her glove, resting on the seat of the sofa, had thrilled at the touch of an old velvet brocade, a wondrous texture that she could recognize, would have recognized among a thousand, without dropping her eyes on it. They stuck to the cabinet with a kind of dissimulated dread, while she painfully asked herself whether she should notice it, notice everything, or just pretend not to be affected. How could she pretend not to be affected, with the very pendants of the lustres tinkling at her and with Mrs. Gereth, beside her and staring at her even as she herself stared at the cabinet, hunching up a back like Atlas under his globe? She was appalled at this image of what Mrs. Gereth had on her shoulders. That lady was waiting and watching her, bracing herself, and preparing the same face of confession and defiance she had shown the day, at Poynton, she had been surprised in the corridor. It was farcical not to speak; and yet to exclaim, to participate, would give one a bad sense of being mixed up with a theft. This ugly word sounded, for herself, in Fleda's silence, and the very violence of it jarred her into a scared glance, as of a creature detected, to right and left. But what again the full picture most showed her was the far-away empty sockets, a scandal of nakedness in high, bare walls. She at last uttered something formal and incoherent—she didn't know what: it had no relation to either house. Then she felt Mrs. Gereth's hand once more on her arm. "I've arranged a charming room for you—it's really lovely. You'll be very happy there." This was spoken with extraordinary sweetness and with a smile that meant, "Oh, I know what you're thinking; but what does it matter when you're so loyally on my side?" It had come indeed to a question of "sides," Fleda thought, for the whole place was in battle array. In the soft lamplight, with one fine feature after another looming up into sombre richness, it defied her not to pronounce it a triumph of taste. Her passion for beauty leaped back into life; and was not what now most appealed to it a certain gorgeous audacity? Mrs. Gereth's high hand was, as mere great effect, the climax of the impression.

"It's too wonderful, what you've done with the house!"—the visitor met her friend's eyes. They lighted up with joy—that friend herself so pleased with what she had done. This was not at all, in its accidental air of enthusiasm, what Fleda wanted to have said: it offered her as stupidly announcing from the first minute on whose side she was. Such was clearly the way Mrs. Gereth took it: she threw herself upon the delightful girl and tenderly embraced her again; so that Fleda soon went on, with a studied difference and a cooler inspection: "Why, you brought away absolutely everything!"

"Oh no, not everything; I saw how little I could get into this scrap of a house. I only brought away what I required."

Fleda had got up; she took a turn round the room. "You 'required' the very best pieces—the *morceaux de musée*, the individual gems!"

"I certainly didn't want the rubbish, if that's what you mean." Mrs. Gereth, on the sofa, followed the direction of her companion's eyes; with the light of her satisfaction still in her face, she slowly rubbed her large, handsome hands. Wherever she was, she was herself the great piece in the gallery. It was the first Fleda had heard of there being "rubbish" at Poynton, but she didn't for the moment take up this insincerity; she only, from where she stood in the room, called out, one after the other, as if she had had a list in her hand, the pieces that in the great house had been scattered and that now, if they had a fault, were too much like a minuet danced on a hearth-rug.

She knew them each, in every chink and charm—knew them by the personal name their distinctive sign or story had given them; and a second time she felt how, against her intention, this uttered knowledge struck her hostess as so much free approval. Mrs. Gereth was never indifferent to approval, and there was nothing she could so love you for as for doing justice to her deep morality. There was a particular gleam in her eyes when Fleda exclaimed at last, dazzled by the display: "And even the Maltese cross!" That description, though technically incorrect, had always been applied, at Poynton, to a small but marvelous crucifix of ivory, a masterpiece of delicacy, of expression, and of the great Spanish period, the existence and precarious accessibility of which she had heard of at Malta, years before, by an odd and romantic chance—a clue followed through mazes of secrecy till the treasure was at last unearthed.

"'Even' the Maltese cross?" Mrs. Gereth rose as she sharply echoed the words. "My dear child, you don't suppose I'd have sacrificed *that*! For what in the world would you have taken me?"

"A *bibelot* the more or the less," Fleda said, "could have made little difference in this grand general view of you. I take you simply for the greatest of all conjurers. You've operated with a quickness—and with a quietness!" Her voice trembled a little as she spoke, for the plain meaning of her words was that what her friend had achieved belonged to the class of operation essentially involving the protection of darkness. Fleda felt she really could say nothing at all if she couldn't say that she knew what the danger had been. She completed her thought by a resolute and perfectly candid question: "How in the world did you get off with them?"

Mrs. Gereth confessed to the fact of danger with a cynicism that surprised the girl. "By calculating, by choosing my time. I *was* quiet, and I *was* quick. I manœuvred; then at the last rushed!" Fleda drew a long breath: she saw in the poor woman something much better than sophistical ease, a crude elation that was a comparatively simple state to deal with. Her elation, it was true, was not so much from what she had done as from the way she had done it—by as brilliant a stroke as any commemorated in the annals of crime. "I succeeded because I had thought it all out and left nothing to chance: the whole process was organized in advance, so that the mere carrying it into effect took but a few hours. It was largely a matter of money: oh, I was horribly extravagant—I had to turn on so many people. But they were all to be had—a little army of workers, the packers, the porters, the helpers of every sort, the men with the mighty vans. It was a question of arranging in Tottenham Court Road and of paying the price. I haven't paid it yet; there'll be a horrid bill; but at least the thing's done! Expedition pure and simple was the essence of the bargain. 'I can give you two days,' I said; 'I can't give you another second.' They undertook the job, and the two days saw them through. The people came down on a Tuesday morning; they were off on the Thursday. I admit that some of them worked all Wednesday night. I had thought it all out; I stood over them; I showed them how. Yes, I coaxed them, I made love to them. Oh, I was inspired—they found me wonderful. I neither ate nor slept, but I was as calm as I am now. I didn't know what was in me; it was worth finding out. I'm very remarkable, my dear: I lifted tons with my own arms. I'm tired, very, very tired; but there's neither a scratch nor a nick, there isn't a teacup missing." Magnificent both in her exhaustion and in her triumph, Mrs. Gereth sank on the sofa again, the sweep of her eyes a rich synthesis and the restless friction of her hands a clear betrayal. "Upon my word," she laughed, "they really look better here!"

Fleda had listened in awe. "And no one at Poynton said anything? There was no alarm?"

"What alarm should there have been? Owen left me almost defiantly alone: I had taken a time that I had reason to believe was safe from a descent." Fleda had another wonder, which she hesitated to express: it would scarcely do to ask Mrs. Gereth if she hadn't stood in fear of her servants. She knew, moreover, some of the secrets of her humorous household rule, all made up of shocks to shyness and provocations to curiosity—a diplomacy so artful that several of the maids quite yearned to accompany her to Ricks. Mrs. Gereth, reading sharply the whole of her visitor's thought, caught it up with fine frankness. "You mean that I was watched—that he had his myrmidons, pledged to wire him if they should see what I was 'up to'? Precisely. I know the three persons you have in mind: I had them in mind myself. Well, I took a line with them—I settled them."

Fleda had had no one in particular in mind; she had never believed in the myrmidons; but the tone in which Mrs. Gereth spoke added to her suspense. "What did you do to them?"

"I took hold of them hard—I put them in the forefront. I made them work."

"To move the furniture?"

"To help, and to help so as to please me. That was the way to take them; it was what they had least expected. I marched up to them and looked each straight in the eye, giving him the chance to choose if he'd gratify me or gratify my son. He gratified *me*. They were too stupid!"

Mrs. Gereth massed herself there more and more as an immoral woman, but Fleda had to recognize that she too would have been stupid and she too would have gratified her. "And when did all this take place?"

"Only last week; it seems a hundred years. We've worked here as fast as we worked there, but I'm not settled yet: you'll see in the rest of the house. However, the worst is over."

"Do you really think so?" Fleda presently inquired. "I mean, does he, after the fact, as it were, accept it?"

"Owen—what I've done? I haven't the least idea," said Mrs. Gereth.

"Does Mona?"

"You mean that she'll be the soul of the row?"

"I hardly see Mona as the 'soul' of anything," the girl replied. "But have they made no sound? Have you heard nothing at all?"

"Not a whisper, not a step, in all the eight days. Perhaps they don't know. Perhaps they're crouching for a leap."

"But wouldn't they have gone down as soon as you left?"

"They may not have known of my leaving." Fleda wondered afresh; it struck her as scarcely supposable that some sign shouldn't have flashed from

Poynton to London. If the storm was taking this term of silence to gather, even in Mona's breast, it would probably discharge itself in some startling form. The great hush of every one concerned was strange; but when she pressed Mrs. Gereth for some explanation of it, that lady only replied, with her brave irony: "Oh, I took their breath away!" She had no illusions, however; she was still prepared to fight. What indeed was her spoliation of Poynton but the first engagement of a campaign?

All this was exciting, but Fleda's spirit dropped, at bedtime, in the chamber embellished for her pleasure, where she found several of the objects that in her earlier room she had most admired. These had been reinforced by other pieces from other rooms, so that the quiet air of it was a harmony without a break, the finished picture of a maiden's bower. It was the sweetest Louis Seize, all assorted and combined—old chastened, figured, faded France. Fleda was impressed anew with her friend's genius for composition. She could say to herself that no girl in England, that night, went to rest with so picked a guard; but there was no joy for her in her privilege, no sleep even for the tired hours that made the place, in the embers of the fire and the winter dawn, look gray, somehow, and loveless. She couldn't care for such things when they came to her in such ways; there was a wrong about them all that turned them to ugliness. In the watches of the night she saw Poynton dishonored; she had cared for it as a happy whole, she reasoned, and the parts of it now around her seemed to suffer like chopped limbs. Before going to bed she had walked about with Mrs. Gereth and seen at whose expense the whole house had been furnished. At poor Owen's, from top to bottom—there wasn't a chair he hadn't sat upon. The maiden aunt had been exterminated—no trace of her to tell her tale. Fleda tried to think of some of the things at Poynton still unappropriated, but her memory was a blank about them, and in trying to focus the old combinations she saw again nothing but gaps and scars, a vacancy that gathered at moments into something worse. This concrete image was her greatest trouble, for it was Owen Gereth's face, his sad, strange eyes, fixed upon her now as they had never been. They stared at her out of the darkness, and their expression was more than she could bear: it seemed to say that he was in pain and that it was somehow her fault. He had looked to her to help him, and this was what her help had been. He had done her the honor to ask her to exert herself in his interest, confiding to her a task of difficulty, but of the highest delicacy. Hadn't that been exactly the sort of service she longed to render him? Well, her way of rendering it had been simply to betray him and hand him over to his enemy. Shame, pity, resentment oppressed her in turn; in the last of these feelings the others were quickly submerged. Mrs. Gereth had imprisoned her in that torment of taste; but it was clear to her for an hour at least that she might hate Mrs. Gereth.

Something else, however, when morning came, was even more intensely definite: the most odious thing in the world for her would be ever again to meet Owen. She took on the spot a resolve to neglect no precaution that could lead to her going through life without that accident. After this, while she dressed, she took still another. Her position had become, in a few hours, intolerably false; in as few more hours as possible she would therefore put an end to it. The way to put an end to it would be to inform Mrs. Gereth that, to her great regret, she couldn't be with her now, couldn't cleave to her to the point that everything about her so plainly urged. She dressed with a sort of violence, a symbol of the manner in which this purpose was precipitated. The more they parted company the less likely she was to come across Owen; for Owen would be drawn closer to his mother now by the very necessity of bringing her down. Fleda, in the inconsequence of distress, wished to have nothing to do with her fall; she had had too much to do with everything. She was well aware of the importance, before breakfast and in view of any light they might shed on the question of motive, of not suffering her invidious expression of a difference to be accompanied by the traces of tears; but it none the less came to pass, downstairs, that after she had subtly put her back to the window, to make a mystery of the state of her eyes, she stupidly let a rich sob escape her before she could properly meet the consequences of being asked if she wasn't delighted with her room. This accident struck her on the spot as so grave that she felt the only refuge to be instant hypocrisy, some graceful impulse that would charge her emotion to the quickened sense of her friend's generosity—a demonstration entailing a flutter round the table and a renewed embrace, and not so successfully improvised but that Fleda fancied Mrs. Gereth to have been only half reassured. She had been startled, at any rate, and she might remain suspicious: this reflection interposed by the time, after breakfast, the girl had recovered sufficiently to say what was in her heart. She accordingly didn't say it that morning at all: she had absurdly veered about; she had encountered the shock of the fear that Mrs. Gereth, with sharpened eyes, might wonder why the deuce (she often wondered in that phrase) she had grown so warm about Owen's rights. She would doubtless, at a pinch, be able to defend them on abstract grounds, but that would involve a discussion, and the idea of a discussion made her nervous for her secret. Until in some way Poynton should return the blow and give her a cue, she must keep nervousness down; and she called herself a fool for having forgotten, however briefly, that her one safety was in silence.

Directly after luncheon Mrs. Gereth took her into the garden for a glimpse of the revolution—or at least, said the mistress of Ricks, of the great row—that had been decreed there; but the ladies had scarcely placed themselves for this view before the younger one found herself embracing a prospect that opened in quite another quarter. Her attention was called to it, oddly, by the streamers of the parlor-maid's cap, which, flying straight behind the neat young woman who unexpectedly burst from the house and showed a long red face as she ambled over the grass, seemed to articulate in their flutter the name that Fleda lived at present only to catch. "Poynton—Poynton!" said the morsels of muslin; so that the parlor-maid became on the instant an actress in the drama, and Fleda, assuming pusillanimously that she herself was only a spectator, looked across the footlights at the exponent of the principal part. The manner in which this artist returned her look showed that she was equally preoccupied. Both were haunted alike by possibilities, but the apprehension of neither, before the announcement was made, took the form of the arrival at Ricks, in the flesh, of Mrs. Gereth's victim. When the messenger informed them that Mr. Gereth was in the drawing-room, the blank "Oh!" emitted by Fleda was quite as precipitate as the sound on her hostess's lips, besides being, as she felt, much less pertinent. "I thought it would be somebody," that lady afterwards said; "but I expected on the whole a solicitor's clerk." Fleda didn't mention that she herself had expected on the whole a pair of constables. She was surprised by Mrs. Gereth's question to the parlor-maid.

"For whom did he ask?"

"Why, for *you*, of course, dearest friend!" Fleda interjected, falling instinctively into the address that embodied the intensest pressure. She wanted to put Mrs. Gereth between her and her danger.

"He asked for Miss Vetch, mum," the girl replied, with a face that brought startlingly to Fleda's ear the muffled chorus of the kitchen.

"Quite proper," said Mrs. Gereth austerely. Then to Fleda: "Please go to him."

"But what to do?"

"What you always do—to see what he wants." Mrs. Gereth dismissed the maid. "Tell him Miss Vetch will come." Fleda saw that nothing was in the mother's imagination at this moment but the desire not to meet her son. She had completely broken with him, and there was little in what had just happened to repair the rupture. It would now take more to do so than his presenting himself uninvited at her door. "He's right in asking for you—he's aware that you're still our communicator; nothing has occurred to alter that. To what he wishes to transmit through you I'm ready, as I've been ready before, to listen. As far as *I'm* concerned, if I couldn't meet him a month ago, how am I to meet him to-day? If he has come to say, 'My dear mother, you're here, in the hovel into which I've flung you, with consolations that give me pleasure,' I'll listen to him; but on no other footing. That's what you're to ascertain, please. You'll oblige me as you've obliged me before. There!" Mrs. Gereth turned her back and, with a fine imitation of superiority, began to redress the miseries immediately before her. Fleda meanwhile hesitated, lingered for some minutes where she had been left, feeling secretly that her fate still had her in hand. It had put her face to face with Owen Gereth, and it evidently meant to keep her so. She was reminded afresh of two things: one of which was that, though she judged her friend's rigor, she had never really had the story of the scene enacted in the great awestricken house between the mother and the son weeks before—the day the former took to her bed in her over-throw; the other was, that at Ricks as at Poynton, it was before all things her place to accept thankfully a usefulness not, she must remember, universally acknowledged. What determined her at the last, while Mrs. Gereth disappeared in the shrubbery, was that, though she was at a distance from the house and the drawing-room was turned the other way, she could absolutely see the young man alone there with the sources of his pain. She saw his simple stare at his tapestries, heard his heavy tread on his carpets and the hard breath of his sense of unfairness. At this she went to him fast.

VIII

"I asked for you," he said when she stood there, "because I heard from the flyman who drove me from the station to the inn that he had brought you here yesterday. We had some talk, and he mentioned it."

"You didn't know I was here?"

"No. I knew only that you had had, in London, all that you told me, that day, to do; and it was Mona's idea that after your sister's marriage you were staying on with your father. So I thought you were with him still."

"I am," Fleda replied, idealizing a little the fact. "I'm here only for a moment. But do you mean," she went on, "that if you had known I was with your mother you wouldn't have come down?"

The way Owen hung fire at this question made it sound more playful than she had intended. She had, in fact, no consciousness of any intention but that of confining herself rigidly to her function. She could already see that, in whatever he had now braced himself for, she was an element he had not reckoned with. His preparation had been of a different sort—the sort congruous with his having been careful to go first and lunch solidly at the inn. He had not been forced to ask for her, but she became aware, in his presence, of a particular desire to make him feel that no harm could really come to him. She might upset him, as people called it, but she would take no advantage of having done so. She had never seen a person with whom she wished more to be light and easy, to be exceptionally human. The account he presently gave of the matter was that he indeed wouldn't have come if he had known she was on the spot; because then, didn't she see? he could have written to her. He would have had her there to let fly at his mother.

"That would have saved me—well, it would have saved me a lot. Of course I would rather see you than her," he somewhat awkwardly added. "When the fellow spoke of you, I assure you I quite jumped at you. In fact I've no real desire to see Mummy at all. If she thinks I *like* it—!" He sighed disgustedly. "I only came down because it seemed better than any other way. I didn't want her to be able to say I hadn't been all right. I dare say you know she has taken everything; or if not quite everything, why, a lot more than one ever dreamed. You can see for yourself—she has got half the place down. She has got them crammed—you can see for yourself!" He had his old trick of artless repetition, his helpless iteration of the obvious; but he was sensibly different, for Fleda, if only by the difference of his clear face, mottled over and almost disfigured by little points of pain. He might have been a fine young man with a bad toothache; with the first even of his life. What ailed him above all, she felt, was that trouble was new to him: he had never known a difficulty; he had taken all his fences, his world wholly the world of the personally possible, rounded indeed by a gray suburb into which he had never had occasion to stray. In this vulgar and ill-lighted region he had evidently now lost himself. "We left it quite to her honor, you know," he said ruefully.

"Perhaps you've a right to say that you left it a little to mine." Mixed up with the spoils there, rising before him as if she were in a manner their keeper, she felt that she must absolutely dissociate herself. Mrs. Gereth had made it impossible to do anything but give her away. "I can only tell you that, on my side, I left it to her. I never dreamed either that she would pick out so many things."

"And you don't really think it's fair, do you? You *don't*!" He spoke very quickly; he really seemed to plead.

Fleda faltered a moment. "I think she has gone too far." Then she added: "I shall immediately tell her that I've said that to you."

He appeared puzzled by this statement, but he presently rejoined: "You haven't then said to mamma what you think?"

"Not yet; remember that I only got here last night." She appeared to herself ignobly weak. "I had had no idea what she was doing; I was taken completely by surprise. She managed it wonderfully."

"It's the sharpest thing I ever saw in *my* life!" They looked at each other with intelligence, in appreciation of the sharpness, and Owen quickly broke into a loud laugh. The laugh was in itself natural, but the occasion of it strange; and stranger still, to Fleda, so that she too almost laughed, the inconsequent charity with which he added: "Poor dear old Mummy! That's one of the reasons I asked for you," he went on—"to see if you'd back her up."

Whatever he said or did, she somehow liked him the better for it. "How can I back her up, Mr. Gereth, when I think, as I tell you, that she has made a great mistake?"

"A great mistake! That's all right." He spoke—it wasn't clear to her why—as if this declaration were a great point gained.

"Of course there are many things she hasn't taken," Fleda continued.

"Oh yes, a lot of things. But you wouldn't know the place, all the same." He looked about the room with his discolored, swindled face, which deepened Fleda's compassion for him, conjuring away any smile at so candid an image of the dupe. "You'd know this one soon enough, wouldn't you? These are just the things she ought to have left. Is the whole house full of them?"

"The whole house," said Fleda uncompromisingly. She thought of her lovely room.

"I never knew how much I cared for them. They're awfully valuable, aren't they?" Owen's manner mystified her; she was conscious of a return of the agitation he had produced in her on that last bewildering day, and she reminded herself that, now she was warned, it would be inexcusable of her to allow him to justify the fear that had dropped on her. "Mother thinks I never took any notice, but I assure you I was awfully proud of everything. Upon my honor, I *was* proud, Miss Vetch."

There was an oddity in his helplessness; he appeared to wish to persuade her and to satisfy himself that she sincerely felt how worthy he really was to treat what had happened as an injury. She could only exclaim, almost as helplessly as himself: "Of course you did justice! It's all most painful. I shall instantly let your mother know," she again declared, "the way I've spoken of her to you." She clung to that idea as to the sign of her straightness.

"You'll tell her what you think she ought to do?" he asked with some eagerness.

"What she ought to do?"

"*Don't* you think it—I mean that she ought to give them up?"

"To give them up?" Fleda hesitated again.

"To send them back—to keep it quiet." The girl had not felt the impulse to ask him to sit down among the monuments of his wrong, so that, nervously, awkwardly, he fidgeted about the room with his hands in his pockets and an effect of returning a little into possession through the formulation of his view. "To have them packed and dispatched again, since she knows so well how. She does it beautifully"—he looked close at two or three precious pieces. "What's sauce for the goose is sauce for the gander!"

He had laughed at his way of putting it, but Fleda remained grave. "Is that what you came to say to her?"

"Not exactly those words. But I did come to say"—he stammered, then brought it out—"I did come to say we must have them right back."

"And did you think your mother would see you?"

"I wasn't sure, but I thought it right to try—to put it to her kindly, don't you see? If she won't see me, then she has herself to thank. The only other way would have been to set the lawyers at her."

"I'm glad you didn't do that."

"I'm dashed if I want to!" Owen honestly declared. "But what's a fellow to do if she won't meet a fellow?"

"What do you call meeting a fellow?" Fleda asked, with a smile.

"Why, letting *me* tell her a dozen things she can have."

This was a transaction that Fleda, after a moment, had to give up trying to represent to herself. "If she won't do that—?" she went on.

"I'll leave it all to my solicitor. *He* won't let her off: by Jove, I know the fellow!"

"That's horrible!" said Fleda, looking at him in woe.

"It's utterly beastly!"

His want of logic as well as his vehemence startled her; and with her eyes still on his she considered before asking him the question these things suggested. At last she asked it. "Is Mona very angry?"

"Oh dear, yes!" said Owen.

She had perceived that he wouldn't speak of Mona without her beginning. After waiting fruitlessly now for him to say more, she continued: "She has been there again? She has seen the state of the house?"

"Oh dear, yes!" Owen repeated.

Fleda disliked to appear not to take account of his brevity, but it was just because she was struck by it that she felt the pressure of the desire to know more. What it suggested was simply what her intelligence supplied, for he was incapable of any art of insinuation. Wasn't it at all events the rule of communication with him to say for him what he couldn't say? This truth was present to the girl as she inquired if Mona greatly resented what Mrs. Gereth had done. He satisfied her promptly; he was standing before the fire, his back to it, his long legs apart, his hands, behind him, rather violently jiggling his gloves. "She hates it awfully. In fact, she refuses to put up with it at all. Don't you see?—she saw the place with all the things."

"So that of course she misses them."

"Misses them—rather! She was awfully sweet on them." Fleda remembered how sweet Mona had been, and reflected that if that was the sort of plea he had prepared it was indeed as well he shouldn't see his mother. This was not all she wanted to know, but it came over her that it was all she needed. "You see it puts me in the position of not carrying out what I promised," Owen said. "As she says herself"—he hesitated an instant—"it's just as if I had obtained her under false pretenses." Just before, when he spoke with more drollery than he knew, it had left Fleda serious; but now his own clear gravity had the effect of exciting her mirth. She laughed out, and he looked surprised, but went on: "She regards it as a regular sell."

Fleda was silent; but finally, as he added nothing, she exclaimed: "Of course it makes a great difference!" She knew all she needed, but none the less she risked, after another pause, an interrogative remark. "I forget when it is that your marriage takes place?"

Owen came away from the fire and, apparently at a loss where to turn, ended by directing himself to one of the windows. "It's a little uncertain; the date isn't quite fixed."

"Oh, I thought I remembered that at Poynton you had told me a day, and that it was near at hand."

"I dare say I did; it was for the 19th. But we've altered that—she wants to shift it." He looked out of the window; then he said: "In fact, it won't come off till Mummy has come round."

"Come round?"

"Put the place as it was." In his offhand way he added: "You know what I mean!"

He spoke not impatiently, but with a kind of intimate familiarity, the sweetness of which made her feel a pang for having forced him to tell her what was embarrassing to him, what was even humiliating. Yes indeed, she knew all she needed: all she needed was that Mona had proved apt at putting down that wonderful patent-leather foot. Her type was misleading only to the superficial, and no one in the world was less superficial than Fleda. She had guessed the truth at Waterbath and she had suffered from it at Poynton; at Ricks the only thing she could do was to accept it with the dumb exaltation that she felt rising. Mona had been prompt with her exercise of the member in question, for it might be called prompt to do that sort of thing before marriage. That she had indeed been premature who should say save those who should have read the matter in the full light of results? Neither at Waterbath nor at Poynton had even Fleda's thoroughness discovered all that there was—or rather, all that there was not—in Owen Gereth. "Of course it makes all the difference!" she said in answer to his last words. She pursued, after considering: "What you wish me to say from you then to your mother is that you demand immediate and practically complete restitution?"

"Yes, please. It's tremendously good of you."

"Very well, then. Will you wait?"

"For Mummy's answer?" Owen stared and looked perplexed; he was more and more fevered with so much vivid expression of his case. "Don't you think that if I'm here she may hate it worse—think I may want to make her reply bang off?"

Fleda thought. "You don't, then?"

"I want to take her in the right way, don't you know?—treat her as if I gave her more than just an hour or two."

"I see," said Fleda. "Then, if you don't wait—good-bye."

This again seemed not what he wanted. "Must *you* do it bang off?"

"I'm only thinking she'll be impatient—I mean, you know, to learn what will have passed between us."

"I see," said Owen, looking at his gloves. "I can give her a day or two, you know. Of course I didn't come down to sleep," he went on. "The inn seems a horrid hole. I know all about the trains—having no idea you were here." Almost as soon as his interlocutress he was struck with the absence of the visible, in this, as between effect and cause. "I mean because in that case I should have felt I could stop over. I should have felt I could talk with you a blessed sight longer than with Mummy."

"We've already talked a long time," smiled Fleda.

"Awfully, haven't we?" He spoke with the stupidity she didn't object to. Inarticulate as he was, he had more to say; he lingered perhaps because he was vaguely aware of the want of sincerity in her encouragement to him to go. "There's one thing, please," he mentioned, as if there might be a great many others too. "Please don't say anything about Mona."

She didn't understand. "About Mona?"

"About its being *her* that thinks she has gone too far." This was still lightly obscure, but now Fleda understood. "It mustn't seem to come from *her* at all, don't you know? That would only make Mummy worse."

Fleda knew exactly how much worse, but she felt a delicacy about explicitly assenting: she was already immersed moreover in the deep consideration of what might make "Mummy" better. She couldn't see as yet at all; she could only clutch at the hope of some inspiration after he should go. Oh, there was a remedy, to be sure, but it was out of the question; in spite of which, in the strong light of Owen's troubled presence, of his anxious face and restless step, it hung there before her for some minutes. She felt that, remarkably, beneath the decent rigor of his errand, the poor young man, for reasons, for weariness, for disgust, would have been ready not to insist. His fitness to fight his mother had left him—he wasn't in fighting trim. He had no natural avidity and even no special wrath; he had none that had not been taught him, and it was doing his best to learn the lesson that had made him so sick. He had his delicacies, but he hid them away like presents before Christmas. He was hollow, perfunctory, pathetic; he had been girded by another hand. That hand had naturally been Mona's, and it was heavy even now on his strong, broad back. Why then had he originally rejoiced so in its touch? Fleda dashed aside this question, for it had nothing to do with her problem. Her problem was to help him to live as a gentleman and carry through what he had undertaken; her problem was to reinstate him in his rights. It was quite irrelevant that Mona had no intelligence of what she had lost—quite irrelevant that she was moved not by the privation, but by the insult: she had every reason to be moved, though she was so much more movable, in the vindictive way, at any rate, than one might have supposed—assuredly more than Owen himself had imagined.

"Certainly I shall not mention Mona," Fleda said, "and there won't be the slightest necessity for it. The wrong's quite sufficiently yours, and the demand you make is perfectly justified by it."

"I can't tell you what it is to me to feel you on my side!" Owen exclaimed.

"Up to this time," said Fleda, after a pause, "your mother has had no doubt of my being on hers."

"Then of course she won't like your changing."

"I dare say she won't like it at all."

"Do you mean to say you'll have a regular kick-up with her?"

"I don't exactly know what you mean by a regular kick-up. We shall naturally have a great deal of discussion—if she consents to discuss the matter at all. That's why you must decidedly give her two or three days."

"I see you think she *may* refuse to discuss it at all," said Owen.

"I'm only trying to be prepared for the worst. You must remember that to have to withdraw from the ground she has taken, to make a public surrender of what she has publicly appropriated, will go uncommonly hard with her pride."

Owen considered; his face seemed to broaden, but not into a smile. "I suppose she's tremendously proud, isn't she?" This might have been the first time it had occurred to him.

"You know better than I," said Fleda, speaking with high extravagance.

"I don't know anything in the world half so well as you. If I were as clever as you I might hope to get round her." Owen hesitated; then he went on: "In fact I don't quite see what even you can say or do that will really fetch her."

"Neither do I, as yet. I must think—I must pray!" the girl pursued, smiling. "I can only say to you that I'll try. I *want* to try, you know—I want to help you." He stood looking at her so long on this that she added with much distinctness: "So you must leave me, please, quite alone with her. You must go straight back."

"Back to the inn?"

"Oh no, back to town. I'll write to you to-morrow."

466

He turned about vaguely for his hat.

"There's the chance, of course, that she may be afraid."

"Afraid, you mean, of the legal steps you may take?"

"I've got a perfect case—I could have her up. The Brigstocks say it's simple stealing."

"I can easily fancy what the Brigstocks say!" Fleda permitted herself to remark without solemnity.

"It's none of their business, is it?" was Owen's unexpected rejoinder. Fleda had already noted that no one so slow could ever have had such rapid transitions.

She showed her amusement. "They've a much better right to say it's none of mine."

"Well, at any rate, you don't call her names."

Fleda wondered whether Mona did; and this made it all the finer of her to exclaim in a moment: "You don't know what I shall call her if she holds out!"

Owen gave her a gloomy glance; then he blew a speck off the crown of his hat. "But if you do have a set-to with her?"

He paused so long for a reply that Fleda said: "I don't think I know what you mean by a set-to."

"Well, if she calls *you* names."

"I don't think she'll do that."

"What I mean to say is, if she's angry at your backing me up—what will you do then? She can't possibly like it, you know."

"She may very well not like it; but everything depends. I must see what I shall do. You mustn't worry about me."

She spoke with decision, but Owen seemed still unsatisfied. "You won't go away, I hope?"

"Go away?"

"If she does take it ill of you."

Fleda moved to the door and opened it. "I'm not prepared to say. You must have patience and see."

"Of course I must," said Owen—"of course, of course." But he took no more advantage of the open door than to say: "You want me to be off, and I'm off in a minute. Only, before I go, please answer me a question. If you *should* leave my mother, where would you go?"

Fleda smiled again. "I haven't the least idea."

"I suppose you'd go back to London."

"I haven't the least idea," Fleda repeated.

"You don't—a—live anywhere in particular, do you?" the young man went on. He looked conscious as soon as he had spoken; she could see that he felt himself to have alluded more grossly than he meant to the circumstance of her having, if one were plain about it, no home of her own. He had meant it as an allusion of a tender sort to all that she would sacrifice in the case of a quarrel with his mother; but there was indeed no graceful way of touching on that. One just couldn't be plain about it.

Fleda, wound up as she was, shrank from any treatment at all of the matter, and she made no answer to his question. "I *won't* leave your mother," she said. "I'll produce an effect on her; I'll convince her absolutely."

"I believe you will, if you look at her like that!"

She was wound up to such a height that there might well be a light in her pale, fine little face—a light that, while, for all return, at first, she simply shone back at him, was intensely reflected in his own. "I'll make her see it—I'll make her see it!" She rang out like a silver bell. She had at that moment a perfect faith that she should succeed; but it passed into something else when, the next instant, she became aware that Owen, quickly getting between her and the door she had opened, was sharply closing it, as might be said, in her face. He had done this before she could stop him, and he stood there with his hand on the knob and smiled at her strangely. Clearer than he could have spoken it was the sense of those seconds of silence.

"When I got into this I didn't know you, and now that I know you how can I tell you the difference? And *she's* so different, so ugly and vulgar, in the light of this squabble. No, like *you* I've never known one. It's another thing, it's a new thing altogether. Listen to me a little: can't something be done?" It was what had been in the air in those moments at Kensington, and it only wanted words to be a committed act. The more reason, to the girl's excited mind, why it shouldn't have words; her one thought was not to hear, to keep the act uncommitted. She would do this if she had to be horrid.

"Please let me out, Mr. Gereth," she said; on which he opened the door with an hesitation so very brief that in thinking of these things afterwards—for she was to think of them forever—she wondered in what tone she could have spoken. They went into the hall, where she encountered the parlor-maid, of whom she inquired whether Mrs. Gereth had come in.

"No, miss; and I think she has left the garden. She has gone up the back road." In other words, they had the whole place to themselves. It would have been a pleasure, in a different mood, to converse with that parlor-maid.

"Please open the house-door," said Fleda.

Owen, as if in quest of his umbrella, looked vaguely about the hall— looked even wistfully up the staircase—while the neat young woman complied with Fleda's request. Owen's eyes then wandered out of the open door. "I think it's awfully nice here," he observed; "I assure you I could do with it myself."

"I should think you might, with half your things here! It's Poynton itself—almost. Good-bye, Mr. Gereth," Fleda added. Her intention had naturally been that the neat young woman, opening the front door, should remain to close it on the departing guest. That functionary, however, had acutely vanished behind a stiff flap of green baize which Mrs. Gereth had not yet had time to abolish. Fleda put out her hand, but Owen turned away—he couldn't find his umbrella. She passed into the open air—she was determined to get him out; and in a moment he joined her in the little plastered portico which had small resemblance to any feature of Poynton. It was, as Mrs. Gereth had said, like the portico of a house in Brompton.

"Oh, I don't mean with all the things here," he explained in regard to the opinion he had just expressed. "I mean I could put up with it just as it was; it had a lot of good things, don't you think? I mean if everything was back at Poynton, if everything was all right." He brought out these last words with a sort of smothered sigh. Fleda didn't understand his explanation unless it had reference to another and more wonderful exchange—the restoration to the great house not only of its tables and chairs, but of its alienated mistress. This would imply the installation of his own life at Ricks, and obviously that of another person. Such another person could scarcely be Mona Brigstock. He put out his hand now; and once more she heard his unsounded words: "With everything patched up at the other place, I could live here with *you*. Don't you see what I mean?"

Fleda saw perfectly, and, with a face in which she flattered herself that nothing of this vision appeared, gave him her hand and said: "Good-bye, good-bye."

Owen held her hand very firmly and kept it even after an effort made by her to recover it—an effort not repeated, as she felt it best not to show she was flurried. That solution—of her living with him at Ricks—disposed of him beautifully, and disposed not less so of herself; it disposed admirably too of Mrs. Gereth. Fleda could only vainly wonder how it provided for poor Mona. While he looked at her, grasping her hand, she felt that now indeed she was paying for his mother's extravagance at Poynton—the vividness of that lady's public plea that little Fleda Vetch was the person to insure the general peace. It was to that vividness poor Owen had come back, and if Mrs. Gereth had had more discretion little Fleda Vetch wouldn't have been in a predicament. She saw that Owen had at this moment his sharpest necessity of speech, and so long as he didn't release her hand she could only submit to him. Her defense would be perhaps to look blank and hard; so she looked as blank and as hard as she could, with the reward of an immediate sense that this was not a bit what he wanted. It even made him hang fire, as if he were suddenly ashamed of himself, were recalled to some idea of duty and of honor. Yet he none the less brought it out. "There's one thing I dare say I ought to tell you, if you're going so kindly to act for me; though of course you'll see for yourself it's a thing it won't do to tell *her*." What was it? He made her wait for it again, and while she waited, under firm coercion, she had the extraordinary impression that Owen's simplicity was in eclipse. His natural honesty was like the scent of a flower, and she felt at this moment as if her nose had been brushed by the bloom without the odor. The allusion was undoubtedly to his mother; and was not what he meant about the matter in question the opposite of what he said—that it just *would* do to tell her? It would have been the first time he had said the opposite of what he meant, and there was certainly a fascination in the phenomenon, as well as a challenge to suspense in the ambiguity. "It's just that I understand from Mona, you know," he stammered; "it's just that she has made no bones about bringing home to me—" He tried to laugh, and in the effort he faltered again.

"About bringing home to you?"—Fleda encouraged him.

He was sensible of it, he achieved his performance. "Why, that if I don't get the things back—every blessed one of them except a few *she*'ll pick out—she won't have anything more to say to me."

Fleda, after an instant, encouraged him again. "To say to you?"

"Why, she simply won't marry me, don't you see?"

Owen's legs, not to mention his voice, had wavered while he spoke, and he felt his possession of her hand loosen so that she was free again. Her stare of perception broke into a lively laugh. "Oh, you're all right, for you *will* get them. You will; you're quite safe; don't worry!" She fell back into the house with her hand on the door. "Good-bye, good-bye." She repeated it several times, laughing bravely, quite waving him away and, as he didn't move and save that he was on the other side of it, closing the door in his face quite as he had closed that of the drawing-room in hers. Never had a face, never at least had such a handsome one, been so presented to that offense. She even held the door a minute, lest he should try to come in again. At last, as she heard nothing, she made a dash for the stairs and ran up.

471

IX

In knowing a while before all she needed, Fleda had been far from knowing as much as that; so that once upstairs, where, in her room, with her sense of danger and trouble, the age of Louis Seize suddenly struck her as wanting in taste and point, she felt that she now for the first time knew her temptation. Owen had put it before her with an art beyond his own dream. Mona would cast him off if he didn't proceed to extremities; if his negotiation with his mother should fail he would be completely free. That negotiation depended on a young lady to whom he had pressingly suggested the condition of his freedom; and as if to aggravate the young lady's predicament designing fate had sent Mrs. Gereth, as the parlor-maid said, "up the back road." This would give the young lady more time to make up her mind that nothing should come of the negotiation. There would be different ways of putting the question to Mrs. Gereth, and Fleda might profitably devote the moments before her return to a selection of the way that would most surely be tantamount to failure. This selection indeed required no great adroitness; it was so conspicuous that failure would be the reward of an effective introduction of Mona. If that abhorred name should be properly invoked Mrs. Gereth would resist to the death, and before envenomed resistance Owen would certainly retire. His retirement would be into single life, and Fleda reflected that he had now gone away conscious of having practically told her so. She could only say, as she waited for the back road to disgorge, that she hoped it was a consciousness he enjoyed. There was something *she* enjoyed; but that was a very different matter. To know that she had become to him an object of desire gave her wings that she felt herself flutter in the air: it was like the rush of a flood into her own accumulations. These stored depths had been fathomless and still, but now, for half an hour, in the empty house, they spread till they overflowed. He seemed to have made it right for her to confess to herself her secret. Strange then there should be for him in return nothing that such a confession could make right! How could it make right that he should give up Mona for another woman? His attitude was a sorry appeal to Fleda to legitimate that. But he didn't believe it himself, and he had none of the courage of his suggestion. She could easily see how wrong everything must be when a man so made to be manly was wanting in courage. She had upset him, as people called it, and he had spoken out from the force of the jar of finding her there. He had upset her too, heaven knew, but she was one of those who could pick themselves up. She had the real advantage, she considered, of having kept him from seeing that she had been overthrown.

She had moreover at present completely recovered her feet, though there was in the intensity of the effort required to do so a vibration which throbbed away into an immense allowance for the young man. How could she after all know what, in the disturbance wrought by his mother, Mona's relations with him might have become? If he had been able to keep his wits, such as they were, more about him he would probably have felt—as sharply as she felt on his behalf—that so long as those relations were not ended he had no right to say even the little he had said. He had no right to appear to wish to draw in another girl to help him to an escape. If he was in a plight he must get out of the plight himself, he must get out of it first, and anything he should have to say to any one else must be deferred and detached. She herself, at any rate—it was her own case that was in question—couldn't dream of assisting him save in the sense of their common honor. She could never be the girl to be drawn in, she could never lift her finger against Mona. There was something in her that would make it a shame to her forever to have owed her happiness to an interference. It would seem intolerably vulgar to her to have "ousted" the daughter of the Brigstocks; and merely to have abstained even wouldn't assure her that she had been straight. Nothing was really straight but to justify her little pensioned presence by her use; and now, won over as she was to heroism, she could see her use only as some high and delicate deed. She couldn't do anything at all, in short, unless she could do it with a kind of pride, and there would be nothing to be proud of in having arranged for poor Owen to get off easily. Nobody had a right to get off easily from pledges so deep, so sacred. How could Fleda doubt they had been tremendous when she knew so well what any pledge of her own would be? If Mona was so formed that she could hold such vows light, that was Mona's peculiar business. To have loved Owen apparently, and yet to have loved him only so much, only to the extent of a few tables and chairs, was not a thing she could so much as try to grasp. Of a different way of loving him she was herself ready to give an instance, an instance of which the beauty indeed would not be generally known. It would not perhaps if revealed be generally understood, inasmuch as the effect of the particular pressure she proposed to exercise would be, should success attend it, to keep him tied to an affection that had died a sudden and violent death. Even in the ardor of her meditation Fleda remained in sight of the truth that it would be an odd result of her magnanimity to prevent her friend's shaking off a woman he disliked. If he didn't dislike Mona, what was the matter with him? And if he did, Fleda asked, what was the matter with her own silly self?

Our young lady met this branch of the temptation it pleased her frankly to recognize by declaring that to encourage any such cruelty would be tortuous and base. She had nothing to do with his dislikes; she had only to do with his good-nature and his good name. She had joy of him just as he was, but it was of these things she had the greatest. The worst aversion and the liveliest reaction moreover wouldn't alter the fact—since one was facing facts—that but the other day his strong arms must have clasped a remarkably handsome girl as close as she had permitted. Fleda's emotion at this time was a wondrous mixture, in which Mona's permissions and Mona's beauty figured powerfully as aids to reflection. She herself had no beauty, and *her* permissions were the stony stares she had just practiced in the drawing-room—a consciousness of a kind appreciably to add to the particular sense of triumph that made her generous. I may not perhaps too much diminish the merit of that generosity if I mention that it could take the flight we are considering just because really, with the telescope of her long thought, Fleda saw what might bring her out of the wood. Mona herself would bring her out; at the least Mona possibly might. Deep down plunged the idea that even should she achieve what she had promised Owen, there was still the contingency of Mona's independent action. She might by that time, under stress of temper or of whatever it was that was now moving her, have said or done the things there is no patching up. If the rupture should come from Waterbath they might all be happy yet. This was a calculation that Fleda wouldn't have committed to paper, but it affected the total of her sentiments. She was meanwhile so remarkably constituted that while she refused to profit by Owen's mistake, even while she judged it and hastened to cover it up, she could drink a sweetness from it that consorted little with her wishing it mightn't have been made. There was no harm done, because he had instinctively known, poor dear, with whom to make it, and it was a compensation for seeing him worried that he hadn't made it with some horrid mean girl who would immediately have dished him by making a still bigger one. Their protected error (for she indulged a fancy that it was hers too) was like some dangerous, lovely living thing that she had caught and could keep—keep vivid and helpless in the cage of her own passion and look at and talk to all day long. She had got it well locked up there by the time that, from an upper window, she saw Mrs. Gereth again in the garden. At this she went down to meet her.

Fleda's line had been taken, her word was quite ready; on the terrace of the painted pots she broke out before her interlocutress could put a question. "His errand was perfectly simple: he came to demand that you shall pack everything straight up again and send it back as fast as the railway will carry it."

The back road had apparently been fatiguing to Mrs. Gereth; she rose there rather white and wan with her walk. A certain sharp thinness was in her ejaculation of "Oh!"—after which she glanced about her for a place to sit down. The movement was a criticism of the order of events that offered such a piece of news to a lady coming in tired; but Fleda could see that in turning over the possibilities this particular peril was the one that during the last hour her friend had turned up oftenest. At the end of the short, gray day, which had been moist and mild, the sun was out; the terrace looked to the south, and a bench, formed as to legs and arms of iron representing knotted boughs, stood against the warmest wall of the house. The mistress of Ricks sank upon it and presented to her companion the handsome face she had composed to hear everything. Strangely enough, it was just this fine vessel of her attention that made the girl most nervous about what she must drop in. "Quite a 'demand,' dear, is it?" asked Mrs. Gereth, drawing in her cloak.

"Oh, that's what I should call it!" Fleda laughed, to her own surprise.

"I mean with the threat of enforcement and that sort of thing."

"Distinctly with the threat of enforcement—what would be called, I suppose, coercion."

"What sort of coercion?" said Mrs. Gereth.

"Why, legal, don't you know?—what he calls setting the lawyers at you."

"Is that what he calls it?" She seemed to speak with disinterested curiosity.

"That's what he calls it," said Fleda.

Mrs. Gereth considered an instant. "Oh, the lawyers!" she exclaimed lightly. Seated there almost cosily in the reddening winter sunset, only with her shoulders raised a little and her mantle tightened as if from a slight chill, she had never yet looked to Fleda so much in possession nor so far from meeting unsuspectedness halfway. "Is he going to send them down here?"

"I dare say he thinks it may come to that."

"The lawyers can scarcely do the packing," Mrs. Gereth humorously remarked.

"I suppose he means them—in the first place, at least—to try to talk you over."

"In the first place, eh? And what does he mean in the second?"

Fleda hesitated; she had not foreseen that so simple an inquiry could disconcert her. "I'm afraid I don't know."

"Didn't you ask?" Mrs. Gereth spoke as if she might have said, "What then were you doing all the while?"

"I didn't ask very much," said her companion. "He has been gone some time. The great thing seemed to be to understand clearly that he wouldn't be content with anything less than what he mentioned."

"My just giving everything back?"

"Your just giving everything back."

"Well, darling, what did you tell him?" Mrs. Gereth blandly inquired.

Fleda faltered again, wincing at the term of endearment, at what the words took for granted, charged with the confidence she had now committed herself to betray. "I told him I would tell you!" She smiled, but she felt that her smile was rather hollow and even that Mrs. Gereth had begun to look at her with some fixedness.

"Did he seem very angry?"

"He seemed very sad. He takes it very hard," Fleda added.

"And how does *she* take it?"

"Ah, that—that I felt a delicacy about asking."

"So you didn't ask?" The words had the note of surprise.

Fleda was embarrassed; she had not made up her mind definitely to lie. "I didn't think you'd care." That small untruth she would risk.

"Well—I don't!" Mrs. Gereth declared; and Fleda felt less guilty to hear her, for the statement was as inexact as her own. "Didn't you say anything in return?" Mrs. Gereth presently continued.

"Do you mean in the way of justifying you?"

"I didn't mean to trouble you to do that. My justification," said Mrs. Gereth, sitting there warmly and, in the lucidity of her thought, which nevertheless hung back a little, dropping her eyes on the gravel—"my justification was all the past. My justification was the cruelty—" But at this, with a short, sharp gesture, she checked herself. "It's too good of me to talk—now." She produced these sentences with a cold patience, as if addressing Fleda in the girl's virtual and actual character of Owen's representative. Our young lady crept to and fro before the bench, combating the sense that it was occupied by a judge, looking at her boot-toes, reminding herself in doing so of Mona, and lightly crunching the pebbles as she walked. She moved about because she was afraid, putting off from moment to moment the exercise of the courage she had been sure she possessed. That courage would all come to her if she could only be equally sure that what she should be called upon to do for Owen would be to suffer. She had wondered, while Mrs. Gereth spoke, how that lady would describe her justification. She had described it as if to be irreproachably fair, give her adversary the benefit of every doubt, and then dismiss the question forever. "Of course," Mrs. Gereth went on, "if we didn't succeed in showing him at Poynton the ground we took, it's simply that he shuts his eyes. What I supposed was that you would have given him your opinion that if I was the woman so signally to assert myself, I'm also the woman to rest upon it imperturbably enough."

Fleda stopped in front of her hostess. "I gave him my opinion that you're very logical, very obstinate, and very proud."

"Quite right, my dear: I'm a rank bigot—about that sort of thing!" and Mrs. Gereth jerked her head at the contents of the house. "I've never denied it. I'd kidnap—to save them, to convert them—the children of heretics. When I know I'm right I go to the stake. Oh, he may burn me alive!" she cried with a happy face. "Did he abuse me?" she then demanded.

Fleda had remained there, gathering in her purpose. "How little you know him!"

Mrs. Gereth stared, then broke into a laugh that her companion had not expected. "Ah, my dear, certainly not so well as you!" The girl, at this, turned away again—she felt she looked too conscious; and she was aware that, during a pause, Mrs. Gereth's eyes watched her as she went. She faced about afresh to meet them, but what she met was a question that reinforced them. "Why had you a 'delicacy' as to speaking of Mona?"

She stopped again before the bench, and an inspiration came to her. "I should think *you* would know," she said with proper dignity.

Blankness was for a moment on Mrs. Gereth's brow; then light broke—she visibly remembered the scene in the breakfast-room after Mona's night at Poynton. "Because I contrasted you—told him *you* were the one?" Her eyes looked deep. "You were—you are still!"

Fleda gave a bold dramatic laugh. "Thank you, my love—with all the best things at Ricks!"

Mrs. Gereth considered, trying to penetrate, as it seemed; but at last she brought out roundly: "For you, you know, I'd send them back!"

The girl's heart gave a tremendous bound; the right way dawned upon her in a flash. Obscurity indeed the next moment engulfed this course, but for a few thrilled seconds she had understood. To send the things back "for her" meant of course to send them back if there were even a dim chance that she might become mistress of them. Fleda's palpitation was not allayed as she asked herself what portent Mrs. Gereth had suddenly perceived of such a chance: that perception could come only from a sudden suspicion of her secret. This suspicion, in turn, was a tolerably straight consequence of that implied view of the propriety of surrender from which, she was well aware, she could say nothing to dissociate herself. What she first felt was that if she wished to rescue the spoils she wished also to rescue her secret. So she looked as innocent as she could and said as quickly as possible: "For me? Why in the world for me?"

"Because you're so awfully keen."

"Am I? Do I strike you so? You know I hate him," Fleda went on.

She had the sense for a while of Mrs. Gereth's regarding her with the detachment of some stern, clever stranger. "Then what's the matter with you? Why do you want me to give in?"

Fleda hesitated; she felt herself reddening. "I've only said your son wants it. I haven't said *I* do."

"Then say it and have done with it!"

This was more peremptory than any word her friend, though often speaking in her presence with much point, had ever yet directly addressed to her. It affected her like the crack of a whip, but she confined herself, with an effort, to taking it as a reminder that she must keep her head. "I know he has his engagement to carry out."

"His engagement to marry? Why, it's just that engagement we loathe!"

"Why should *I* loathe it?" Fleda asked with a strained smile. Then, before Mrs. Gereth could reply, she pursued: "I'm thinking of his general undertaking—to give her the house as she originally saw it."

"To give her the house!" Mrs. Gereth brought up the words from the depth of the unspeakable. The effort was like the moan of an autumn wind; it was in the power of such an image to make her turn pale.

"I'm thinking," Fleda continued, "of the simple question of his keeping faith on an important clause of his contract: it doesn't matter whether it's with a stupid girl or with a monster of cleverness. I'm thinking of his honor and his good name."

480

"The honor and good name of a man you hate?"

"Certainly," the girl resolutely answered. "I don't see why you should talk as if one had a petty mind. You don't think so. It's not on that assumption you've ever dealt with me. I can do your son justice, as he put his case to me."

"Ah, then he did put his case to you!" Mrs. Gereth exclaimed, with an accent of triumph. "You seemed to speak just now as if really nothing of any consequence had passed between you."

"Something always passes when one has a little imagination," our young lady declared.

"I take it you don't mean that Owen has any!" Mrs. Gereth cried with her large laugh.

Fleda was silent a moment. "No, I don't mean that Owen has any," she returned at last.

"Why is it you hate him so?" her hostess abruptly inquired.

"Should I love him for all he has made you suffer?"

Mrs. Gereth slowly rose at this and, coming across the walk, took her young friend in her arms and kissed her. She then passed into one of Fleda's an arm perversely and imperiously sociable. "Let us move a little," she said, holding her close and giving a slight shiver. They strolled along the terrace, and she brought out another question. "He *was* eloquent, then, poor dear—he poured forth the story of his wrongs?"

Fleda smiled down at her companion, who, cloaked and perceptibly bowed, leaned on her heavily and gave her an odd, unwonted sense of age and cunning. She took refuge in an evasion. "He couldn't tell me anything that I didn't know pretty well already."

"It's very true that you know everything. No, dear, you haven't a petty mind; you've a lovely imagination and you're the nicest creature in the world. If you were inane, like most girls—like every one, in fact—I would have insulted you, I would have outraged you, and then you would have fled from me in terror. No, now that I think of it," Mrs. Gereth went on, "you wouldn't have fled from me; nothing, on the contrary, would have made you budge. You would have cuddled into your warm corner, but you would have been wounded and weeping and martyrized, and you would have taken every opportunity to tell people I'm a brute—as indeed I should have been!" They went to and fro, and she would not allow Fleda, who laughed and protested, to attenuate with any light civility this spirited picture. She praised her cleverness and her patience; then she said it was getting cold and dark and they must go in to tea. She delayed quitting the place, however, and reverted instead to Owen's ultimatum, about which she asked another question or two; in particular whether it had struck Fleda that he really believed she would comply with such a summons.

"I think he really believes that if I try hard enough I can make you:" after uttering which words our young lady stopped short and emulated the embrace she had received a few moments before.

"And you've promised to try: I see. You didn't tell me that, either," Mrs. Gereth added as they went on. "But you're rascal enough for anything!" While Fleda was occupied in thinking in what terms she could explain why she had indeed been rascal enough for the reticence thus denounced, her companion broke out with an inquiry somewhat irrelevant and even in form somewhat profane. "Why the devil, at any rate, doesn't it come off?"

Fleda hesitated. "You mean their marriage?"

"Of course I mean their marriage!" Fleda hesitated again. "I haven't the least idea."

"You didn't ask him?"

"Oh, how in the world can you fancy?" She spoke in a shocked tone.

"Fancy your putting a question so indelicate? *I* should have put it—I mean in your place; but I'm quite coarse, thank God!" Fleda felt privately that she herself was coarse, or at any rate would presently have to be; and Mrs. Gereth, with a purpose that struck the girl as increasing, continued: "What, then, *was* the day to be? Wasn't it just one of these?"

"I'm sure I don't remember."

It was part of the great rupture and an effect of Mrs. Gereth's character that up to this moment she had been completely and haughtily indifferent to that detail. Now, however, she had a visible reason for being clear about it. She bethought herself and she broke out—"Isn't the day past?" Then, stopping short, she added: "Upon my word, they must have put it off!" As Fleda made no answer to this she sharply went on: "*Have* they put it off?"

"I haven't the least idea," said the girl.

Her hostess was looking at her hard again. "Didn't he tell you—didn't he say anything about it?"

Fleda, meanwhile, had had time to make her reflections, which were moreover the continued throb of those that had occupied the interval between Owen's departure and his mother's return. If she should now repeat his words, this wouldn't at all play the game of her definite vow; it would only play the game of her little gagged and blinded desire. She could calculate well enough the effect of telling Mrs. Gereth how she had had it from Owen's troubled lips that Mona was only waiting for the restitution and would do nothing without it. The thing was to obtain the restitution without imparting that knowledge. The only way, also, not to impart it was not to tell any truth at all about it; and the only way to meet this last condition was to reply to her companion, as she presently did: "He told me nothing whatever: he didn't touch on the subject."

"Not in any way?"

"Not in any way."

Mrs. Gereth watched Fleda and considered. "You haven't any idea if they are waiting for the things?"

"How should I have? I'm not in their counsels."

"I dare say they are—or that Mona is." Mrs. Gereth reflected again; she had a bright idea. "If I don't give in, I'll be hanged if she'll not break off."

"She'll never, never break off!" said Fleda.

"Are you sure?"

"I can't be sure, but it's my belief."

"Derived from *him*?"

The girl hung fire a few seconds. "Derived from him."

Mrs. Gereth gave her a long last look, then turned abruptly away. "It's an awful bore you didn't really get it out of him! Well, come to tea," she added rather dryly, passing straight into the house.

The sense of her adversary's dryness, which was ominous of something she couldn't read, made Fleda, before complying, linger a little on the terrace; she felt the need moreover of taking breath after such a flight into the cold air of denial. When at last she rejoined Mrs. Gereth she found her erect before the drawing-room fire. Their tea had been set out in the same quarter, and the mistress of the house, for whom the preparation of it was in general a high and undelegated function, was in an attitude to which the hissing urn made no appeal. This omission, for Fleda, was such a further sign of something to come that, to disguise her apprehension, she immediately and without an apology took the duty in hand; only, however, to be promptly reminded that she was performing it confusedly and not counting the journeys of the little silver shovel she emptied into the pot. "Not *five*, my dear—the usual three," said her hostess, with the same dryness; watching her then in silence while she clumsily corrected her mistake. The tea took some minutes to draw, and Mrs. Gereth availed herself of them suddenly to exclaim: "You haven't yet told me, you know, how it is you propose to 'make' me!"

"Give everything back?" Fleda looked into the pot again and uttered her question with a briskness that she felt to be a little overdone. "Why, by putting the question well before you; by being so eloquent that I shall persuade you, shall act upon you; by making you sorry for having gone so far," she said boldly; "by simply and earnestly asking it of you, in short; and by reminding you at the same time that it's the first thing I ever have so asked. Oh, you've done things for me—endless and beautiful things," she exclaimed; "but you've done them all from your own generous impulse. I've never so much as hinted to you to lend me a postage-stamp."

"Give me a cup of tea," said Mrs. Gereth. A moment later, taking the cup, she replied: "No, you've never asked me for a postage-stamp."

"That gives me a pull!" Fleda returned, smiling.

"Puts you in the situation of expecting that I shall do this thing just simply to oblige you?"

The girl hesitated. "You said a while ago that for me you *would* do it."

"For you, but not for your eloquence. Do you understand what I mean by the difference?" Mrs. Gereth asked as she stood stirring her tea.

Fleda, to postpone answering, looked round, while she drank it, at the beautiful room. "I don't in the least like, you know, your having taken so much. It was a great shock to me, on my arrival here, to find you had done so."

"Give me some more tea," said Mrs. Gereth; and there was a moment's silence as Fleda poured out another cup. "If you were shocked, my dear, I'm bound to say you concealed your shock."

"I know I did. I was afraid to show it."

Mrs. Gereth drank off her second cup. "And you're not afraid now?"

"No, I'm not afraid now."

"What has made the difference?"

"I've pulled myself together." Fleda paused; then she added: "And I've seen Mr. Owen."

"You've seen Mr. Owen"—Mrs. Gereth concurred. She put down her cup and sank into a chair, in which she leaned back, resting her head and gazing at her young friend. "Yes, I did tell you a while ago that for you I'd do it. But you haven't told me yet what you'll do in return."

Fleda thought an instant. "Anything in the wide world you may require."

"Oh, 'anything' is nothing at all! That's too easily said." Mrs. Gereth, reclining more completely, closed her eyes with an air of disgust, an air indeed of inviting slumber.

Fleda looked at her quiet face, which the appearance of slumber always made particularly handsome; she noted how much the ordeal of the last few weeks had added to its indications of age. "Well then, try me with something. What is it you demand?"

At this, opening her eyes, Mrs. Gereth sprang straight up. "Get him away from her!"

Fleda marveled: her companion had in an instant become young again. "Away from Mona? How in the world—?"

"By not looking like a fool!" cried Mrs. Gereth very sharply. She kissed her, however, on the spot, to make up for this roughness, and summarily took off her hat, which, on coming into the house, our young lady had not removed. She applied a friendly touch to the girl's hair and gave a businesslike pull to her jacket. "I say don't look like an idiot, because you happen not to be one, not the least bit. I'm idiotic; I've been so, I've just discovered, ever since our first days together. I've been a precious donkey; but that's another affair."

Fleda, as if she humbly assented, went through no form of controverting this; she simply stood passive to her companion's sudden refreshment of her appearance. "How *can* I get him away from her?" she presently demanded.

"By letting yourself go."

"By letting myself go?" She spoke mechanically, still more like an idiot, and felt as if her face flamed out the insincerity of her question. It was vividly back again, the vision of the real way to act upon Mrs. Gereth. This lady's movements were now rapid; she turned off from her as quickly as she had seized her, and Fleda sat down to steady herself for full responsibility.

Her hostess, without taking up her ejaculation, gave a violent poke at the fire and then faced her again. "You've done two things, then, to-day—haven't you?—that you've never done before. One has been asking me the service, or favor, or concession—whatever you call it—that you just mentioned; the other has been telling me—certainly too for the first time—an immense little fib."

"An immense little fib?" Fleda felt weak; she was glad of the support of her seat.

"An immense big one, then!" said Mrs. Gereth irritatedly. "You don't in the least 'hate' Owen, my darling. You care for him very much. In fact, my own, you're in love with him—there! Don't tell me any more lies!" cried Mrs. Gereth with a voice and a face in the presence of which Fleda recognized that there was nothing for her but to hold herself and take them. When once the truth was out, it was out, and she could see more and more every instant that it would be the only way. She accepted therefore what had to come; she leaned back her head and closed her eyes as her companion had done just before. She would have covered her face with her hands but for the still greater shame. "Oh, you're a wonder, a wonder," said Mrs. Gereth; "you're magnificent, and I was right, as soon as I saw you, to pick you out and trust you!" Fleda closed her eyes tighter at this last word, but her friend kept it up. "I never dreamed of it till a while ago, when, after he had come and gone, we were face to face. Then something stuck out of you; it strongly impressed me, and I didn't know at first quite what to make of it. It was that you had just been with him and that you were not natural. Not natural to *me*," she added with a smile. "I pricked up my ears, and all that this might mean dawned upon me when you said you had asked nothing about Mona. It put me on the scent, but I didn't show you, did I? I felt it was *in* you, deep down, and that I must draw it out. Well, I *have* drawn it, and it's a blessing. Yesterday, when you shed tears at breakfast, I was awfully puzzled. What has been the matter with you all the while? Why, Fleda, it isn't a crime, don't you know that?" cried the delighted woman. "When I was a girl I was always in love, and not always with such nice people as Owen. I didn't behave as well as you; compared with you I think I must have been horrid. But if you're proud and reserved, it's your own affair; I'm proud too, though I'm not reserved—that's what spoils it. I'm stupid, above all—that's what I am; so dense that I really blush for it. However, no one but you could have deceived me. If I trusted you, moreover, it was exactly to be cleverer than myself. You must be so now more than ever!" Suddenly Fleda felt her hands grasped: Mrs. Gereth had plumped down at her feet and was leaning on her knees. "Save him—save him: you *can*!" she passionately pleaded. "How could you *not* like him, when he's such a dear? He *is* a dear, darling; there's no harm in my own boy! You can do what you will with him—you know you can! What else does he give s all this time for? Get him away from her; it's as if he besought you to, poor wretch! Don't abandon him to such a fate, and I'll never abandon *you*. Think of him with that creature, that future! If you'll take him I'll give up everything. There, it's a solemn promise, the most sacred of my life! Get the better of her, and he shall have every stick I removed. Give me your word, and I'll accept it. I'll write for the packers to-night!"

Fleda, before this, had fallen forward on her companion's neck, and the two women, clinging together, had got up while the younger wailed on the other's bosom. "You smooth it down because you see more in it than there can ever be; but after my hideous double game how will you be able to believe in me again?"

"I see in it simply what *must* be, if you've a single spark of pity. Where on earth was the double game, when you've behaved like such a saint? You've been beautiful, you've been exquisite, and all our trouble is over."

Fleda, drying her eyes, shook her head ever so sadly. "No, Mrs. Gereth, it isn't over. I can't do what you ask—I can't meet your condition."

Mrs. Gereth stared; the cloud gathered in her face again. "Why, in the name of goodness, when you adore him? I know what you see in him," she declared in another tone. "You're right!"

Fleda gave a faint, stubborn smile. "He cares for her too much."

"Then why doesn't he marry her? He's giving you an extraordinary chance."

"He doesn't dream I've ever thought of him," said Fleda. "Why should he, if you didn't?"

"It wasn't with me you were in love, my duck." Then Mrs. Gereth added: "I'll go and tell him."

"If you do any such thing, you shall never see me again,—absolutely, literally never!"

Mrs. Gereth looked hard at her young friend, showing she saw she must believe her. "Then you're perverse, you're wicked. Will you swear he doesn't know?"

"Of course he doesn't know!" cried Fleda indignantly.

Her interlocutress was silent a little. "And that he has no feeling on *his* side?"

"For me?" Fleda stared. "Before he has even married her?"

Mrs. Gereth gave a sharp laugh at this. "He ought at least to appreciate your wit. Oh, my dear, you *are* a treasure! Doesn't he appreciate anything? Has he given you absolutely no symptom—not looked a look, not breathed a sigh?"

"The case," said Fleda coldly, "is as I've had the honor to state it."

"Then he's as big a donkey as his mother! But you know you must account for their delay," Mrs. Gereth remarked.

"Why must I?" Fleda asked after a moment.

"Because you were closeted with him here so long. You can't pretend at present, you know, not to have any art."

The girl hesitated an instant; she was conscious that she must choose between two risks. She had had a secret and the secret was gone. Owen had one, which was still unbruised, and the greater risk now was that his mother should lay her formidable hand upon it. All Fleda's tenderness for him moved her to protect it; so she faced the smaller peril. "Their delay," she brought herself to reply, "may perhaps be Mona's doing. I mean because he has lost her the things."

Mrs. Gereth jumped at this. "So that she'll break altogether if I keep them?"

Fleda winced. "I've told you what I believe about that. She'll make scenes and conditions; she'll worry him. But she'll hold him fast; she'll never give him up."

Mrs. Gereth turned it over. "Well, I'll keep them, to try her," she finally pronounced; at which Fleda felt quite sick, as if she had given everything and got nothing.

"I must in common decency let him know that I've talked of the matter with you," she said to her hostess that evening. "What answer do you wish me to write to him?"

"Write to him that you must see him again," said Mrs. Gereth.

Fleda looked very blank. "What on earth am I to see him for?"

"For anything you like."

The girl would have been struck with the levity of this had she not already, in an hour, felt the extent of the change suddenly wrought in her commerce with her friend—wrought above all, to that friend's view, in her relation to the great issue. The effect of what had followed Owen's visit was to make that relation the very key of the crisis. Pressed upon her, goodness knew, the crisis had been, but it now seemed to put forth big, encircling arms— arms that squeezed till they hurt and she must cry out. It was as if everything at Ricks had been poured into a common receptacle, a public ferment of emotion and zeal, out of which it was ladled up to be tasted and talked about; everything at least but the one little treasure of knowledge that she kept back. She ought to have liked this, she reflected, because it meant sympathy, meant a closer union with the source of so much in her life that had been beautiful and renovating; but there were fine instincts in her that stood off. She had had—and it was not merely at this time—to recognize that there were things for which Mrs. Gereth's *flair* was not so happy as for bargains and "marks." It wouldn't be happy now as to the best action on the knowledge she had just gained; yet as from this moment they were still more intimately together, so a person deeply in her debt would simply have to stand and meet what was to come. There were ways in which she could sharply incommode such a person, and not only with the best conscience in the world, but with a sort of brutality of good intentions. One of the straightest of these strokes, Fleda saw, would be the dance of delight over the mystery Mrs. Gereth had laid bare—

the loud, lawful, tactless joy of the explorer leaping upon the strand. Like any other lucky discoverer, she would take possession of the fortunate island. She was nothing if not practical: almost the only thing she took account of in her young friend's soft secret was the excellent use she could make of it—a use so much to her taste that she refused to feel a hindrance in the quality of the material. Fleda put into Mrs. Gereth's answer to her question a good deal more meaning than it would have occurred to her a few hours before that she was prepared to put, but she had on the spot a foreboding that even so broad a hint would live to be bettered.

"Do you suggest that I shall propose to him to come down here again?" she presently inquired.

"Dear, no; say that you'll go up to town and meet him." It *was* bettered, the broad hint; and Fleda felt this to be still more the case when, returning to the subject before they went to bed, her companion said: "I make him over to you wholly, you know—to do what you please with. Deal with him in your own clever way—I ask no questions. All I ask is that you succeed."

"That's charming," Fleda replied, "but it doesn't tell me a bit, you'll be so good as to consider, in what terms to write to him. It's not an answer from you to the message I was to give you."

"The answer to his message is perfectly distinct: he shall have everything in the place the minute he'll say he'll marry you."

"You really pretend," Fleda asked, "to think me capable of transmitting him that news?"

"What else can I really pretend when you threaten so to cast me off if I speak the word myself?"

"Oh, if *you* speak the word!" the girl murmured very gravely, but happy at least to know that in this direction Mrs. Gereth confessed herself warned and helpless. Then she added: "How can I go on living with you on a footing of which I so deeply disapprove? Thinking as I do that you've despoiled him far more than is just or merciful—for if I expected you to take something, I didn't in the least expect you to take everything—how can I stay here without a sense that I'm backing you up in your cruelty and participating in your ill-gotten gains?" Fleda was determined that if she had the chill of her exposed and investigated state she would also have the convenience of it, and that if Mrs. Gereth popped in and out of the chamber of her soul she would at least return the freedom. "I shall quite hate, you know, in a day or two, every object that surrounds you—become blind to all the beauty and rarity that I formerly delighted in. Don't think me harsh; there's no use in my not being frank now. If I leave you, everything's at an end."

Mrs. Gereth, however, was imperturbable: Fleda had to recognize that her advantage had become too real. "It's too beautiful, the way you care for him; it's music in my ears. Nothing else but such a passion could make you say such things; that's the way I should have been too, my dear. Why didn't you tell me sooner? I'd have gone right in for you; I never would have moved a candlestick. Don't stay with me if it torments you; don't, if you suffer, be where you see the old rubbish. Go up to town—go back for a little to your father's. It need be only for a little; two or three weeks will see us through. Your father will take you and be glad, if you only will make him understand what it's a question of—of your getting yourself off his hands forever. I'll make him understand, you know, if you feel shy. I'd take you up myself, I'd go with you, to spare your being bored; we'd put up at an hotel and we might amuse ourselves a bit. We haven't had much pleasure since we met, have we? But of course that wouldn't suit our book. I should be a bugaboo to Owen—I should be fatally in the way. Your chance is there—your chance is to be alone; for God's sake, use it to the right end. If you're in want of money I've a little I can give you. But I ask no questions—not a question as small as your shoe!"

She asked no questions, but she took the most extraordinary things for granted. Fleda felt this still more at the end of a couple of days. On the second of these our young lady wrote to Owen; her emotion had to a certain degree cleared itself—there was something she could say briefly. If she had given everything to Mrs. Gereth and as yet got nothing, so she had on the other hand quickly reacted—it took but a night—against the discouragement of her first check. Her desire to serve him was too passionate, the sense that he counted upon her too sweet: these things caught her up again and gave her new patience and a new subtlety. It shouldn't really be for nothing that she had given so much; deep within her burned again the resolve to get something back. So what she wrote to Owen was simply that she had had a great scene with his mother, but that he must be patient and give her time. It was difficult, as they both had expected, but she was working her hardest for him. She had made an impression—she would do everything to follow it up. Meanwhile he must keep intensely quiet and take no other steps; he must only trust her and pray for her and believe in her perfect loyalty. She made no allusion whatever to Mona's attitude, nor to his not being, as regarded that young lady, master of the situation; but she said in a postscript, in reference to his mother, "Of course she wonders a good deal why your marriage doesn't take place." After the letter had gone she regretted having used the word "loyalty;" there were two or three milder terms which she might as well have employed. The answer she immediately received from Owen was a little note of which she met all the deficiencies by describing it to herself as pathetically simple, but which, to prove that Mrs. Gereth might ask as many questions as she liked, she at once made his mother read. He had no art with his pen, he had not even a good hand, and his letter, a short profession of friendly confidence, consisted of but a few familiar and colorless words of acknowledgment and assent. The gist of it was that he would certainly, since Miss Vetch recommended it, not hurry mamma too much. He would not for the present cause her to be approached by any one else, but he would nevertheless continue to hope that she would see she *must* come round. "Of course, you know," he added, "she can't keep me waiting indefinitely. Please give her my love and tell her that. If it can be done peaceably I know you're just the one to do it."

Fleda had awaited his rejoinder in deep suspense; such was her imagination of the possibility of his having, as she tacitly phrased it, let himself go on paper that when it arrived she was at first almost afraid to open it. There was indeed a distinct danger, for if he should take it into his head to write her love-letters the whole chance of aiding him would drop: she would have to return them, she would have to decline all further communication with him: it would be quite the end of the business. This imagination of Fleda's was a faculty that easily embraced all the heights and depths and extremities of things; that made a single mouthful, in particular, of any tragic or desperate necessity. She was perhaps at first just a trifle disappointed not to find in the note in question a syllable that strayed from the text; but the next moment she had risen to a point of view from which it presented itself as a production almost inspired in its simplicity. It was simple even for Owen, and she wondered what had given him the cue to be more so than usual. Then she saw how natures that are right just do the things that are right. He wasn't clever—his manner of writing showed it; but the cleverest man in England couldn't have had more the instinct that, under the circumstances, was the supremely happy one, the instinct of giving her something that would do beautifully to be shown to Mrs. Gereth. This was a kind of divination, for naturally he couldn't know the line Mrs. Gereth was taking. It was furthermore explained—and that was the most touching part of all—by his wish that she herself should notice how awfully well he was behaving. His very bareness called her attention to his virtue; and these were the exact fruits of her beautiful and terrible admonition. He was cleaving to Mona; he was doing his duty; he was making tremendously sure he should be without reproach.

If Fleda handed this communication to her friend as a triumphant gage of the innocence of the young man's heart, her elation lived but a moment after Mrs. Gereth had pounced upon the tell-tale spot in it. "Why in the world, then," that lady cried, "does he still not breathe a breath about the day, the *day*, the day?" She repeated the word with a crescendo of superior acuteness; she proclaimed that nothing could be more marked than its absence—an absence that simply spoke volumes. What did it prove in fine but that she was producing the effect she had toiled for—that she had settled or was rapidly settling Mona?

Such a challenge Fleda was obliged in some manner to take up. "You may be settling Mona," she returned with a smile, "but I can hardly regard it as sufficient evidence that you're settling Mona's lover."

"Why not, with such a studied omission on his part to gloss over in any manner the painful tension existing between them—the painful tension that, under providence, I've been the means of bringing about? He gives you by his silence clear notice that his marriage is practically off."

"He speaks to me of the only thing that concerns me. He gives me clear notice that he abates not one jot of his demand."

"Well, then, let him take the only way to get it satisfied."

Fleda had no need to ask again what such a way might be, nor was her support removed by the fine assurance with which Mrs. Gereth could make her argument wait upon her wish. These days, which dragged their length into a strange, uncomfortable fortnight, had already borne more testimony to that element than all the other time the two women had passed together. Our young lady had been at first far from measuring the whole of a feature that Owen himself would probably have described as her companion's "cheek." She lived now in a kind of bath of boldness, felt as if a fierce light poured in upon her from windows opened wide; and the singular part of the ordeal was that she couldn't protest against it fully without incurring, even to her own mind, some reproach of ingratitude, some charge of smallness. If Mrs. Gereth's apparent determination to hustle her into Owen's arms was accompanied with an air of holding her dignity rather cheap, this was after all only as a consequence of her being held in respect to some other attributes rather dear. It was a new version of the old story of being kicked upstairs. The wonderful woman was the same woman who, in the summer, at Poynton, had been so puzzled to conceive why a good-natured girl shouldn't have contributed more to the personal rout of the Brigstocks—shouldn't have been grateful even for the handsome puff of Fleda Vetch. Only her passion was keener now and her scruple more absent; the fight made a demand upon her, and her pugnacity had become one with her constant habit of using such weapons as she could pick up. She had no imagination about anybody's life save on the side she bumped against. Fleda was quite aware that she would have otherwise been a rare creature; but a rare creature was originally just what she had struck her as being. Mrs. Gereth had really no perception of anybody's nature—had only one question about persons: were they clever or stupid? To be clever meant to know the marks. Fleda knew them by direct inspiration, and a warm recognition of this had been her friend's tribute to her character. The girl had hours, now, of sombre wishing that she might never see anything good again: that kind of experience was evidently not an infallible source of peace. She would be more at peace in some vulgar little place that should owe its *cachet* to Tottenham Court Road. There were nice strong horrors in West Kensington; it was as if they beckoned her and wooed her back to them. She had a relaxed recollection of Waterbath; and of her reasons for staying on at Ricks the force was rapidly ebbing. One of these was her pledge to Owen—her vow to press his mother close; the other was the fact that of the two discomforts, that of being prodded by Mrs. Gereth and that of appearing to run after somebody else, the former remained for a while the more endurable.

As the days passed, however, it became plainer to Fleda that her only chance of success would be in lending herself to this low appearance. Then, moreover, at last, her nerves settling the question, the choice was simply imposed by the violence done to her taste—to whatever was left of that high principle, at least, after the free and reckless meeting, for months, of great drafts and appeals. It was all very well to try to evade discussion: Owen Gereth was looking to her for a struggle, and it wasn't a bit of a struggle to be disgusted and dumb. She was on too strange a footing—that of having presented an ultimatum and having had it torn up in her face. In such a case as that the envoy always departed; he never sat gaping and dawdling before the city. Mrs. Gereth, every morning, looked publicly into "The Morning Post," the only newspaper she received; and every morning she treated the blankness of that journal as fresh evidence that everything was "off." What did the Post exist for but to tell you your children were wretchedly married?—so that if such a source of misery was dry, what could you do but infer that for once you had miraculously escaped? She almost taunted Fleda with supineness in not getting something out of somebody—in the same breath indeed in which she drenched her with a kind of appreciation more onerous to the girl than blame. Mrs. Gereth herself had of course washed her hands of the matter; but Fleda knew people who knew Mona and would be sure to be in her confidence—inconceivable people who admired her and had the privilege of Waterbath. What was the use therefore of being the most natural and the easiest of letter-writers, if no sort of side-light—in some pretext for correspondence—was, by a brilliant creature, to be got out of such barbarians? Fleda was not only a brilliant creature, but she heard herself commended in these days for new and strange attractions; she figured suddenly, in the queer conversations of Ricks, as a distinguished, almost as a dangerous beauty. That retouching of her hair and dress in which her friend had impulsively indulged on a first glimpse of her secret was by implication very frequently repeated. She had the sense not only of being advertised and offered, but of being counseled and enlightened in ways that she scarcely understood—arts obscure even to a poor girl who had had, in good society and motherless poverty, to look straight at realities and fill out blanks.

These arts, when Mrs. Gereth's spirits were high, were handled with a brave and cynical humor with which Fleda's fancy could keep no step: they left our young lady wondering what on earth her companion wanted her to do. "I want you to cut in!"—that was Mrs. Gereth's familiar and comprehensive phrase for the course she prescribed. She challenged again and again Fleda's picture, as she called it (though the sketch was too slight to deserve the name), of the indifference to which a prior attachment had committed the proprietor of Poynton. "Do you mean to say that, Mona or no Mona, he could see you that way, day after day, and not have the ordinary feelings of a man?" This was the sort of interrogation to which Fleda was fitfully and irrelevantly treated. She had grown almost used to the refrain. "Do you mean to say that when, the other day, one had quite made you over to him, the great gawk, and he was, on this very spot, utterly alone with you—?" The poor girl at this point never left any doubt of what she meant to say, but Mrs. Gereth could be trusted to break out in another place and at another time. At last Fleda wrote to her father that he must take her in for a while; and when, to her companion's delight, she returned to London, that lady went with her to the station and wafted her on her way. "The Morning Post" had been delivered as they left the house, and Mrs. Gereth had brought it with her for the traveler, who never spent a penny on a newspaper. On the platform, however, when this young person was ticketed, labeled, and seated, she opened it at the window of the carriage, exclaiming as usual, after looking into it a moment: "Nothing—nothing—nothing: don't tell *me!*" Every day that there was nothing was a nail in the coffin of the marriage. An instant later the train was off, but, moving quickly beside it, while Fleda leaned inscrutably forth, Mrs. Gereth grasped her friend's hand and looked up with wonderful eyes. "Only let yourself go, darling—only let yourself go!"

XIII

That she desired to ask no questions Mrs. Gereth conscientiously proved by closing her lips tight after Fleda had gone to London. No letter from Ricks arrived at West Kensington, and Fleda, with nothing to communicate that could be to the taste of either party, forbore to open a correspondence. If her heart had been less heavy she might have been amused to perceive how much rope this reticence of Ricks seemed to signify to her that she could take. She had at all events no good news for her friend save in the sense that her silence was not bad news. She was not yet in a position to write that she had "cut in;" but neither, on the other hand, had she gathered material for announcing that Mona was undisseverable from her prey. She had made no use of the pen so glorified by Mrs. Gereth to wake up the echoes of Waterbath; she had sedulously abstained from inquiring what in any quarter, far or near, was said or suggested or supposed. She only spent a matutinal penny on "The Morning Post;" she only saw, on each occasion, that that inspired sheet had as little to say about the imminence as about the abandonment of certain nuptials. It was at the same time obvious that Mrs. Gereth triumphed on these occasions much more than she trembled, and that with a few such triumphs repeated she would cease to tremble at all. What was most manifest, however, was that she had had a rare preconception of the circumstances that would have ministered, had Fleda been disposed, to the girl's cutting in. It was brought home to Fleda that these circumstances would have particularly favored intervention; she was quickly forced to do them a secret justice. One of the effects of her intimacy with Mrs. Gereth was that she had quite lost all sense of intimacy with any one else. The lady of Ricks had made a desert around her, possessing and absorbing her so utterly that other partakers had fallen away. Hadn't she been admonished, months before, that people considered they had lost her and were reconciled on the whole to the privation? Her present position in the great unconscious town defined itself as obscure: she regarded it at any rate with eyes suspicious of that lesson. She neither wrote notes nor received them; she indulged in no reminders nor knocked at any doors; she wandered vaguely in the western wilderness or cultivated shy forms of that "household art" for which she had had a respect before tasting the bitter tree of knowledge. Her only plan was to be as quiet as a mouse, and when she failed in the attempt to lose herself in the flat suburb she felt like a lonely fly crawling over a dusty chart.

How had Mrs. Gereth known in advance that if she had chosen to be "vile" (that was what Fleda called it) everything would happen to help her?—especially the way her poor father, after breakfast, doddered off to his club, showing seventy when he was really fifty-seven, and leaving her richly alone for the day. He came back about midnight, looking at her very hard and not risking long words—only making her feel by inimitable touches that the presence of his family compelled him to alter all his hours. She had in their common sitting-room the company of the objects he was fond of saying that he had collected—objects, shabby and battered, of a sort that appealed little to his daughter: old brandy-flasks and match-boxes, old calendars and hand-books, intermixed with an assortment of pen-wipers and ash-trays, a harvest he had gathered in from penny bazaars. He was blandly unconscious of that side of Fleda's nature which had endeared her to Mrs. Gereth, and she had often heard him wish to goodness there was something striking she cared for. Why didn't she try collecting something?—it didn't matter what. She would find it gave an interest to life, and there was no end of little curiosities one could easily pick up. He was conscious of having a taste for fine things which his children had unfortunately not inherited. This indicated the limits of their acquaintance with him—limits which, as Fleda was now sharply aware, could only leave him to wonder what the mischief she was there for. As she herself echoed this question to the letter she was not in a position to clear up the mystery. She couldn't have given a name to her errand in town or explained it save by saying that she had had to get away from Ricks. It was intensely provisional, but what was to come next? Nothing could come next but a deeper anxiety. She had neither a home nor an outlook—nothing in all the wide world but a feeling of suspense.

Of course she had her duty—her duty to Owen—a definite undertaking, reaffirmed, after his visit to Ricks, under her hand and seal; but there was no sense of possession attached to that; there was only a horrible sense of privation. She had quite moved from under Mrs. Gereth's wide wing; and now that she was really among the pen-wipers and ash-trays she was swept, at the thought of all the beauty she had forsworn, by short, wild gusts of despair. If her friend should really keep the spoils she would never return to her. If that friend should on the other hand part with them, what on earth would there be to return to? The chill struck deep as Fleda thought of the mistress of Ricks reduced, in vulgar parlance, to what she had on her back; there was nothing to which she could compare such an image but her idea of Marie Antoinette in the Conciergerie, or perhaps the vision of some tropical bird, the creature of hot, dense forests, dropped on a frozen moor to pick up a living. The mind's eye could see Mrs. Gereth, indeed, only in her thick, colored air; it took all the light of her treasures to make her concrete and distinct. She loomed for a moment, in any mere house, gaunt and unnatural; then she vanished as if she had suddenly sunk into a quicksand. Fleda lost herself in the rich fancy of how, if *she* were mistress of Poynton, a whole province, as an abode, should be assigned there to the august queen-mother. She would have returned from her campaign with her baggage-train and her loot, and the palace would unbar its shutters and the morning flash back from its halls. In the event of a surrender the poor woman would never again be able to begin to collect: she was now too old and too moneyless, and times were altered and good things impossibly dear. A surrender, furthermore, to any daughter-in-law save an oddity like Mona needn't at all be an abdication in fact; any other fairly nice girl whom Owen should have taken it into his head to marry would have been positively glad to have, for the museum, a custodian who was a walking catalogue and who understood beyond any one in England the hygiene and temperament of rare pieces. A fairly nice girl would somehow be away a good deal and would at such times count it a blessing to feel Mrs. Gereth at her post.

Fleda had fully recognized, the first days, that, quite apart from any question of letting Owen know where she was, it would be a charity to give him some sign: it would be weak, it would be ugly, to be diverted from that kindness by the fact that Mrs. Gereth had attached a tinkling bell to it. A frank relation with him was only superficially discredited: she ought for his own sake to send him a word of cheer. So she repeatedly reasoned, but she as repeatedly delayed performance: if her general plan had been to be as still as a mouse, an interview like the interview at Ricks would be an odd contribution to that ideal. Therefore with a confused preference of practice to theory she let the days go by; she felt that nothing was so imperative as the gain of precious time. She shouldn't be able to stay with her father forever, but she might now reap the benefit of having married her sister. Maggie's union had been built up round a small spare room. Concealed in this apartment she might try to paint again, and abetted by the grateful Maggie—for Maggie at least was grateful—she might try to dispose of her work. She had not indeed struggled with a brush since her visit to Waterbath, where the sight of the family splotches had put her immensely on her guard. Poynton moreover had been an impossible place for producing; no active art could flourish there but a Buddhistic contemplation. It had stripped its mistress clean of all feeble accomplishments; her hands were imbrued neither with ink nor with water-color. Close to Fleda's present abode was the little shop of a man who mounted and framed pictures and desolately dealt in artists' materials. She sometimes paused before it to look at a couple of shy experiments for which its dull window constituted publicity, small studies placed there for sale and full of warning to a young lady without fortune and without talent. Some such young lady had brought them forth in sorrow; some such young lady, to see if they had been snapped up, had passed and repassed as helplessly as she herself was doing. They never had been, they never would be, snapped up; yet they were quite above the actual attainment of some other young ladies. It was a matter of discipline with Fleda to take an occasional lesson from them; besides which, when she now quitted the house, she had to look for reasons after she was out. The only place to find them was in the shop-windows. They made her feel like a servant-girl taking her "afternoon," but that didn't signify: perhaps some day she would resemble such a person still more closely. This continued a fortnight, at the end of which the feeling was suddenly dissipated. She had stopped as usual in the presence of the little pictures; then, as she turned away, she had found herself face to face with Owen Gereth.

At the sight of him two fresh waves passed quickly across her heart, one at the heels of the other. The first was an instant perception that this encounter was not an accident; the second a consciousness as prompt that the best place for it was the street. She knew before he told her that he had been to see her, and the next thing she knew was that he had had information from his mother. Her mind grasped these things while he said with a smile: "I saw only your back, but I was sure. I was over the way. I've been at your house."

"How came you to know my house?" Fleda asked.

"I like that!" he laughed. "How came you not to let me know that you were there?"

Fleda, at this, thought it best also to laugh. "Since I didn't let you know, why did you come?"

"Oh, I say!" cried Owen. "Don't add insult to injury. Why in the world didn't you let me know? I came because I want awfully to see you." He hesitated, then he added: "I got the tip from mother: she has written to me—fancy!"

They still stood where they had met. Fleda's instinct was to keep him there; the more so that she could already see him take for granted that they would immediately proceed together to her door. He rose before her with a different air: he looked less ruffled and bruised than he had done at Ricks, he showed a recovered freshness. Perhaps, however, this was only because she had scarcely seen him at all as yet in London form, as he would have called it—"turned out" as he was turned out in town. In the country, heated with the chase and splashed with the mire, he had always rather reminded her of a picturesque peasant in national costume. This costume, as Owen wore it, varied from day to day; it was as copious as the wardrobe of an actor; but it never failed of suggestions of the earth and the weather, the hedges and the ditches, the beasts and the birds. There had been days when it struck her as all nature in one pair of boots. It didn't make him now another person that he was delicately dressed, shining and splendid—that he had a higher hat and light gloves with black seams, and a spearlike umbrella; but it made him, she soon decided, really handsomer, and that in turn gave him—for she never could think of him, or indeed of some other things, without the aid of his vocabulary—a tremendous pull. Yes, this was for the moment, as he looked at her, the great fact of their situation—his pull was tremendous. She tried to keep the acknowledgement of it from trembling in her voice as she said to him with more surprise than she really felt: "You've then reopened relations with her?"

"It's she who has reopened them with me. I got her letter this morning. She told me you were here and that she wished me to know it. She didn't say much; she just gave me your address. I wrote her back, you know, 'Thanks no end. Shall go to-day.' So we *are* in correspondence again, aren't we? She means of course that you've something to tell me from her, eh? But if you have, why haven't you let a fellow know?" He waited for no answer to this, he had so much to say. "At your house, just now, they told me how long you've been here. Haven't you known all the while that I'm counting the hours? I left a word for you—that I would be back at six; but I'm awfully glad to have caught you so much sooner. You don't mean to say you're not going home!" he exclaimed in dismay. "The young woman there told me you went out early."

"I've been out a very short time," said Fleda, who had hung back with the general purpose of making things difficult for him. The street would make them difficult; she could trust the street. She reflected in time, however, that to betray to him she was afraid to admit him would give him more a feeling of facility than of anything else. She moved on with him after a moment, letting him direct their course to her door, which was only round a corner: she considered as they went that it might not prove such a stroke to have been in London so long and yet not to have called him. She desired he should feel she was perfectly simple with him, and there was no simplicity in that. None the less, on the steps of the house, though she had a key, she rang the bell; and while they waited together and she averted her face she looked straight into the depths of what Mrs. Gereth had meant by giving him the "tip." This had been perfidious, had been monstrous of Mrs. Gereth, and Fleda wondered if her letter had contained only what Owen repeated.

<u>XIV</u>

When Owen and Fleda were in her father's little place and, among the brandy-flasks and pen-wipers, still more disconcerted and divided, the girl—to do something, though it would make him stay—had ordered tea, he put the letter before her quite as if he had guessed her thought. "She's still a bit nasty—fancy!" He handed her the scrap of a note which he had pulled out of his pocket and from its envelope. "Fleda Vetch," it ran, "is at 10 Raphael Road, West Kensington. Go to see her, and try, for God's sake, to cultivate a glimmer of intelligence." When in handing it back to him she took in his face she saw that its heightened color was the effect of his watching her read such an allusion to his want of wit. Fleda knew what it was an allusion to, and his pathetic air of having received this buffet, tall and fine and kind as he stood there, made her conscious of not quite concealing her knowledge. For a minute she was kept silent by an angered sense of the trick that had been played her. It was a trick because Fleda considered there had been a covenant; and the trick consisted of Mrs. Gereth's having broken the spirit of their agreement while conforming in a fashion to the letter. Under the girl's menace of a complete rupture she had been afraid to make of her secret the use she itched to make; but in the course of these days of separation she had gathered pluck to hazard an indirect betrayal. Fleda measured her hesitations and the impulse which she had finally obeyed and which the continued procrastination of Waterbath had encouraged, had at last made irresistible. If in her high-handed manner of playing their game she had not named the thing hidden, she had named the hiding-place. It was over the sense of this wrong that Fleda's lips closed tight: she was afraid of aggravating her case by some ejaculation that would make Owen prick up his ears. A great, quick effort, however, helped her to avoid the danger; with her constant idea of keeping cool and repressing a visible flutter, she found herself able to choose her words. Meanwhile he had exclaimed with his uncomfortable laugh: "That's a good one for me, Miss Vetch, isn't it?"

"Of course you know by this time that your mother's very sharp," said Fleda.

"I think I can understand well enough when I know what's to be nderstood," the young man asserted. "But I hope you won't mind my saying hat you've kept me pretty well in the dark about that. I've been waiting, aiting, waiting; so much has depended on your news. If you've been orking for me I'm afraid it has been a thankless job. Can't she say what he'll do, one way or the other? I can't tell in the least where I am, you know. haven't really learnt from you, since I saw you there, where *she* is. You wrote ne to be patient, and upon my soul I have been. But I'm afraid you don't uite realize what I'm to be patient with. At Waterbath, don't you know? ve simply to account and answer for the damned things. Mona looks at me nd waits, and I, hang it, I look at you and do the same." Fleda had gathered uller confidence as he continued; so plain was it that she had succeeded n not dropping into his mind the spark that might produce the glimmer nvoked by his mother. But even this fine assurance gave a start when, after n appealing pause, he went on: "I hope, you know, that after all you're not eeping anything back from me."

In the full face of what she was keeping back such a hope could only nake her wince; but she was prompt with her explanations in proportion as he felt they failed to meet him. The smutty maid came in with tea-things, nd Fleda, moving several objects, eagerly accepted the diversion of arranging place for them on one of the tables. "I've been trying to break your mother lown because it has seemed there may be some chance of it. That's why I've et you go on expecting it. She's too proud to veer round all at once, but I hink I speak correctly in saying that I've made an impression."

In spite of ordering tea she had not invited him to sit down; she herself nade a point of standing. He hovered by the window that looked into Raphael Road; she kept at the other side of the room; the stunted slavey, gazing wide-yed at the beautiful gentleman and either stupidly or cunningly bringing but ne thing at a time, came and went between the tea-tray and the open door.

"You pegged at her so hard?" Owen asked.

"I explained to her fully your position and put before her much more trongly than she liked what seemed to me her absolute duty."

Owen waited a little. "And having done that, you departed?"

Fleda felt the full need of giving a reason for her departure; but at first she only said with cheerful frankness: "I departed."

Her companion again looked at her in silence. "I thought you had gone to her for several months."

"Well," Fleda replied, "I couldn't stay. I didn't like it. I didn't like it at all—I couldn't bear it," she went on. "In the midst of those trophies of Poynton, living with them, touching them, using them, I felt as if I were backing her up. As I was not a bit of an accomplice, as I hate what she has done, I didn't want to be, even to the extent of the mere look of it—what is it you call such people?—an accessory after the fact." There was something she kept back so rigidly that the joy of uttering the rest was double. She felt the sharpest need of giving him all the other truth. There was a matter as to which she had deceived him, and there was a matter as to which she had deceived Mrs. Gereth, but her lack of pleasure in deception as such came home to her now. She busied herself with the tea and, to extend the occupation, cleared the table still more, spreading out the coarse cups and saucers and the vulgar little plates. She was aware that she produced more confusion than symmetry, but she was also aware that she was violently nervous. Owen tried to help her with something: this made rather for disorder. "My reason for not writing to you," she pursued, "was simply that I was hoping to hear more from Ricks. I've waited from day to day for that."

"But you've heard nothing?"

"Not a word."

"Then what I understand," said Owen, "is that, practically, you and Mummy have quarreled. And you've done it—I mean you personally—for *me*."

"Oh no, we haven't quarreled a bit!" Then with a smile: "We've only diverged."

"You've diverged uncommonly far!"—Owen laughed back. Fleda, with her hideous crockery and her father's collections, could conceive that these objects, to her visitor's perception even more strongly than to her own, measured the length of the swing from Poynton and Ricks; she was aware too that her high standards figured vividly enough even to Owen's simplicity to make him reflect that West Kensington was a tremendous fall. If she had fallen it was because she had acted for him. She was all the more content he should thus see she *had* acted, as the cost of it, in his eyes, was none of her own showing. "What seems to have happened," he exclaimed, "is that you've had a row with her and yet not moved her!"

Fleda considered a moment; she was full of the impression that, notwithstanding her scant help, he saw his way clearer than he had seen it at Ricks. He might mean many things; and what if the many should mean in their turn only one? "The difficulty is, you understand, that she doesn't really see into your situation." She hesitated. "She doesn't comprehend why your marriage hasn't yet taken place."

Owen stared. "Why, for the reason I told you: that Mona won't take another step till mother has given full satisfaction. Everything must be there. You see, everything *was* there the day of that fatal visit."

"Yes, that's what I understood from you at Ricks," said Fleda; "but I haven't repeated it to your mother." She had hated, at Ricks, to talk with him about Mona, but now that scruple was swept away. If he could speak of Mona's visit as fatal, she need at least not pretend not to notice it. It made all the difference that she had tried to assist him and had failed: to give him any faith in her service she must give him all her reasons but one. She must give him, in other words, with a corresponding omission, all Mrs. Gereth's. "You can easily see that, as she dislikes your marriage, anything that may seem to make it less certain works in her favor. Without my telling her, she has suspicions and views that are simply suggested by your delay. Therefore it didn't seem to me right to make them worse. By holding off long enough, she thinks she may put an end to your engagement. If Mona's waiting, she believes she may at last tire Mona out." That, in all conscience, Fleda felt was lucid enough.

So the young man, following her attentively, appeared equally to feel. "So far as that goes," he promptly declared, "she *has* at last tired Mona out." He uttered the words with a strange approach to hilarity.

Fleda's surprise at this aberration left her a moment looking at him. "Do you mean your marriage is off?"

Owen answered with a kind of gay despair. "God knows, Miss Vetch, where or when or what my marriage is! If it isn't 'off,' it certainly, at the point things have reached, isn't *on*. I haven't seen Mona for ten days, and for a week I haven't heard from her. She used to write me every week, don't you know? She won't budge from Waterbath, and I haven't budged from town." Then he suddenly broke out: "If she *does* chuck me, will mother come round?"

Fleda, at this, felt that her heroism had come to its real test—felt that in telling him the truth she should effectively raise a hand to push his impediment out of the way. Was the knowledge that such a motion would probably dispose forever of Mona capable of yielding to the conception of still giving her every chance she was entitled to? That conception was heroic, but at the same moment it reminded Fleda of the place it had held in her plan, she was also reminded of the not less urgent claim of the truth. Ah, the truth—there was a limit to the impunity with which one could juggle with it! Wasn't what she had most to remember the fact that Owen had a right to his property and that he had also her vow to stand by him in the effort to recover it? How did she stand by him if she hid from him the single way to recover it of which she was quite sure? For an instant that seemed to her the fullest of her life she debated. "Yes," she said at last, "if your marriage is really abandoned, she will give up everything she has taken."

"That's just what makes Mona hesitate!" Owen honestly exclaimed. "I mean the idea that I shall get back the things only if she gives me up."

Fleda thought an instant. "You mean makes her hesitate to keep you—not hesitate to renounce you?"

Owen looked a trifle bewildered. "She doesn't see the use of hanging on, as I haven't even yet put the matter into legal hands. She's awfully keen about that, and awfully disgusted that I don't. She says it's the only real way, and she thinks I'm afraid to take it. She has given me time and then has given me again more. She says I give Mummy too much. She says I'm a muff to go pottering on. That's why she's drawing off so hard, don't you see?"

"I don't see very clearly. Of course you must give her what you offered her; of course you must keep your word. There must be no mistake about *that!*" the girl declared.

Owen's bewilderment visibly increased. "You think, then, as she does, that I *must* send down the police?"

The mixture of reluctance and dependence in this made her feel how much she was failing him. She had the sense of "chucking" him too. "No, no, not yet!" she said, though she had really no other and no better course to prescribe. "Doesn't it occur to you," she asked in a moment, "that if Mona is, as you say, drawing away, she may have, in doing so, a very high motive? She knows the immense value of all the objects detained by your mother, and to restore the spoils of Poynton she is ready—is that it!—to make a sacrifice. The sacrifice is that of an engagement she had entered upon with joy."

Owen had been blank a moment before, but he followed this argument with success—a success so immediate that it enabled him to produce with decision: "Ah, she's not that sort! She wants them herself," he added; "she wants to feel they're hers; she doesn't care whether I have them or not! And if she can't get them she doesn't want *me*. If she can't get them she doesn't want anything at all."

This was categoric; Fleda drank it in. "She takes such an interest in them?"

"So it appears."

"So much that they're *all*, and that she can let everything else absolutely depend upon them?"

Owen weighed her question as if he felt the responsibility of his answer. But that answer came in a moment, and, as Fleda could see, out of a wealth of memory. "She never wanted them particularly till they seemed to be in danger. Now she has an idea about them; and when she gets hold of an idea— Oh dear me!" He broke off, pausing and looking away as with a sense of the futility of expression: it was the first time Fleda had ever heard him explain a matter so pointedly or embark at all on a generalization. It was striking, it was touching to her, as he faltered, that he appeared but half capable of floating his generalization to the end. The girl, however, was so far competent to fill up his blank as that she had divined, on the occasion of Mona's visit to Poynton, what would happen in the event of the accident at which he glanced. She had there with her own eyes seen Owen's betrothed get hold of an idea. "I say, you know, *do* give me some tea!" he went on irrelevantly and familiarly.

Her profuse preparations had all this time had no sequel, and, with a laugh that she felt to be awkward, she hastily complied with his request. "It's sure to be horrid," she said; "we don't have at all good things." She offered him also bread and butter, of which he partook, holding his cup and saucer in his other hand and moving slowly about the room. She poured herself a cup, but not to take it; after which, without wanting it, she began to eat a small stale biscuit. She was struck with the extinction of the unwillingness she had felt at Ricks to contribute to the bandying between them of poor Mona's name; and under this influence she presently resumed: "Am I to understand that she engaged herself to marry you without caring for you?"

Owen looked out into Raphael Road. "She *did* care for me awfully. But she can't stand the strain."

"The strain of what?"

"Why, of the whole wretched thing."

"The whole thing has indeed been wretched, and I can easily conceive its effect upon her," Fleda said.

Her visitor turned sharp round. "You *can*?" There was a light in his strong stare. "You can understand it's spoiling her temper and making her come down on *me*? She behaves as if I were of no use to her at all!"

Fleda hesitated. "She's rankling under the sense of her wrong."

"Well, was it *I*, pray, who perpetrated the wrong? Ain't I doing what I an to get the thing arranged?"

The ring of his question made his anger at Mona almost resemble for minute an anger at Fleda; and this resemblance in turn caused our young ady to observe how handsome he looked when he spoke, for the first time in ter hearing, with that degree of heat, and used, also for the first time, such a erm as "perpetrated." In addition, his challenge rendered still more vivid to ter the mere flimsiness of her own aid. "Yes, you've been perfect," she said. You've had a most difficult part. You've *had* to show tact and patience, as vell as firmness, with your mother, and you've strikingly shown them. It's I vho, quite unintentionally, have deceived you. I haven't helped you at all to our remedy."

"Well, you wouldn't at all events have ceased to like me, would you?")wen demanded. It evidently mattered to him to know if she really justified Mona. "I mean of course if you *had* liked me—liked me as *she* liked me," he xplained.

Fleda looked this inquiry in the face only long enough to recognize that, n her embarrassment, she must take instant refuge in a superior one. "I can nswer that better if I know how kind to her you've been. *Have* you been kind o her?" she asked as simply as she could.

"Why, rather, Miss Vetch!" Owen declared. "I've done every blessed hing she wished. I rushed down to Ricks, as you saw, with fire and sword, nd the day after that I went to see her at Waterbath." At this point he hecked himself, though it was just the point at which her interest deepened. \ different look had come into his face as he put down his empty teacup. But why should I tell you such things, for any good it does me? I gather that ou've no suggestion to make me now except that I shall request my solicitor o act. *Shall* I request him to act?"

Fleda scarcely heard his words; something new had suddenly come into ter mind. "When you went to Waterbath after seeing me," she asked, "did ou tell her all about that?"

Owen looked conscious. "All about it?"

"That you had had a long talk with me, without seeing your mother at all?"

"Oh yes, I told her exactly, and that you had been most awfully kind and that I had placed the whole thing in your hands."

Fleda was silent a moment. "Perhaps that displeased her," she at last suggested.

"It displeased her fearfully," said Owen, looking very queer.

"Fearfully?" broke from the girl. Somehow, at the word, she was startled.

"She wanted to know what right you had to meddle. She said you were not honest."

"Oh!" Fleda cried, with a long wail. Then she controlled herself. "I see."

"She abused you, and I defended you. She denounced you—"

She checked him with a gesture. "Don't tell me what she did!" She had colored up to her eyes, where, as with the effect of a blow in the face, she quickly felt the tears gathering. It was a sudden drop in her great flight, a shock to her attempt to watch over what Mona was entitled to. While she had been straining her very soul in this attempt, the object of her magnanimity had been pronouncing her "not honest." She took it all in, however, and after an instant was able to speak with a smile. She would not have been surprised to learn, indeed, that her smile was strange. "You had said a while ago that your mother and I quarreled about you. It's much more true that you and Mona have quarreled about *me*."

Owen hesitated, but at last he brought it out. "What I mean to say is, don't you know, that Mona, if you don't mind my saying so, has taken it into her head to be jealous."

"I see," said Fleda. "Well, I dare say our conferences have looked very odd."

"They've looked very beautiful, and they've been very beautiful. Oh, I've told her the sort you are!" the young man pursued.

"That of course hasn't made her love me better."

"No, nor love me," said Owen. "Of course, you know, she says she loves me."

"And do you say you love her?"

"I say nothing else—I say it all the while. I said it the other day a dozen times." Fleda made no immediate rejoinder to this, and before she could choose one he repeated his question of a moment before. "*Am* I to tell my solicitor to act?"

She had at that moment turned away from this solution, precisely because she saw in it the great chance of her secret. If she should determine him to adopt it she might put out her hand and take him. It would shut in Mrs. Gereth's face the open door of surrender: she would flare up and fight, flying the flag of a passionate, an heroic defense. The case would obviously go against her, but the proceedings would last longer than Mona's patience or Owen's propriety. With a formal rupture he would be at large; and she had only to tighten her fingers round the string that would raise the curtain on that scene. "You tell me you 'say' you love her, but is there nothing more in it than your saying so? You wouldn't say so, would you, if it's not true? What in the world has become, in so short a time, of the affection that led to your engagement?"

"The deuce knows what has become of it, Miss Vetch!" Owen cried. "It seemed all to go to pot as this horrid struggle came on." He was close to her now, and, with his face lighted again by the relief of it, he looked all his helpless history into her eyes. "As I saw you and noticed you more, as I knew you better and better, I felt less and less—I couldn't help it—about anything or any one else. I wished I had known you sooner—I knew I should have liked you better than any one in the world. But it wasn't you who made the difference," he eagerly continued, "and I was awfully determined to stick to Mona to the death. It was she herself who made it, upon my soul, by the

515

state she got into, the way she sulked, the way she took things, and the way she let me have it! She destroyed our prospects and our happiness, upon my honor. She made just the same smash of them as if she had kicked over that tea-table. She wanted to know all the while what was passing between us, between you and me; and she wouldn't take my solemn assurance that nothing was passing but what might have directly passed between me and old Mummy. She said a pretty girl like you was a nice old Mummy for me, and, if you'll believe it, she never called you anything else but that. I'll be hanged if I haven't been good, haven't I? I haven't breathed a breath of any sort to you, have I? You'd have been down on me hard if I had, wouldn't you? You're down on me pretty hard as it is, I think, aren't you? But I don't care what you say now, or what Mona says, either, or a single rap what any one says: she has given me at last, by her confounded behavior, a right to speak out, to utter the way I feel about it. The way I feel about it, don't you know, is that it had all better come to an end. You ask me if I don't love her, and I suppose it's natural enough you should. But you ask it at the very moment I'm half mad to say to you that there's only one person on the whole earth I *really* love, and that that person—" Here Owen pulled up short, and Fleda wondered if it was from the effect of his perceiving, through the closed door, the sound of steps and voices on the landing of the stairs. She had caught this sound herself with surprise and a vague uneasiness: it was not an hour at which her father ever came in, and there was no present reason why she should have a visitor. She had a fear, which after a few seconds deepened: a visitor was at hand; the visitor would be simply Mrs. Gereth. That lady wished for a near view of the consequence of her note to Owen. Fleda straightened herself with the instant thought that if this was what Mrs. Gereth desired Mrs. Gereth should have it in a form not to be mistaken. Owen's pause was the matter of a moment, but during that moment our young couple stood with their eyes holding each other's eyes and their ears catching the suggestion, still through the door, of a murmured conference in the hall. Fleda had begun to make the movement to cut it short when Owen stopped her with a grasp of her arm. "You're surely able to guess," he said, with his voice dropped and her arm pressed as she had never known such a drop or such a pressure—"you're surely able to guess the one person on earth I love?"

The handle of the door turned, and Fleda had only time to jerk at him: "Your mother!"

The door opened, and the smutty maid, edging in, announced "Mrs. Brigstock!"

Mrs. Brigstock, in the doorway, stood looking from one of the occupants of the room to the other; then they saw her eyes attach themselves to a small object that had lain hitherto unnoticed on the carpet. This was the biscuit of which, on giving Owen his tea, Fleda had taken a perfunctory nibble: she had immediately laid it on the table, and that subsequently, in some precipitate movement, she should have brushed it off was doubtless a sign of the agitation that possessed her. For Mrs. Brigstock there was apparently more in it than met the eye. Owen at any rate picked it up, and Fleda felt as if he were removing the traces of some scene that the newspapers would have characterized as lively. Mrs. Brigstock clearly took in also the sprawling tea-things and the mark as of high water in the full faces of her young friends. These elements made the little place a vivid picture of intimacy. A minute was filled by Fleda's relief at finding her visitor not to be Mrs. Gereth, and a longer space by the ensuing sense of what was really more compromising in the actual apparition. It dimly occurred to her that the lady of Ricks had also written to Waterbath. Not only had Mrs. Brigstock never paid her a call, but Fleda would have been unable to figure her so employed. A year before the girl had spent a day under her roof, but never feeling that Mrs. Brigstock regarded this as constituting a bond. She had never stayed in any house but Poynton where the imagination of a bond, one way or the other, prevailed. After the first astonishment she dashed gayly at her guest, emphasizing her welcome and wondering how her whereabouts had become known at Waterbath. Had not Mrs. Brigstock quitted that residence for the very purpose of laying her hand on the associate of Mrs. Gereth's misconduct? The spirit in which this hand was to be laid our young lady was yet to ascertain; but she was a person who could think ten thoughts at once—a circumstance which, even putting her present plight at its worst, gave her a great advantage over a person who required easy conditions for dealing even with one. The very vibration of the air, however, told her that whatever Mrs. Brigstock's spirit might originally have been, it had been sharply affected by the sight of Owen. He was essentially a surprise: she had reckoned with everything that concerned him but his presence. With that, in awkward silence, she was reckoning now, as Fleda could see, while she effected with friendly aid an embarrassed transit to the sofa. Owen would be useless, would be deplorable: that aspect of the case Fleda had taken in as well. Another aspect was that he would admire her, adore her, exactly in proportion as she herself should rise gracefully superior. Fleda felt for the first time free to let herself "go," as Mrs. Gereth had said, and she was full of the sense that to "go" meant now to aim straight at the effect of moving Owen to rapture at her simplicity and tact. It was her impression that he had no positive dislike of Mona's mother; but she couldn't entertain that notion without a glimpse of the implication that he had a positive dislike of Mrs. Brigstock's daughter. Mona's mother declined tea, declined a better seat, declined a cushion, declined to remove her boa: Fleda guessed that she had not come on purpose to be dry, but that the voice of the invaded room had itself given her the hint.

"I just came on the mere chance," she said. "Mona found yesterday, somewhere, the card of invitation to your sister's marriage that you sent us, or your father sent us, some time ago. We couldn't be present—it was impossible; but as it had this address on it I said to myself that I might find you here."

"I'm very glad to be at home," Fleda responded.

"Yes, that doesn't happen very often, does it?" Mrs. Brigstock looked round afresh at Fleda's home.

"Oh, I came back from Ricks last week. I shall be here now till I don't know when."

"We thought it very likely you would have come back. We knew of course of your having been at Ricks. If I didn't find you I thought I might perhaps find Mr. Vetch," Mrs. Brigstock went on.

"I'm sorry he's out. He's always out—all day long."

Mrs. Brigstock's round eyes grew rounder. "All day long?"

"All day long," Fleda smiled.

"Leaving you quite to yourself?"

"A good deal to myself, but a little, to-day, as you see, to Mr. Gereth,—" and the girl looked at Owen to draw him into their sociability. For Mrs. Brigstock he had immediately sat down; but the movement had not corrected the sombre stiffness taking possession of him at the sight of her. Before he found a response to the appeal addressed to him Fleda turned again to her other visitor. "Is there any purpose for which you would like my father to call on you?"

Mrs. Brigstock received this question as if it were not to be unguardedly answered; upon which Owen intervened with pale irrelevance: "I wrote to Mona this morning of Miss Vetch's being in town; but of course the letter hadn't arrived when you left home."

"No, it hadn't arrived. I came up for the night—I've several matters to attend to." Then looking with an intention of fixedness from one of her companions to the other, "I'm afraid I've interrupted your conversation," Mrs. Brigstock said. She spoke without effectual point, had the air of merely announcing the fact. Fleda had not yet been confronted with the question of the sort of person Mrs. Brigstock was; she had only been confronted with the question of the sort of person Mrs. Gereth scorned her for being. She was really, somehow, no sort of person at all, and it came home to Fleda that if Mrs. Gereth could see her at this moment she would scorn her more than ever. She had a face of which it was impossible to say anything but that it was pink, and a mind that it would be possible to describe only if one had been able to mark it in a similar fashion. As nature had made this organ neither green nor blue nor yellow, there was nothing to know it by: it strayed and bleated like an unbranded sheep. Fleda felt for it at this moment much of the kindness of compassion, since Mrs. Brigstock had brought it with her to do something for her that she regarded as delicate. Fleda was quite prepared to help it to perform, if she should be able to gather what it wanted to do. What she gathered, however, more and more, was that it wanted to do something different from what it had wanted to do in leaving Waterbath. There was still nothing to enlighten her more specifically in the way her visitor continued: "You must be very much taken up. I believe you quite espouse his dreadful quarrel."

Fleda vaguely demurred. "His dreadful quarrel?"

"About the contents of the house. Aren't you looking after them for him?"

"She knows how awfully kind you've been to me," Owen said. He showed such discomfiture that he really gave away their situation; and Fleda found herself divided between the hope that he would take leave and the wish that he should see the whole of what the occasion might enable her to bring to pass for him.

She explained to Mrs. Brigstock. "Mrs. Gereth, at Ricks, the other day, asked me particularly to see him for her."

"And did she ask you also particularly to see him here in town?" Mrs. Brigstock's hideous bonnet seemed to argue for the unsophisticated truth; and it was on Fleda's lips to reply that such had indeed been Mrs. Gereth's request. But she checked herself, and before she could say anything else Owen had addressed their companion.

"I made a point of letting Mona know that I should be here, don't you see? That's exactly what I wrote her this morning."

"She would have had no doubt you would be here, if you had a chance," Mrs. Brigstock returned. "If your letter had arrived it might have prepared me for finding you here at tea. In that case I certainly wouldn't have come."

"I'm glad, then, it didn't arrive. Shouldn't you like him to go?" Fleda asked.

Mrs. Brigstock looked at Owen and considered: nothing showed in her face but that it turned a deeper pink. "I should like him to go with *me*." There was no menace in her tone, but she evidently knew what she wanted. As Owen made no response to this Fleda glanced at him to invite him to assent; then, for fear that he wouldn't, and would thereby make his case worse, she took upon herself to declare that she was sure he would be very glad to meet such a wish. She had no sooner spoken than she felt that the words had a bad effect of intimacy: she had answered for him as if she had been his wife. Mrs. Brigstock continued to regard him as if she had observed nothing, and she continued to address Fleda: "I've not seen him for a long time—I've particular things to say to him."

"So have I things to say to you, Mrs. Brigstock!" Owen interjected. With this he took up his hat as if for an immediate departure.

The other visitor meanwhile turned to Fleda. "What is Mrs. Gereth going to do?"

"Is that what you came to ask me?" Fleda demanded.

"That and several other things."

"Then you had much better let Mr. Gereth go, and stay by yourself and make me a pleasant visit. You can talk with him when you like, but it is the first time you've been to see me."

This appeal had evidently a certain effect; Mrs. Brigstock visibly wavered. "I can't talk with him whenever I like," she returned; "he hasn't been near us since I don't know when. But there are things that have brought me here."

"They are not things of any importance," Owen, to Fleda's surprise, suddenly asserted. He had not at first taken up Mrs. Brigstock's expression of a wish to carry him off: Fleda could see that the instinct at the bottom of this was that of standing by her, of seeming not to abandon her. But abruptly, all his soreness working within him, it had struck him that he should abandon her still more if he should leave her to be dealt with by her other visitor. "You must allow me to say, you know, Mrs. Brigstock, that I don't think you should come down on Miss Vetch about anything. It's very good of her to take the smallest interest in us and our horrid little squabble. If you want to talk about it, talk about it with *me*." He was flushed with the idea of protecting Fleda, of exhibiting his consideration for her. "I don't like your cross-questioning her, don't you see? She's as straight as a die: *I'*ll tell you all about her!" he declared with an excited laugh. "Please come off with me and let her alone."

Mrs. Brigstock, at this, became vivid at once; Fleda thought she looked most peculiar. She stood straight up, with a queer distention of her whole person and of everything in her face but her mouth, which she gathered into a small, tight orifice. Fleda was painfully divided; her joy was deep within, but it was more relevant to the situation that she should not appear to associate herself with the tone of familiarity in which Owen addressed a lady who had been, and was perhaps still, about to become his mother-in-law. She laid on Mrs. Brigstock's arm a repressive hand. Mrs. Brigstock, however, had already exclaimed on her having so wonderful a defender. "He speaks, upon my word, as if I had come here to be rude to you!"

At this, grasping her hard, Fleda laughed; then she achieved the exploit of delicately kissing her. "I'm not in the least afraid to be alone with you, or of your tearing me to pieces. I'll answer any question that you can possibly dream of putting to me."

"I'm the proper person to answer Mrs. Brigstock's questions," Owen broke in again, "and I'm not a bit less ready to meet them than you are." He was firmer than she had ever seen him: it was as if she had not known he could be so firm.

"But she'll only have been here a few minutes. What sort of a visit is that?" Fleda cried.

"It has lasted long enough for my purpose. There was something I wanted to know, but I think I know it now."

"Anything you don't know I dare say I can tell you!" Owen observed as he impatiently smoothed his hat with the cuff of his coat.

Fleda by this time desired immensely to keep his companion, but she saw she could do so only at the cost of provoking on his part a further exhibition of the sheltering attitude, which he exaggerated precisely because it was the first thing, since he had begun to "like" her, that he had been able frankly to do for her. It was not in her interest that Mrs. Brigstock should be more struck than she already was with that benevolence. "There may be things you know that I don't," she presently said to her, with a smile. "But I've a sort of sense that you're laboring under some great mistake."

Mrs. Brigstock, at this, looked into her eyes more deeply and yearningly than she had supposed Mrs. Brigstock could look; it was the flicker of a certain willingness to give her a chance. Owen, however, quickly spoiled everything. "Nothing is more probable than that Mrs. Brigstock is doing what you say; but there's no one in the world to whom you owe an explanation. I may owe somebody one—I dare say I do; but not you, no!"

"But what if there's one that it's no difficulty at all for me to give?" Fleda inquired. "I'm sure that's the only one Mrs. Brigstock came to ask, if she came to ask any at all."

Again the good lady looked hard at her young hostess. "I came, I believe, Fleda, just, you know, to plead with you."

Fleda, with a bright face, hesitated a moment. "As if I were one of those bad women in a play?"

The remark was disastrous. Mrs. Brigstock, on whom her brightness was lost, evidently thought it singularly free. She turned away, as from a presence that had really defined itself as objectionable, and Fleda had a vain sense that her good humor, in which there was an idea, was taken for impertinence, or at least for levity. Her allusion was improper, even if she herself wasn't; Mrs. Brigstock's emotion simplified: it came to the same thing. "I'm quite ready," that lady said to Owen rather mildly and woundedly. "I do want to speak to you very much."

"I'm completely at your service." Owen held out his hand to Fleda. "Good-bye, Miss Vetch. I hope to see you again to-morrow." He opened the door for Mrs. Brigstock, who passed before the girl with an oblique, averted salutation. Owen and Fleda, while he stood at the door, then faced each other darkly and without speaking. Their eyes met once more for a long moment, and she was conscious there was something in hers that the darkness didn't quench, that he had never seen before and that he was perhaps never to see again. He stayed long enough to take it—to take it with a sombre stare that just showed the dawn of wonder; then he followed Mrs. Brigstock out of the house.

XVI

He had uttered the hope that he should see her the next day, but Fleda could easily reflect that he wouldn't see her if she were not there to be seen. If there was a thing in the world she desired at that moment, it was that the next day should have no point of resemblance with the day that had just lapsed. She accordingly aspired to an absence: she would go immediately down to Maggie. She ran out that evening and telegraphed to her sister, and in the morning she quitted London by an early train. She required for this step no reason but the sense of necessity. It was a strong personal need; she wished to interpose something, and there was nothing she could interpose but distance, but time. If Mrs. Brigstock had to deal with Owen she would allow Mrs. Brigstock the chance. To be there, to be in the midst of it, was the reverse of what she craved: she had already been more in the midst of it than had ever entered into her plan. At any rate she had renounced her plan; she had no plan now but the plan of separation. This was to abandon Owen, to give up the fine office of helping him back to his own; but when she had undertaken that office she had not foreseen that Mrs. Gereth would defeat it by a manœuvre so simple. The scene at her father's rooms had extinguished all offices, and the scene at her father's rooms was of Mrs. Gereth's producing. Owen, at all events, must now act for himself: he had obligations to meet, he had satisfactions to give, and Fleda fairly ached with the wish that he might be equal to them. She never knew the extent of her tenderness for him till she became conscious of the present force of her desire that he should be superior, be perhaps even sublime. She obscurely made out that superiority, that sublimity, mightn't after all be fatal. She closed her eyes and lived for a day or two in the mere beauty of confidence. It was with her on the short journey; it was with her at Maggie's; it glorified the mean little house in the stupid little town. Owen had grown larger to her: he would do, like a man, whatever he should have to do. He wouldn't be weak—not as she was: she herself was weak exceedingly.

Arranging her few possessions in Maggie's fewer receptacles, she caught a glimpse of the bright side of the fact that her old things were not such a problem as Mrs. Gereth's. Picking her way with Maggie through the local puddles, diving with her into smelly cottages and supporting her, at smellier shops, in firmness over the weight of joints and the taste of cheese, it was still her own secret that was universally inter-woven In the puddles, the cottages, the shops she was comfortably alone with it; that comfort prevailed even while, at the evening meal, her brother-in-law invited her attention to a diagram, drawn with a fork on too soiled a tablecloth, of the scandalous drains of the Convalescent Home. To be alone with it she had come away from Ricks; and now she knew that to be alone with it she had come away from London. This advantage was of course menaced, but not immediately destroyed, by the arrival, on the second day, of the note she had been sure she should receive from Owen. He had gone to West Kensington and found her flown, but he had got her address from the little maid and then hurried to a club and written to her. "Why have you left me just when I want you most?" he demanded. The next words, it was true, were more reassuring on the question of his steadiness. "I don't know what your reason may be," they went on, "nor why you've not left a line for me; but I don't think you can feel that I did anything yesterday that it wasn't right for me to do. As regards Mrs. Brigstock, certainly, I just felt what was right and I did it. She had no business whatever to attack you that way, and I should have been ashamed if I had left her there to worry you. I won't have you worried by any one; no one shall be disagreeable to you but me. I didn't mean to be so yesterday, and I don't to-day; but I'm perfectly free now to want you, and I want you much more than you've allowed me to explain. You'll see if I'm not all right, if you'll let me come to you. Don't be afraid—I'll not hurt you nor trouble you. I give you my honor I'll not hurt any one. Only I *must* see you, on what I had to say to Mrs. B. She was nastier than I thought she could be, but I'm behaving like an angel. I assure you I'm all right—that's exactly what I want you to see. You owe me something, you know, for what you said you would do and haven't done; what your departure without a word gives me to understand—doesn't it?—that you definitely can't do. Don't simply forsake me. See me, if you only see me once. I shan't wait for any leave—I shall come down to-morrow. I've been looking into trains and find there's something that will bring me down just after lunch and something very good for getting me back. I won't stop long. For God's sake, be there."

This communication arrived in the morning, but Fleda would still have had time to wire a protest. She debated on that alternative; then she read the note over and found in one phrase an exact statement of her duty. Owen's simplicity had expressed it, and her subtlety had nothing to answer. She owed him something for her obvious failure, and what she owed him was to receive him. If indeed she had known he would make this attempt she might have been held to have gained nothing by her flight. Well, she had gained what she had gained—she had gained the interval. She had no compunction for the greater trouble she should give the young man; it was now doubtless right that he should have as much trouble as possible. Maggie, who thought she was in her confidence, but was immensely not, had reproached her for having left Mrs. Gereth, and Maggie was just in this proportion gratified to hear of the visitor with whom, early in the afternoon, she would have to ask to be left alone. Maggie liked to see far, and now she could sit upstairs and rake the whole future. She had known that, as she familiarly said, there was something the matter with Fleda, and the value of that knowledge was augmented by the fact that there was apparently also something the matter with Mr. Gereth.

Fleda, downstairs, learned soon enough what this was. It was simply that, as he announced the moment he stood before her, he was now all right. When she asked him what he meant by that state he replied that he meant he could practically regard himself henceforth as a free man: he had had at West Kensington, as soon as they got into the street, such a horrid scene with Mrs. Brigstock.

"I knew what she wanted to say to me: that's why I was determined to get her off. I knew I shouldn't like it, but I was perfectly prepared," said Owen. "She brought it out as soon as we got round the corner; she asked me point-blank if I was in love with you."

"And what did you say to that?"

"That it was none of her business."

"Ah," said Fleda, "I'm not so sure!"

"Well, *I* am, and I'm the person most concerned. Of course I didn't use just those words: I was perfectly civil, quite as civil as she. But I told her I didn't consider she had a right to put me any such question. I said I wasn't sure that even Mona had, with the extraordinary line, you know, that Mona has taken. At any rate the whole thing, the way *I* put it, was between Mona and me; and between Mona and me, if she didn't mind, it would just have to remain."

Fleda was silent a little. "All that didn't answer her question."

"Then you think I ought to have told her?"

Again our young lady reflected. "I think I'm rather glad you didn't."

"I knew what I was about," said Owen. "It didn't strike me that she had the least right to come down on us that way and ask for explanations."

Fleda looked very grave, weighing the whole matter. "I dare say that when she started, when she arrived, she didn't mean to 'come down.'"

"What then did she mean to do?"

"What she said to me just before she went: she meant to plead with me."

"Oh, I heard her!" said Owen. "But plead with you for what?"

"For you, of course—to entreat me to give you up. She thinks me awfully designing—that I've taken some sort of possession of you."

Owen stared. "You haven't lifted a finger! It's I who have taken possession."

"Very true, you've done it all yourself." Fleda spoke gravely and gently, without a breath of coquetry. "But those are shades between which she's probably not obliged to distinguish. It's enough for her that we're singularly intimate."

"I am, but you're not!" Owen exclaimed.

Fleda gave a dim smile. "You make me at least feel that I'm learning to know you very well when I hear you say such a thing as that. Mrs. Brigstock came to get round me, to supplicate me," she went on; "but to find you there, looking so much at home, paying me a friendly call and shoving the tea-things about—that was too much for her patience. She doesn't know, you see, that I'm after all a decent girl. She simply made up her mind on the spot that I'm a very bad case."

"I couldn't stand the way she treated you, and that was what I had to say to her," Owen returned.

"She's simple and slow, but she's not a fool: I think she treated me, on the whole, very well." Fleda remembered how Mrs. Gereth had treated Mona when the Brigstocks came down to Poynton.

Owen evidently thought her painfully perverse. "It was you who carried it off; you behaved like a brick. And so did I, I consider. If you only knew the difficulty I had! I told her you were the noblest and straightest of women."

"That can hardly have removed her impression that there are things I put you up to."

"It didn't," Owen replied with candor. "She said our relation, yours and mine, isn't innocent."

"What did she mean by that?"

"As you may suppose, I particularly inquired. Do you know what she had the cheek to tell me?" Owen asked. "She didn't better it much: she said she meant that it's excessively unnatural."

Fleda considered afresh. "Well, it is!" she brought out at last.

"Then, upon my honor, it's only you who make it so!" Her perversity was distinctly too much for him. "I mean you make it so by the way you keep me off."

"Have I kept you off to-day?" Fleda sadly shook her head, raising her arms a little and dropping them.

Her gesture of resignation gave him a pretext for catching at her hand, but before he could take it she had put it behind her. They had been seated together on Maggie's single sofa, and her movement brought her to her feet, while Owen, looking at her reproachfully, leaned back in discouragement. "What good does it do me to be here when I find you only a stone?"

She met his eyes with all the tenderness she had not yet uttered, and she had not known till this moment how great was the accumulation. "Perhaps, after all," she risked, "there may be even in a stone still some little help for you."

Owen sat there a minute staring at her. "Ah, you're beautiful, more beautiful than any one," he broke out, "but I'll be hanged if I can ever understand you! On Tuesday, at your father's, you were beautiful—as beautiful, just before I left, as you are at this instant. But the next day, when I went back, I found it had apparently meant nothing; and now, again, that you let me come here and you shine at me like an angel, it doesn't bring you an inch nearer to saying what I want you to say." He remained a moment longer in the same position; then he jerked himself up. "What I want you to say is that you like me—what I want you to say is that you pity me." He sprang up and came to her. "What I want you to say is that you'll *save* me!"

Fleda hesitated. "Why do you need saving, when you announced to me just now that you're a free man?"

He too hesitated, but he was not checked. "It's just for the reason that I'm free. Don't you know what I mean, Miss Vetch? I want you to marry me."

Fleda, at this, put out her hand in charity; she held his own, which quickly grasped it a moment, and if he had described her as shining at him it may be assumed that she shone all the more in her deep, still smile. "Let me hear a little more about your freedom first," she said. "I gather that Mrs. Brigstock was not wholly satisfied with the way you disposed of her question."

"I dare say she wasn't. But the less she's satisfied the more I'm free."

"What bearing have *her* feelings, pray?" Fleda asked.

"Why, Mona's much worse than her mother. She wants much more to give me up."

"Then why doesn't she do it?"

"She will, as soon as her mother gets home and tells her."

"Tells her what?" Fleda inquired.

"Why, that I'm in love with *you!*"

Fleda debated. "Are you so very sure she will?"

"Certainly I'm sure, with all the evidence I already have. That will finish ᴀer!" Owen declared.

This made his companion thoughtful again. "Can you take such pleasure ɪn her being 'finished'—a poor girl you've once loved?"

Owen waited long enough to take in the question; then with a ᴇerenity startling even to her knowledge of his nature, "I don't think I can ʜave *really* loved her, you know," he replied.

Fleda broke into a laugh which gave him a surprise as visible as the ᴍmotion it testified to. "Then how am I to know that you 'really' love— ɪnybody else?"

"Oh, I'll show you that!" said Owen.

"I must take it on trust," the girl pursued. "And what if Mona doesn't ɢive you up?" she added.

Owen was baffled but a few seconds; he had thought of everything. ʜWhy, that's just where you come in."

"To save you? I see. You mean I must get rid of her for you." His ʙlankness showed for a little that he felt the chill of her cold logic; but as she ᴡaited for his rejoinder she knew to which of them it cost most. He gasped a ᴍninute, and that gave her time to say: "You see, Mr. Owen, how impossible ɪt is to talk of such things yet!"

Like lightning he had grasped her arm. "You mean you *will* talk of them?" Then as he began to take the flood of assent from her eyes: "You *will* listen to ᴍne? Oh, you dear, you dear—when, when?"

531

"Ah, when it isn't mere misery!" The words had broken from her in a sudden loud cry, and what next happened was that the very sound of her pain upset her. She heard her own true note; she turned short away from him; in a moment she had burst into sobs; in another his arms were round her; the next she had let herself go so far that even Mrs. Gereth might have seen it. He clasped her, and she gave herself—she poured out her tears on his breast; something prisoned and pent throbbed and gushed; something deep and sweet surged up—something that came from far within and far off, that had begun with the sight of him in his indifference and had never had rest since then. The surrender was short, but the relief was long: she felt his lips upon her face and his arms tighten with his full divination. What she did, what she *had* done, she scarcely knew: she only was aware, as she broke from him again, of what had taken place in his own quick breast. What had taken place was that, with the click of a spring, he saw. He had cleared the high wall at a bound; they were together without a veil. She had not a shred of a secret left; it was as if a whirlwind had come and gone, laying low the great false front that she had built up stone by stone. The strangest thing of all was the momentary sense of desolation.

"Ah, all the while you *cared*?" Owen read the truth with a wonder so great that it was visibly almost a sadness, a terror caused by his sudden perception of where the impossibility was not. That made it all perhaps elsewhere.

"I cared, I cared, I cared!" Fleda moaned it as defiantly as if she were confessing a misdeed. "How couldn't I care? But you mustn't, you must never, never ask! It isn't for us to talk about!" she insisted. "Don't speak of it, don't speak!"

It was easy indeed not to speak when the difficulty was to find words. He clasped his hands before her as he might have clasped them at an altar; his pressed palms shook together while he held his breath and while she stilled herself in the effort to come round again to the real and the right. He helped this effort, soothing her into a seat with a touch as light as if she had really been something sacred. She sank into a chair and he dropped before her on his knees; she fell back with closed eyes and he buried his face in her lap. There was no way to thank her but this act of prostration, which lasted, in silence, till she laid consenting hands on him, touched his head and stroked it, held it in her tenderness till he acknowledged his long density. He made the avowal seem only his—made her, when she rose again, raise him at last, softly, as if from the abasement of shame. If in each other's eyes now, however, they saw the truth, this truth, to Fleda, looked harder even than before—all the harder that when, at the very moment she recognized it, he murmured to her ecstatically, in fresh possession of her hands, which he drew up to his breast, holding them tight there with both his own: "I'm saved, I'm saved,—I *am*! I'm ready for anything. I have your word. Come!" he cried, as if from the sight of a response slower than he needed, and in the tone he so often had of a great boy at a great game.

She had once more disengaged herself, with the private vow that he shouldn't yet touch her again. It was all too horribly soon—her sense of this was rapidly surging back. "We mustn't talk, we mustn't talk; we must *wait*!" she intensely insisted. "I don't know what you mean by your freedom; I don't see it, I don't feel it. Where is it yet, where, your freedom? If it's real there's plenty of time, and if it isn't there's more than enough. I hate myself," she protested, "for having anything to say about her: it's like waiting for dead men's shoes! What business is it of mine what she does? She has her own trouble and her own plan. It's too hideous to watch her and count on her!"

Owen's face, at this, showed a reviving dread, the fear of some darksome process of her mind. "If you speak for yourself I can understand, but why is it hideous for *me*?"

"Oh, I mean for myself!" Fleda said impatiently.

"*I* watch her, *I* count on her: how can I do anything else? If I count on her to let me definitely know how we stand, I do nothing in life but what she herself has led straight up to. I never thought of asking you to 'get rid of her' for me, and I never would have spoken to you if I hadn't held that I *am* rid of her, that she has backed out of the whole thing. Didn't she do so from the moment she began to put it off? I had already applied for the license; the very invitations were half addressed. Who but she, all of a sudden, demanded an unnatural wait? It was none of *my* doing; I had never dreamed of anything but coming up to the scratch." Owen grew more and more lucid, and more confident of the effect of his lucidity. "She called it 'taking a stand,' to see what mother would do. I told her mother would do what I would make her do; and to that she replied that she would like to see me make her first. I said I would arrange that everything should be all right, and she said she really preferred to arrange it herself. It was a flat refusal to trust me in the smallest degree. Why then had she pretended so tremendously to care for me? And of course, at present," said Owen, "she trusts me, if possible, still less."

Fleda paid this statement the homage of a minute's muteness. "As to that, naturally, she has reason."

"Why on earth has she reason?" Then, as his companion, moving away, simply threw up her hands, "I never looked at you—not to call looking—till she had regularly driven me to it," he went on. "I know what I'm about. I do assure you I'm all right!"

"You're not all right—you're all wrong!" Fleda cried in despair. "You mustn't stay here, you mustn't!" she repeated with clear decision. "You make me say dreadful things, and I feel as if I made *you* say them." But before he could reply she took it up in another tone. "Why in the world, if everything had changed, didn't you break off?"

"I?—" The inquiry seemed to have moved him to stupefaction. "Can you ask me that question when I only wanted to please you? Didn't you seem to show me, in your wonderful way, that that was exactly how? I didn't break off just on purpose to leave it to *her*. I didn't break off so that there shouldn't be a thing to be said against me."

The instant after her challenge Fleda had faced him again in self-reproof. "There *isn't* a thing to be said against you, and I don't know what nonsense you make me talk! You *have* pleased me, and you've been right and good, and it's the only comfort, and you must go. Everything must come from Mona, and if it doesn't come we've said entirely too much. You must leave me alone—forever."

"Forever?" Owen gasped.

"I mean unless everything is different."

"Everything *is* different—when I *know*!"

Fleda winced at what he knew; she made a wild gesture which seemed to whirl it out of the room. The mere allusion was like another embrace. "You know nothing—and you must go and wait! You mustn't break down at this point."

He looked about him and took up his hat: it was as if, in spite of frustration, he had got the essence of what he wanted and could afford to agree with her to the extent of keeping up the forms. He covered her with his fine, simple smile, but made no other approach. "Oh, I'm so awfully happy!" he exclaimed.

She hesitated: she would only be impeccable even though she should have to be sententious. "You'll be happy if you're perfect!" she risked.

He laughed out at this, and she wondered if, with a new-born acuteness, he saw the absurdity of her speech, and that no one was happy just because no one could be what she so lightly prescribed. "I don't pretend to be perfect, but I shall find a letter to-night!"

"So much the better, if it's the kind of one you desire." That was the most she could say, and having made it sound as dry as possible she lapsed into a silence so pointed as to deprive him of all pretext for not leaving her. Still, nevertheless, he stood there, playing with his hat and filling the long pause with a strained and anxious smile. He wished to obey her thoroughly, to appear not to presume on any advantage he had won from her; but there was clearly something he longed for beside. While he showed this by hanging on she thought of two other things. One of these was that his countenance, after all, failed to bear out his description of his bliss. As for the other, it had no sooner come into her head than she found it seated, in spite of her resolution, on her lips. It took the form of an inconsequent question. "When did you say Mrs. Brigstock was to have gone back?"

Owen stared. "To Waterbath? She was to have spent the night in town, don't you know? But when she left me, after our talk, I said to myself that she would take an evening train. I know I made her want to get home."

"Where did you separate?" Fleda asked.

"At the West Kensington station—she was going to Victoria. I had walked with her there, and our talk was all on the way."

Fleda pondered a moment. "If she did go back that night you would have heard from Waterbath by this time."

"I don't know," said Owen. "I thought I might hear this morning."

"She can't have gone back," Fleda declared. "Mona would have written on the spot."

"Oh yes, she *will* have written bang off!" Owen cheerfully conceded.

Fleda thought again. "Then, even in the event of her mother's not having got home till the morning, you would have had your letter at the latest to-day. You see she has had plenty of time."

Owen hesitated; then, "Oh, she's all right!" he laughed. "I go by Mrs. Brigstock's certain effect on her—the effect of the temper the old lady showed when we parted. Do you know what she asked me?" he sociably continued. "She asked me in a kind of nasty manner if I supposed you 'really' cared anything about me. Of course I told her I supposed you didn't—not a solitary rap. How could I suppose you *do*, with your extraordinary ways? It doesn't matter; I could see she thought I lied."

"You should have told her, you know, that I had seen you in town only that one time," Fleda observed.

"By Jove, I did—for *you*! It was only for you."

Something in this touched the girl so that for a moment she could not trust herself to speak. "You're an honest man," she said at last. She had gone to the door and opened it. "Good-bye."

Even yet, however, he hung back; and she remembered how, at the end of his hour at Ricks, she had been put to it to get him out of the house. He had in general a sort of cheerful slowness which helped him at such times, though she could now see his strong fist crumple his big, stiff gloves as if they had been paper. "But even if there's no letter—" he began. He began, but here he left it.

"You mean, even if she doesn't let you off? Ah, you ask me too much!" Fleda spoke from the tiny hall, where she had taken refuge between the old barometer and the old mackintosh. "There are things too utterly for yourselves alone. How can I tell? What do I know? Good-bye, good-bye! If she doesn't let you off, it will be because she *is* attached to you."

"She's not, she's not: there's nothing in it! Doesn't a fellow know?—except with *you*!" Owen ruefully added. With this he came out of the room, lowering his voice to secret supplication, pleading with her really to meet him on the ground of the negation of Mona. It was this betrayal of his need of support and sanction that made her retreat—harden herself in the effort to save what might remain of all she had given, given probably for nothing. The very vision of him as he thus morally clung to her was the vision of a weakness somewhere in the core of his bloom, a blessed manly weakness of which, if she had only the valid right, it would be all a sweetness to take care. She faintly sickened, however, with the sense that there was as yet no valid right poor Owen could give. "You can take it from my honor, you know," he whispered, "that she loathes me."

Fleda had stood clutching the knob of Maggie's little painted stair-rail; she took, on the stairs, a step backward. "Why then doesn't she prove it in the only clear way?"

"She *has* proved it. Will you believe it if you see the letter?"

"I don't want to see any letter," said Fleda. "You'll miss your train."

Facing him, waving him away, she had taken another upward step; but he sprang to the side of the stairs and brought his hand, above the banister, down hard on her wrist. "Do you mean to tell me that I must marry a woman I hate?"

From her step she looked down into his raised face. "Ah, you see it's not true that you're free!" She seemed almost to exult. "It's not true—it's not true!"

He only, at this, like a buffeting swimmer, gave a shake of his head and repeated his question. "Do you mean to tell me I must marry such a woman?"

Fleda hesitated; he held her fast. "No. Anything is better than that."

"Then, in God's name, what must I do?"

"You must settle that with her. You mustn't break faith. Anything is better than that. You must at any rate be utterly sure. She *must* love you—how can she help it? *I* wouldn't give you up!" said Fleda. She spoke in broken bits, panting out her words. "The great thing is to keep faith. Where *is* a man if he doesn't? If he doesn't he may be so cruel. So cruel, so cruel, so cruel!" Fleda repeated. "I couldn't have a hand in *that*, you know: that's my position—that's mine. You offered her marriage: it's a tremendous thing for her." Then looking at him another moment, "*I* wouldn't give you up!" she said again. He still had hold of her arm; she took in his blank alarm. With a quick dip of her face she reached his hand with her lips, pressing them to the back of it with a force that doubled the force of her words. "Never, never, never!" she cried; and before he could succeed in seizing her she had turned and, scrambling up the stairs, got away from him even faster than she had got away from him at Ricks.

XVII

Ten days after his visit she received a communication from Mrs. Gereth—a telegram of eight words, exclusive of signature and date. "Come up immediately and stay with me here"—it was characteristically sharp, as Maggie said; but, as Maggie added, it was also characteristically kind. "Here" was an hotel in London, and Maggie had embraced a condition of life which already began to produce in her some yearning for hotels in London. She would have responded in an instant, and she was surprised that her sister seemed to hesitate. Fleda's hesitation, which lasted but an hour, was expressed in that young lady's own mind by the reflection that in obeying her friend's summons she shouldn't know what she should be "in for." Her friend's summons, however, was but another name for her friend's appeal; and Mrs. Gereth's bounty had laid her under obligations more sensible than any reluctance. In the event—that is at the end of her hour—she testified to her gratitude by taking the train and to her mistrust by leaving her luggage. She went as if she had gone up for the day. In the train, however, she had another thoughtful hour, during which it was her mistrust that mainly deepened. She felt as if for ten days she had sat in darkness, looking to the east for a dawn that had not yet glimmered. Her mind had lately been less occupied with Mrs. Gereth; it had been so exceptionally occupied with Mona. If the sequel was to justify Owen's prevision of Mrs. Brigstock's action upon her daughter, this action was at the end of a week as much a mystery as ever. The stillness, all round, had been exactly what Fleda desired, but it gave her for the time a deep sense of failure, the sense of a sudden drop from a height at which she had all things beneath her. She had nothing beneath her now; she herself was at the bottom of the heap. No sign had reached her from Owen—poor Owen, who had clearly no news to give about his precious letter from Waterbath. If Mrs. Brigstock had hurried back to obtain that this letter should be written, Mrs. Brigstock might then have spared herself so great an inconvenience. Owen had been silent for the best of all reasons—the reason that he had had nothing in life to say. If the letter had not been written he would simply have had to introduce some large qualification into his account of his freedom. He had left his young friend under her refusal to listen to him until he should be able, on the contrary, to extend that picture; and his present submission was all in keeping with the rigid honesty that his young friend had prescribed.

It was this that formed the element through which Mona loomed large; Fleda had enough imagination, a fine enough feeling for life, to be impressed with such an image of successful immobility. The massive maiden at Waterbath *was* successful from the moment she could entertain her resentments as if they had been poor relations who needn't put her to expense. She was a magnificent dead weight; there was something positive and portentous in her quietude. "What game are they all playing?" poor Fleda could only ask; for she had an intimate conviction that Owen was now under the roof of his betrothed. That was stupefying if he really hated Mona; and if he didn't really hate her what had brought him to Raphael Road and to Maggie's? Fleda had no real light, but she felt that to account for the absence of any result of their last meeting would take a supposition of the full sacrifice to charity that she had held up before him. If he had gone to Waterbath it had been simply because he had to go. She had as good as told him that he would have to go; that this was an inevitable incident of his keeping perfect faith—faith so literal that the smallest subterfuge would always be a reproach to him. When she tried to remember that it was for herself he was taking his risk, she felt how weak a way that was of expressing Mona's supremacy. There would be no need of keeping him up if there were nothing to keep him up to. Her eyes grew wan as she discerned in the impenetrable air that Mona's thick outline never wavered an inch. She wondered fitfully what Mrs. Gereth had by this time made of it, and reflected with a strange elation that the sand on which the mistress of Ricks had built a momentary triumph was quaking beneath the surface. As The Morning Post still held its peace, she would be, of course, more confident; but the hour was at hand at which Owen would have absolutely to do either one thing or the other. To keep perfect faith was to inform against his mother, and to hear the police at her door would be Mrs. Gereth's awakening. How much she was beguiled Fleda could see from her having been for a whole month quite as deep and dark as Mona. She had let her young friend alone because of the certitude, cultivated at Ricks, that Owen had done the opposite. He had done the opposite indeed, but much good had that brought forth! To have sent for her now, Fleda felt, was from this point of view wholly natural: she had sent for her to show at last how much she had scored. If, however, Owen was really at Waterbath the refutation of that boast was easy.

Fleda found Mrs. Gereth in modest apartments and with an air of fatigue in her distinguished face—a sign, as she privately remarked, of the strain of that effort to be discreet of which she herself had been having the benefit. It was a constant feature of their relation that this lady could make Fleda blench a little, and that the effect proceeded from the intense pressure of her confidence. If the confidence had been heavy even when the girl, in the early flush of devotion, had been able to feel herself most responsive, it drew her heart into her mouth now that she had reserves and conditions, now that she couldn't simplify with the same bold hand as her protectress. In the very brightening of the tired look, and at the moment of their embrace, Fleda felt on her shoulders the return of the load, so that her spirit frankly quailed as she asked herself what she had brought up from her trusted seclusion to support it. Mrs. Gereth's free manner always made a joke of weakness, and there was in such a welcome a richness, a kind of familiar nobleness, that suggested shame to a harried conscience. Something had happened, she could see, and she could also see, in the bravery that seemed to announce it had changed everything, a formidable assumption that what had happened was what a healthy young woman must like. The absence of luggage had made this young woman feel meagre even before her companion, taking in the bareness at a second glance, exclaimed upon it and roundly rebuked her. Of course she had expected her to stay.

Fleda thought best to show bravery too, and to show it from the first. "What you expected, dear Mrs. Gereth, is exactly what I came up to ascertain. It struck me as right to do that first. I mean to ascertain, without making preparations."

"Then you'll be so good as to make them on the spot!" Mrs. Gereth was most emphatic. "You're going abroad with me."

Fleda wondered, but she also smiled. "To-night—to-morrow?"

541

"In a few days as possible. That's all that's left for me now." Fleda's heart, at this, gave a bound; she wondered to what particular difference in Mrs. Gereth's situation as last known to her it was an allusion. "I've made my plan," her friend continued: "I go for at least a year. We shall go straight to Florence; we can manage there. I of course don't look to you, however," she added, "to stay with me all that time. That will require to be settled. Owen will have to join us as soon as possible; he may not be quite ready to get off with us. But I'm convinced it's quite the right thing to go. It will make a good change; it will put in a decent interval."

Fleda listened; she was deeply mystified. "How kind you are to me!" she presently said. The picture suggested so many questions that she scarcely knew which to ask first. She took one at a venture. "You really have it from Mr. Gereth that he'll give us his company?"

If Mr. Gereth's mother smiled in response to this, Fleda knew that her smile was a tacit criticism of such a form of reference to her son. Fleda habitually spoke of him as Mr. Owen, and it was a part of her present vigilance to appear to have relinquished that right. Mrs. Gereth's manner confirmed a certain impression of her pretending to more than she felt; her very first words had conveyed it, and it reminded Fleda of the conscious courage with which, weeks before, the lady had met her visitor's first startled stare at the clustered spoils of Poynton. It was her practice to take immensely for granted whatever she wished. "Oh, if you'll answer for him, it will do quite as well!" she said. Then she put her hands on the girl's shoulders and held them at arm's length, as if to shake them a little, while in the depths of her shining eyes Fleda discovered something obscure and unquiet. "You bad, false thing, why didn't you tell me?" Her tone softened her harshness, and her visitor had never had such a sense of her indulgence. Mrs. Gereth could show patience; it was a part of the general bribe, but it was also like the handing in of a heavy bill before which Fleda could only fumble in a penniless pocket. "You must perfectly have known at Ricks, and yet you practically denied it. That's why I call you bad and false!" It was apparently also why she again almost roughly kissed her.

"I think that before I answer you I had better know what you're talking about," Fleda said.

Mrs. Gereth looked at her with a slight increase of hardness. "You've done everything you need for modesty, my dear! If he's sick with love of you, you haven't had to wait for me to inform you."

Fleda hesitated. "Has he informed *you*, dear Mrs. Gereth?"

Dear Mrs. Gereth smiled sweetly. "How could he, when our situation is such that he communicates with me only through you, and that you are so virtuous you conceal everything?"

"Didn't he answer the note in which you let him know that I was in town?" Fleda asked.

"He answered it sufficiently by rushing off on the spot to see you."

Mrs. Gereth met that allusion with a prompt firmness that made almost insolently light of any ground of complaint, and Fleda's own sense of responsibility was now so vivid that all resentments turned comparatively pale. She had no heart to produce a grievance; she could only, left as she was with the little mystery on her hands, produce, after a moment, a question. "How then do you come to know that your son has ever thought—"

"That he would give his ears to get you?" Mrs. Gereth broke in. "I had a visit from Mrs. Brigstock."

Fleda opened her eyes. "She went down to Ricks?"

"The day after she had found Owen at your feet. She knows everything."

Fleda shook her head sadly; she was more startled than she cared to know. This odd journey of Mrs. Brigstock's, which, with a simplicity equal for once to Owen's, she had not divined, now struck her as having produced the hush of the last ten days. "There are things she doesn't know!" she presently exclaimed.

"She knows he would do anything to marry you."

"He hasn't told her so," Fleda said.

"No, but he has told you. That's better still!" laughed Mrs. Gereth. "My dear child," she went on with an air that affected the girl as a sort of blind profanity, "don't try to make yourself out better than you are. *I* know what you are. I haven't lived with you so much for nothing. You're not quite a saint in heaven yet. Lord, what a creature you'd have thought me in my good time! But you do like it, fortunately, you idiot. You're pale with your passion, you sweet thing. That's exactly what I wanted to see. I can't for the life of me think where the shame comes in." Then with a finer significance, a look that seemed to Fleda strange, she added: "It's all right."

"I've seen him but twice," said Fleda.

"But twice?" Mrs. Gereth still smiled.

"On the occasion, at papa's, that Mrs. Brigstock told you of, and one day, since then, down at Maggie's."

"Well, those things are between yourselves, and you seem to me both poor creatures at best." Mrs. Gereth spoke with a rich humor which tipped with light for an instant a real conviction. "I don't know what you've got in your veins: you absurdly exaggerated the difficulties. But enough is as good as a feast, and when once I get you abroad together—!" She checked herself as if from excess of meaning; what might happen when she should get them abroad together was to be gathered only from the way she slowly rubbed her hands.

The gesture, however, made the promise so definite that for a moment her companion was almost beguiled. But there was nothing to account as yet, for the wealth of Mrs. Gereth's certitude: the visit of the lady of Waterbath appeared but half to explain it. "Is it permitted to be surprised," Fleda deferentially asked, "at Mrs. Brigstock's thinking it would help her to see you?"

"It's never permitted to be surprised at the aberrations of born fools," said Mrs. Gereth. "If a cow should try to calculate, that's the kind of happy thought she'd have. Mrs. Brigstock came down to plead with me."

Fleda mused a moment. "That's what she came to do with *me*," she then honestly returned. "But what did she expect to get of you, with your opposition so marked from the first?"

"She didn't know I want *you*, my dear. It's a wonder, with all my violence—the gross publicity I've given my desires. But she's as stupid as an owl—she doesn't feel your charm."

Fleda felt herself flush slightly, but she tried to smile. "Did you tell her all about it? Did you make her understand you want me?"

"For what do you take me? I wasn't such a donkey."

"So as not to aggravate Mona?" Fleda suggested.

"So as not to aggravate Mona, naturally. We've had a narrow course to steer, but thank God we're at last in the open!"

"What do you call the open, Mrs. Gereth?" Fleda demanded. Then as the other faltered: "Do you know where Mr. Owen is to-day?"

Mrs. Gereth stared. "Do you mean he's at Waterbath? Well, that's your own affair. I can bear it if *you* can."

"Wherever he is, I can bear it," Fleda said. "But I haven't the least idea where he is."

"Then you ought to be ashamed of yourself!" Mrs. Gereth broke out with a change of note that showed how deep a passion underlay everything she had said. The poor woman, catching her companion's hand, however, the next moment, as if to retract something of this harshness, spoke more patiently. "Don't you understand, Fleda, how immensely, how devotedly, I've trusted you?" Her tone was indeed a supplication.

Fleda was infinitely shaken; she was silent a little. "Yes, I understand. Did she go to you to complain of me?"

"She came to see what she could do. She had been tremendously upset, the day before, by what had taken place at your father's, and she had posted down to Ricks on the inspiration of the moment. She hadn't meant it on leaving home; it was the sight of you closeted there with Owen that had suddenly determined her. The whole story, she said, was written in your two faces: she spoke as if she had never seen such an exhibition. Owen was on the brink, but there might still be time to save him, and it was with this idea she had bearded me in my den. 'What won't a mother do, you know?'—that was one of the things she said. What wouldn't a mother do indeed? I thought I had sufficiently shown her what! She tried to break me down by an appeal to my good nature, as she called it, and from the moment she opened on *you*, from the moment she denounced Owen's falsity, I was as good-natured as she could wish. I understood that it was a plea for mere mercy, that you and he between you were killing her child. Of course I was delighted that Mona should be killed, but I was studiously kind to Mrs. Brigstock. At the same time I was honest, I didn't pretend to anything I couldn't feel. I asked her why the marriage hadn't taken place months ago, when Owen was perfectly ready; and I showed her how completely that fatuous mistake on Mona's part cleared his responsibility. It was she who had killed *him*—it was she who had destroyed his affection, his illusions. Did she want him now when he was estranged, when he was disgusted, when he had a sore grievance? She reminded me that Mona had a sore grievance too, but she admitted that she hadn't come to me to speak of that. What she had come to me for was not to get the old things back, but simply to get Owen. What she wanted was that I would, in simple pity, see fair play. Owen had been awfully bedeviled—she didn't call it that, she called it 'misled'—but it was simply you who had bedeviled him. He would be all right still if I would see that you were out of the way. She asked me point-blank if it was possible I could want him to marry you."

Fleda had listened in unbearable pain and growing terror, as if her interlocutress, stone by stone, were piling some fatal mass upon her breast. She had the sense of being buried alive, smothered in the mere expansion of another will; and now there was but one gap left to the air. A single word, she felt, might close it, and with the question that came to her lips as Mrs. Gereth paused she seemed to herself to ask, in cold dread, for her doom. "What did you say to that?" she inquired.

"I was embarrassed, for I saw my danger—the danger of her going home and saying to Mona that I was backing you up. It had been a bliss to learn that Owen had really turned to you, but my joy didn't put me off my guard. I reflected intensely for a few seconds; then I saw my issue."

"Your issue?" Fleda murmured.

"I remembered how you had tied my hands about saying a word to Owen."

Fleda wondered. "And did you remember the little letter that, with your hands tied, you still succeeded in writing to him?"

"Perfectly; my little letter was a model of reticence. What I remembered was all that in those few words I forbade myself to say. I had been an angel of delicacy—I had effaced myself like a saint. It was not for me to have done all that and then figure to such a woman as having done the opposite. Besides, it was none of her business."

"Is that what you said to her?" Fleda asked.

"I said to her that her question revealed a total misconception of the nature of my present relations with my son. I said to her that I had no relations with him at all, and that nothing had passed between us for months. I said to her that my hands were spotlessly clean of any attempt to make him make up to you. I said to her that I had taken from Poynton what I had a right to take, but had done nothing else in the world. I was determined that if I had bit my tongue off to oblige you I would at least have the righteousness that my sacrifice gave me."

"And was Mrs. Brigstock satisfied with your answer?"

"She was visibly relieved."

"It was fortunate for you," said Fleda, "that she's apparently not aware of the manner in which, almost under her nose, you advertised me to him at Poynton."

Mrs. Gereth appeared to recall that scene; she smiled with a serenity remarkably effective as showing how cheerfully used she had grown to invidious allusions to it. "How should she be aware of it?"

"She would if Owen had described your outbreak to Mona."

"Yes, but he didn't describe it. All his instinct was to conceal it from Mona. He wasn't conscious, but he was already in love with you!" Mrs. Gereth declared.

Fleda shook her head wearily. "No—I was only in love with him!"

Here was a faint illumination with which Mrs. Gereth instantly mingled her fire. "You dear old wretch!" she exclaimed; and she again, with ferocity, embraced her young friend.

Fleda submitted like a sick animal: she would submit to everything now. "Then what further passed?"

"Only that she left me thinking she had got something."

"And what had she got?"

"Nothing but her luncheon. But *I* got everything!"

"Everything?" Fleda quavered.

Mrs. Gereth, struck apparently by something in her tone, looked at her from a tremendous height. "Don't fail me now!"

It sounded so like a menace that, with a full divination at last, the poor girl fell weakly into a chair. "What on earth have you done?"

Mrs. Gereth stood there in all the glory of a great stroke. "I've settled you." She filled the room, to Fleda's scared vision, with the glare of her magnificence. "I've sent everything back."

"Everything?" Fleda gasped.

"To the smallest snuff-box. The last load went yesterday. The same people did it. Poor little Ricks is empty." Then as if, for a crowning splendor, check all deprecation, "They're yours, you goose!" Mrs. Gereth concluded, olding up her handsome head and rubbing her white hands. Fleda saw that here were tears in her deep eyes.

XVIII

She was slow to take in the announcement, but when she had done so
she felt it to be more than her cup of bitterness would hold. Her bitterness
was her anxiety, the taste of which suddenly sickened her. What had she
become, on the spot, but a traitress to her friend? The treachery increased
with the view of the friend's motive, a motive magnificent as a tribute to her
value. Mrs. Gereth had wished to make sure of her and had reasoned that
there would be no such way as by a large appeal to her honor. If it be true,
as men have declared, that the sense of honor is weak in women, some of
the bearings of this stroke might have thrown a light on the question. What
was now, at all events, put before Fleda was that she had been made sure of,
for the greatness of the surrender imposed an obligation as great. There was
an expression she had heard used by young men with whom she danced: the
only word to fit Mrs. Gereth's intention was that Mrs. Gereth had designed
to "fetch" her. It was a calculated, it was a crushing bribe; it looked her in
the eyes and said simply: "That's what I do for you!" What Fleda was to do
in return required no pointing out. The sense, at present, of how little she
had done made her almost cry aloud with pain; but her first endeavor, in the
face of the fact, was to keep such a cry from reaching her companion. How
little she had done Mrs. Gereth didn't yet know, and possibly there would
be still some way of turning round before the discovery. On her own side
too Fleda had almost made one: she had known she was wanted, but she
had not after all conceived how magnificently much. She had been treated
by her friend's act as a conscious prize, but what made her a conscious prize
was only the power the act itself imputed to her. As high, bold diplomacy it
dazzled and carried her off her feet. She admired the noble risk of it, a risk
Mrs. Gereth had faced for the utterly poor creature that the girl now felt
herself. The change it instantly wrought in her was, moreover, extraordinary:
it transformed at a touch her emotion on the subject of concessions. A few
weeks earlier she had jumped at the duty of pleading for them, practically
quarreling with the lady of Ricks for her refusal to restore what she had taken.

She had been sore with the wrong to Owen, she had bled with the wounds of Poynton; now however, as she heard of the replenishment of the void that had so haunted her, she came as near sounding an alarm as if from the deck of a ship she had seen a person she loved jump into the sea. Mrs. Gereth had become in a flash the victim; poor little Ricks had been laid bare in a night. If Fleda's feeling about the old things had taken precipitate form the form would have been a frantic command. It was indeed for mere want of breath that she didn't shout: "Oh, stop them—it's no use; bring them back—it's too late!" And what most kept her breathless was her companion's very grandeur. Fleda distinguished as never before the purity of such a passion; it made Mrs. Gereth august and almost sublime. It was absolutely unselfish—she cared nothing for mere possession. She thought solely and incorruptibly of what was best for the things; she had surrendered them to the presumptive care of the one person of her acquaintance who felt about them as she felt herself, and whose long lease of the future would be the nearest approach that could be compassed to committing them to a museum. Now it was indeed that Fleda knew what rested on her; now it was also that she measured as if for the first time Mrs. Gereth's view of the natural influence of a fine acquisition. She had adopted the idea of blowing away the last doubt of what her young friend would gain, of making good still more than she was obliged to make it the promise of weeks before. It was one thing for the girl to have heard that in a certain event restitution would be made; it was another for her to see the condition, with a noble trust, treated in advance as performed, and to be able to feel that she should have only to open a door to find every old piece in every old corner. To have played such a card was therefore, practically, for Mrs. Gereth, to have won the game. Fleda had certainly to recognize that, so far as the theory of the matter went, the game had been won. Oh, she had been made sure of!

She couldn't, however, succeed for so very many minutes in deferring her exposure. "Why didn't you wait, dearest? Ah, why didn't you wait?"—if that inconsequent appeal kept rising to her lips to be cut short before it was spoken, this was only because at first the humility of gratitude helped her to gain time, enabled her to present herself very honestly as too overcome to be clear. She kissed her companion's hands, she did homage at her feet, she murmured soft snatches of praise, and yet in the midst of it all was conscious that what she really showed most was the wan despair at her heart. She saw Mrs. Gereth's glimpse of this despair suddenly widen, heard the quick chill of her voice pierce through the false courage of endearments. "Do you mean to tell me at such an hour as this that you've really lost him?"

The tone of the question made the idea a possibility for which Fleda had nothing from this moment but terror. "I don't know, Mrs. Gereth; how can I say?" she asked. "I've not seen him for so long; as I told you just now, I don't even know where he is. That's by no fault of his," she hurried on: "he would have been with me every day if I had consented. But I made him understand, the last time, that I'll receive him again only when he's able to show me that his release has been complete and definite. Oh, he can't yet, don't you see, and that's why he hasn't been back. It's far better than his coming only that we should both be miserable. When he does come he'll be in a better position. He'll be tremendously moved by the splendid thing you've done. I know you wish me to feel that you've done it as much for me as for Owen, but your having done it for me is just what will delight him most! When he hears of it," said Fleda, in desperate optimism, "when he hears of it—" There indeed, regretting her advance, she quite broke down. She was wholly powerless to say what Owen would do when he heard of it. "I don't know what he won't make of you and how he won't hug you!" she had to content herself with lamely declaring. She had drawn Mrs. Gereth to a sofa with a vague instinct of pacifying her and still, after all, gaining time; but it was a position in which her great duped benefactress, portentously patient again during this demonstration, looked far from inviting a "hug." Fleda found herself tricking out the situation with artificial flowers, trying to talk even herself into the fancy that Owen, whose name she now made simple and sweet, might come in upon them at any moment. She felt an immense need to be understood and justified; she averted her face in dread from all that she might have to be forgiven. She pressed on her companion's arm as if to keep her quiet till she should really know, and then, after a minute, she poured out the clear essence of what in happier days had been her "secret." "You mustn't think I don't adore him when I've told him so to his face. I love him so that I'd die for him—I love him so that it's horrible. Don't look at me therefore as if I had not been kind, as if I had not been as tender as if he were dying and my tenderness were what would save him. Look at me as if you believe me, as if you feel what I've been through. Darling Mrs. Gereth, I could kiss the ground he walks on. I haven't a rag of pride; I used to have, but it's gone. I used to have a secret, but every one knows it now, and any one who looks at me can say, I think, what's the matter with me. It's not so very fine, my secret, and the less one really says about it the better; but I want you to have it from me because I was stiff before. I want you to see for yourself that I've been brought as low as a girl can very well be. It serves me right," Fleda laughed, "if I was ever proud and horrid to you! I don't know what you wanted me, in those days at Ricks, to do, but I don't think you can have wanted much more than what I've done. The other day at Maggie's I did things that made me, afterwards, think of you! I don't know what girls may do; but if he doesn't know that there isn't an inch of me that isn't his—!" Fleda sighed as if she couldn't express it; she piled it up, as she would have said; holding Mrs. Gereth with dilated eyes, she seemed to sound her for the effect of these words. "It's idiotic," she wearily smiled; "it's so strange that I'm almost angry for it, and the strangest part of all is that it isn't even happiness. It's anguish—it was from the first; from the first there was a bitterness and a kind of dread. But I owe you every word of the truth. You don't do him justice, either: he's a dear, I assure you he's a dear. I'd trust him to the last breath; I don't think you really know him. He's ever so much cleverer than he makes a show of; he's remarkable in his own shy way. You told me at Ricks that you wanted me to let myself go, and I've 'gone' quite far enough to discover as much as that, as well as all sorts of other delightful things about him. You'll tell me I make myself out worse than I am," said the girl, feeling more and more in her companion's attitude a quality that treated her speech as a desperate rigmarole and even perhaps as a piece of cold immodesty. She wanted to make herself out "bad"—it was a part of her justification; but it suddenly occurred to her that such a picture of her extravagance imputed a want of gallantry to the young man. "I don't care for anything you think," she declared, "because Owen, don't you know, sees me as I am. He's so kind that it makes up for everything!"

This attempt at gayety was futile; the silence with which, for a minute, her adversary greeted her troubled plea brought home to her afresh that she was on the bare defensive. "Is it a part of his kindness never to come near you?" Mrs. Gereth inquired at last. "Is it a part of his kindness to leave you without an inkling of where he is?" She rose again from where Fleda had kept her down; she seemed to tower there in the majesty of her gathered wrong. "Is it a part of his kindness that, after I've toiled as I've done for six days, and with my own weak hands, which I haven't spared, to denude myself, in your interest, to that point that I've nothing left, as I may say, but what I have on my back—is it a part of his kindness that you're not even able to produce him for me?"

There was a high contempt in this which was for Owen quite as much, and in the light of which Fleda felt that her effort at plausibility had been mere groveling. She rose from the sofa with an humiliated sense of rising from ineffectual knees. That discomfort, however, lived but an instant: it was swept away in a rush of loyalty to the absent. She herself could bear his mother's scorn; but to avert it from his sweet innocence she broke out with a quickness that was like the raising of an arm. "Don't blame him—don't blame him: he'd do anything on earth for me! It was I," said Fleda, eagerly, "who sent him back to her; I made him go; I pushed him out of the house; I declined to have anything to say to him except on another footing."

Mrs. Gereth stared as at some gross material ravage. "Another footing? What other footing?"

"The one I've already made so clear to you: my having it in black and white, as you may say, from her that she freely gives him up."

"Then you think he lies when he tells you that he has recovered his liberty?"

Fleda hesitated a moment; after which she exclaimed with a certain hard pride: "He's enough in love with me for anything!"

"For anything, apparently, except to act like a man and impose his reason and his will on your incredible folly. For anything except to put an end, as any man worthy of the name would have put it, to your systematic, to your idiotic perversity. What are you, after all, my dear, I should like to know, hat a gentleman who offers you what Owen offers should have to meet such onderful exactions, to take such extraordinary precautions about your sweet ttle scruples?" Her resentment rose to a strange insolence which Fleda took ill in the face and which, for the moment at least, had the horrible force) present to her vengefully a showy side of the truth. It gave her a blinding limpse of lost alternatives. "I don't know what to think of him," Mrs. Gereth ent on; "I don't know what to call him: I'm so ashamed of him that I can carcely speak of him even to *you*. But indeed I'm so ashamed of you both gether that I scarcely know in common decency where to look." She paused) give Fleda the full benefit of this remarkable statement; then she exclaimed: Any one but a jackass would have tucked you under his arm and marched ou off to the Registrar!"

Fleda wondered; with her free imagination she could wonder even while er cheek stung from a slap. "To the Registrar?"

"That would have been the sane, sound, immediate course to adopt. Vith a grain of gumption you'd both instantly have felt it. *I* should have und a way to take you, you know, if I'd been what Owen's supposed to e. *I* should have got the business over first; the rest could come when you ked! Good God, girl, your place was to stand before me as a woman honestly narried. One doesn't know what one has hold of in touching you, and you nust excuse my saying that you're literally unpleasant to me to meet as you re. Then at least we could have talked, and Owen, if he had the ghost of a nse of humor, could have snapped his fingers at your refinements."

This stirring speech affected our young lady as if it had been the shake of tambourine borne towards her from a gypsy dance: her head seemed to go und and she felt a sudden passion in her feet. The emotion, however, was ut meagerly expressed in the flatness with which she heard herself presently y: "I'll go to the Registrar now."

"Now?" Magnificent was the sound Mrs. Gereth threw into this nonosyllable. "And pray who's to take you?" Fleda gave a colorless smile, and er companion continued: "Do you literally mean that you can't put your and upon him?" Fleda's wan grimace appeared to irritate her; she made a nort, imperious gesture. "Find him for me, you fool—*find* him for me!"

"What do you want of him," Fleda sadly asked, "feeling as you do to both of us?"

"Never mind how I feel, and never mind what I say when I'm furious!" Mrs. Gereth still more incisively added. "Of course I cling to you, you wretches, or I shouldn't suffer as I do. What I want of him is to see that he takes you; what I want of him is to go with you myself to the place." She looked round the room as if, in feverish haste, for a mantle to catch up; she bustled to the window as if to spy out a cab: she would allow half an hour for the job. Already in her bonnet, she had snatched from the sofa a garment for the street: she jerked it on as she came back. "Find him, find him," she repeated; "come straight out with me, to try, at least, to get at him!"

"How can I get at him? He'll come when he's ready," Fleda replied.

Mrs. Gereth turned on her sharply. "Ready for what? Ready to see me ruined without a reason or a reward?"

Fleda was silent; the worst of it all was that there was something unspoken between them. Neither of them dared to utter it, but the influence of it was in the girl's tone when she returned at last, with great gentleness: "Don't be harsh to me—I'm very unhappy." The words produced a visible impression on Mrs. Gereth, who held her face averted and sent off through the window a gaze that kept pace with the long caravan of her treasures. Fleda knew she was watching it wind up the avenue of Poynton—Fleda participated indeed fully in the vision; so that after a little the most consoling thing seemed to her to add: "I don't see why in the world you take so for granted that he's, as you say, 'lost.'"

Mrs. Gereth continued to stare out of the window, and her stillness denoted some success in controlling herself. "If he's not lost, why are you unhappy?"

"I'm unhappy because I torment you, and you don't understand me."

"No, Fleda, I don't understand you," said Mrs. Gereth, finally facing her again. "I don't understand you at all, and it's as if you and Owen were of quite another race and another flesh. You make me feel very old-fashioned and simple and bad. But you must take me as I am, since you take so much else *with* me!" She spoke now with the drop of her resentment, with a dry and weary calm. "It would have been better for me if I had never known you," she pursued, "and certainly better if I hadn't taken such an extraordinary fancy to you. But that too was inevitable: everything, I suppose, is inevitable. It was all my own doing—you didn't run after me: I pounced on you and caught you up. You're a stiff little beggar, in spite of your pretty manners: yes, you're hideously misleading. I hope you feel how handsome it is of me to recognize the independence of your character. It was your clever sympathy that did it—your extraordinary feeling for those accursed vanities. You were sharper about them than any one I had ever known, and that was a thing I simply couldn't resist. Well," the poor lady concluded after a pause, "you see where it has landed us!"

"If you'll go for him yourself, I'll wait here," said Fleda.

Mrs. Gereth, holding her mantle together, appeared for a while to consider.

"To his club, do you mean?"

"Isn't it there, when he's in town, that he has a room? He has at present no other London address," Fleda said: "it's there one writes to him."

"How do *I* know, with my wretched relations with him?" Mrs. Gereth asked.

"Mine have not been quite so bad as that," Fleda desperately smiled. Then she added: "His silence, *her* silence, our hearing nothing at all—what are these but the very things on which, at Poynton and at Ricks, you rested your assurance that everything is at an end between them?"

Mrs. Gereth looked dark and void. "Yes, but I hadn't heard from you then that you could invent nothing better than, as you call it, to send him back to her."

"Ah, but, on the other hand, you've learned from them what you didn't know—you've learned by Mrs. Brigstock's visit that he cares for me." Fleda found herself in the position of availing herself of optimistic arguments that she formerly had repudiated; her refutation of her companion had completely changed its ground.

She was in a fever of ingenuity and painfully conscious, on behalf of her success, that her fever was visible. She could herself see the reflection of it glitter in Mrs. Gereth's sombre eyes.

"You plunge me in stupefaction," that lady answered, "and at the same time you terrify me. Your account of Owen is inconceivable, and yet I don't know what to hold on by. He cares for you, it does appear, and yet in the same breath you inform me that nothing is more possible than that he's spending these days at Waterbath. Excuse me if I'm so dull as not to see my way in such darkness. If he's at Waterbath he doesn't care for you. If he cares for you he's not at Waterbath."

"Then where is he?" poor Fleda helplessly wailed. She caught herself up, however; she did her best to be brave and clear. Before Mrs. Gereth could reply, with due obviousness, that this was a question for her not to ask, but to answer, she found an air of assurance to say: "You simplify far too much. You always did and you always will. The tangle of life is much more intricate than you've ever, I think, felt it to be. You slash into it," cried Fleda finely, "with a great pair of shears, you nip at it as if you were one of the Fates! If Owen's at Waterbath he's there to wind everything up."

Mrs. Gereth shook her head with slow austerity. "You don't believe a word you're saying. I've frightened you, as you've frightened me: you're whistling in the dark to keep up our courage. I do simplify, doubtless, if to simplify is to fail to comprehend the insanity of a passion that bewilders a young blockhead with bugaboo barriers, with hideous and monstrous sacrifices. I can only repeat that you're beyond me. Your perversity's a thing to howl over. However," the poor woman continued with a break in her voice, a long hesitation and then the dry triumph of her will, "I'll never mention it to you again! Owen I can just make out; for Owen *is* a blockhead. Owen's a blockhead," she repeated with a quiet, tragic finality, looking straight into Fleda's eyes. "I don't know why you dress up so the fact that he's disgustingly weak."

Fleda hesitated; at last, before her companion's, she lowered her look. "Because I love him. It's because he's weak that he needs me," she added.

"That was why his father, whom he exactly resembles, needed *me*. And I didn't fail his father," said Mrs. Gereth. She gave Fleda a moment to appreciate the remark; after which she pursued: "Mona Brigstock isn't weak; she's stronger than you!"

"I never thought she was weak," Fleda answered. She looked vaguely round the room with a new purpose: she had lost sight of her umbrella.

"I did tell you to let yourself go, but it's clear enough that you really haven't," Mrs. Gereth declared. "If Mona has got him—"

Fleda had accomplished her search; her interlocutress paused. "If Mona has got him?" the girl inquired, tightening the umbrella.

"Well," said Mrs. Gereth profoundly, "it will be clear enough that Mona *has*."

"Has let herself go?"

"Has let herself go." Mrs. Gereth spoke as if she saw it in every detail.

Fleda felt the tone and finished her preparation; then she went and opened the door. "We'll look for him together," she said to her friend, who stood a moment taking in her face. "They may know something about him at the Colonel's."

"We'll go there." Mrs. Gereth had picked up her gloves and her purse. "But the first thing," she went on, "will be to wire to Poynton."

"Why not to Waterbath at once?" Fleda asked.

Her companion hesitated. "In *your* name?"

"In my name. I noticed a place at the corner."

While Fleda held the door open Mrs. Gereth drew on her gloves. "Forgive me," she presently said. "Kiss me," she added.

Fleda, on the threshold, kissed her; then they went out.

XIX

In the place at the corner, on the chance of its saving time, Fleda wrote her telegram—wrote it in silence under Mrs. Gereth's eye and then in silence handed it to her. "I send this to Waterbath, on the possibility of your being there, to ask you to come to me." Mrs. Gereth held it a moment, read it more than once; then keeping it, and with her eyes on her companion, seemed to consider. There was the dawn of a kindness in her look; Fleda perceived in it, as if as the reward of complete submission, a slight relaxation of her rigor.

"Wouldn't it perhaps after all be better," she asked, "before doing this, to see if we can make his whereabouts certain?"

"Why so? It will be always so much done," said Fleda. "Though I'm poor," she added with a smile, "I don't mind the shilling."

"The shilling's *my* shilling," said Mrs. Gereth.

Fleda stayed her hand. "No, no—I'm superstitious."

"Superstitious?"

"To succeed, it must be all me!"

"Well, if that will make it succeed!" Mrs. Gereth took back her shilling, but she still kept the telegram. "As he's most probably not there—"

"If he shouldn't be there," Fleda interrupted, "there will be no harm done."

"If he 'shouldn't be' there!" Mrs. Gereth ejaculated. "Heaven help us, how you assume it!"

"I'm only prepared for the worst. The Brigstocks will simply send any telegram on."

"Where will they send it?"

"Presumably to Poynton."

"They'll read it first," said Mrs. Gereth.

"Read it?"

"Yes, Mona will. She'll open it under the pretext of having it repeated; and then she'll probably do nothing. She'll keep it as a proof of your immodesty."

"What of that?" asked Fleda.

"You don't mind her seeing it?"

Rather musingly and absently Fleda shook her head. "I don't mind anything."

"Well, then, that's all right," said Mrs. Gereth as if she had only wanted to feel that she had been irreproachably considerate. After this she was gentler still, but she had another point to clear up. "Why have you given, for a reply, your sister's address?"

"Because if he *does* come to me he must come to me there. If that telegram goes," said Fleda, "I return to Maggie's to-night."

Mrs. Gereth seemed to wonder at this. "You won't receive him here with me?"

"No, I won't receive him here with you. Only where I received him last—only there again." She showed her companion that as to that she was firm.

But Mrs. Gereth had obviously now had some practice in following queer movements prompted by queer feelings. She resigned herself, though she fingered the paper a moment longer. She appeared to hesitate; then she brought out: "You couldn't then, if I release you, make your message a little stronger?"

Fleda gave her a faint smile. "He'll come if he can."

Mrs. Gereth met fully what this conveyed; with decision she pushed in the telegram. But she laid her hand quickly upon another form and with still greater decision wrote another message. "From *me*, this," she said to Fleda when she had finished: "to catch him possibly at Poynton. Will you read it?"

561

Fleda turned away. "Thank you."

"It's stronger than yours."

"I don't care," said Fleda, moving to the door. Mrs. Gereth, having paid for the second missive, rejoined her, and they drove together to Owen's club where the elder lady alone got out. Fleda, from the hansom, watched through the glass doors her brief conversation with the hall-porter and then met in silence her return with the news that he had not seen Owen for a fortnight and was keeping his letters till called for. These had been the last orders; there were a dozen letters lying there. He had no more information to give, but they would see what they could find at Colonel Gereth's. To any connection with this inquiry, however, Fleda now roused herself to object, and her friend had indeed to recognize that on second thoughts it couldn't be quite to the taste of either of them to advertise in the remoter reaches of the family that they had forfeited the confidence of the master of Poynton. The letters lying at the club proved effectively that he was not in London, and this was the question that immediately concerned them. Nothing could concern them further till the answers to their telegrams should have had time to arrive. Mrs. Gereth had got back into the cab, and, still at the door of the club, they sat staring at their need of patience. Fleda's eyes rested, in the great hard street, on passing figures that struck her as puppets pulled by strings. After a little the driver challenged them through the hole in the top. "Anywhere in particular, ladies?"

Fleda decided. "Drive to Euston, please."

"You won't wait for what we may hear?" Mrs. Gereth asked.

"Whatever we hear, I must go." As the cab went on she added: "But needn't drag *you* to the station."

Mrs. Gereth was silent a moment; then "Nonsense!" she sharply replied.

In spite of this sharpness they were now almost equally and almost tremulously mild; though their mildness took mainly the form of an inevitable sense of nothing left to say. It was the unsaid that occupied them—the thing that for more than an hour they had been going round and round without naming it. Much too early for Fleda's train, they encountered at the station a long half-hour to wait. Fleda made no further allusion to Mrs. Gereth's leaving her; their dumbness, with the elapsing minutes, grew to be in itself a reconstituted bond. They slowly paced the great gray platform, and presently Mrs. Gereth took the girl's arm and leaned on it with a hard demand for support. It seemed to Fleda not difficult for each to know of what the other was thinking—to know indeed that they had in common two alternating visions, one of which, at moments, brought them as by a common impulse to a pause. This was the one that was fixed; the other filled at times the whole space and then was shouldered away. Owen and Mona glared together out of the gloom and disappeared, but the replenishment of Poynton made a shining, steady light. The old splendor was there again, the old things were in their places. Our friends looked at them with an equal yearning; face to face, on the platform, they counted them in each other's eyes. Fleda had come back to them by a road as strange as the road they themselves had followed. The wonder of their great journeys, the prodigy of this second one, was the question that made her occasionally stop. Several times she uttered it, asked how this and that difficulty had been met. Mrs. Gereth replied with pale lucidity—was naturally the person most familiar with the truth that what she undertook was always somehow achieved. To do it was to do it—she had more than one kind of magnificence. She confessed there, audaciously enough, to a sort of arrogance of energy, and Fleda, going on again, her inquiry more than answered and her arm rendering service, flushed, in her diminished identity, with the sense that such a woman was great.

"You do mean literally everything, to the last little miniature on the last little screen?"

"I mean literally everything. Go over them with the catalogue!"

Fleda went over them while they walked again; she had no need of the catalogue. At last she spoke once more: "Even the Maltese cross?"

"Even the Maltese cross. Why not that as well as everything else?—especially as I remembered how you like it."

Finally, after an interval, the girl exclaimed: "But the mere fatigue of it, the exhaustion of such a feat! I drag you to and fro here while you must be ready to drop."

"I'm very, very tired." Mrs. Gereth's slow head-shake was tragic. "I couldn't do it again."

"I doubt if they'd bear it again!"

"That's another matter: they'd bear it if I could. There won't have been, this time either, a shake or a scratch. But I'm too tired—I very nearly don't care."

"You must sit down, then, till I go," said Fleda. "We must find a bench."

"No. I'm tired of *them*: I'm not tired of you. This is the way for you to feel most how much I rest on you." Fleda had a compunction, wondering as they continued to stroll whether it was right after all to leave her. She believed, however, that if the flame might for the moment burn low, it was far from dying out; an impression presently confirmed by the way Mrs. Gereth went on: "But one's fatigue is nothing. The idea under which one worked kept one up. For you I *could*—I can still. Nothing will have mattered if *she's* not there."

There was a question that this imposed, but Fleda at first found no voice to utter it: it was the thing that, between them, since her arrival, had been so consciously and vividly unsaid. Finally she was able to breathe: "And if she *is* there—if she's there already?"

Mrs. Gereth's rejoinder too hung back; then when it came—from sad eyes as well as from lips barely moved—it was unexpectedly merciful. "It will be very hard." That was all, now; and it was poignantly simple. The train Fleda was to take had drawn up; the girl kissed her as if in farewell. Mrs. Gereth submitted, then after a little brought out: "If we *have* lost—"

"If we have lost?" Fleda repeated as she paused again.

"You'll all the same come abroad with me?"

"It will seem very strange to me if you want me. But whatever you ask, whatever you need, that I will always do."

"I shall need your company," said Mrs. Gereth. Fleda wondered an instant if this were not practically a demand for penal submission—for a surrender that, in its complete humility, would be a long expiation. But there was none of the latent chill of the vindictive in the way Mrs. Gereth pursued: "We can always, as time goes on, talk of them together."

"Of the old things?" Fleda had selected a third-class compartment: she stood a moment looking into it and at a fat woman with a basket who had already taken possession. "Always?" she said, turning again to her companion. "Never!" she exclaimed. She got into the carriage, and two men with bags and boxes immediately followed, blocking up door and window so long that when she was able to look out again Mrs. Gereth had gone.

XX

There came to her at her sister's no telegram in answer to her own: the rest of that day and the whole of the next elapsed without a word either from Owen or from his mother. She was free, however, to her infinite relief, from any direct dealing with suspense, and conscious, to her surprise, of nothing that could show her, or could show Maggie and her brother-in-law, that she was excited. Her excitement was composed of pulses as swift and fine as the revolutions of a spinning top: she supposed she was going round, but she went round so fast that she couldn't even feel herself move. Her emotion occupied some quarter of her soul that had closed its doors for the day and shut out even her own sense of it; she might perhaps have heard something if she had pressed her ear to a partition. Instead of that she sat with her patience in a cold, still chamber from which she could look out in quite another direction. This was to have achieved an equilibrium to which she couldn't have given a name: indifference, resignation, despair were the terms of a forgotten tongue. The time even seemed not long, for the stages of the journey were the items of Mrs. Gereth's surrender. The detail of that performance, which filled the scene, was what Fleda had now before her eyes. The part of her loss that she could think of was the reconstituted splendor of Poynton. It was the beauty she was most touched by that, in tons, she had lost—the beauty that, charged upon big wagons, had safely crept back to its home. But the loss was a gain to memory and love; it was to her too, at last, that, in condonation of her treachery, the old things had crept back. She greeted them with open arms; she thought of them hour after hour; they made a company with which solitude was warm and a picture that, at this crisis, overlaid poor Maggie's scant mahogany. It was really her obliterated passion that had revived, and with it an immense assent to Mrs. Gereth's early judgment of her. She too, she felt, was of the religion, and like any other of the passionately pious she could worship now even in the desert. Yes, it was all for her; far round as she had gone she had been strong enough: her love had gathered in the spoils. She wanted indeed no catalogue to count them over; the array of them, miles way, was complete; each piece, in its turn, was perfect to her; she could ave drawn up a catalogue from memory. Thus again she lived with them, nd she thought of them without a question of any personal right. That they might have been, that they might still be hers, that they were perhaps already nother's, were ideas that had too little to say to her. They were nobody's at l—too proud, unlike base animals and humans, to be reducible to anything narrow. It was Poynton that was theirs; they had simply recovered their wn. The joy of that for them was the source of the strange peace in which he girl found herself floating.

It was broken on the third day by a telegram from Mrs. Gereth. "Shall e with you at 11.30—don't meet me at station." Fleda turned this over, but as sufficiently expert not to disobey the injunction. She had only an hour take in its meaning, but that hour was longer than all the previous time. Maggie had studied her convenience the day Owen came, Maggie was also t the present juncture a miracle of refinement. Increasingly and resentfully mystified, in spite of all reassurance, by the impression that Fleda suffered more than she gained from the grandeur of the Gereths, she had it at heart to exemplify the perhaps truer distinction of nature that characterized the house f Vetch. She was not, like poor Fleda, at every one's beck, and the visitor as to see no more of her than what the arrangement of luncheon might tantalizingly show. Maggie described herself to her sister as intending for a 1st provocation even the understanding she had had with her husband that e also should remain invisible. Fleda accordingly awaited alone the subject f so many manœuvres—a period that was slightly prolonged even after the rawing-room door, at 11.30, was thrown open. Mrs. Gereth stood there with face that spoke plain, but no sound fell from her till the withdrawal of the naid, whose attention had immediately attached itself to the rearrangement f a window-blind and who seemed, while she bustled at it, to contribute to he pregnant silence; before the duration of which, however, she retreated vith a sudden stare.

"He has done it," said Mrs. Gereth, turning her eyes avoidingly but ot unperceivingly about her and in spite of herself dropping an opinion pon the few objects in the room. Fleda, on her side, in her silence, observed how characteristically she looked at Maggie's possessions before looking a Maggie's sister. The girl understood and at first had nothing to say; she wa still dumb while Mrs. Gereth selected, with hesitation, a seat less distasteful than the one that happened to be nearest. On the sofa near the window the poor woman finally showed what the two past days had done for the age o her face. Her eyes at last met Fleda's. "It's the end."

"They're married?"

"They're married."

Fleda came to the sofa in obedience to the impulse to sit down by her then paused before her while Mrs. Gereth turned up a dead gray mask. A tired old woman sat there with empty hands in her lap. "I've heard nothing, said Fleda. "No answer came."

"That's the only answer. It's the answer to everything." So Fleda saw for a minute she looked over her companion's head and far away. "He wasn' at Waterbath; Mrs. Brigstock must have read your telegram and kept it. Bu mine, the one to Poynton, brought something. 'We are here—what do you want?'" Mrs. Gereth stopped as if with a failure of voice; on which Fleda sank upon the sofa and made a movement to take her hand. It met no response there could be no attenuation. Fleda waited; they sat facing each other like strangers. "I wanted to go down," Mrs. Gereth presently continued. "Well I went."

All the girl's effort tended for the time to a single aim—that of taking the thing with outward detachment, speaking of it as having happened to Owen and to his mother and not in any degree to herself. Something at leas of this was in the encouraging way she said: "Yesterday morning?"

"Yesterday morning. I saw him."

Fleda hesitated. "Did you see *her*?"

"Thank God, no!"

Fleda laid on her arm a hand of vague comfort, of which Mrs. Gereth took no notice. "You've been capable, just to tell me, of this wretched journey of this consideration that I don't deserve?"

"We're together, we're together," said Mrs. Gereth. She looked helpless as she sat there, her eyes, unseeingly enough, on a tall Dutch clock, old but rather poor, that Maggie had had as a wedding-gift and that eked out the bareness of the room.

To Fleda, in the face of the event, it appeared that this was exactly what they were not: the last inch of common ground, the ground of their past intercourse, had fallen from under them. Yet what was still there was the grand style of her companion's treatment of her. Mrs. Gereth couldn't stand upon small questions, couldn't, in conduct, make small differences. "You're magnificent!" her young friend exclaimed. "There's a rare greatness in your generosity."

"We're together, we're together," Mrs. Gereth lifelessly repeated. "That's all we *are* now; it's all we have." The words brought to Fleda a sudden vision of the empty little house at Ricks; such a vision might also have been what her companion found in the face of the stopped Dutch clock. Yet with this it was clear that she would now show no bitterness: she had done with that, had given the last drop to those horrible hours in London. No passion even was left to her, and her forbearance only added to the force with which she represented the final vanity of everything.

Fleda was so far from a wish to triumph that she was absolutely ashamed of having anything to say for herself; but there was one thing, all the same, that not to say was impossible. "That he has done it, that he couldn't *not* do it, shows how right I was." It settled forever her attitude, and she spoke as if for her own mind; then after a little she added very gently, for Mrs. Gereth's: "That's to say, it shows that he was bound to her by an obligation that, however much he may have wanted to, he couldn't in any sort of honor break."

Blanched and bleak, Mrs. Gereth looked at her. "What sort of an obligation do you call that? No such obligation exists for an hour between any man and any woman who have hatred on one side. He had ended by hating her, and now he hates her more than ever."

"Did he tell you so?" Fleda asked.

"No. He told me nothing but the great gawk of a fact. I saw him but for three minutes." She was silent again, and Fleda, as before some lurid image of this interview, sat without speaking. "Do you wish to appear as if you don't care?" Mrs. Gereth presently demanded.

"I'm trying not to think of myself."

"Then if you're thinking of Owen, how can you *bear* to think?"

Sadly and submissively Fleda shook her head; the slow tears had come into her eyes. "I can't. I don't understand—I don't understand!" she broke out.

"*I* do, then." Mrs. Gereth looked hard at the floor. "There was no obligation at the time you saw him last—when you sent him, hating her as he did, back to her."

"If he went," Fleda asked, "doesn't that exactly prove that he recognized one?"

"He recognized rot! You know what *I* think of him." Fleda knew; she had no wish to challenge a fresh statement. Mrs. Gereth made one—it was her sole, faint flicker of passion—to the extent of declaring that he was too abjectly weak to deserve the name of a man. For all Fleda cared!—it was his weakness she loved in him. "He took strange ways of pleasing you!" her friend went on. "There was no obligation till suddenly, the other day, the situation changed."

Fleda wondered. "The other day?"

"It came to Mona's knowledge—I can't tell you how, but it came—that the things I was sending back had begun to arrive at Poynton. I had sent them for you, but it was *her* I touched." Mrs. Gereth paused; Fleda was too absorbed in her explanation to do anything but take blankly the full, cold breath of this. "They were there, and that determined her."

"Determined her to what?"

"To act, to take means."

"To take means?" Fleda repeated.

"I can't tell you what they were, but they were powerful. She knew how," said Mrs. Gereth.

Fleda received with the same stoicism the quiet immensity of this allusion to the person who had not known how. But it made her think a little, and the thought found utterance, with unconscious irony, in the simple interrogation: "Mona?"

"Why not? She's a brute."

"But if he knew that so well, what chance was there in it for her?"

"How can I tell you? How can I talk of such horrors? I can only give you, of the situation, what I see. He knew it, yes. But as she couldn't make him forget it, she tried to make him like it. She tried and she succeeded: that's what she did. She's after all so much less of a fool than he. And what *else* had he originally liked?" Mrs. Gereth shrugged her shoulders. "She did what you wouldn't!" Fleda's face had grown dark with her wonder, but her friend's empty hands offered no balm to the pain in it. "It was that if it was anything. Nothing else meets the misery of it. Then there was quick work. Before he could turn round he was married."

Fleda, as if she had been holding her breath, gave the sigh of a listening child. "At that place you spoke of in town?"

"At the Registrar's, like a pair of low atheists."

The girl hesitated. "What do people say of that? I mean the 'world.'"

"Nothing, because nobody knows. They're to be married on the 17th, at Waterbath church. If anything else comes out, everybody is a little prepared. It will pass for some stroke of diplomacy, some move in the game, some outwitting of *me*. It's known there has been a row with me."

Fleda was mystified. "People surely knew at Poynton," she objected, "if, as you say, she's there."

"She was there, day before yesterday, only for a few hours. She met him in London and went down to see the things."

Fleda remembered that she had seen them only once. "Did *you* see them?" she then ventured to ask.

"Everything."

"Are they right?"

"Quite right. There's nothing like them," said Mrs. Gereth. At this her companion took up one of her hands again and kissed it as she had done in London. "Mona went back that night; she was not there yesterday. Owen stayed on," she added.

Fleda stared. "Then she's not to live there?"

"Rather! But not till after the public marriage." Mrs. Gereth seemed to muse; then she brought out: "She'll live there alone."

"Alone?"

"She'll have it to herself."

"He won't live with her?"

"Never! But she's none the less his wife, and you're not," said Mrs. Gereth, getting up. "Our only chance is the chance she may die."

Fleda appeared to consider: she appreciated her visitor's magnanimous use of the plural. "Mona won't die," she replied.

"Well, *I* shall, thank God! Till then"—and with this, for the first time, Mrs. Gereth put out her hand—"don't desert me."

Fleda took her hand, and her clasp of it was a reiteration of a promise already given. She said nothing, but her silence was an acceptance as responsible as the vow of a nun. The next moment something occurred to her. "I mustn't put myself in your son's way."

Mrs. Gereth gave a dry, flat laugh. "You're prodigious! But how shall you possibly be more out of it? Owen and I—" She didn't finish her sentence.

"That's your great feeling about *him*," Fleda said; "but how, after what has happened, can it be his about you?"

Mrs. Gereth hesitated. "How do you know what has happened? You •n't know what I said to him."

"Yesterday?"

"Yesterday."

They looked at each other with a long, deep gaze. Then, as Mrs. Gereth emed again about to speak, the girl, closing her eyes, made a gesture of ong prohibition. "Don't tell me!"

"Merciful powers, how you worship him!" Mrs. Gereth wonderingly oaned. It was, for Fleda, the shake that made the cup overflow. She had pause, that of the child who takes time to know that he responds to an cident with pain; then, dropping again on the sofa, she broke into tears. 1ey were beyond control, they came in long sobs, which for a moment Mrs. ereth, almost with an air of indifference, stood hearing and watching. At st Mrs. Gereth too sank down again. Mrs. Gereth soundlessly, wearily wept.

"It looks just like Waterbath; but, after all, we bore *that* together
these words formed part of a letter in which, before the 17th, Mrs. Geret
writing from disfigured Ricks, named to Fleda the day on which she wou
be expected to arrive there on a second visit. "I sha'n't, for a long time t
come," the missive continued, "be able to receive any one who may *like* i
who would try to smooth it down, and me with it; but there are always thing
you and I can comfortably hate together, for you're the only person wh
comfortably understands. You don't understand quite everything, but of a
my acquaintance you're far away the least stupid. For action you're no goo
at all; but action is over, for me, forever, and you will have the great merit
knowing, when I'm brutally silent, what I shall be thinking about. Withou
setting myself up for your equal, I dare say I shall also know what are you
own thoughts. Moreover, with nothing else but my four walls, you'll at an
rate be a bit of furniture. For that, you know, a little, I've always taken you–
quite one of my best finds. So come, if possible, on the 15th."

The position of a bit of furniture was one that Fleda could conscientious
accept, and she by no means insisted on so high a place in the list. Th
communication made her easier, if only by its acknowledgment that he
friend had some thing left: it still implied recognition of the principle
property. Something to hate, and to hate "comfortably," was at least not th
utter destitution to which, after their last interview, she had helplessly seeme
to see Mrs. Gereth go forth. She remembered indeed that, in the state in whic
they first saw it, she herself had "liked" the blessed refuge of Ricks; and sh
now wondered if the tact for which she was commended had then operated t
make her keep her kindness out of sight. She was at present ashamed of suc
obliquity, and made up her mind that if this happy impression, quenche
in the spoils of Poynton, should revive on the spot, she would utter it to he
companion without reserve. Yes, she was capable of as much "action" as tha
all the more that the spirit of her hostess seemed, for the time at least, wholl
to have failed. Mrs. Gereth's three minutes with Owen had been a blow to a

talk of travel, and after her woeful hour at Maggie's she had, like some great moaning, wounded bird, made her way, with wings of anguish, back to the nest she knew she should find empty. Fleda, on that dire day, could neither keep her nor give her up; she had pressingly offered to return with her, but Mrs. Gereth, in spite of the theory that their common grief was a bond, had even declined all escort to the station, conscious apparently of something abject in her collapse and almost fiercely eager, as with a personal shame, to be unwatched. All she had said to Fleda was that she would go back to Ricks that night, and the girl had lived for days after with a dreadful image of her position and her misery there. She had had a vision of her now lying prone on some unmade bed, now pacing a bare floor like a lioness deprived of her cubs. There had been moments when her mind's ear was strained to listen for some sound of grief wild enough to be wafted from afar. But the first sound, at the end of a week, had been a note announcing, without reflections, that the plan of going abroad had been abandoned. "It has come to me indirectly, but with much appearance of truth, that *they* are going—for an indefinite time. That quite settles it; I shall stay where I am, and as soon as I've turned round again I shall look for you." The second letter had come a week later, and on the 15th Fleda was on her way to Ricks.

Her arrival took the form of a surprise very nearly as violent as that of the other time. The elements were different, but the effect, like the other, arrested her on the threshold: she stood there stupefied and delighted at the magic of a passion of which such a picture represented the low-water mark. Wound up but sincere, and passing quickly from room to room, Fleda broke out before she even sat down. "If you turn me out of the house for it, my dear, there isn't a woman in England for whom it wouldn't be a privilege to live here." Mrs. Gereth was as honestly bewildered as she had of old been falsely calm. She looked about at the few sticks that, as she afterwards phrased it, she had gathered in, and then hard at her guest, as if to protect herself against a joke sufficiently cruel. The girl's heart gave a leap, for this stare was the sign of an opportunity. Mrs. Gereth was all unwitting; she didn't in the least know what she had done, and as Fleda could tell her Fleda suddenly became the one who knew most. That counted for the moment as a magnificent position; it almost made all the difference. Yet what contradicted it was the vivid presence of the artist's idea. "Where on earth did you put your hand on such beautiful things?"

"Beautiful things?" Mrs. Gereth turned again to the little worn, bleached stuffs and the sweet spindle-legs. "They're the wretched things that were here—that stupid, starved old woman's."

"The maiden aunt's, the nicest, the dearest old woman that ever lived? I thought you had got rid of the maiden aunt."

"She was stored in an empty barn—stuck away for a sale; a matter that, fortunately, I've had neither time nor freedom of mind to arrange. I've simply, in my extremity, fished her out again."

"You've simply, in your extremity, made a delight of her." Fleda took the highest line and the upper hand, and as Mrs. Gereth, challenging her cheerfulness, turned again a lustreless eye over the contents of the place, she broke into a rapture that was unforced, but that she was conscious of an advantage in being able to feel. She moved, as she had done on the previous occasion, from one piece to another, with looks of recognition and hands that lightly lingered, but she was as feverishly jubilant now as she had formerly been anxious and mute. "Ah, the little melancholy, tender, tell-tale things: how can they *not* speak to you and find a way to your heart? It's not the great chorus of Poynton; but you're not, I'm sure, either so proud or so broken as to be reached by nothing but that. This is a voice so gentle, so human, so feminine—a faint, far-away voice with the little quaver of a heart-break. You've listened to it unawares; for the arrangement and effect of everything— when I compare them with what we found the first day we came down— shows, even if mechanically and disdainfully exercised, your admirable, infallible hand. It's your extraordinary genius; you make things 'compose' in spite of yourself. You've only to be a day or two in a place with four sticks for something to come of it!"

"Then if anything has come of it here, it has come precisely of just four. That's literally, by the inventory, all there are!" said Mrs. Gereth.

"If there were more there would be too many to convey the impression in which half the beauty resides—the impression, somehow, of something dreamed and missed, something reduced, relinquished, resigned: the poetry, as it were, of something sensibly *gone*." Fleda ingeniously and triumphantly worked it out. "Ah, there's something here that will never be in the inventory!"

"Does it happen to be in your power to give it a name?" Mrs. Gereth's face showed the dim dawn of an amusement at finding herself seated at the feet of her pupil.

"I can give it a dozen. It's a kind of fourth dimension. It's a presence, a perfume, a touch. It's a soul, a story, a life. There's ever so much more here than you and I. We're in fact just three!"

"Oh, if you count the ghosts!"

"Of course I count the ghosts. It seems to me ghosts count double—for what they were and for what they are. Somehow there were no ghosts at Poynton," Fleda went on. "That was the only fault."

Mrs. Gereth, considering, appeared to fall in with the girl's fine humor. "Poynton was too splendidly happy."

"Poynton was too splendidly happy," Fleda promptly echoed.

"But it's cured of that now," her companion added.

"Yes, henceforth there'll be a ghost or two."

Mrs. Gereth thought again: she found her young friend suggestive. "Only *she* won't see them."

"No, 'she' won't see them." Then Fleda said, "What I mean is, for this dear one of ours, that if she had (as I *know* she did; it's in the very taste of the air!) a great accepted pain—"

She had paused an instant, and Mrs. Gereth took her up. "Well, if she had?"

Fleda still hesitated. "Why, it was worse than yours."

577

Mrs. Gereth reflected. "Very likely." Then she too hesitated. "The question is if it was worse than yours."

"Mine?" Fleda looked vague.

"Precisely. Yours."

At this our young lady smiled. "Yes, because it was a disappointment. She had been so sure."

"I see. And you were never sure."

"Never. Besides, I'm happy," said Fleda.

Mrs. Gereth met her eyes awhile. "Goose!" she quietly remarked as she turned away. There was a curtness in it; nevertheless it represented a considerable part of the basis of their new life.

On the 18th The Morning Post had at last its clear message, a brief account of the marriage, from the residence of the bride's mother, of Mr. Owen Gereth of Poynton Park to Miss Mona Brigstock of Waterbath. There were two ecclesiastics and six bridesmaids and, as Mrs. Gereth subsequently said, a hundred frumps, as well as a special train from town: the scale of the affair sufficiently showed that the preparations had been complete for weeks. The happy pair were described as having taken their departure for Mr. Gereth's own seat, famous for its unique collection of artistic curiosities. The newspapers and letters, the fruits of the first London post, had been brought to the mistress of Ricks in the garden; and she lingered there alone a long time after receiving them. Fleda kept at a distance; she knew what must have happened, for from one of the windows she saw her rigid in a chair, her eyes strange and fixed, the newspaper open on the ground and the letters untouched in her lap. Before the morning's end she had disappeared, and the rest of that day she remained in her room: it recalled to Fleda, who had picked up the newspaper, the day, months before, on which Owen had come down to Poynton to make his engagement known. The hush of the house was at least the same, and the girl's own waiting, her soft wandering, through the hours: there was a difference indeed sufficiently great, of which her companion's absence might in some degree have represented a considerate

cognition. That was at any rate the meaning Fleda, devoutly glad to be
one, attached to her opportunity. Mrs. Gereth's sole allusion, the next day,
the subject of their thoughts, has already been mentioned: it was a dazzled
ance at the fact that Mona's quiet pace had really never slackened.

Fleda fully assented. "I said of our disembodied friend here that she had
ffered in proportion as she had been sure. But that's not always a source of
ffering. It's Mona who must have been sure!"

"She was sure of *you*!" Mrs. Gereth returned. But this didn't diminish
e satisfaction taken by Fleda in showing how serenely and lucidly she could
k.

579

XXII

Her relation with her wonderful friend had, however, in becoming new one, begun to shape itself almost wholly on breaches and omission Something had dropped out altogether, and the question between then which time would answer, was whether the change had made them strange or yokefellows. It was as if at last, for better or worse, they were, in a cleare cruder air, really to know each other. Fleda wondered how Mrs. Gereth ha escaped hating her: there were hours when it seemed that such a feat migl leave after all a scant margin for future accidents. The thing indeed th now came out in its simplicity was that even in her shrunken state the lad of Ricks was larger than her wrongs. As for the girl herself, she had mad up her mind that her feelings had no connection with the case. It was he pretension that they had never yet emerged from the seclusion into which after her friend's visit to her at her sister's, we saw them precipitately retire: she should suddenly meet them in straggling procession on the road it woul be time enough to deal with them. They were all bundled there together, lik with dislikes and memories with fears; and she had for not thinking of then the excellent reason that she was too occupied with the actual. The actual wa not that Owen Gereth had seen his necessity where she had pointed it out; was that his mother's bare spaces demanded all the tapestry that the recipien of her bounty could furnish. There were moments during the month tha followed when Mrs. Gereth struck her as still older and feebler, and as likel to become quite easily amused.

At the end of it, one day, the London paper had another piece of news "Mr. and Mrs. Owen Gereth, who arrived in town last week, proceed thi morning to Paris." They exchanged no word about it till the evening, an none indeed would then have been uttered had not Mrs. Gereth irrelevantl broken out: "I dare say you wonder why I declared the other day with suc assurance that he wouldn't live with her. He apparently *is* living with her."

"Surely it's the only proper thing for him to do."

"They're beyond me—I give it up," said Mrs. Gereth.

"I don't give it up—I never did," Fleda returned.

"Then what do you make of his aversion to her?"

"Oh, she has dispelled it."

Mrs. Gereth said nothing for a minute. "You're prodigious in your choice of terms!" she then simply ejaculated.

But Fleda went luminously on; she once more enjoyed her great command of her subject: "I think that when you came to see me at Maggie's you saw too many things, you had too many ideas."

"You had none," said Mrs. Gereth: "you were completely bewildered."

"Yes, I didn't quite understand—but I think I understand now. The case is simple and logical enough. She's a person who's upset by failure and who blooms and expands with success. There was something she had set her heart upon, set her teeth about—the house exactly as she had seen it."

"She never saw it at all, she never looked at it!" cried Mrs. Gereth.

"She doesn't look with her eyes; she looks with her ears. In her own way she had taken it in; she knew, she felt when it had been touched. That probably made her take an attitude that was extremely disagreeable. But the attitude lasted only while the reason for it lasted."

"Go on—I can bear it now," said Mrs. Gereth. Her companion had just perceptibly paused.

"I know you can, or I shouldn't dream of speaking. When the pressure was removed she came up again. From the moment the house was once more what it had to be, her natural charm reasserted itself."

"Her natural charm!" Mrs. Gereth could barely articulate.

581

"It's very great; everybody thinks so; there must be something in it. It operated as it had operated before. There's no need of imagining anything very monstrous. Her restored good humor, her splendid beauty, and Mr. Owen's impressibility and generosity sufficiently cover the ground. His great bright sun came out!"

"And his great bright passion for another person went in. Your explanation would doubtless be perfection if he didn't love you."

Fleda was silent a little. "What do you know about his 'loving' me?"

"I know what Mrs. Brigstock herself told me."

"You never in your life took her word for any other matter."

"Then won't yours do?" Mrs. Gereth demanded. "Haven't I had it from your own mouth that he cares for you?"

Fleda turned pale, but she faced her companion and smiled. "You confound, Mrs. Gereth, you mix things up. You've only had it from my own mouth that I care for *him*!"

It was doubtless in contradictious allusion to this (which at the time had made her simply drop her head as in a strange, vain reverie) that Mrs. Gereth, a day or two later, said to Fleda: "Don't think I shall be a bit affected if I'm here to see it when he comes again to make up to you."

"He won't do that," the girl replied. Then she added, smiling: "But if he should be guilty of such bad taste, it wouldn't be nice of you not to be disgusted."

"I'm not talking of disgust; I'm talking of its opposite," said Mrs. Gereth.

"Of its opposite?"

"Why, of any reviving pleasure that one might feel in such an exhibition. I shall feel none at all. You may personally take it as you like; but what conceivable good will it do?"

Fleda wondered. "To me, do you mean?"

"Deuce take you, no! To what we don't, you know, by your wish, ever talk about."

"The old things?" Fleda considered again. "It will do no good of any sort to anything or any one. That's another question I would rather we shouldn't discuss, please," she gently added.

Mrs. Gereth shrugged her shoulders.

"It certainly isn't worth it!"

Something in her manner prompted her companion, with a certain inconsequence, to speak again. "That was partly why I came back to you, you know—that there should be the less possibility of anything painful."

"Painful?" Mrs. Gereth stared. "What pain can I ever feel again?"

"I meant painful to myself," Fleda, with a slight impatience, explained.

"Oh, I see." Her friend was silent a minute. "You use sometimes such odd expressions. Well, I shall last a little, but I sha'n't last forever."

"You'll last quite as long—" Here Fleda suddenly hesitated.

Mrs. Gereth took her up with a cold smile that seemed the warning of experience against hyperbole. "As long as what, please?"

The girl thought an instant; then met the difficulty by adopting, as an amendment, the same tone. "As any danger of the ridiculous."

That did for the time, and she had moreover, as the months went on, the protection of suspended allusions. This protection was marked when, in the following November, she received a letter directed in a hand at which a quick glance sufficed to make her hesitate to open it. She said nothing, then or afterwards; but she opened it, for reasons that had come to her, on the morrow. It consisted of a page and a half from Owen Gereth, dated from Florence, but with no other preliminary. She knew that during the summer he had returned to England with his wife, and that after a couple of months they had again gone abroad. She also knew, without communication, that Mrs. Gereth, round whom Ricks had grown submissively and indescribably sweet, had her own interpretation of her daughter-in-law's share in this second migration. It was a piece of calculated insolence—a stroke odiously directed at showing whom it might concern that now she had Poynton fast she was perfectly indifferent to living there. The Morning Post, at Ricks, had again been a resource: it was stated in that journal that Mr. and Mrs. Owen Gereth proposed to spend the winter in India. There was a person to whom it was clear that she led her wretched husband by the nose. Such was the light in which contemporary history was offered to Fleda until, in her own room, late at night, she broke the seal of her letter.

"I want you, inexpressibly, to have, as a remembrance, something of mine—something of real value. Something from Poynton is what I mean and what I should prefer. You know everything there, and far better than I what's best and what isn't. There are a lot of differences, but aren't some of the smaller things the most remarkable? I mean for judges, and for what they'd bring. What I want you to take from me, and to choose for yourself, is the thing in the whole house that's most beautiful and precious. I mean the 'gem of the collection,' don't you know? If it happens to be of such a sort that you can take immediate possession of it—carry it right away with you—so much the better. You're to have it on the spot, whatever it is. I humbly beg of you to go down there and see. The people have complete instructions: they'll act for you in every possible way and put the whole place at your service. There's a thing mamma used to call the Maltese cross and that I think I've heard her say is very wonderful. Is *that* the gem of the collection? Perhaps you would take it, or anything equally convenient. Only I do want you awfully to let it be the very pick of the place. Let me feel that I can trust you for this. You won't refuse if you will think a little what it must be that makes me ask."

Fleda read that last sentence over more times even than the rest; she was baffled—she couldn't think at all of what it might be. This was indeed because it might be one of so many things. She made for the present no answer; she merely, little by little, fashioned for herself the form that her answer should eventually wear. There was only one form that was possible—the form of doing, at her time, what he wished. She would go down to Poynton as a pilgrim might go to a shrine, and as to this she must look out for her chance.

ie lived with her letter, before any chance came, a month, and even after a
onth it had mysteries for her that she couldn't meet. What did it mean, what
d it represent, to what did it correspond in his imagination or his soul? What
as behind it, what was beyond it, what was, in the deepest depth, within it?
ie said to herself that with these questions she was under no obligation to
al. There was an explanation of them that, for practical purposes, would do
 well as another: he had found in his marriage a happiness so much greater
an, in the distress of his dilemma, he had been able to take heart to believe,
at he now felt he owed her a token of gratitude for having kept him in the
raight path. That explanation, I say, she could throw off; but no explanation
 the least mattered: what determined her was the simple strength of her
ipulse to respond. The passion for which what had happened had made no
fference, the passion that had taken this into account before as well as after,
und here an issue that there was nothing whatever to choke. It found even a
lief to which her imagination immensely contributed. Would she act upon
s offer? She would act with secret rapture. To have as her own something
lendid that he had given her, of which the gift had been his signed desire,
ould be a greater joy than the greatest she had supposed to be left to her,
id she felt that till the sense of this came home she had even herself not
iown what burned in her successful stillness. It was an hour to dream of
id watch for; to be patient was to draw out the sweetness. She was capable
f feeling it as an hour of triumph, the triumph of everything in her recent
e that had not held up its head. She moved there in thought—in the great
oms she knew; she should be able to say to herself that, for once at least, her
ossession was as complete as that of either of the others whom it had filled
ily with bitterness. And a thousand times yes—her choice should know no
ruple: the thing she should go down to take would be up to the height of
er privilege. The whole place was in her eyes, and she spent for weeks her
rivate hours in a luxury of comparison and debate. It should be one of the
nallest things because it should be one she could have close to her; and it
iould be one of the finest because it was in the finest he saw his symbol.
ie said to herself that of what it would symbolize she was content to know
othing more than just what her having it would tell her. At bottom she
iclined to the Maltese cross—with the added reason that he had named it.

585

But she would look again and judge afresh; she would on the spot so hand[
and ponder that there shouldn't be the shade of a mistake.

Before Christmas she had a natural opportunity to go to London; the[
was her periodical call upon her father to pay as well as a promise to Magg[
to redeem. She spent her first night in West Kensington, with the idea [
carrying out on the morrow the purpose that had most of a motive. H[
father's affection was not inquisitive, but when she mentioned to him th[
she had business in the country that would oblige her to catch an early trai[
he deprecated her excursion in view of the menace of the weather. It w[
spoiling for a storm; all the signs of a winter gale were in the air. She repli[
that she would see what the morning might bring; and it brought, in fac[
what seemed in London an amendment. She was to go to Maggie the ne[
day, and now that she had started her eagerness had become suddenly a pai[
She pictured her return that evening with her trophy under her cloak; so th[
after looking, from the doorstep, up and down the dark street, she decide[
with a new nervousness, and sallied forth to the nearest place of access to th[
"Underground." The December dawn was dolorous, but there was neith[
rain nor snow; it was not even cold, and the atmosphere of West Kensingto[
purified by the wind, was like a dirty old coat that had been bettered by [
dirty brush. At the end of almost an hour, in the larger station, she had take[
her place in a third-class compartment; the prospect before her was the ru[
of eighty minutes to Poynton. The train was a fast one, and she was familia[
with the moderate measure of the walk to the park from the spot at which [
would drop her.

Once in the country, indeed, she saw that her father was right: the breat[
of December was abroad with a force from which the London labyrint[
had protected her. The green fields were black, the sky was all alive wit[
the wind; she had, in her anxious sense of the elements, her wonder at wha[
might happen, a reminder of the surmises, in the old days of going to th[
Continent, that used to worry her on the way, at night, to the horrid chea[
crossings by long sea. Something, in a dire degree, at this last hour, had begu[
to press on her heart: it was the sudden imagination of a disaster, or at lea[
of a check, before her errand was achieved. When she said to herself th[

something might happen she wanted to go faster than the train. But nothing could happen save a dismayed discovery that, by some altogether unlikely chance, the master and mistress of the house had already come back. In that case she must have had a warning, and the fear was but the excess of her hope. It was every one's being exactly where every one was that lent the quality to her visit. Beyond lands and seas and alienated forever, they in their different ways gave her the impression to take as she had never taken it. At last it was already there, though the darkness of the day had deepened; they had whizzed past Chater—Chater, which was the station before the right one. Off in that quarter was an air of wild rain, but there shimmered straight across it a brightness that was the color of the great interior she had been haunting. That vision settled before her—in the house the house was all; and as the train drew up she rose, in her mean compartment, quite proudly erect with the thought that all for Fleda Vetch then the house was standing there.

But with the opening of the door she encountered a shock, though for an instant she couldn't have named it; the next moment she saw it was given her by the face of the man advancing to let her out, an old lame porter of the station, who had been there in Mrs. Gereth's time and who now recognized her. He looked up at her so hard that she took an alarm and before alighting broke out to him: "They've come back?" She had a confused, absurd sense that even he would know that in this case she mustn't be there. He hesitated, and in the few seconds her alarm had completely changed its ground: it seemed to leap, with her quick jump from the carriage, to the ground that was that of his stare at her. "Smoke?" She was on the platform with her frightened sniff: it had taken her a minute to become aware of an extraordinary smell. The air was full of it, and there were already heads at the window of the train, looking out at something she couldn't see. Some one, the only other passenger, had got out of another carriage, and the old porter hobbled off to close his door. The smoke was in her eyes, but she saw the station-master, from the end of the platform, recognize her too and come straight to her. He brought her a finer shade of surprise than the porter, and while he was coming she heard a voice at a window of the train say that something was "a good bit off—a mile from the town." That was just what Poynton was. Then her heart stood still at the white wonder in the station-master's face.

"You've come down to it, miss, already?"

At this she knew. "Poynton's on fire?"

"Gone, miss—with this awful gale. You weren't wired? Look out!" he cried in the next breath, seizing her; the train was going on, and she had given a lurch that almost made it catch her as it passed. When it had drawn away she became more conscious of the pervading smoke, which the wind seemed to hurl in her face.

"*Gone?*" She was in the man's hands; she clung to him.

"Burning still, miss. Ain't it quite too dreadful? Took early this morning—the whole place is up there."

In her bewildered horror she tried to think. "Have they come back?"

"Back? They'll be there all day!"

"Not Mr. Gereth, I mean—nor his wife?"

"Nor his mother, miss—not a soul of *them* back. A pack o' servants in charge—not the old lady's lot, eh? A nice job for care-takers! Some rotten chimley or one of them portable lamps set down in the wrong place. What has done it is this cruel, cruel night." Then as a great wave of smoke half choked them, he drew her with force to the little waiting room. "Awkward for you, miss—I see!"

She felt sick; she sank upon a seat, staring up at him. "Do you mean that great house is *lost?*"

"It was near it, I was told, an hour ago—the fury of the flames had got such a start. I was there myself at six, the very first I heard of it. They were fighting it then, but you couldn't quite say they had got it down."

Fleda jerked herself up. "Were they saving the things?"

"That's just where it was, miss—to get *at* the blessed things. And the want of right help—it maddened me to stand and see 'em muff it. This ain't a place, like, for anything organized. They don't come up to a *reel* emergency."

She passed out of the door that opened toward the village and met a great acrid gust. She heard a far-off windy roar which, in her dismay, she took for that of flames a mile away, and which, the first instant, acted upon her as a wild solicitation. "I must go there." She had scarcely spoken before the same omen had changed into an appalling check.

Her vivid friend, moreover, had got before her; he clearly suffered from the nature of the control he had to exercise. "Don't do that, miss—you won't care for it at all." Then as she waveringly stood her ground, "It's not a place for a young lady, nor, if you'll believe me, a sight for them as are in any way affected."

Fleda by this time knew in what way she was affected: she became limp and weak again; she felt herself give everything up. Mixed with the horror, with the kindness of the station-master, with the smell of cinders and the riot of sound, was the raw bitterness of a hope that she might never again in life have to give up so much at such short notice. She heard herself repeat mechanically, yet as if asking it for the first time: "Poynton's *gone?*"

The man hesitated. "What can you call it, miss, if it ain't really saved?"

A minute later she had returned with him to the waiting-room, where, in the thick swim of things, she saw something like the disk of a clock. "Is there an up-train?" she asked.

"In seven minutes."

She came out on the platform: everywhere she met the smoke. She covered her face with her hands. "I'll go back."

589

About Author

Henry James OM (15 April 1843 – 28 February 1916) was an American-British author regarded as a key transitional figure between literary realism and literary modernism, and is considered by many to be among the greatest novelists in the English language. He was the son of Henry James Sr. and the brother of renowned philosopher and psychologist William James and diarist Alice James.

He is best known for a number of novels dealing with the social and marital interplay between émigré Americans, English people, and continental Europeans. Examples of such novels include The Portrait of a Lady, The Ambassadors, and The Wings of the Dove. His later works were increasingly experimental. In describing the internal states of mind and social dynamics of his characters, James often made use of a style in which ambiguous or contradictory motives and impressions were overlaid or juxtaposed in the discussion of a character's psyche. For their unique ambiguity, as well as for other aspects of their composition, his late works have been compared to impressionist painting.

His novella The Turn of the Screw has garnered a reputation as the most analysed and ambiguous ghost story in the English language and remains his most widely adapted work in other media. He also wrote a number of other highly regarded ghost stories and is considered one of the greatest masters of the field.

James published articles and books of criticism, travel, biography, autobiography, and plays. Born in the United States, James largely relocated to Europe as a young man and eventually settled in England, becoming a British subject in 1915, one year before his death. James was nominated for the Nobel Prize in Literature in 1911, 1912 and 1916.

Life

Early years, 1843–1883

James was born at 2 Washington Place in New York City on 15 Apr 1843. His parents were Mary Walsh and Henry James Sr. His father wa intelligent and steadfastly congenial. He was a lecturer and philosopher wh had inherited independent means from his father, an Albany banker an investor. Mary came from a wealthy family long settled in New York Cit Her sister Katherine lived with her adult family for an extended period c time. Henry Jr. had three brothers, William, who was one year his senior, an younger brothers Wilkinson (Wilkie) and Robertson. His younger sister wa Alice. Both of his parents were of Irish and Scottish descent.

The family first lived in Albany, at 70 N. Pearl St., and then moved t Fourteenth Street in New York City when James was still a young boy. H education was calculated by his father to expose him to many influence primarily scientific and philosophical; it was described by Percy Lubbock, th editor of his selected letters, as "extraordinarily haphazard and promiscuous. James did not share the usual education in Latin and Greek classics. Betwee 1855 and 1860, the James' household traveled to London, Paris, Geneva Boulogne-sur-Mer and Newport, Rhode Island, according to the father' current interests and publishing ventures, retreating to the United State when funds were low. Henry studied primarily with tutors and brief attended schools while the family traveled in Europe. Their longest stays wer in France, where Henry began to feel at home and became fluent in French He was afflicted with a stutter, which seems to have manifested itself onl when he spoke English; in French, he did not stutter.

In 1860 the family returned to Newport. There Henry became a frien of the painter John La Farge, who introduced him to French literature, an in particular, to Balzac. James later called Balzac his "greatest master," an said that he had learned more about the craft of fiction from him than fror anyone else.

In the autumn of 1861 Henry received an injury, probably to his back while fighting a fire. This injury, which resurfaced at times throughout hi life, made him unfit for military service in the American Civil War.

In 1864 the James family moved to Boston, Massachusetts to be near William, who had enrolled first in the Lawrence Scientific School at Harvard and then in the medical school. In 1862 Henry attended Harvard Law School, but realised that he was not interested in studying law. He pursued his interest in literature and associated with authors and critics William Dean Howells and Charles Eliot Norton in Boston and Cambridge, formed lifelong friendships with Oliver Wendell Holmes Jr., the future Supreme Court Justice, and with James and Annie Fields, his first professional mentors.

His first published work was a review of a stage performance, "Miss Maggie Mitchell in Fanchon the Cricket," published in 1863. About a year later, A Tragedy of Error, his first short story, was published anonymously. James's first payment was for an appreciation of Sir Walter Scott's novels, written for the North American Review. He wrote fiction and non-fiction pieces for The Nation and Atlantic Monthly, where Fields was editor. In 1871 he published his first novel, Watch and Ward, in serial form in the Atlantic Monthly. The novel was later published in book form in 1878.

During a 14-month trip through Europe in 1869–70 he met Ruskin, Dickens, Matthew Arnold, William Morris, and George Eliot. Rome impressed him profoundly. "Here I am then in the Eternal City," he wrote to his brother William. "At last—for the first time—I live!" He attempted to support himself as a freelance writer in Rome, then secured a position as Paris correspondent for the New York Tribune, through the influence of its editor John Hay. When these efforts failed he returned to New York City. During 1874 and 1875 he published Transatlantic Sketches, A Passionate Pilgrim, and Roderick Hudson. During this early period in his career he was influenced by Nathaniel Hawthorne.

In 1869 he settled in London. There he established relationships with Macmillan and other publishers, who paid for serial installments that they would later publish in book form. The audience for these serialized novels was largely made up of middle-class women, and James struggled to fashion serious literary work within the strictures imposed by editors' and publishers' notions of what was suitable for young women to read. He lived in rented rooms but was able to join gentlemen's clubs that had libraries and where he could entertain male friends. He was introduced to English society by Henry Adams and Charles Milnes Gaskell, the latter introducing him to the Travellers' and the Reform Clubs.

In the fall of 1875 he moved to the Latin Quarter of Paris. Aside from two trips to America, he spent the next three decades—the rest of his life—in Europe. In Paris he met Zola, Alphonse Daudet, Maupassant, Turgenev, and others. He stayed in Paris only a year before moving to London.

In England he met the leading figures of politics and culture. He continued to be a prolific writer, producing The American (1877), The Europeans (1878), a revision of Watch and Ward (1878), French Poets and Novelists (1878), Hawthorne (1879), and several shorter works of fiction. In 1878 Daisy Miller established his fame on both sides of the Atlantic. It drew notice perhaps mostly because it depicted a woman whose behavior is outside the social norms of Europe. He also began his first masterpiece, The Portrait of a Lady, which would appear in 1881.

In 1877 he first visited Wenlock Abbey in Shropshire, home of his friend Charles Milnes Gaskell whom he had met through Henry Adams. He was much inspired by the darkly romantic Abbey and the surrounding countryside, which features in his essay Abbeys and Castles. In particular the gloomy monastic fishponds behind the Abbey are said to have inspired the lake in The Turn of the Screw.

While living in London, James continued to follow the careers of the "French realists", Émile Zola in particular. Their stylistic methods influenced his own work in the years to come. Hawthorne's influence on him faded during this period, replaced by George Eliot and Ivan Turgenev. 1879–1882 saw the publication of The Europeans, Washington Square, Confidence, and The Portrait of a Lady. He visited America in 1882–1883, then returned to London.

The period from 1881 to 1883 was marked by several losses. His mother died in 1881, followed by his father a few months later, and then by his brother Wilkie. Emerson, an old family friend, died in 1882. His friend Turgenev died in 1883.

Middle years, 1884–1897

In 1884 James made another visit to Paris. There he met again with Zola, Daudet, and Goncourt. He had been following the careers of the French "realist" or "naturalist" writers, and was increasingly influenced by them. In 1886, he published The Bostonians and The Princess Casamassima, both influenced by the French writers he'd studied assiduously. Critical reaction and sales were poor. He wrote to Howells that the books had hurt his career rather than helped because they had "reduced the desire, and demand, for my productions to zero". During this time he became friends with Robert Louis Stevenson, John Singer Sargent, Edmund Gosse, George du Maurier, Paul Bourget, and Constance Fenimore Woolson. His third novel from the 1880s was The Tragic Muse. Although he was following the precepts of Zola in his novels of the '80s, their tone and attitude are closer to the fiction of Alphonse Daudet. The lack of critical and financial success for his novels during this period led him to try writing for the theatre. (His dramatic works and his experiences with theatre are discussed below.)

In the last quarter of 1889, he started translating "for pure and copious lucre" Port Tarascon, the third volume of Alphonse Daudet adventures of Tartarin de Tarascon. Serialized in Harper's Monthly Magazine from June 1890, this translation praised as "clever" by The Spectator was published in January 1891 by Sampson Low, Marston, Searle & Rivington.

After the stage failure of Guy Domville in 1895, James was near despair and thoughts of death plagued him. The years spent on dramatic works were not entirely a loss. As he moved into the last phase of his career he found ways to adapt dramatic techniques into the novel form.

In the late 1880s and throughout the 1890s James made several trips through Europe. He spent a long stay in Italy in 1887. In that year the short novel The Aspern Papers and The Reverberator were published.

Late years, 1898–1916

In 1897–1898 he moved to Rye, Sussex, and wrote The Turn of the Screw. 1899–1900 saw the publication of The Awkward Age and The Sacred

Fount. During 1902–1904 he wrote The Ambassadors, The Wings of the Dove, and The Golden Bowl.

In 1904 he revisited America and lectured on Balzac. In 1906–1910 he published The American Scene and edited the "New York Edition", a 24-volume collection of his works. In 1910 his brother William died; Henry had just joined William from an unsuccessful search for relief in Europe on what then turned out to be his (Henry's) last visit to the United States (from summer 1910 to July 1911), and was near him, according to a letter he wrote, when he died.

In 1913 he wrote his autobiographies, A Small Boy and Others, and Notes of a Son and Brother. After the outbreak of the First World War in 1914 he did war work. In 1915 he became a British subject and was awarded the Order of Merit the following year. He died on 28 February 1916, in Chelsea, London. As he requested, his ashes were buried in Cambridge Cemetery in Massachusetts.

Biographers

James regularly rejected suggestions that he should marry, and after settling in London proclaimed himself "a bachelor". F. W. Dupee, in several volumes on the James family, originated the theory that he had been in love with his cousin Mary ("Minnie") Temple, but that a neurotic fear of sex kept him from admitting such affections: "James's invalidism ... was itself the symptom of some fear of or scruple against sexual love on his part." Dupee used an episode from James's memoir A Small Boy and Others, recounting a dream of a Napoleonic image in the Louvre, to exemplify James's romanticism about Europe, a Napoleonic fantasy into which he fled.

Dupee had not had access to the James family papers and worked principally from James's published memoir of his older brother, William, and the limited collection of letters edited by Percy Lubbock, heavily weighted toward James's last years. His account therefore moved directly from James's childhood, when he trailed after his older brother, to elderly invalidism. As more material became available to scholars, including the diaries of contemporaries and hundreds of affectionate and sometimes erotic letters ritten by James to younger men, the picture of neurotic celibacy gave way a portrait of a closeted homosexual.

Between 1953 and 1972, Leon Edel authored a major five-volume ography of James, which accessed unpublished letters and documents after del gained the permission of James's family. Edel's portrayal of James included e suggestion he was celibate. It was a view first propounded by critic Saul osenzweig in 1943. In 1996 Sheldon M. Novick published Henry James: e Young Master, followed by Henry James: The Mature Master (2007). e first book "caused something of an uproar in Jamesian circles" as it allenged the previous received notion of celibacy, a once-familiar paradigm biographies of homosexuals when direct evidence was non-existent. Novick so criticised Edel for following the discounted Freudian interpretation of omosexuality "as a kind of failure." The difference of opinion erupted in series of exchanges between Edel and Novick which were published by the line magazine Slate, with the latter arguing that even the suggestion of libacy went against James's own injunction "live!"—not "fantasize!"

A letter James wrote in old age to Hugh Walpole has been cited as an plicit statement of this. Walpole confessed to him of indulging in "high ks", and James wrote a reply endorsing it: "We must know, as much as ossible, in our beautiful art, yours & mine, what we are talking about — & e only way to know it is to have lived & loved & cursed & floundered & njoyed & suffered — I don't think I regret a single 'excess' of my responsive outh".

The interpretation of James as living a less austere emotional life has een subsequently explored by other scholars. The often intense politics f Jamesian scholarship has also been the subject of studies. Author Colm óibín has said that Eve Kosofsky Sedgwick's Epistemology of the Closet ade a landmark difference to Jamesian scholarship by arguing that he be ad as a homosexual writer whose desire to keep his sexuality a secret shaped s layered style and dramatic artistry. According to Tóibín such a reading emoved James from the realm of dead white males who wrote about posh eople. He became our contemporary."

James's letters to expatriate American sculptor Hendrik Christian Andersen have attracted particular attention. James met the 27-year-old Andersen in Rome in 1899, when James was 56, and wrote letters to Andersen that are intensely emotional: "I hold you, dearest boy, in my innermost love & count on your feeling me—in every throb of your soul". In a letter of 6 May 1904, to his brother William, James referred to himself as "always your hopelessly celibate even though sexagenarian Henry". How accurate that description might have been is the subject of contention among James biographers, but the letters to Andersen were occasionally quasi-erotic: "I put, my dear boy, my arm around you, & feel the pulsation, thereby, as it were, of our excellent future & your admirable endowment." To his homosexual friend Howard Sturgis, James could write: "I repeat, almost to indiscretion, that I could live with you. Meanwhile I can only try to live without you."

His numerous letters to the many young gay men among his close male friends are more forthcoming. In a letter to Howard Sturgis, following a long visit, James refers jocularly to their "happy little congress of two" and in letters to Hugh Walpole he pursues convoluted jokes and puns about their relationship, referring to himself as an elephant who "paws you oh so benevolently" and winds about Walpole his "well meaning old trunk". His letters to Walter Berry printed by the Black Sun Press have long been celebrated for their lightly veiled eroticism.

He corresponded in almost equally extravagant language with his many female friends, writing, for example, to fellow novelist Lucy Clifford: "Dearest Lucy! What shall I say? when I love you so very, very much, and see you nine times for once that I see Others! Therefore I think that—if you want it made clear to the meanest intelligence—I love you more than I love Others." To his New York friend Mary Cadwalader Jones: "Dearest Mary Cadwalader. I yearn over you, but I yearn in vain; & your long silence really breaks my heart, mystifies, depresses, almost alarms me, to the point even of making me wonder if poor unconscious & doting old Célimare [Jones's pet name for James] has 'done' anything, in some dark somnambulism of the spirit, which has ... given you a bad moment, or a wrong impression, or a 'colourable pretext' ... However these things may be, he loves you as tenderly as ever nothing, to the end of time, will ever detach him from you, & he remembers those Eleventh St. matutinal intimes hours, those telephonic matinées, as the most romantic of his life ..." His long friendship with American novelist Constance Fenimore Woolson, in whose house he lived for a number of weeks in Italy in 1887, and his shock and grief over her suicide in 1894, are discussed in detail in Edel's biography and play a central role in a study by Lyndall Gordon. (Edel conjectured that Woolson was in love with James and killed herself in part because of his coldness, but Woolson's biographers have objected to Edel's account.)

Works

Style and themes

James is one of the major figures of trans-Atlantic literature. His works frequently juxtapose characters from the Old World (Europe), embodying a feudal civilisation that is beautiful, often corrupt, and alluring, and from the New World (United States), where people are often brash, open, and assertive and embody the virtues—freedom and a more highly evolved moral character—of the new American society. James explores this clash of personalities and cultures, in stories of personal relationships in which power is exercised well or badly. His protagonists were often young American women facing oppression or abuse, and as his secretary Theodora Bosanquet remarked in her monograph Henry James at Work:

> When he walked out of the refuge of his study and into the world and looked around him, he saw a place of torment, where creatures of prey perpetually thrust their claws into the quivering flesh of doomed, defenseless children of light ... His novels are a repeated exposure of this wickedness, a reiterated and passionate plea for the fullest freedom of development, unimperiled by reckless and barbarous stupidity.

Critics have jokingly described three phases in the development of James's prose: "James I, James II, and The Old Pretender." He wrote short stories and plays. Finally, in his third and last period he returned to the long, serialised novel. Beginning in the second period, but most noticeably in the third, he increasingly abandoned direct statement in favour of frequent double negatives, and complex descriptive imagery. Single paragraphs began to run for page after page, in which an initial noun would be succeeded by pronouns surrounded by clouds of adjectives and prepositional clauses, far from their original referents, and verbs would be deferred and then preceded by a series of adverbs. The overall effect could be a vivid evocation of a scene as perceived by a sensitive observer. It has been debated whether this change of style was engendered by James's shifting from writing to dictating to a typist, a change made during the composition of What Maisie Knew.

In its intense focus on the consciousness of his major characters, James's later work foreshadows extensive developments in 20th century fiction. Indeed, he might have influenced stream-of-consciousness writers such as Virginia Woolf, who not only read some of his novels but also wrote essays about them. Both contemporary and modern readers have found the late style difficult and unnecessary; his friend Edith Wharton, who admired him greatly, said that there were passages in his work that were all but incomprehensible. James was harshly portrayed by H. G. Wells as a hippopotamus laboriously attempting to pick up a pea that had got into a corner of its cage. The "late James" style was ably parodied by Max Beerbohm in "The Mote in the Middle Distance".

More important for his work overall may have been his position as an expatriate, and in other ways an outsider, living in Europe. While he came from middle-class and provincial beginnings (seen from the perspective of European polite society) he worked very hard to gain access to all levels of society, and the settings of his fiction range from working class to aristocratic, and often describe the efforts of middle-class Americans to make their way in European capitals. He confessed he got some of his best story ideas from gossip at the dinner table or at country house weekends. He worked for a living, however, and lacked the experiences of select schools, university, and army service, the common bonds of masculine society. He was furthermore a man whose tastes and interests were, according to the prevailing standards of Victorian era Anglo-American culture, rather feminine, and who was shadowed by the cloud of prejudice that then and later accompanied suspicions of his homosexuality. Edmund Wilson famously compared James's objectivity to Shakespeare's:

One would be in a position to appreciate James better if one compared him with the dramatists of the seventeenth century—Racine and Molière, whom he resembles in form as well as in point of view, and even Shakespeare, when allowances are made for the most extreme differences in subject and form. These poets are not, like Dickens and Hardy, writers of melodrama—either humorous or pessimistic, nor secretaries of society like Balzac, nor prophets like Tolstoy: they are occupied simply with the presentation of conflicts of moral character, which they do not concern themselves about softening or averting. They do not indict society for these situations: they regard them as universal and inevitable. They do not even blame God for allowing them: they accept them as the conditions of life.

It is also possible to see many of James's stories as psychological thought-experiments. In his preface to the New York edition of The American he describes the development of the story in his mind as exactly such: the "situation" of an American, "some robust but insidiously beguiled and betrayed, some cruelly wronged, compatriot..." with the focus of the story being on the response of this wronged man. The Portrait of a Lady may be an experiment to see what happens when an idealistic young woman suddenly becomes very rich. In many of his tales, characters seem to exemplify alternative futures and possibilities, as most markedly in "The Jolly Corner", in which the protagonist and a ghost-doppelganger live alternative American and European lives; and in others, like The Ambassadors, an older James seems fondly to regard his own younger self facing a crucial moment.

Major novels

The first period of James's fiction, usually considered to have culminated in The Portrait of a Lady, concentrated on the contrast between Europe and America. The style of these novels is generally straightforward and, though personally characteristic, well within the norms of 19th-century fiction. Roderick Hudson (1875) is a Künstlerroman that traces the development of the title character, an extremely talented sculptor. Although the book shows some signs of immaturity—this was James's first serious attempt at a full-length novel—it has attracted favourable comment due to the vivid realisation of the three major characters: Roderick Hudson, superbly gifted but unstable and unreliable; Rowland Mallet, Roderick's limited but much more mature friend and patron; and Christina Light, one of James's most enchanting and maddening femmes fatales. The pair of Hudson and Mallet has been seen as representing the two sides of James's own nature: the wildly imaginative artist and the brooding conscientious mentor.

In The Portrait of a Lady (1881) James concluded the first phase of his career with a novel that remains his most popular piece of long fiction. The story is of a spirited young American woman, Isabel Archer, who "affronts her destiny" and finds it overwhelming. She inherits a large amount of money and subsequently becomes the victim of Machiavellian scheming by two American expatriates. The narrative is set mainly in Europe, especially in England and Italy. Generally regarded as the masterpiece of his early phase, The Portrait of a Lady is described as a psychological novel, exploring the minds of his characters, and almost a work of social science, exploring the differences between Europeans and Americans, the old and the new worlds.

The second period of James's career, which extends from the publication of The Portrait of a Lady through the end of the nineteenth century, features less popular novels including The Princess Casamassima, published serially in The Atlantic Monthly in 1885–1886, and The Bostonians, published serially in The Century Magazine during the same period. This period also featured James's celebrated Gothic novella, The Turn of the Screw.

The third period of James's career reached its most significant achievement in three novels published just around the start of the 20th century: The Wings of the Dove (1902), The Ambassadors (1903), and The Golden Bowl (1904). Critic F. O. Matthiessen called this "trilogy" James's major phase, and these novels have certainly received intense critical study. It was the second-written of the books, The Wings of the Dove (1902) that was the first published because it attracted no serialization. This novel tells the story of Milly Theale, an American heiress stricken with a serious disease, and her impact on the people around her. Some of these people befriend Milly with honourable motives, while others are more self-interested. James ted in his autobiographical books that Milly was based on Minny Temple, s beloved cousin who died at an early age of tuberculosis. He said that he tempted in the novel to wrap her memory in the "beauty and dignity of t".

Shorter narratives

James was particularly interested in what he called the "beautiful and est nouvelle", or the longer form of short narrative. Still, he produced a umber of very short stories in which he achieved notable compression of metimes complex subjects. The following narratives are representative of mes's achievement in the shorter forms of fiction.

- "A Tragedy of Error" (1864), short story

- "The Story of a Year" (1865), short story

- A Passionate Pilgrim (1871), novella

- Madame de Mauves (1874), novella

- Daisy Miller (1878), novella

- The Aspern Papers (1888), novella

- The Lesson of the Master (1888), novella

- The Pupil (1891), short story

- "The Figure in the Carpet" (1896), short story

- The Beast in the Jungle (1903), novella

- An International Episode (1878)

- Picture and Text

- Four Meetings (1885)

- A London Life, and Other Tales (1889)

- The Spoils of Poynton (1896)

- Embarrassments (1896)

- The Two Magics: The Turn of the Screw, Covering End (1898)

- A Little Tour of France (1900)

- The Sacred Fount (1901)

- Views and Reviews (1908)

- The Wings of the Dove, Volume I (1902)

- The Wings of the Dove, Volume II (1909)

- The Finer Grain (1910)

- The Outcry (1911)

- Lady Barbarina: The Siege of London, An International Episod and Other Tales (1922)

- The Birthplace (1922)

Plays

At several points in his career James wrote plays, beginning with one-ac plays written for periodicals in 1869 and 1871 and a dramatisation of hi popular novella Daisy Miller in 1882. From 1890 to 1892, having receive a bequest that freed him from magazine publication, he made a strenuou effort to succeed on the London stage, writing a half-dozen plays of whic only one, a dramatisation of his novel The American, was produced. This pla was performed for several years by a touring repertory company and had respectable run in London, but did not earn very much money for James. Hi other plays written at this time were not produced.

In 1893, however, he responded to a request from actor-manage George Alexander for a serious play for the opening of his renovated St James's Theatre, and wrote a long drama, Guy Domville, which Alexande produced. There was a noisy uproar on the opening night, 5 January 1895 with hissing from the gallery when James took his bow after the final curtair and the author was upset. The play received moderately good reviews an

604

had a modest run of four weeks before being taken off to make way for Oscar Wilde's The Importance of Being Earnest, which Alexander thought would have better prospects for the coming season.

After the stresses and disappointment of these efforts James insisted that he would write no more for the theatre, but within weeks had agreed to write a curtain-raiser for Ellen Terry. This became the one-act "Summersoft", which he later rewrote into a short story, "Covering End", and then expanded into a full-length play, The High Bid, which had a brief run in London in 1907, when James made another concerted effort to write for the stage. He wrote three new plays, two of which were in production when the death of Edward VII on 6 May 1910 plunged London into mourning and theatres closed. Discouraged by failing health and the stresses of theatrical work, James did not renew his efforts in the theatre, but recycled his plays as successful novels. The Outcry was a best-seller in the United States when it was published in 1911. During the years 1890–1893 when he was most engaged with the theatre, James wrote a good deal of theatrical criticism and assisted Elizabeth Robins and others in translating and producing Henrik Ibsen for the first time in London.

Leon Edel argued in his psychoanalytic biography that James was traumatised by the opening night uproar that greeted Guy Domville, and that it plunged him into a prolonged depression. The successful later novels, in Edel's view, were the result of a kind of self-analysis, expressed in fiction, which partly freed him from his fears. Other biographers and scholars have not accepted this account, however; the more common view being that of F.O. Matthiessen, who wrote: "Instead of being crushed by the collapse of his hopes [for the theatre]... he felt a resurgence of new energy."

Non-fiction

Beyond his fiction, James was one of the more important literary critics in the history of the novel. In his classic essay The Art of Fiction (1884), he argued against rigid prescriptions on the novelist's choice of subject and method of treatment. He maintained that the widest possible freedom in content and approach would help ensure narrative fiction's continued vitality.

James wrote many valuable critical articles on other novelists; typical is his book-length study of Nathaniel Hawthorne, which has been the subject of critical debate. Richard Brodhead has suggested that the study was emblematic of James's struggle with Hawthorne's influence, and constituted an effort to place the elder writer "at a disadvantage." Gordon Fraser, meanwhile, has suggested that the study was part of a more commercial effort by James to introduce himself to British readers as Hawthorne's natural successor.

When James assembled the New York Edition of his fiction in his final years, he wrote a series of prefaces that subjected his own work to searching, occasionally harsh criticism.

At 22 James wrote The Noble School of Fiction for The Nation's first issue in 1865. He would write, in all, over 200 essays and book, art, and theatre reviews for the magazine.

For most of his life James harboured ambitions for success as a playwright. He converted his novel The American into a play that enjoyed modest returns in the early 1890s. In all he wrote about a dozen plays, most of which went unproduced. His costume drama Guy Domville failed disastrously on its opening night in 1895. James then largely abandoned his efforts to conquer the stage and returned to his fiction. In his Notebooks he maintained that his theatrical experiment benefited his novels and tales by helping him dramatise his characters' thoughts and emotions. James produced a small but valuable amount of theatrical criticism, including perceptive appreciations of Henrik Ibsen.

With his wide-ranging artistic interests, James occasionally wrote on the visual arts. Perhaps his most valuable contribution was his favourable assessment of fellow expatriate John Singer Sargent, a painter whose critical status has improved markedly in recent decades. James also wrote sometimes charming, sometimes brooding articles about various places he visited and lived in. His most famous books of travel writing include Italian Hours (an example of the charming approach) and The American Scene (most definitely on the brooding side).

James was one of the great letter-writers of any era. More than ten thousand of his personal letters are extant, and over three thousand have been published in a large number of collections. A complete edition of James's letters began publication in 2006, edited by Pierre Walker and Greg Zacharias. As of 2014, eight volumes have been published, covering the period from 1855 to 1880. James's correspondents included celebrated contemporaries like Robert Louis Stevenson, Edith Wharton and Joseph Conrad, along with many others in his wide circle of friends and acquaintances. The letters range from the "mere twaddle of graciousness" to serious discussions of artistic, social and personal issues.

Very late in life James began a series of autobiographical works: A Small Boy and Others, Notes of a Son and Brother, and the unfinished The Middle Years. These books portray the development of a classic observer who was passionately interested in artistic creation but was somewhat reticent about participating fully in the life around him.

Reception

Criticism, biographies and fictional treatments

James's work has remained steadily popular with the limited audience of educated readers to whom he spoke during his lifetime, and has remained firmly in the canon, but, after his death, some American critics, such as Van Wyck Brooks, expressed hostility towards James for his long expatriation and eventual naturalisation as a British subject. Other critics such as E. M. Forster complained about what they saw as James's squeamishness in the treatment of sex and other possibly controversial material, or dismissed his late style as difficult and obscure, relying heavily on extremely long sentences and excessively latinate language. Similarly Oscar Wilde criticised him for writing "fiction as if it were a painful duty". Vernon Parrington, composing a canon of American literature, condemned James for having cut himself off from America. Jorge Luis Borges wrote about him, "Despite the scruples and delicate complexities of James, his work suffers from a major defect: the absence of life." And Virginia Woolf, writing to Lytton Strachey, asked, "Please tell me what you find in Henry James. ... we have his works here, and

607

I read, and I can't find anything but faintly tinged rose water, urbane and sleek, but vulgar and pale as Walter Lamb. Is there really any sense in it?" The novelist W. Somerset Maugham wrote, "He did not know the English as an Englishman instinctively knows them and so his English characters never to my mind quite ring true," and argued "The great novelists, even in seclusion, have lived life passionately. Henry James was content to observe it from a window." Maugham nevertheless wrote, "The fact remains that those last novels of his, notwithstanding their unreality, make all other novels, except the very best, unreadable." Colm Tóibín observed that James "never really wrote about the English very well. His English characters don't work for me."

Despite these criticisms, James is now valued for his psychological and moral realism, his masterful creation of character, his low-key but playful humour, and his assured command of the language. In his 1983 book, The Novels of Henry James, Edward Wagenknecht offers an assessment that echoes Theodora Bosanquet's:

> "To be completely great," Henry James wrote in an early review, "a work of art must lift up the heart," and his own novels do this to an outstanding degree ... More than sixty years after his death, the great novelist who sometimes professed to have no opinions stands foursquare in the great Christian humanistic and democratic tradition. The men and women who, at the height of World War II, raided the secondhand shops for his out-of-print books knew what they were about. For no writer ever raised a braver banner to which all who love freedom might adhere.

William Dean Howells saw James as a representative of a new realist school of literary art which broke with the English romantic tradition epitomised by the works of Charles Dickens and William Makepeace Thackeray. Howells wrote that realism found "its chief exemplar in Mr. James... A novelist he is not, after the old fashion, or after any fashion but his own." F.R. Leavis championed Henry James as a novelist of "established pre-eminence" in The Great Tradition (1948), asserting that The Portrait of a Lady and The Bostonians were "the two most brilliant novels in the language." James is now prized as a master of point of view who moved literary fiction forward by insisting in showing, not telling, his stories to the reader. (Source: Wikipedia)

NOTABLE WORKS

NOVELS

Watch and Ward (1871)

Roderick Hudson (1875)

The American (1877)

The Europeans (1878)

Confidence (1879)

Washington Square (1880)

The Portrait of a Lady (1881)

The Bostonians (1886)

The Princess Casamassima (1886)

The Reverberator (1888)

The Tragic Muse (1890)

The Other House (1896)

The Spoils of Poynton (1897)

What Maisie Knew (1897)

The Awkward Age (1899)

The Sacred Fount (1901)

The Wings of the Dove (1902)

The Ambassadors (1903)

The Golden Bowl (1904)

The Whole Family (collaborative novel with eleven other authors, 1908

The Outcry (1911)

The Ivory Tower (unfinished, published posthumously 1917)

The Sense of the Past (unfinished, published posthumously 1917)

SHORT STORIES AND NOVELLAS

A Tragedy of Error (1864)

The Story of a Year (1865)

A Landscape Painter (1866)

A Day of Days (1866)

My Friend Bingham (1867)

Poor Richard (1867)

The Story of a Masterpiece (1868)

A Most Extraordinary Case (1868)

A Problem (1868)

De Grey: A Romance (1868)

Osborne's Revenge (1868)

The Romance of Certain Old Clothes (1868)

A Light Man (1869)

Gabrielle de Bergerac (1869)

Travelling Companions (1870)

A Passionate Pilgrim (1871)

At Isella (1871)

Lady Barberina (1884)

Pandora (1884)

The Author of Beltraffio (1884)

Georgina's Reasons (1884)

A New England Winter (1884)

The Path of Duty (1884)

Mrs. Temperly (1887)

Louisa Pallant (1888)

The Aspern Papers (1888)

The Liar (1888)

The Modern Warning (1888, originally published as The Two Countries)

A London Life (1888)

The Patagonia (1888)

The Lesson of the Master (1888)

The Solution (1888)

The Pupil (1891)

Brooksmith (1891)

The Marriages (1891)

The Chaperon (1891)

Sir Edmund Orme (1891)

Nona Vincent (1892)

The Real Thing (1892)

The Private Life (1892)

Lord Beaupré (1892)

The Visits (1892)

Sir Dominick Ferrand (1892)

Greville Fane (1892)

Collaboration (1892)

Owen Wingrave (1892)

The Wheel of Time (1892)

The Middle Years (1893)

The Death of the Lion (1894)

The Coxon Fund (1894)

The Next Time (1895)

Glasses (1896)

The Altar of the Dead (1895)

The Figure in the Carpet (1896)

The Way It Came (1896, also published as The Friends of the Friends)

The Turn of the Screw (1898)

Covering End (1898)

In the Cage (1898)

John Delavoy (1898)

The Given Case (1898)

Europe (1899)

The Great Condition (1899)

The Real Right Thing (1899)

Paste (1899)

The Great Good Place (1900)

Maud-Evelyn (1900)

Miss Gunton of Poughkeepsie (1900)

The Tree of Knowledge (1900)

The Abasement of the Northmores (1900)

The Third Person (1900)

The Special Type (1900)

The Tone of Time (1900)

Broken Wings (1900)

The Two Faces (1900)

Mrs. Medwin (1901)

The Beldonald Holbein (1901)

The Story in It (1902)

Flickerbridge (1902)

The Birthplace (1903)

The Beast in the Jungle (1903)

The Papers (1903)

Fordham Castle (1904)

Julia Bride (1908)

The Jolly Corner (1908)

The Velvet Glove (1909)

Mora Montravers (1909)

Crapy Cornelia (1909)

The Bench of Desolation (1909)

A Round of Visits (1910)

OTHER

Transatlantic Sketches (1875)

French Poets and Novelists (1878)

Hawthorne (1879)

Portraits of Places (1883)

A Little Tour in France (1884)

Partial Portraits (1888)

Essays in London and Elsewhere (1893)

Picture and Text (1893)

Terminations (1893)

Theatricals (1894)

Theatricals: Second Series (1895)

Guy Domville (1895)

The Soft Side (1900)

William Wetmore Story and His Friends (1903)

The Better Sort (1903)

English Hours (1905)

The Question of our Speech; The Lesson of Balzac. Two Lectures (1905)

The American Scene (1907)

Views and Reviews (1908)

Italian Hours (1909)

A Small Boy and Others (1913)

Notes on Novelists (1914)

Notes of a Son and Brother (1914)

Within the Rim (1918)

Travelling Companions (1919)

Notebooks (various, published posthumously)

The Middle Years (unfinished, published posthumously 1917)

A Most Unholy Trade (1925, published posthumously)

The Art of the Novel : Critical Prefaces (1934)

CPSIA information can be obtained
at www.ICGtesting.com
Printed in the USA
LVHW052039021120
670493LV00002B/128